Advanced Mathematical Concepts

Glen D. Vannatta
Supervisor of Mathematics
Indianapolis Public Schools
Indianapolis, Indiana

F. Joe Crosswhite
Professor of Mathematics Education
The Ohio State University
Columbus, Ohio

Charles E. Merrill Publishing Co.
A Bell & Howell Company
Columbus, Ohio

MERRILL MATHEMATICS SERIES

for secondary schools

F. Joe Crosswhite, Consultant

DISCOVERIES IN MODERN MATHEMATICS: Course One

DISCOVERIES IN MODERN MATHEMATICS: Course Two

ALGEBRA ONE

GEOMETRY

ALGEBRA TWO With Circular Functions

ADVANCED MATHEMATICAL CONCEPTS

ISBN O-675-07900-4

Copyright ©, 1971, by

CHARLES E. MERRILL PUBLISHING COMPANY

A Bell and Howell Company

Columbus, Ohio 43216

Portions of this book formerly copyrighted ©, 1965, 1961,
under the title, *Advanced High School Mathematics*.

PREFACE

The major objective of *Advanced Mathematical Concepts* is to provide a course in pre-calculus mathematics that encompasses topics and concepts which grow out of intermediate algebra. This course prepares students for a rigorous course in calculus. The content includes the elementary functions, with polynomial functions and circular functions being given special emphasis. Many topics are similar to those traditionally found in trigonometry, analytic geometry, and college algebra, but in *Advanced Mathematical Concepts* the treatment has been updated to satisfy contemporary needs.

The text is intended as the fourth year of college preparatory mathematics, usually taught in the junior or senior year of high school. Students should have a good background in intermediate algebra, preferably including an introduction to circular functions. The function concept should be reasonably well developed and understood. Students using this text should be either mathematically oriented, or they should be seeking a broad terminal course in secondary mathematics. Most of those who elect this course will be planning to enter a technical area such as science or engineering. The material is broad enough to satisfy these varied needs.

In the first chapter, the development of mathematical systems, with emphasis on groups and fields, is investigated. The concepts are built upon the knowledge of properties of familiar number sets studied in previous mathematics courses. The examples and exercises present familiar ideas in a fresh and challenging light.

Chapter 5 presents a thorough investigation and development of the circular functions. For students who have studied some trigonometry or circular functions in intermediate algebra (as in *Algebra Two With Circular Functions*, the third book in the Merrill Mathematics Series for Secondary Schools), this chapter will serve as a review and extension of the material previously covered. The subsequent chapters on trigonometry present a standard course in this subject using the definitions in terms of an angle in standard position. The exercises in these trigonometry chapters will challenge students even though they have had a previous introduction to this topic.

iii

The final chapter on limits of functions will prepare students for a thorough course in calculus. Other topics, such as absolute value, inequalities, and graphing of the elementary functions, have been upgraded in preparation for calculus. The derivative is introduced in Chapter 3 as a special limit—slope of a function—which provides an enriched background for a study of mathematical analysis.

The explanations in the text are carefully presented, and the examples and illustrations have been chosen for clarity and relevance. It is appropriate to use this book in a small group or "self-teaching" format if students are well-motivated. In this instructional mode, the teacher becomes a guide and consultant.

Students who successfully complete a course based on this text will be well prepared for a course in calculus. Many of the included topics help to accomplish this goal. Also many topics and applications, statistics for example, will provide a broad base for students who are interested in general education.

The authors have relied on teachers' experiences with *Advanced High School Mathematics* in developing this text. The content and the sequence should satisfy the mathematical needs of students of the Seventies. The authors wish to express particular thanks and appreciation to the members of the editorial staff of Charles E. Merrill Publishing Company, each of whom has made many significant contributions.

Glen D. Vannatta
F. Joe Crosswhite

CONTENTS

3 Theory of Equations

4 Matrices and Vectors

5 The Circular Functions

6 The Trigonometric Functions

7 Graphical Representation of Trigonometric Functions

8 Applications of Trigonometry

9 Inverses of Trigonometric Functions and Trigonometric Equations

10 Sequences and Series

11 Special Theorems and Functions

ix

12 The Straight Line

13 The Circle

14 The Parabola

15 The Ellipse

16 The Hyperbola

17 Permutations, Combinations, and Probability

18 Empirical Relations—Statistics

19 Limits

Appendix: Computation

Tables

Selected Answers

Index

Glossary of Symbols

Sets

{ }	set
$\in$	is an element of
$\notin$	is not an element of
{|}	set-builder notation
ϕ	null set or empty set
U	universal set
$\cup$	union
$\cap$	intersection

Number Sets

N	natural numbers
W	whole numbers
Z	integers
Q	rational numbers
R	real numbers

Relations

$=$	is equal to
$\neq$	is not equal to
$\approx$	is approximately equal to
$>$	is greater than
$\not>$	is not greater than
$\geqq$	is greater than or equal to
$<$	is less than
$\not<$	is not less than
$\leqq$	is less than or equal to
$\sim$	is similar to
$\cong$	is congruent to

Statistics

$_nP_r$	number of permutations of n elements taken r at a time
$_nC_r$	number of combinations of n elements taken r at a time
$\bar{X}$	arithmetic mean of a sample
σ	standard deviation
$\sigma_{\bar{x}}$	standard error of the mean
$!$	factorial notation

Calculus and Analysis

Δx	increment in x
$D_x y$	the derivative of y with respect to x
$\sum$	summation symbol
$\lim\limits_{x \to a} y$	limit of y as x approaches a
e	Euler's constant

Other Symbols

$\cdots$	ellipsis
$\therefore$	therefore
$\|n\|$	the absolute value of n
$f(x)$	the value of function f at x
$p \to q$	if p, then q
$p \leftrightarrow q$	p if and only if q
$\overline{AB}$	directed distance AB
$\vec{A}$	the vector A
i	$\sqrt{-1}$

The Structure
of Our Number System

1

1.1 Mathematical systems

The most important characteristic of modern mathematics is the use of the *axiomatic,* or *postulational method* to develop *mathematical systems.* You may have used this method when you studied the rational number system or the real number system, but you were probably most aware of using it when you studied Euclidean geometry.

Every mathematical system begins with a set of *undefined elements.* Some of the undefined elements in geometry are "point," "line," and "plane." Physical models can give you an intuitive feeling for what these terms mean, but any attempt to define them within the system leads to *circular definitions.* In geometry, physical models also suggest relations such as "is contained in" and "is between." These also remain undefined unless a definition can be given in terms of properties already assigned to the undefined elements.

The next step in building a mathematical system is to assign properties to the undefined elements and relations to give them meaning. To do this, a set of *assumptions* is selected. Assumptions that are accepted in a mathematical system are called *axioms*, or *postulates*. These postulates provide the working information necessary for building a system and giving it a certain character. All that can be known about the system must be derived logically from the set of postulates.

In geometry, you accepted these postulates.

1. Every line contains at least two distinct points.

2. For every pair of points, there corresponds one and only one positive real number that represents the distance between the points.

From a foundation of postulates such as these and from a set of undefined terms and relations, you defined new terms such as "line segment" and "angle," and new relations such as "is similar to" and "is congruent to." If the new terms and relations were to have properties not already inherent in the system, additional postulates were needed. The only restriction was that new postulates had to be consistent with the system, that is, their addition should not lead to a contradiction.

The final step in building a mathematical system is to identify and prove theorems. *Theorems* are neither definitions nor assumptions, but rather statements about the elements and relations that are logical consequences of the postulates. These statements must be tested to determine whether they can be logically derived by an accepted pattern of proof from the statements that are already part of the system. Those statements for which such proofs can be found are then added to the system as theorems. Much of your work in geometry involved proving theorems deductively.

The development of our number system parallels the development of Euclidean geometry. If we begin with the set of natural numbers, N, and a set of axioms originally stated by the Italian mathematician George Peano (1858–1932), it is possible to derive the properties of the natural numbers under the usual operations and relations. By making suitable definitions, we can extend the set of natural numbers to the system of complex numbers in a continuous, logical development. You have already studied these extensions and, in doing so, have become familiar with the properties of the subsets of our number system.

In this chapter, we explore some of the algebraic systems for which subsets of the complex numbers provide interpretations. We will be concerned with abstract properties of operations and relations in these systems. These are the primary objects of study in modern algebra.

Exercises

1. List the steps in the development of a mathematical system and identify the components of such a system.
2. Select an ordinary, nontechnical word and use a standard dictionary to trace its definition to circularity. (*Hint:* For example, trace the definition of the word "explain" to circularity. Explain means "To make plain; to expound." Expound means "To lay open the meaning of; to interpret." Interpret means "To explain or tell the meaning of.")
3. Recall and list three postulates from your study of geometry. Why do you feel these were postulates rather than theorems?
4. List three assumptions (assumptions you accept) that assign initial properties to the natural numbers as undefined elements.
5. Explain what is meant by the statement, "One man's assumption is another man's theorem."
6. *Special Project:* Study the historical development of non-Euclidean geometries as examples of systems that were not physically motivated. Try to find references to recent developments in science that make use of some of these non-Euclidean geometries.

1.2   Relations

Every mathematical system contains relations defined on the elements of the system. The most common relation in mathematics is equality. In elementary algebra, when we say $x + 4 = 7$, we mean that $x + 4$ and 7 are different names for the same number. In geometry, when we say $\angle A = \angle B$, we mean that A and B are different names for the same angle. In mathematics *equality* always has the meaning of *identity*. Two sets with the same number of elements are said to be *equivalent*, but they are equal only if their elements are identical.

In your study of algebra, a relation may have been defined as a set of ordered pairs. It is that, but it is more, too. The process which determines the set of ordered pairs is critical. To be "in the relation," a pair of elements must satisfy a well-defined set of conditions. Suppose N is the set of natural numbers and $a, b \in N$. We define $a < b$ to mean that $a + c = b$ for some $c \in N$. Since $4 + 3 = 7$, we know that $4 < 7$ and say "4 is in the relation $<$ to 7," or "$(4, 7)$ is in the relation $<$." Because there is no natural number c such that $5 + c = 3$, we say "5 is not in the relation $<$ to 3," or "$(5, 3)$ is not in the relation $<$" and we write $5 \not< 3$. Notice that the *order* of the pair is very important: $4 < 7$ but $7 \not< 4$.

> **Definition:** A *relation R* is defined on a set S if for each ordered pair of elements, (s, t), of S, the statement "s is in relation R to t" is either true or false.

When we use the alternate definition that a relation R is a set of ordered pairs, we mean the set of ordered pairs for which the statement is true.

Equality is a special case of a more general type of relation, an equivalence relation.

> **Definition:** A relation $\square$ defined on a set A is an *equivalence relation* if for every choice of elements a, b, c in A, the following properties are satisfied.
> 1. *Reflexive Property.* $a \square a$.
> 2. *Symmetric Property.* If $a \square b$, then $b \square a$.
> 3. *Transitive Property.* If $a \square b$ and $b \square c$, then $a \square c$.

The special property of equality that distinguishes it from all other equivalence relations is that it permits unrestricted substitution. That is, if $m = n$, then m may be substituted for n in any statement or expression. Other equivalence relations permit only restricted substitution. For example, congruence defined on the angles in a plane is an equivalence relation. Can you verify this? If $\angle A \cong \angle B$, it would be proper to substitute $\angle A$ for $\angle B$ in the statement, "The measure of $\angle B$ is 30°." This substitution is possible because all pairs of angles that are congruent have the same measure. But we could not substitute $\angle A$ for $\angle B$ in the statement, " $\angle B$ is adjacent to $\angle C$." With all equivalence relations other than equality, substitutions must be made with great care.

You have worked with several equivalence relations other than equality.

EXAMPLE. Define the relation *is similar to*, symbolized $\sim$, on the set of triangles in a plane. Show that this is an equivalence relation.

Solution. (a) Every triangle is similar to itself. Thus the relation is reflexive.

(b) If $\triangle ABC \sim \triangle DEF$, then $\triangle DEF \sim \triangle ABC$. The relation is symmetric.

(c) If $\triangle ABC \sim \triangle DEF$ and $\triangle DEF \sim \triangle RST$, then $\triangle ABC \sim \triangle RST$. The relation is transitive.

Therefore the relation *is similar to* is an equivalence relation.

Other relations with which you have worked may not be equivalence relations. The relation $\leq$, as defined on the set of real numbers R, is reflexive (since $a \leq a$ for all $a \in R$) and transitive (since $a \leq b$, $b \leq c \rightarrow a \leq c$ for all a, b, $c \in R$), but it is not symmetric (since $3 \leq 5$ but $5 \not\leq 3$). Notice that a single *counterexample* is sufficient to show that a given relation does not satisfy a stated property. Since the relation does not satisfy all three properties, it is not an equivalence relation.

Exercises

Determine whether each relation is (a) reflexive, (b) symmetric, (c) transitive, and (d) an equivalence relation. For each relation which is an equivalence relation, give an example of a statement in which substitution would be appropriate and a second statement in which substitution would not be appropriate.

1. *Is parallel to* for lines in a plane
2. *Has the same slope as* for lines in a plane
3. *Is perpendicular to* for lines in a plane
4. *Is greater than* for positive integers
5. *Has the same area as* for rectangles in a plane
6. *Has the same circumference as* for circles in a plane
7. *Is the brother of* for all men
8. *Is the complement of* for acute angles
9. *Is a subset of* for sets
10. *Is a multiple or divisor of* for even integers
11. *Is congruent to* for triangles in a plane
12. *Lives within two miles of* for students in your school
13. Let Z be the set of all integers. For a, $b \in Z$, define $a \bigcirc b$ if $a - b$ is divisible by 3. Prove that $\bigcirc$, relation circle, is an equivalence relation. (*Hint:* $a - b$ is divisible by 3 if and only if $a - b = k \cdot 3$ such that k is an integer.)

1.3 Operations

Every algebraic system has at least one operation defined on its set of elements. The nature of the system depends upon the properties satisfied by these operations. Therefore the study of algebraic systems is the study of properties of operations.

The four fundamental operations of arithmetic—addition, subtraction, multiplication, and division—are binary operations, that is, they are defined for *pairs of elements*.

> **Definition:** Let S be any set. A *binary operation* $\oplus$ on the set S is a correspondence that associates with each ordered pair of elements, (s, t), of S, a unique element $s \oplus t$ in S.

The operations of squaring and taking the square root of a number are called *unary operations*. We could also define operations for ordered triples, *ternary operations*, or even for ordered n-tuples of elements.

Three important conditions must be satisfied for a correspondence to qualify as an operation on a set.

1. *Uniqueness.* The element $s \oplus t$ must be unique. Consider a correspondence that associates with any pair of integers, (a, b), a number c such that $c^2 = ab$. For the pair $(2, 8)$ the correspondence would be $(2, 8) \rightarrow 4$ and $(2, 8) \rightarrow -4$. Thus the correspondence is not unique and, therefore, is not an operation.

   Uniqueness also requires that the correspondence associate the same element with the ordered pair regardless of how the elements may be represented. If $a = b$ and $c = d$, then $a \oplus c = b \oplus d$. A property of real numbers analogous to this type of correspondence is, "If equals are added to equals the sums are equal." Since equality always means identity, this is just another way of saying an operation must be unique. For example, in the set of rational numbers $\frac{1}{2} = \frac{2}{4}$ and $\frac{1}{3} = \frac{3}{9}$, so $\frac{1}{2} + \frac{1}{3} = \frac{2}{4} + \frac{3}{9}$ since the operation is independent of the representation of the elements. We must be sure this is the case before we can say an operation is *well-defined*.

2. *Closure.* The element $s \oplus t$ must be in the set S. Consider the correspondence that associates with each ordered pair of natu-

ral numbers, (a, b), the number c such that $a + c = b$. For the pair $(7, 3)$ the correspondence would be $(7, 3) \rightarrow -4$ because $7 + (-4) = 3$. But -4 is not a natural number. Therefore we say the natural numbers are not closed under this correspondence, and it is not an operation on the set of natural numbers. (*Note:* Some definitions of operation do not insist on closure. Under these definitions it is appropriate to ask if a set is closed under an operation. For example, one might ask whether the natural numbers are closed under the operation of subtraction. The answer would be "no." We prefer to make closure a part of every operation and would ask, "Is subtraction an operation on the set of natural numbers?" or simply, "Is the set of natural numbers closed under the subtraction correspondence?" The answer, of course, is still "no." This is an example of our privilege of selection in making a definition.)

3. The correspondence must be defined for every pair of elements in the set.

The familiar operation of division presents some interesting problems with respect to the previous definition. Consider the set of rational numbers Q. If $a, b \in Q, b \neq 0$, we define $a \div b = c$ to mean that $a = bc$. What happens if we try to apply this definition when the rational number zero is used as a divisor? To define $a \div 0$, we must find a number c such that $0 \cdot c = a$. If $a = 0$, *any number c* will satisfy this relation and thus the correspondence will not be unique. If $a \neq 0$, there is *no number* c which satisfies the condition because $0 \cdot c = 0$ for *all* rational numbers c. Thus $\div$ is not defined for all pairs of rational numbers. Specifically, it is not defined for any pair $(a, 0)$. The definition of an operation is violated, so $\div$ cannot be an operation on Q. Is division an operation on the nonzero rational numbers?

The property of closure plays an important role in the logical development of our number system. Since the natural numbers are not closed under subtraction, one motivation for inventing zero and the negative integers is to provide a set of numbers upon which subtraction *is* an operation. Similarly, since the integers are not closed under division, the invention of the set of rational numbers makes division an operation provided zero divisors are excluded.

Since a binary operation is defined for *ordered pairs* of elements, it is natural to wonder if the order really matters. That is, would the result be the same if the order were reversed? Would the pair (s, t)

and the pair (t, s) be associated with the same element? More simply, would $s \oplus t = t \oplus s$? An operation which possesses this property for all pairs of elements is said to be commutative.

> **Definition:** An operation $\oplus$ defined on a set S is *commutative* if for every pair of elements, (s, t), in S, $s \oplus t = t \oplus s$.

Another question that arises naturally is whether we can extend the operation to more than two elements, to *ordered triples*, (s, t, u), or even beyond. Binary operation was defined only for pairs of elements, but since $s \oplus t$ is itself an element of the set, we can consider the pair $(s \oplus t, u)$ and obtain $(s \oplus t) \oplus u$ as a correspondence for the ordered triple (s, t, u). Notice that we arbitrarily chose to pair s and t to obtain $s \oplus t$ *first*.

What if we had chosen t and u and formed the pair $(s, t \oplus u)$ to obtain $s \oplus (t \oplus u)$? Would the final outcome have been the same? Would $(s \oplus t) \oplus u = s \oplus (t \oplus u)$? Nothing in the definition of binary operation suggests that this should be the case. So for any operation this is one of the questions that must be explored.

> **Definition:** An operation $\oplus$ defined on a set S is *associative* if for every ordered triple of elements, (s, t, u), in S, $s \oplus (t \oplus u) = (s \oplus t) \oplus u$.

Notice that the order of the three elements has not been changed. Only the *grouping* is altered. If an operation is associative, we can interpret $s \oplus t \oplus u$ as either $(s \oplus t) \oplus u$ or $s \oplus (t \oplus u)$. If the operation is not associative, then either symbols of grouping must be supplied or we must agree to perform the operation in a specific order (usually left to right) before we can interpret $s \oplus t \oplus u$. Although the definition is stated for ordered triples, the Associative Property can usually be applied repeatedly to any number of elements. For example, for four elements, $[(a \oplus b) \oplus c] \oplus d = a \oplus [b \oplus (c \oplus d)]$.

Exercises

For each of the following, tell whether the indicated correspondence, as usually defined, is an operation on the given set.

1. Natural numbers, multiplication
2. Natural numbers, subtraction
3. Integers, subtraction
4. Integers, division
5. Rational numbers, squaring the number

6. Rational numbers, taking the square root

7. Suppose we define ★ on the set of natural numbers by $a ★ b = a^2 - b^2 + 1$. Is this an operation on the natural numbers?

8. Is $\triangle$, defined by $a \triangle b = ab - a$, an operation on the set of positive integers?

9. Is $*$, defined by $a * b = 2 - (a - b)$, an operation on the set of positive integers?

10. Define $\square$ such that it is an operation on the set $\{-3, -2, -1, 0, 1, 2, 3\}$.

1.4   A finite mathematical system

Let us examine a small finite system which contains a set A of elements $\{a, b, c, d\}$, an equivalence relation $=$, and a correspondence defined as follows.

$$
\begin{array}{llll}
a \circ a = b & b \circ a = d & c \circ a = a & d \circ a = c \\
a \circ b = d & b \circ b = c & c \circ b = b & d \circ b = a \\
a \circ c = a & b \circ c = b & c \circ c = c & d \circ c = d \\
a \circ d = c & b \circ d = a & c \circ d = d & d \circ d = b
\end{array}
$$

Where are the assumptions that are a necessary part of any mathematical system? They are imbedded in the correspondence as defined. The properties of this correspondence are completely specified in the previous display.

For finite systems, such as the one above, it is helpful to display the correspondence in a table.

SECOND ELEMENT

$\circ$	a	b	c	d
a	b	d	a	c
b	d	c	b	a
c	a	b	c	d
d	c	a	d	b

FIRST ELEMENT

Is the correspondence $\circ$ an operation on the set A? Does it associate a unique element in A with each ordered pair of elements from A? It does. Therefore it is an operation on A.

Is the operation commutative? Since the system is finite, we can check for commutativity by inspecting each set of pairs of the form (s, t) and (t, s). If $s \circ t = t \circ s$ for all pairs, the operation is commutative. If there exists a single example such that $s \circ t \neq t \circ s$, then the operation is not commutative. Check this property.

The test for associativity is more difficult, even for a small system. There is a total of twelve ordered triples to be checked. We will check one of them for you.

Check. $(a \circ b) \circ d = d \circ d = b$
$a \circ (b \circ d) = a \circ a = b$
$\therefore (a \circ b) \circ d = a \circ (b \circ d)$

Notice that we used the Substitution Property of the equivalence relation $=$ in the above check.

Perhaps as you examined the system above for commutativity and associativity (both properties hold) you noticed that the element c has a special property. Can you determine that property? Do you see that when c is paired with any element, the operation results in that element? When an element such as c has this special property it is called an identity element.

> **Definition:** An element e of a set S is an *identity element* for the set under the operation $\oplus$ if for every $s \in S$, $e \oplus s = s = s \oplus e$.

The number zero is the identity element for the set of integers, Z, under addition since $a + 0 = a = 0 + a$ for all integers a. What is the identity element for the integers under multiplication?

The existence of an identity element for a set raises another question about operations. Perhaps for each element a in the set there exists a second element a' such that the correspondence associates this pair of elements with the identity element e. Is this true for the set A under the operation $\circ$? Is there an x in A such that $a \circ x = e$? Is this true for each of the elements?

> **Definition:** If e is an identity element for a set S under the operation $\oplus$, then an element $a' \in S$ is an *inverse element* for the element $a \in S$ if $a \oplus a' = e = a' \oplus a$.

In the set of integers, each element has an inverse under addition. The inverse element for 3 is -3 since $3 + (-3) = 0 = (-3) + 3$. Of course, this also means that 3 is an inverse element for -3. In general, the inverse of any integer under addition is the negative of that integer because $n + (-n) = 0 = (-n) + n$. We call zero the *additive identity* for the set of integers, and the inverse elements relative to this identity are called *additive inverses*.

The set of integers also has a *multiplicative identity*, one. Does it have *multiplicative inverses* for all elements? For any elements? What set can be constructed from the integers to provide a set of numbers which does contain multiplicative inverse elements? Does this set have inverses for all its elements?

Exercises

1. Write the additive inverse and the multiplicative inverse of each of the following real numbers.

   a. -3 c. $2 + \sqrt{3}$ e. $4\frac{1}{2}$
   b. $\frac{2}{3}$ d. 0.3 f. $\sqrt{13}$

2. A mathematical system consists of the set $\{\bigcirc, \triangle, \square\}$, the equivalence relation $=$, and an operation $\otimes$ defined by the table below.

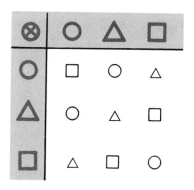

FIGURE 1–1

   a. What is the identity element?
   b. List each element with its inverse.
   c. Is $\otimes$ commutative?
   d. Is $\otimes$ associative?
   e. Solve the equation $\bigcirc \otimes x = \square$ for x.

3. Construct a mathematical system from the set $\{0, 1, 2, 3\}$ by displaying the table for an operation $\oplus$ where the "sum" $a \oplus b$ is the remainder when $a + b$ is divided by 4. List all the properties you can find for this system.

4. Define $\circ$ on the set of natural numbers by $a \circ b = ab + 1$. Is this an operation on the natural numbers? If so, is it commutative? Does an identity element exist?

5. Suppose we define $*$ on the set of rational numbers by $a * b = a^2 - b^2 - 1$. Is this an operation on the rational numbers? If so, is it commutative? Does an identity element exist?

1.5   Groups

Algebraic systems are classified according to the properties their operations and relations satisfy. Even the few properties discussed in the preceding sections are sufficient to classify several important algebraic systems. The simplest system we shall consider is the group.

> **Definition:** A *group* is a mathematical system consisting of a non-empty set G, the equivalence relation $=$, and a binary operation $\circ$ defined on G with the following properties.
> 1. *Associative Property.* If a, b, $c \in G$, then $(a \circ b) \circ c = a \circ (b \circ c)$.
> 2. *Existence of Identity Element.* There exists an element $e \in G$ such that $e \circ a = a = a \circ e$ for all $a \in G$.
> 3. *Existence of Inverse Elements.* If $a \in G$, there exists an element $a' \in G$ such that $a \circ a' = e = a' \circ a$.

Note: The symbol $(G, \circ)$ represents a mathematical system consisting of set G under operation $\circ$.

Notice that three properties of the operation are required for the system to be a group—associativity, existence of an identity element, and existence of an inverse element for each element of G. If the operation is also commutative, then the group is called an *Abelian* or commutative group.

> **Definition:** $(G, \circ)$ is a *commutative group* if the operation $\circ$ also has the following property.
> 4. *Commutative Property.* If a, $b \in G$, then $a \circ b = b \circ a$.

Your familiarity with the usual operations of multiplication and addition should enable you to identify several subsets of our number system which are groups under one or both of these operations. (See the exercises following this section.)

A group may be specified in two ways. If the set of elements is finite, the elements can be listed and the operation exhibited in a table (see Section 1.4). In this case, the properties of the operation can be determined by examining every possible instance. If the number of elements is infinite, the properties of the operation must be assumed or proved from known properties. In the development of our number system, the original properties assumed for the set of natural numbers are used to prove properties for the integers, the rational numbers, the real numbers, and the complex numbers.

Let us review the requirements for a group by considering an unfamiliar example.

EXAMPLE 1. Consider the set of rational numbers Q with the equivalence relation $=$ and a binary operation $\#$ defined as follows.

$$a \# b = (a \times b) + (a + b) = ab + a + b \text{ for all } a, b \in Q$$

Solution. We will assume the properties of $+$ and $\times$ on Q and an additional property that connects the two operations.

> **Definition:** A binary operation $\times$ defined on a set S is said
> to be *distributive* with respect to a second operation $+$ on
> S if for every ordered triple of elements, (a, b, c) that are in
> $S, a \times (b + c) = (a \times b) + (a \times c)$.

You are already familiar with the Distributive Property and know that it applies both from the right and the left in our number system.

To determine the structure of $(Q, \#)$, you should first verify that $\#$ is a well-defined binary operation.

Now examine the properties of $\#$ on Q. You should be able to cite properties of $+$ and $\times$ to justify each step. For simplicity, we write $a \times b$ as ab.

1. *Associative Property.*

$$
\begin{aligned}
a \# (b \# c) &= a \# (bc + b + c) \\
&= a(bc + b + c) + a + (bc + b + c) \\
&= abc + ab + ac + a + bc + b + c \\
&= abc + ab + ac + bc + a + b + c \\
(a \# b) \# c &= (ab + a + b) \# c \\
&= (ab + a + b)c + (ab + a + b) + c \\
&= abc + ac + bc + ab + a + b + c \\
&= abc + ab + ac + bc + a + b + c \\
\therefore a \# (b \# c) &= (a \# b) \# c \text{ and } \# \text{ is associative.}
\end{aligned}
$$

2. *Existence of an Identity Element.*

We need to find an element e such that $a \# e = a = e \# a$ for all $a \in Q$. To find a candidate for e, we assume $a \# e = ae + a + e = a$ and solve for e. We know $a \# e = e \# a$ since $ae + a + e = ea + e + a$ from the Commutative and Associative Properties of $\times$ and $+$ on Q.

$$ae + a + e = a$$
$$ae + e + a = a$$
$$(ae + e) + a = a$$
$$ae + e = 0$$
$$e(a + 1) = 0$$
$$e = \frac{0}{a + 1} \text{ if } a \neq -1$$

For all $a \neq -1$, we would have $e = 0$. If $a = -1$, then $\frac{0}{a + 1}$ is undefined.

Let us consider what happens under $\#$ to the pair $(-1, 0)$.

$$-1 \# 0 = (-1 \times 0) + (-1) + 0 = -1$$

So zero could serve as an identity element for negative one. But so far zero is only a candidate for the identity element. We have shown that it holds for -1; we must now show that it holds for all $a \in Q$. For $a \in Q$,

$$a \# 0 = (a \times 0) + a + 0 = a$$

and thus zero is the identity element for Q under $\#$.

3. *Existence of Inverse Elements.*

For each $a \in Q$, we need to find an element $a' \in Q$ such that $a \# a' = 0$. To find a candidate for the inverse of an arbitrary $a \in Q$, we suppose $a \# x = ax + a + x = 0$ and solve for x. Again, $a \# x = x \# a$ since $ax + a + x = xa + x + a$.

$$ax + a + x = 0$$
$$ax + x = -a$$
$$x(a + 1) = -a$$
$$x = \frac{-a}{a + 1} \text{ if } a \neq -1$$

Again we must carefully consider -1 since $\frac{-a}{a + 1}$ is not defined for this element. Let us examine $-1 \# x$ separately. Suppose $-1 \# x = 0$.

$$(-1 \times x) + (-1) + x = 0$$
$$-x - 1 + x = 0$$
$$-1 = 0$$

This contradicts a known fact $(-1 \neq 0)$ and thus $-1 \# x \neq 0$ for all x, and -1 has no inverse for $\#$ on Q. Therefore $(Q, \#)$ is not a group. The problem encountered here is similar to one involving zero as a potential divisor in Q.

Suppose we eliminate -1 from the set of rational numbers and form a new set S. Is $(S, \#)$ a group? If so, is it a commutative group? This investigation is left to the student as an exercise.

Exercises

In Exercises 1–10, assuming that the Associative Property holds, decide whether each set forms a group under the given operation. Indicate which properties are or are not satisfied in each case.

1. Integers, multiplication
2. Integers, addition $(-3, 2)$
3. Odd integers, addition
4. Odd integers, multiplication
5. Even integers, addition
6. Even integers, multiplication
7. $\{0, 1, 2, \cdots, 9\}$, $\circ$ where $a \circ b$ is equal to the smaller of a and b
8. The subsets of a set, union
9. The subsets of a set, intersection
10. Rational numbers except 1, $\circ$ defined by $a \circ b = a + b - ab$
11. Prove or disprove that the set of rational numbers forms a commutative group under addition.
12. Prove or disprove that the set of rational numbers forms a commutative group under multiplication.
13. Show that the set $\{1, -1, i, -i\}$, consisting of these four complex numbers, the equivalence relation $=$, and multiplication as usually defined $(i \cdot i = -1)$ forms a commutative group.

1.6   Theorems about groups

The theorems concerning groups that will be proved in this section are for *all* groups. Therefore, they apply to each of the subsets of our number system which forms a group with respect to some given operation. Assume $(G, \circ)$ is a group in each of the following theorems.

We usually refer to *the* identity element or to *the* inverse element because we can prove quite easily that there is a unique identity element for $\circ$ and that each element in G has a unique inverse.

● THEOREM 1

The identity element of a group $(G, \circ)$ is unique.

Proof: We use an *indirect proof* for this theorem. Assume e_1 and e_2 are distinct identity elements.

$\quad\quad e_1 \circ e_2 = e_1$ because e_2 is an identity.
$\quad\quad e_1 \circ e_2 = e_2$ because e_1 is an identity.

But $e_1 \circ e_2 = e_1 \circ e_2$, and therefore, by substitution, $e_1 = e_2$ contradicting the assumption that they are distinct elements. Thus the identity element must be unique.

● THEOREM 2

Each element in a group $(G, \circ)$ has a unique inverse element.

We leave the proof of this theorem to the student as an exercise. An indirect approach similar to that used in the preceding theorem is suggested.

● THEOREM 3

For all $a, b, c, d \in G$, if $a = b$ and $c = d$, then $a \circ c = b \circ d$.

Proof: The proof of this theorem is a direct consequence of the Uniqueness Property of an operation.

1. $a = b, c = d$	Hypothesis
2. $a \circ c = a \circ c$	Uniqueness of $\circ$
3. $a \circ c = b \circ c$	Substitution
4. $a \circ c = b \circ d$	Substitution

● THEOREM 4

For all $a, b, c \in G$, if $a \circ c = b \circ c$, then $a = b$.

Proof: 1. $a \circ c = b \circ c$	Hypothesis
2. There exists an identity element e for G under $\circ$.	Group Property 2

3. There exists an element   Group Property 3
   $c' \in G$ such that $c \circ c' = e$.

4. $(a \circ c) \circ c' = (b \circ c) \circ c'$ Theorem 3

5. $a \circ (c \circ c') = b \circ (c \circ c')$ Group Property 1

6. $a \circ e = b \circ e$ Group Property 3
                                       and Substitution

7. $a = b$ Group Property 2
                                       and Substitution

• THEOREM 5

For all $a, b \in G$, there exists a unique element $c \in G$ such that $a \circ c = b$.

Proof: In proving this theorem, we must consider two cases: *uniqueness* and *existence*.

Case I. Uniqueness.

    Let us assume that $a \circ x = b$.

1. $a' \circ (a \circ x) = a' \circ b$ Theorem 3

2. $(a' \circ a) \circ x = a' \circ b$ Group Property 1

3. $e \circ x = a' \circ b$ Group Property 3
                                     and Substitution

4. $x = a' \circ b$ Group Property 2
                                     and Substitution

Therefore if such an element x exists, it is $a' \circ b$.

Case II. Existence.

    Consider $a' \circ b$ where a' is the inverse element for a.

1. $a \circ (a' \circ b) = (a \circ a') \circ b$ Group Property 1

2. $a \circ a' = e$ Group Property 3

3. $a \circ (a' \circ b) = e \circ b$ Substitution

4. $a \circ (a' \circ b) = b$ Group Property 2
                                      and Substitution

Therefore $c = a' \circ b$ is the required element.

These theorems and their proofs are not difficult, but they are important in terms of what they mean in our number system. Theorem 3 is the familiar "If equals are multiplied by equals (or added to equals), the products (sums) are equal." Theorem 4 is the familiar Cancellation Property that you use to solve equations. Theorem 5 guarantees a solution to simple equations such as $3 + x = 7$ or $2x = 4$. Moreover, it guarantees that the solution is unique.

Now we consider a familiar property from algebra and seek to translate it into group language. If you were to simplify the expression $3x - (-2)$, you would write $3x + 2$. You interpret the expression $3x - (-2)$ as $3x + [-(-2)]$ and assume that $-(-2)$ is 2. In group terminology this would translate as in Theorem 6.

● THEOREM 6

   For all $a \in G$, $(a')' = a$.

This is a simple and direct theorem which justifies a procedure you have used many times. Another example similar to this is shown in Theorem 7.

● THEOREM 7

   $(a \circ b)' = b' \circ a'$ for all $a, b \in G$.

The following corollary can be derived from Theorem 7.

   Corollary 1: If $(G, \circ)$ is a commutative group, then $(a \circ b)' = a' \circ b'$.

This theorem and its corollary justify another procedure for simplifying algebraic expressions that you have used many times. For example, $7x - (3x + 4)$ means $7x + [-(3x + 4)]$. You would rewrite this as $7x - 3x - 4$ which means $7x + [-3x + (-4)]$.

Exercises

Write proofs for Exercises 1–3 and justify each step with the appropriate theorem or property.

1. Prove Theorem 6.
2. Prove Theorem 7.
3. Prove Corollary 1.
4. Supply numerical examples to illustrate the use of each theorem and corollary for groups.
5. Prove that a group also has a left cancellation property, that is, if $c \circ a = c \circ b$, then $a = b$.
6. Prove that the equation $x \circ a = b$ in $(G, \circ)$ has a unique solution for all $x, a, b \in G$.
7. Prove that $(a \circ b')' = b \circ a' = a' \circ b$ in any commutative group. Interpret this theorem for a specific case in each of the following

systems. We represent the set of integers with the letter Z and the set of nonzero rational numbers with $Q - 0$.

a. $(Z, +)$ **b.** $(Q - 0, \times)$

8. Solve each equation in the system indicated. Justify each step with a group theorem.

a. $x + 3 = 7$ in $(Z, +)$ **c.** $\frac{1}{3}x = 2$ in $(Q, \times)$

b. $3x = 9$ in $(Q, \times)$ **d.** $2 - x = 5$ in $(Z, +)$

1.7   Fields

The structure of a group is quite simple and yet it enables us to explore many properties of our number system. However, when we encounter problems that involve two or more operations, we need to consider the properties of more complicated algebraic structures.

The basic structure of the real number system is like that of the rational number system considered in Section 1.5. Let us summarize the properties of the rational number system.

SUMMARY

Consider the set of rational numbers under the operations of addition and multiplication symbolized $(Q, +, \times)$.

1. Both $+$ and $\times$ are commutative operations.
2. Both $+$ and $\times$ are associative operations.
3. There is an identity element, 0, for $+$.
4. There is an identity element, 1, for $\times$.
5. Each $a \in Q$ has an additive inverse $-a \in Q$.

6. Each $a \in Q$, $a \neq 0$, has a multiplicative inverse $\frac{1}{a} \in Q$.

7. The operation $\times$ distributes over $+$, that is, $a \times (b + c) =$
   $(a \times b) + (a \times c)$ for all $a, b, c \in Q$.

One additional property is necessary to characterize the algebraic structure of which the rational number system provides an example. There are several ways to formulate this property as an assumption. We will examine three alternatives to illustrate the options a mathematician has in building a mathematical system.

8. If $a, b \in Q$ and $ab = 0$, then $a = 0$ or $b = 0$.

Any system that has each of the Properties 1–8 is a *field*. Property 8 states that there are no nonzero elements whose product is zero. This is a property that you have used many times. However, since it cannot be derived from Properties 1–7, it must be assumed or derived from still other assumptions. For our number system, this property is usually derived from the properties of the order relation to be discussed in Section 1.9. Not all fields are ordered. Thus, we must provide for this property in some other way if we are to characterize fields in general. One way is to add Property 8 to Properties 1–7 as stated. We can also use the following statement in conjunction with Properties 1–7.

8A. If $a, b, c \in Q$ and $ac = bc$, $c \neq 0$, then $a = b$.

Property 8A is the familiar Cancellation Property for Multiplication. Let us prove that Properties 8 and 8A are equivalent assumptions.

• THEOREM

Assumption 8 $\leftrightarrow$ Assumption 8A.

Proof: There are two parts in the proof of this theorem.
Case I. Assumption 8 $\rightarrow$ Assumption 8A.
If Q has Property 8 and $ac = bc$, $c \neq 0$, then

$$ac + (-bc) = 0$$
$$ac - bc = 0$$
$$(a - b)c = 0$$

Since $c \neq 0$, Property 8 states that $a - b = 0$. Thus $a = b$ and Property 8A holds.
Case II. Assumption 8A $\rightarrow$ Assumption 8.
If Q has Property 8A and $ab = 0$ for $a, b \in Q$, then $0 \cdot b = 0 = ab$ or $0 \cdot b = ab$. If $b \neq 0$, Property 8A states that $0 = a$. Thus $a = 0$ or $b = 0$ and Property 8 holds.

Here is another example of the mathematician's privilege of selection within the bounds of logical constraints.

Since the set of rational numbers under addition and multiplication satisfies Properties 1–8 (or 1–8A), it is a field. The real numbers and complex numbers are also fields. We now state a formal definition of this important algebraic structure.

Definition: A *field* is a mathematical system consisting of a nonempty set F with an equivalence relation $=$ and two binary operations, multiplication ($\times$) and addition ($+$), defined on F such that:

1. $(F, +)$ is a commutative group.
2. The set of nonzero elements of F forms a commutative group under multiplication.
3. Multiplication distributes over addition for all a, b, $c \in F$.

Check to see if all the properties listed for rational numbers correspond to Field Properties 1–3 above. You may wonder what happened to Property 8 (or 8A) that was discussed. Do Field Properties 1, 2, or 3 contain information that was not stated earlier in the list of properties for Q (see page 19)? Think carefully about Field Property 2 and you will see that it involves the assumption that the set of all nonzero elements is closed under multiplication. This is not stated explicitly in the properties listed for Q on page 19. We did say that multiplicative inverses exist for all nonzero elements and we already knew that multiplication was associative and commutative, but we did not know that the nonzero elements formed a group under multiplication. What if $a \cdot b = 0$ for some pair where $a \neq 0$ and $b \neq 0$? Then multiplication would not be closed on the set of nonzero elements. Assuming Field Property 2 is equivalent to adding Property 8 (or 8A) to the list for Q. This is another example of the privilege of selection.

Are there algebraic systems based on subsets of the real numbers other than the rational numbers? The answer is yes. The integers with addition and multiplication satisfy all the field properties but one. They do not contain inverse elements with respect to multiplication for all nonzero elements. A structure with these properties is called an *integral domain*. Any theorem proved for an integral domain will be true for a field. However, only those theorems for a field which do not involve inverse elements for multiplication in any way will apply to integral domains.

A *ring* is a structure with two operations, addition and multiplication, that possesses the following properties.

1. It is a commutative group under addition.
2. Multiplication is associative.
3. Multiplication distributes over addition.

Unlike an integral domain, a ring need not have a multiplicative identity element, multiplication need not be commutative, and zero divisors are not excluded. An example of a ring is the set of all 2×2 matrices under matrix addition and multiplication. You will examine this structure in Chapter 4.

Now let us consider a set from *modular arithmetic*. Which of the field properties do you think apply?

FIGURE 1–2

EXAMPLE. Consider the set of integers, $\{0, 1, 2, 3, 4\}$, modulo 5. You can make addition and multiplication tables by referring to a "clock" labeled with these five integers.

Solution. To add 2 and 1, start at 2 and count clockwise one unit. The sum is 3. What is the sum of 2 and 3? Start at 2 and count clockwise three units. The sum is 0.

In a modulo 5 addition table, the sum of any two numbers in the system is found by locating the number at the intersection of the column and row of the addends.

SECOND ELEMENT

+	0	1	2	3	4
0	0	1	2	3	4
1	1	2	3	4	0
2	2	3	4	0	1
3	3	4	0	1	2
4	4	0	1	2	3

FIRST ELEMENT

Multiplication modulo 5 is defined by the following table. Check each product with the clock to see that it satisfies your intuitive understanding of multiplication.

SECOND ELEMENT

		×	0	1	2	3	4
		0	0	0	0	0	0
		1	0	1	2	3	4
FIRST ELEMENT		2	0	2	4	1	3
		3	0	3	1	4	2
		4	0	4	3	2	1

Exercises

In Exercises 1–12, refer to the modulo 5 system in the preceding example.

1. Is addition a commutative operation in this system? Is multiplication commutative? Verify each answer with a specific example.

2. Are addition and multiplication associative in this system? Verify each answer with a specific example.

3. What is the identity element under addition? under multiplication?

4. Does each number in the system have an additive inverse? Verify your answer with a specific example.

5. Does each number in the system have a multiplicative inverse? Verify your answer with a specific example.

6. Does the Distributive Property hold in this system? Give two examples.

7. Is this system a commutative group under addition? under multiplication?

8. Do the nonzero elements form a group under multiplication?

9. Is the modulo 5 system a field?

10. Solve for x: $2x - 4 = x + 4 + 2$ (mod 5).

11. Solve for t: $3t + 2 = t + 3$ (mod 5).

12. Solve for n: $4n - 2 = n + 4$ (mod 5).

13. Set up a modulo 4 system, with tables, like the modulo 5 system we just investigated. Which of the field properties hold in this system? What type of structure is this system?

14. Solve for y: $3(3y) + y - (3 + 1) = 3y - 2 \pmod 4$.

15. Solve for z: $2z + 3 = 5z + 2 \pmod 6$.

Which of the field properties apply to each set of numbers under addition and multiplication as usually defined?

16. $\{-1, 0, 1\}$ **17.** $\{\cdots -2, 0, 2, \cdots\}$

18. $\{x \mid x = 0\} \cup \{x \mid |x| = 2^n, n \in Z\}$

19. Prove that $(a')' = a$ in any integral domain.

20. We have seen that the rational numbers form a field. Do the irrational numbers also form a field?

1.8   Theorems about fields

When you have proved a theorem for a field, you have established a property of the rational, real, and complex numbers simultaneously. You should think about such interpretations as you study these theorems. The system $(F, +)$ is a commutative group. The system $(F - 0, \times)$, where $F - 0$ represents the nonzero elements of F, is also a commutative group. We can, therefore, apply the theorems proved for these groups in fields. We must, however, be careful about zero when working with multiplication. Since the Distributive Property is the only property involving the two operations, we may expect to use it frequently in proving field theorems.

In each of the following theorems, assume that $(F, +, \times)$ is a field. Remember that $-a$ names inverse elements with respect to addition and $\frac{1}{a}$ names inverse elements with respect to multiplication.

● THEOREM 8

If $a \in F$, then $a \cdot 0 = 0$.

Proof: 1. $a + 0 = a$ Additive Identity
2. $a \cdot (a + 0) = a \cdot a$ Theorem 3
3. $a \cdot a + a \cdot 0 = a \cdot a$ Distributive Property
4. $a \cdot a + a \cdot 0 = a \cdot a + 0$ Additive Identity
5. $a \cdot 0 = 0$ Theorem 4

Theorem 9 is a corollary of Theorem 8 and is the converse of Property 8 stated in Section 1.7.

● THEOREM 9

If $a = 0$ or $b = 0$, then $a \cdot b = 0$ for all $a, b \in F$.

Proof: There are three cases in the proof of this theorem.

Case I. If $b = 0$, then $a \cdot b = 0$.   Theorem 8

Case II. If $a = 0$, then

1. $a \cdot b = b \cdot a$	Commutative Property
2. $b \cdot a = 0$	Theorem 8
3. $a \cdot b = 0$	Substitution

Case III. If $a = b = 0$,   Theorem 8
then $a \cdot b = 0$.

● THEOREM 10

For all $a, b \in F$, $a(-b) = -(ab)$.

Corollary 2: For all $a, b \in F$, $(-a)(b) = a(-b) = -(ab)$.

Theorem 11 may appear to be like Theorem 7 and Corollary 1, but it is not. Theorem 7, for groups, involves only one operation. Theorem 11 involves two operations, as do Theorem 10 and Corollary 2, since the inverses are with respect to addition and the operation is multiplication.

● THEOREM 11

For all $a, b \in F$, $(-a)(-b) = ab$.

Do you recognize that these theorems are the familiar properties of positive and negative numbers?

Exercises

Justify each step of the proofs in Exercises 1–3 with the appropriate property, definition, or theorem.

1. Prove Theorem 10.
2. Prove Corollary 2.
3. Prove Theorem 11.

Solve each equation justifying each step with the appropriate reason.

4. $3x + 14 = 2x - 5$
5. $8(x - 3) + 2(12 - x) = 0$
6. $\dfrac{x + 2}{35} + \dfrac{(1 - x)}{20} = 0$
7. $12x - 13 = 3(x - 9) + 4$
8. $5x - 2(x - 3) = 4(x + 7)$

9. $\dfrac{6}{x-3} + 2 = \dfrac{3}{2x-6}$

10. Interpret each of the field theorems by supplying specific instances from the set of rational numbers.

1.9 Ordered fields

The rational number system and the real number system are *ordered fields* because the *order relation* is defined on these sets of numbers.

> **Definition:** For all real numbers a and b, $a < b$ means that there exists a positive real number p such $a + p = b$. Also, $b > a$ means $a < b$. The meaning of $a \leqq b$ is that either $a = b$ or $a < b$.

Formally, we take the word positive as undefined and define the symbol $<$ in terms of the positive numbers. By *positive* we mean the set of all real numbers a for which $0 < a$. We obviously cannot use the symbol $<$ to define positive and then use positive to define the symbol $<$. In this section, you will need to know that the set of positive numbers is closed under addition and multiplication.

There exists a *one-to-one correspondence* between the set of real numbers, R, and the set of points on the number line. If the points representing real numbers a and b are located on the line, then a lies to the left of b if $a < b$ (see Figure 1–3). If point b lies between a and

FIGURE 1–3

c, then the relation $a < b < c$ means that $a < b$ and $b < c$ are both true statements.

PROPERTIES OF THE ORDER RELATION IN A FIELD

1. *Trichotomy Property.* If $a,\, b \in F$, exactly one of the following holds.

$$a < b \text{ or } a = b \text{ or } a > b$$

2. *Transitive Property.* If $a, b, c \in F$ such that $a < b$ and $b < c$, then $a < c$.

We can use these properties to derive theorems that state the familiar facts about our number system. These theorems can be used to find solution sets of inequalities.

● THEOREM 12

For all real numbers a, b, and c, if $a < b$, then $a + c < b + c$. Similarly if $a > b$, then $a + c > b + c$.

Proof: 1. $a < b$ Hypothesis
        2. $a + p = b$ Definition of $<$
        3. $(a + p) + c = b + c$ Theorem 3
        4. $(a + c) + p = b + c$ Commutative and Associative Properties
        5. $a + c < b + c$ Definition of $<$

The proof for the second part of this theorem is similar to this proof.

EXAMPLE. If $7 > -4$, then $7 + 3 > -4 + 3$ or $10 > -1$.

● THEOREM 13

For all real numbers a, b, and c, if $a < b$ and $c > 0$, then $a \cdot c < b \cdot c$. Similarly if $a > b$ and $c > 0$, then $a \cdot c > b \cdot c$.

EXAMPLE. If $-3 < -1$, then $-3 \cdot 5 < -1 \cdot 5$ or $-15 < -5$.

● THEOREM 14

For all real numbers a, b, and c, if $a < b$ and $c < 0$, then $a \cdot c > b \cdot c$. Similarly if $a > b$ and $c < 0$, then $a \cdot c < b \cdot c$.

EXAMPLE. If $4 < 10$, then $4 \cdot -2 > 10 \cdot -2$ or $-8 > -20$.
The following converses of these theorems are also true.

● THEOREM 12A

For all real numbers a, b, and c, if $a + c < b + c$, then $a < b$. Similarly if $a + c > b + c$, then $a > b$.

● THEOREM 13A

For all real numbers a, b, and c, if $a \cdot c < b \cdot c$ and $c > 0$, then $a < b$. Similarly if $a \cdot c > b \cdot c$ and $c > 0$, then $a > b$.

● THEOREM 14A

For all real numbers a, b, and c, if $a \cdot c < b \cdot c$ and $c < 0$, then $a > b$. Similarly if $a \cdot c > b \cdot c$ and $c < 0$, then $a < b$.

In addition to these theorems, it is often necessary to use the Substitution Principle which was mentioned in Section 1.2. For example, if $x = y$ and $y < 0$, then $x < 0$.

The absolute value of a real number may be involved in an inequality relation.

Definition: The *absolute value* of a real number n, symbolized $|n|$, is defined as follows.

$$|n| = n \text{ if } n \geq 0$$
$$|n| = -n \text{ if } n < 0$$

If we write $|x| < 1$, we know that any real number *between* -1 and $+1$ may replace x and produce a true sentence. The following theorem states this for the general case.

● THEOREM 15

For all real numbers x and a, if $a > 0$ and $|x| < a$, then $-a < x < a$. Similarly if $a > 0$ and $|x| \leq a$, then $-a \leq x \leq a$.

● THEOREM 16

For all real numbers x and a, if $a > 0$ and $|x| > a$, then *either* $x < -a$ *or* $x > a$. Similarly if $a > 0$ and $|x| \geq a$, then *either* $x \leq -a$ *or* $x \geq a$.

EXAMPLE 1. Explain the meaning of $|x| > 10$ and graph the solution set on a number line.

Solution. $|x| > 10$ means that $x < -10$ or $x > 10$.

FIGURE 1–4

EXAMPLE 2. Explain the meaning of $|x| \leq 5$ and graph the solution set on a number line.

Solution. $|x| \leq 5$ means that $x \geq -5$ and $x \leq 5$, or $-5 \leq x \leq 5$.

FIGURE 1–5

In each of the following examples, an inequality is solved for x and the solution set is graphed on a number line.

EXAMPLE 3. Solve $2x + 3 \leq x + 5$.

Solution. $2x + 3 \leq x + 5$ Hypothesis
              $2x \leq x + 2$ Theorem 12A
                $x \leq 2$ Theorem 12A
The solution set is $\{x \mid x \leq 2\}$.

FIGURE 1–6

EXAMPLE 4. Solve $7 - 2x < 13$.

Solution. $7 - 2x < 13$ Hypothesis
            $-2x < 6$ Theorem 12A
              $x > -3$ Theorem 14 (Multiply by $-\frac{1}{2}$ and note the reversal of order.)

The solution set is $\{x \mid x > -3\}$.

FIGURE 1–7

EXAMPLE 5. Solve $x^2 > 1$.

Solution. $x^2 > 1$ Hypothesis
         $x^2 - 1 > 0$ Theorem 12A
    $(x + 1)(x - 1) > 0$ Factor

Since the product of $x + 1$ and $x - 1$ is positive, then either (1) $x + 1 > 0$ *and* $x - 1 > 0$ or (2) $x + 1 < 0$ *and* $x - 1 < 0$. From (1) we have $x > -1$ and $x > 1$ which is true only when $x > 1$. From (2) we have $x < -1$ and $x < 1$ which is true only if $x < -1$. The solution set is $\{x \mid x > 1\} \cup \{x \mid x < -1\}$.

FIGURE 1–8

Exercises

Write the following statements in symbols.

1. **a.** x is a real number greater than y.
   b. a is a negative integer.
   c. r is greater than its reciprocal.
   d. x is a number between 5 and 20, inclusive.
   e. x is a number between 5 and 20, exclusive.
   f. x is a number between -4 and 4. Use two methods.
   g. The average of two different numbers lies between the numbers.
   h. The absolute value of the sum of x and y is less than or equal to the sum of their absolute values.

In Exercises 2–19, find the values for x in each solution set and graph each solution set on a number line.

2. $\{x \mid 2x > 1\}$

3. $\{x \mid 3x > 12\}$

4. $\{x \mid 4x < 1\}$

5. $\{x \mid x + 2 > 0\}$
6. $\{x \mid x - 3 < 7\}$

7. $\{x \mid x - 1 < 0\}$

8. $\{x \mid -2x - 3 < 5\}$
9. $\{x \mid 3x + 1 > 0\}$
10. $\{x \mid -5x - 2 < 4\}$

11. $\left\{x \mid \dfrac{1}{2} x < 7\right\}$

12. $\left\{x \mid 2\dfrac{1}{2} x > 3\right\}$

13. $\left\{x \mid -\dfrac{2}{3} x < 1\right\}$

14. $\{x \mid 2x - 1 > 3x + 2\}$
15. $\{x \mid 5x + 3 < x - 2\}$

16. $\left\{x \mid \dfrac{1}{2} x + 6 > \dfrac{1}{3} x - 3\right\}$

17. $\{x \mid x^2 > 0\}$
18. $\{x \mid x^2 - 2 < 1\}$
19. $\{x \mid x^2 - x - 6 < 0\}$

20. Interpret Theorems 12A, 13A, and 14A by supplying specific instances from the set of rational numbers.

21. Prove the second part of Theorem 12.

22. Prove Theorem 13.

23. Prove that if $a > 0$, then $-a < 0$.

24. Prove Theorem 14.

25. Prove Theorems 12A, 13A, and 14A.

26. Prove that any nonzero real number and its reciprocal have the same sign.

27. Prove that if $a < b$ and $c < d$, then $a + c < b + d$.

28. Prove that if $a < b$, then $-a > -b$.

29. Prove that if $ab < 0$, then $a > 0$ *and* $b < 0$ or $a < 0$ *and* $b > 0$.

30. Prove that if $a \neq 0$, then $a^2 > 0$.

1.10   The complex numbers

Not all fields are *ordered*. One important example is the complex number system.

A complex number may be defined as an ordered pair of real numbers (a, b). We often write such a number as $a + bi$ where a and b are real numbers and i is defined by $i^2 = -1$. The *real part* of the complex number $a + bi$ is a, and the *imaginary part* is b.

How can powers of i be simplified? If we know that $i^1 = i$ and $i^2 = -1$, we can build higher powers of i by multiplication. Here are the first few powers of i.

$$i^3 = -i \qquad\qquad i^6 = -1$$
$$i^4 = 1 \qquad\qquad i^7 = -i$$
$$i^5 = i \qquad\qquad i^8 = 1$$

In general, i^n, where n is a natural number, can be reduced to 1, i, -1, or $-i$. Noting the cyclic nature of the results and observing that $i^n = 1$ whenever n is divisible by 4, we deduce that $i^n = i^{4r+s} = i^s$ where $s = 0, 1, 2,$ or 3. The simplification of i^n is accomplished by dividing n by 4 and expressing the result as 1, i, -1, or $-i$ if the remainder is 0, 1, 2, or 3, respectively.

EXAMPLE. $i^{35} = i^{4 \cdot 8 + 3} = i^3 = -i$.

The four fundamental operations with complex numbers are defined by the following equations where $a + bi$ and $c + di$ are any two complex numbers.

ADDITION: $(a + bi) + (c + di) = (a + c) + (b + d)i$

SUBTRACTION: $(a + bi) - (c + di) = (a + bi) + [-(c + di)]$
$$= (a + bi) + (-c - di)$$
$$= (a - c) + (b - d)i$$

MULTIPLICATION: $(a + bi)(c + di) = (ac - bd) + (ad + bc)i$

DIVISION: $\dfrac{(a + bi)}{(c + di)} = \dfrac{(ac + bd) + (bc - ad)i}{c^2 + d^2}$, provided c and d are not both zero.

The relationship of the set of real numbers to the set of complex numbers is evident if we set b equal to zero and let a be a real number. We see that the set of real numbers is a subset of the set of complex numbers.

Similarly, if $a = 0$ and b is a nonzero real number, we obtain numbers of the form bi that are called *pure imaginary* numbers.

For positive real numbers a: $\sqrt{-a} = i\sqrt{a}.$

When both a and b are not equal to zero, the complex number is neither a real nor a pure imaginary number.

Now that the fundamental operations with complex numbers have been defined, it is possible to compare the properties of the real numbers with those of the complex numbers. The notable exception in comparing the properties is the matter of *order*. We cannot say that one complex number is greater or less than another; we can only say that two complex numbers are equal or they are not equal. For the purpose of consistency we make the following definition.

Definition: $a + bi = c + di$ if and only if $a = c$ and $b = d$.

In the following exercises, the field properties of Section 1.7 are investigated in relation to the complex number field.

Exercises

1. Show that the set of complex numbers forms a commutative group under addition. Write the identity element for this group and the inverse element for $a + bi$.

2. Show that the set of nonzero complex numbers forms a commutative group under multiplication. Write the identity element for this group and the inverse element of $a + bi$ if a, $b \neq 0$.

3. Show that the Distributive Property for Multiplication over Addition holds in the set of complex numbers.

Perform the indicated operations.

4. $(3 - 7i) + (2 + 5i)$

5. $(-12 + 3i) - (7 - 5i)$

6. $(6 - 3i)(\sqrt{2} - i\sqrt{3})$

7. $(\sqrt[3]{4} + i\sqrt{2})(2 + i)$

8. $\dfrac{-15 + i}{4 + 2i}$

9. $\dfrac{4 - 3i}{2 + i}$

10. $(3 - 2i)^3$

11. $(1 - i)^4$

12. Find $\sqrt{2i}$. (*Hint:* The form is $a + bi$.)

Chapter Review

1. Why must every mathematical system contain undefined elements?

2. What is the difference between a theorem and a postulate in a mathematical system?

3. What is the role of an assumption in a mathematical system? of a definition? of a theorem?

4. What are the advantages of creating and studying abstract mathematical systems?

5. An equivalence relation satisfies what properties?

6. What property of equality distinguishes it from all other equivalence relations?

7. Give three examples of relations that satisfy some, but not all, of the properties of an equivalence relation. Identify the property or properties satisfied and show why the remaining properties are not satisfied.

8. To be an operation on a given set, what conditions must a correspondence satisfy?

9. Give an example of a correspondence that is not an operation on each set.
   a. The set of natural numbers
   b. The set of integers
   c. The set of rational numbers

10. Give an example of an operation that is not commutative on some set S.

11. Give numerical examples to show how the Associative Property is used to simplify expressions involving addition and multiplication on the set of real numbers.

12. Give numerical examples to show that both subtraction and division are neither commutative nor associative operations on the set of real numbers.

13. Given the set $S = \{\square, \triangle, \bigcirc, \times\}$, define a commutative operation $*$ on S such that $\times$ is the identity element and each element is its own inverse. Display your operation in a table. What type of algebraic system have you created?

14. Do the even integers form a group under addition? the odd integers?

15. Give an algebraic example to illustrate each of the theorems for groups and fields.

16. Given the commutative groups $(S, +)$ and $(S - 0, \times)$, what additional property is required for S to be a field?

17. Given that the domain of x is the set of real numbers, find the solution set for each sentence justifying each step.
   a. $3(x - 2) = x + 4$ **c.** $3x - 1 < x + 4$
   b. $x^2 - 3x - 4 = 0$ **d.** $x^2 - 4 < 0$
                    e. $x < x^2 - 3$

18. What is the multiplicative inverse of the complex number $3 - 2i$?

19. Simplify $\dfrac{\sqrt{2} + i\sqrt{3}}{4 - i\sqrt{2}}$.

20. Expand $(1 - i)^3$.

CHAPTER OUTLINE

Linear Relations

2

2.1 Linear functions

A *variable* is any symbol which represents an element of a specified set. The set may be the set of the integers, the rational numbers, the real numbers, the set of complex numbers, or any other set.

If x is a variable, an expression such as $2x - 5$ is also a variable. The value of the expression $2x - 5$ depends upon the value of x. We can also say that the value of x depends upon the value of the expression $2x - 5$ because if we specify a value of the expression, that value of x which makes the statement true is determined. Thus, if we specify that $2x - 5 = 7$, then it follows that $x = 6$. Often we represent a variable such as $2x - 5$ by a symbol such as y and write $y = 2x - 5$. We call x the *independent variable* and $2x - 5$, or y, the *dependent variable*. The equation $y = 2x - 5$ is solved for the dependent variable in terms of the independent variable.

A sentence relating two variables is sometimes called a *set-selector*. This sentence can be stated in words, as an equation, or as an inequality. For example, if the statement of the relation between x and y is $y = 2x$, then we can select from the set of real numbers sample replacements for x and compute corresponding replacements for y. Thus, if we select the number 2 as a replacement for x, then $y = 4$ and we have the sample ordered pair $(2, 4)$. In a similar way, we find that $(-1, -2)$ satisfies $y = 2x$. We can find other sample ordered pairs.

$$\{(+2, +4), (-1, -2), (0, 0), (1, 2), (-2, -4), \cdots\}$$

An expression such as $\{(x, y) \mid y = 2x\}$ may be called a *set-builder*. This is read "the set of all ordered pairs (x, y) such that $y = 2x$." It designates the set of all ordered pairs (x, y) defined by the set-selector $y = 2x$.

The concept of pairing the elements of one set with the elements of another set is one of the most important in mathematics. We call such a pairing a mathematical relation.

✷ **Definition:** A *relation* is defined when a rule assigns one or more elements of a set R to each element of a set D. A relation can be expressed as a set of ordered pairs.

The set D from which the first members of the ordered pairs are selected is called the *domain*, or the domain of definition. Each element of set D is paired with an element of set R, called the *range*. Let us consider some examples of relations.

Suppose x is a variable representing an element of the set of positive integers less than 6, and y is a variable representing a number found by multiplying each replacement of x by 5. The equation $y = 5x$ can be written to show this relationship. The relation thus established can be expressed as the following set of ordered pairs.

$$\{(1, 5), (2, 10), (3, 15), (4, 20), (5, 25)\}$$

The domain set is $\{1, 2, 3, 4, 5\}$. The range set is $\{5, 10, 15, 20, 25\}$.

Now suppose we have the same domain as in the previous example, but the rule which assigns numbers to be paired is expressed by the inequality $y > 2x$ where y represents an integer. In this case we can write some of the ordered pairs in the relation as follows.

$$\{(1, 3), (2, 8), (5, 21), (2, 5), (1, 10), \cdots\}$$

Notice that the same first element can be paired with more than one second element in this relation.

This concept of pairing of elements of two sets can be extended to include sets where the elements are not necessarily numbers. The sets may involve elements of any kind; the essential characteristic which determines a relation is the nature of the rule which establishes it. We are now ready to make a formal definition of function.

> **Definition:** A *function* is defined when a rule assigns *exactly one* element of a set R to each element of a set D.

An alternate definition equivalent to that given in the preceding statement is: A function is a set of ordered pairs in which no two pairs have the same first element. The rule for a relation or function may be a formal rule stated as an equation such as $y = x^2 - 8x + 2$, or $2x + 3y = 5$. Elements of the domain set are represented by x, the independent variable; the elements of the range set are represented by y, the dependent variable. Other symbols may be used for the variables. The rule may also be given as a graph, a table of values, in words or symbols, or as a list of ordered pairs. The last method is useful when there is no pattern so that the rule is implied by the set of ordered pairs itself.

The most common way of representing the rule for a function is by a letter, usually f. We write $y = f(x)$ which indicates that for each selected element which replaces x, the function assigns one and only one replacement of y. The symbol $f(x)$ is read "f of x" but should be interpreted as "the value of function f at x." The ordered pairs of the function are written in the form (x, y) or $(x, f(x))$.

EXAMPLE. If $f(x) = 3x - 2$, find $f(-1)$.

Solution. $f(-1) = 3(-1) - 2 = -3 - 2 = -5$

Of the many functions ordinarily studied in algebra, the linear function is the simplest. A function is *linear* if it is defined by an equation of the form $y = ax + b$ where a and b are real numbers and the replacement set for x is the set of real numbers. Every first degree equation in two variables can be written in this form. The name "linear" is applied to such equations and to the functions they define because the set of points $(x, ax + b)$ determines a straight line.

One important problem in the study of functions is to identify values of the independent variable for which the value of the function is zero. Such values are called *zeros of the function*. For a linear function, these values are found by solving the equation $ax + b = 0$. If $a \neq 0$, the solution set of this equation is $\left\{ -\dfrac{b}{a} \right\}$ and $-\dfrac{b}{a}$ is the only zero of the function. This means that $\left(-\dfrac{b}{a}, 0 \right)$ is one member of $\{(x, y) \mid y = ax + b\}$.

When $a = 0$, the defining equation for the linear function becomes $y = b$, and the value of the function is the same for all values of x. Therefore, in this case, there are either no zeros of the function ($b \neq 0$), or every value of x is a zero of the function ($b = 0$).

There is a one-to-one correspondence between the set of all possible ordered pairs of real numbers and the set of all points in a coordinate plane. That is, if any ordered pair (x, y) is stated, there is a unique point corresponding to it in the coordinate plane. Conversely, for any point in the coordinate plane, there corresponds a unique ordered pair. For example, in Figure 2–1, the points A, B, C, D, and E correspond respectively to the ordered pairs $(-2, -2.5)$, $(-1, -2)$, $(0, -1.5)$, $(+3, 0)$, and $(+5, +1)$.

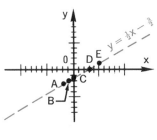

FIGURE 2–1

If the points are connected by a smooth curve, in this case a straight line, we get the graph of the function defined by the set-selector $y = \dfrac{1}{2}x - \dfrac{3}{2}$ which is satisfied by the given ordered pairs. In a later section of this chapter you will learn how to write the equation of a line if you are given two points of the line.

Exercises

For each of the following functions, select 5 sample integral values of the independent variable and compute corresponding values of the dependent variable.

1. $(x, -x + 3)$

2. $y = x^2$

3. $y = x^3$

4. $\{(x, y) \mid y = x^2 + 2\}$

5. $\{(s, t) \mid t = s^2 - s - 6\}$

Find the value of the function for each indicated value of the independent variable.

6. If $f(x) = x + 2$, find $f(1)$

7. If $f(x) = 3x - 1$, find $f(-1)$

8. If $f(n) = n^2$, find $f(-2)$

9. If $f(v) = 1 - 4v$, find $f(0)$

10. If $f(r) = 7 - r^2$, find $f(4)$

11. If $f(y) = 1 + y - y^2$, find $f(0)$

12. Copy the table and fill the blanks given that $f(x) = 7x - 2$.

x	-3	-2	-1	0	$+1$	$+2$	$+3$	$+5$
$f(x)$	-23							

13. Use the set-selector $y = 3x - 1$ to determine a set of sample ordered pairs of numbers. If the domain is the set of real numbers, what is the range? What is the independent variable?

14. Use the set-selector $y = x^2 - x - 2$ to determine a set of sample ordered pairs. If the domain is the set of real numbers, what is the range? What is the independent variable? What is the dependent variable?

15. If $f(x) = \dfrac{x + 3}{x - 2}$, find a set of sample ordered pairs. What number is not in the domain?

16. Find the zero of each linear function.

a. $x + 3y = 7$

b. $\dfrac{x - 2}{3} = y + 4$

c. $2x - y = \dfrac{4x - 3}{2}$

d. $3y - 2x = x + y$

17. Use the field properties of the real numbers to verify that
$$\{x \mid ax + b = 0, a \neq 0\} = \left\{x \mid x = -\frac{b}{a}\right\}.$$

18. Write an equation which defines a linear function whose zero is $\dfrac{4}{3}$.

19. Write a linear function which has the same zero as the function defined by $y = 2x - 5$.

20. Describe a family of straight lines in a coordinate plane which is *not* defined by equations of the form $y = ax + b$.

Graph each of the given functions by finding sample ordered pairs and plotting them on a coordinate plane. The graph of each is a straight line.

21. $\{(x, 3x - 2)\}$

22. $\{(x, f(x)) \mid f(x) = .5x + 1\}$

23. $\{(x, f(x)) \mid f(x) = .3 - .2x\}$

24. $\{(x, y) \mid 4x + y = -5\}$

25. $\{(x, y) \mid x + y = 2.5\}$

2.2 Distance on a line

It is often necessary to find the distance between two points in the coordinate plane. First, however, we shall investigate the distance between two points on a number line.

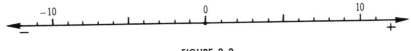

FIGURE 2–2

Let A and B be two points on the line with coordinates a and b, respectively. The distance between A and B is defined to be $|b - a|$ (read, "the absolute value of $b - a$"). Note that the distance between two points is always positive. If we wish to take into account the direction of the line segment, we shall write this in the form of a vector $\overrightarrow{AB}$. Thus, the distance between A and B can be designated as $|AB|$ or $|b - a|$, but the directed line segment from A to B is $\overrightarrow{AB}$ and from B to A is $\overrightarrow{BA}$ or $-\overrightarrow{AB}$.

As a specific example, let A be at $+2$ and B be at $+7$ on the number line. The distance between A and B is $|7 - 2|$ or 5; the distance between B and A is $|2 - 7|$ or 5. The directed distance from A to B $(\overrightarrow{AB})$ is $7 - 2$ or $+5$; the directed distance from B to A $(\overrightarrow{BA})$ is $2 - 7$ or -5.

Note: Following this chapter, we will drop the absolute value signs and simply use AB. The context will tell you whether we are referring to the *line segment* or to the *measure* of the segment. A similar convention will be adopted with angles and arcs in later chapters. Since equality must mean identity, the context will determine whether the reference is to the figure or the measure. For example, corresponding *angles* of two congruent triangles are *congruent,* but their *measures* are *equal.*

Now let us turn our attention to the coordinate plane. We shall first consider the special case where we are to find the distance between the points $R(2, 3)$ and $S(6, 6)$. Draw the line segment RS. If ST is drawn parallel to the y-axis and RT is drawn parallel to the x-axis, right triangle RTS is formed. Why? The coordinates of vertex T are $(6, 3)$. Why?

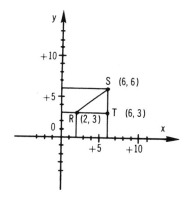

FIGURE 2–3

Since R and T have the same ordinates, the distance $|RT|$ is equal to the absolute value of the difference of the abscissas of the points. Thus, $|RT| = |6 - 2|$ = 4. Since S and T have the same abscissas, the distance $|TS|$ equals the absolute value of the difference of the ordinates of the points. Thus, $|TS| = |6 - 3| = 3$. By the Pythagorean Theorem the distance between R and S is

$$|RS| = \sqrt{|RT|^2 + |TS|^2}$$
$$|RS| = \sqrt{4^2 + 3^2}$$
$$|RS| = 5$$

The distance between R and S is 5 units.

Now suppose $P(x_1, y_1)$ and $Q(x_2, y_2)$ are any two points in the coordinate plane. How can we find the distance between P and Q? As in the example above we shall draw PA parallel to the x-axis and QB parallel to the y-axis. We know that PA will intersect QB at some point H. Why are the coordinates of H (x_2, y_1) ? Is angle PHQ a right angle?

The distance between P and H is

$$|PH| = |x_2 - x_1|$$

The distance between Q and H is

$$|QH| = |y_2 - y_1|$$

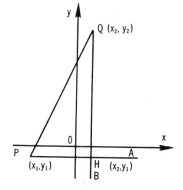

FIGURE 2–4

By the Pythagorean Theorem the distance between P and Q is

$$|PQ| = \sqrt{|PH|^2 + |QH|^2}$$

or

$$|PQ| = \sqrt{|x_2 - x_1|^2 + |y_2 - y_1|^2}$$

Since $|x_2 - x_1|^2 = (x_2 - x_1)^2$ the *distance formula* is usually written in this form:

$$|PQ| = \sqrt{(x_2 - x_1)^2 + (y_2 - y_1)^2} \qquad (I)$$

Note that the distance between two points in the coordinate plane is always measured by a positive number.

EXAMPLE. Find the distance between $P(3, -5)$ and $Q(-1, 2)$.

Solution. Let $(x_1, y_1) = (3, -5)$ and $(x_2, y_2) = (-1, 2)$, so that we can apply the distance formula.

$$|PQ| = \sqrt{(x_2 - x_1)^2 + (y_2 - y_1)^2}$$
$$|PQ| = \sqrt{(-1 - 3)^2 + [2 - (-5)]^2}$$
$$|PQ| = \sqrt{(-4)^2 + (7)^2}$$
$$|PQ| = \sqrt{16 + 49}$$
$$|PQ| = \sqrt{65}$$

Alternate solution. Let $(x_1, y_1) = (-1, 2)$ and $(x_2, y_2) = (3, -5)$. Then,

$$|PQ| = \sqrt{[3 - (-1)]^2 + (-5 - 2)^2}$$
$$|PQ| = \sqrt{(4)^2 + (-7)^2}$$
$$|PQ| = \sqrt{16 + 49}$$
$$|PQ| = \sqrt{65}$$

We see that either P or Q can be (x_1, y_1) and the distance does not depend upon the order of the points.

Exercises

Find the distance between the given points.

1. $A(4, 1)$, $B(7, 1)$
2. $C(7, 1)$, $D(4, 1)$
3. $E(5, 1)$, $F(5, 11)$
4. $G(-1, -3)$, $H(-1, 3)$
5. $J(0, 0)$, $K(-4, -3)$
6. $L(-1, 1)$, $M(4, 13)$
7. $P(-2, 2)$, $Q(0, 4)$
8. $R(1, -5)$, $S(-7, 11)$
9. Find the perimeter of the triangle with vertices at $R(2, 3)$, $S(14, 3)$, and $T(14, 8)$.
10. Find the perimeter of the triangle with vertices at $A(3, 8)$, $B(-2, 4)$, and $C(0, -2)$.

2.3　Slope of a line

Every line in a plane either is parallel to the x-axis or intersects the x-axis. If a line intersects the x-axis, the angle between the axis and the line is called the *angle of inclination* of the line. The angle of inclination is measured from the positive direction of the x-axis counter-clockwise to the line.

In the drawing, line l_1 has an angle of inclination α_1 and line l_2 has an angle of inclination α_2 . If line l_3 is a line parallel to the x-axis, l_1 makes an angle with l_3 equal to α_1 . Why?

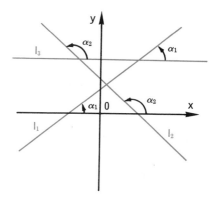

The angle of inclination of a line parallel to the x-axis is zero. Can the angle of inclination of a line ever be greater than 180°? What is the angle of inclination of a line parallel to the y-axis?

FIGURE 2–5

A very important property of a line is that it has a *slope* which is constant. Before we define the slope of a line let us select two points A and B on a line and determine right triangle ACB by constructing AC parallel to the x-axis and BC parallel to the y-axis.

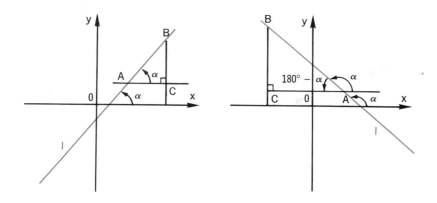

FIGURE 2–6

There are two special cases where no triangle can be formed by this procedure. How can a line be situated so that no triangle is formed when two points are selected on it and parallels to the axes drawn? We shall consider these two special cases later.

If α is the angle of inclination of line l, angle BAC is equal either to α or to the supplement of α, as you can see in the figures above. We shall define the *slope of a line* as the ratio of the directed distances $\dfrac{\overrightarrow{CB}}{\overrightarrow{AC}}$. This ratio is frequently expressed as the *rise* divided by the *run*. The direction of the line segments is important. The slope is positive or negative according to the sign of the ratio. If α is an acute angle, the slope is positive. Why? If α is an obtuse angle, the slope is negative. Why?

An equivalent definition of the slope of a line to that given above is *the slope of a line equals the tangent of the angle of inclination*. If m is the slope of a line, then the definitions can be summarized as follows.

Slope of a line:

(a) $m = \dfrac{\overrightarrow{CB}}{\overrightarrow{AC}}$, where A and B are any two points on the line and C

is the vertex of the right triangle formed when a line parallel to the x-axis is drawn through A and a line parallel to the y-axis is drawn through B.

(b) $m = \tan \alpha$, where α is the angle of inclination of the line.

If a line is parallel to the x-axis, its slope is defined to be zero. Is this consistent with the definition of slope? If a line is parallel to the y-axis, the line has no slope, that is, the slope of such a line does not exist. Is this consistent with the definition? Why? You must distinguish between zero slope and undefined slope.

EXAMPLE 1. Find the slope of a line which passes through the points $A(-3, 2)$ and $B(5, 7)$.

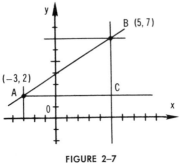

FIGURE 2-7

Solution. Make a drawing of the line on the coordinate plane. Through A and B draw lines parallel to the axes determining point C as shown. What are the coordinates of vertex C? Is angle ACB a right angle?

The directed distance $\overrightarrow{AC}$ is equal to $5 - (-3) = 8$. Why? The directed distance $\overrightarrow{CB} = 7 - 2 = 5$. Why? Thus the slope of the line is

$$m = \frac{\overrightarrow{CB}}{\overrightarrow{AC}}; \; m = \frac{5}{8}$$

EXAMPLE 2. A line intersects the x-axis at $+5$ and passes through the point $(-3, 4)$. Find the slope of the line.

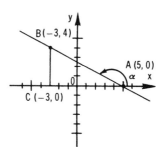

Solution. Select the points on the line $A(5, 0)$ and $B(-3, 4)$. The coordinates of C in right triangle ACB are $(-3, 0)$. The slope of the line is

$$m = \frac{\overrightarrow{CB}}{\overrightarrow{AC}} = \frac{4 - 0}{-3 - 5} = \frac{4}{-8} = -\frac{1}{2}$$

FIGURE 2–8

Note that the slope of a line is positive if it extends to the upper right and negative if it extends to the lower right.

EXAMPLE 3. Find the tangent of the angle of inclination of the line $x + y = 5$.

Solution. Find the coordinates of two points on the line. If $x = 1$, then $y = 4$, and point $A(1, 4)$ is on the line. Point $B(5, 0)$ is also on the line. Vertex C of right triangle ACB is at $(5, 4)$. The tangent of the angle of inclination is equal to the slope; therefore

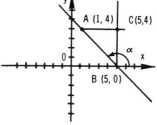

$$\tan \alpha = m = \frac{\overrightarrow{CB}}{\overrightarrow{AC}}$$

$$\tan \alpha = \frac{0 - 4}{5 - 1} = \frac{-4}{4} = -1$$

FIGURE 2–9

Exercises

Graph the given points and find the slope of the line passing through them if there is a slope.

1. $A(2, 2)$, $B(6, 6)$ **2.** $C(-1, 3)$, $D(3, 7)$

3. $E(0, 2), F(-4, 7)$ **6.** $L(4, 2), M(11, 2)$

4. $G(0, 0), H(-1, -5)$ **7.** $R(-3, 2), S(-8, 2)$

5. $J(1, -3), K(-1, 3)$ **8.** $T(4, 2), U(4, 7)$

9. What is the tangent of the angle of inclination of the line
$2x - y + 4 = 0$?

10. What "run" will produce a "rise" of 6 units for the line
$3y = 2x + 9$?

2.4   General equation of a line

The general form of the equation of a line is

$$Ax + By + C = 0$$

where A, B, and C are real numbers, but A and B cannot both be zero. For convenience we shall restrict A, B, and C in our examples to the set of rational numbers.

If we wish to find the point at which the line intersects the x-axis (if it does), we can set $y = 0$, since any point on the x-axis will be of the form $(a, 0)$. Solving for x, we get

$$Ax + B \cdot 0 + C = 0$$

$$x = -\frac{C}{A}$$

The x-intercept of a line is $-\dfrac{C}{A}$. Can you show that the y-intercept is $-\dfrac{C}{B}$? What value has A if there is no x-intercept? What value has B if there is no y-intercept?

How can we find the slope of a line if we are given the equation of the line? If the equation is not already in general form, it can be transformed so that it is. Assume $A \neq 0$ and $B \neq 0$. We can find immediately the coordinates of two points on the line, namely, the x-intercept and the y-intercept. Let P be the x-intercept which has the coordinates $(-\dfrac{C}{A},\ 0)$; let Q be the y-intercept which has the

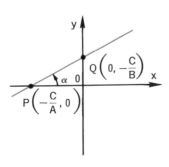

FIGURE 2-10

coordinates $\left(0, -\dfrac{C}{B}\right)$. Then triangle POQ is a right triangle and we can determine the slope of the line through P and Q.

$$m = \frac{\overrightarrow{OQ}}{\overrightarrow{PO}} = \frac{-\dfrac{C}{B} - 0}{0 - \left(-\dfrac{C}{A}\right)} = \frac{-\dfrac{C}{B}}{\dfrac{C}{A}} = -\frac{A}{B}$$

Thus, the slope of a line in general form ($B \neq 0$) is $-\dfrac{A}{B}$.

EXAMPLE. Find the x- and y-intercepts of the line $2x - 5y = 15$. Find the slope of the line.

Solution. The equation in general form is $2x - 5y - 15 = 0$, where $A = 2$, $B = -5$, and $C = -15$.

The x-intercept is $-\dfrac{C}{A} = -\dfrac{-15}{2} = 7\frac{1}{2}$. The y-intercept is

$-\dfrac{C}{B} = -\dfrac{-15}{-5} = -3$.

The slope is $-\dfrac{A}{B} = -\dfrac{2}{-5} = \dfrac{2}{5}$.

Exercises

Find the x- and y-intercepts of each of the following lines. Find the slope if it exists. Graph each equation.

1. $2x - 5 = 0$ $x = 2.5$
2. $x - 2y - 4 = 0$
3. $3x + y = 2$
4. $3y - 1 = 0$
5. $8x = 2y - 1$
6. $2x - 5y - 10 = 0$
7. $4x + 3y = 0$
8. $7x + 2y = -12$

9. Find the slope of each side of the triangle with the sides $4x + 3y + 1 = 0$, $4x - 3y - 17 = 0$, and $4x - 9y + 13 = 0$.

10. Find the vertices of the triangle in Exercises 9 by solving the equations as simultaneous pairs.

2.5   Other equations of a line

The position of a line in the coordinate plane is fully determined if

    a. two points on the line are known, or

    b. the slope and one point on the line are known.

As we have seen, the slope of a line is constant. If any two points on the line, $P(x_1, y_1)$ and $Q(x_2, y_2)$, are known, it can be shown that the slope is given by the formula

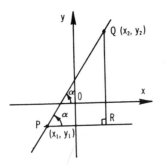

FIGURE 2–11

$$m = \frac{y_2 - y_1}{x_2 - x_1} \qquad \text{(II)}$$

The proof is left to the student as an exercise. (*Hint:* Find the coordinates of R.) Thus, if any two points on a line are known, or can be found, the slope can be readily computed.

Suppose the equation of a line is desired when two points on the line are known. By means of Formula (II) the slope can always be computed unless $x_1 = x_2$, that is, unless the line is perpendicular to the x-axis. If the slope is known and one or more points on the line known, how can we write the equation of the line?

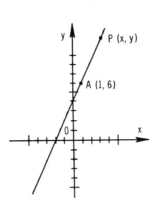

FIGURE 2–12

Let us consider the example where a line passes through the point $A(1, 6)$ and has a slope of $+2$. Select any other point on the line $P(x, y)$. Formula (II) gives us the slope of the line as

$$m = \frac{y_2 - y_1}{x_2 - x_1}$$

We can replace (x_1, y_1) with the coordinates of A, (x_2, y_2) with the coordinates of P, and the slope, m, with $+2$ to obtain

$$+2 = \frac{y - 6}{x - 1} \quad \text{or} \quad 2x - 2 = y - 6$$

In general form the equation of the line is

$$2x - y + 4 = 0$$

Several standard forms of the equation of a line may be defined based upon the general principles illustrated above. We shall list these forms for reference, but you are reminded that the equation of a line can be written using Formula (II) whenever the slope and one point are known or can be found.

If the slope m does not exist, the equation of the line will be of the form $x = a$ where a is the x-intercept; the line is parallel to the y-axis.

SUMMARY OF METHODS FOR FORMING THE EQUATION OF A LINE

1. The *slope-intercept* form. The general form of the equation of a line can be transformed as follows.

$$Ax + By + C = 0$$

or
$$By = -Ax - C$$

or
$$y = -\frac{A}{B}x - \frac{C}{B}$$

Note that the coefficient of x, $-\dfrac{A}{B}$, is the slope m, and the constant term, $-\dfrac{C}{B}$, is the y-intercept which we shall call b. The slope-intercept form of the equation of a line is

$$y = mx + b \tag{III}$$

2. The *point-slope* form. If the point $P(x_1, y_1)$ lies on a line and the slope is m, from Formula (II), we can immediately write the point-slope form of the equation of a line as

$$m = \frac{y - y_1}{x - x_1} \tag{IV}$$

or
$$y - y_1 = m(x - x_1)$$

3. The *two-point* form. If two points $P(x_1, y_1)$ and $Q(x_2, y_2)$ are known, the slope can be computed by Formula (II) as follows.

$$m = \frac{y_2 - y_1}{x_2 - x_1}$$

Then, considering either P or Q as a known point, the slope is also given by

$$m = \frac{y - y_1}{x - x_1} \quad \text{or} \quad \frac{y - y_2}{x - x_2}$$

Since the slope is constant we can equate the two values of the slope and write the two-point form of the equation of a line as follows.

$$\frac{y - y_1}{x - x_1} = \frac{y_2 - y_1}{x_2 - x_1} \tag{V}$$

or

$$y - y_1 = \left(\frac{y_2 - y_1}{x_2 - x_1}\right)(x - x_1)$$

Note that this form is similar to the point-slope form except that here the slope must first be computed.

EXAMPLE 1. Find the equation of a line which passes through the points $A(1, 4)$ and $B(5, 7)$.

Solution. Computing the slope of the line by Formula (II), we have

$$m = \frac{7 - 4}{5 - 1} = \frac{3}{4}$$

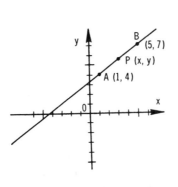

FIGURE 2–13

Now, selecting a general point $P(x, y)$ on the line, we can write, also by Formula (II), the slope is

$$m = \frac{y - 4}{x - 1}$$

Since $m = \frac{3}{4}$, the equation becomes

$$\frac{3}{4} = \frac{y - 4}{x - 1}$$

In general form the equation of the line is $3x - 4y + 13 = 0$. The two-point form of the equation of a line could be applied directly to give the same result.

EXAMPLE 2. A line passing through the point $(0, -4)$ has a slope of -2. Write the equation of the line in general form.

Solution. Applying the slope-intercept form of the equation of a line, we see that $m = -2$ and $b = -4$. Thus, the equation $y = mx + b$ becomes $y = -2x - 4$.

In general form this is

$$2x + y + 4 = 0$$

As an alternate solution, the equation of the line can be written by referring to Formula (II) which gives us

$$-2 = \frac{y - (-4)}{x - 0} \text{ or } -2x = y + 4$$

In general form the equation is

$$2x + y + 4 = 0$$

EXAMPLE 3. Find the y-intercept of the line passing through $(-4, 1)$ having a slope of $\frac{2}{3}$.

Solution. Write the equation of the line by means of the point-slope form. We get

$$y - y_1 = m(x - x_1)$$

$$y - 1 = \frac{2}{3}[x - (-4)]$$

y = mx + b

y = ⅔x + 1

The equation in general form is

$$2x - 3y + 11 = 0$$

Now that we have the equation, the y-intercept can be found by three methods.

a. y-intercept $= -\dfrac{C}{B} = -\dfrac{11}{-3} = \dfrac{11}{3}$

b. Setting $x = 0$ in the equation we get $2(0) - 3y + 11 = 0$; hence, $y = \dfrac{11}{3}$.

c. If we transform the equation to slope-intercept form we get $y = \dfrac{2}{3}x + \dfrac{11}{3}$. Thus b, the y-intercept, is $\dfrac{11}{3}$.

Exercises

In Exercises 1–6 find the slope and y-intercept of the given equations.

1. $3x - 2y = 7$
2. $5x + 11y = 2$
3. $-3x + 4y = 0$
4. $15y - x = 1$
5. $7x = y$
6. $4x = 0$

In Exercises 7–10 find the slope of the line passing through the given points.

7. $A(5, 2)$, $B(7, 9)$
8. $C(-2, 0)$, $D(1, -3)$
9. $E(4, 2)$, $F(7, 2)$
10. $G(-1, 4)$, $H(-1, 7)$

In Exercises 11–16 write the equation of the line passing through the given points.

11. $A(2, 5)$, $B(7, 8)$ **14.** $G(6, 6)$, $H(-6, -6)$

12. $C(3, 1)$, $D(-2, 4)$ **15.** $I(-7, -1)$, $J(4, -2)$

13. $E(3, -5)$, $F(2, -1)$ **16.** $K(-3, 11)$, $L(2, 11)$

17. Find the distance between the points in Exercises 11–16.

18. Write the equations of the sides of the triangle with vertices at $A(2, -7)$, $B(5, 1)$, and $C(-3, 2)$. Find the perimeter of the triangle.

2.6 Linear inequalities

You have already seen that inequalities in one variable can be represented by points on the number line. Equations in two variables can be graphed in the coordinate plane. Linear equations such as $x + 2y = 4$ can be represented by a line in the plane. Ordered pairs (x, y) which satisfy the equation are in a one-to-one correspondence with coordinates of points of the line.

We may also represent inequalities in two variables graphically on a coordinate plane. Consider the inequality $x + 2y > 4$. Compare the ordered pairs determined by this relation with those obtained from $x + 2y = 4$. Note that $(0, 2)$ satisfies the equation, but $(0, y > 2)$ or $(x > 0, 2)$ satisfies the inequality. The graph of the equation $x + 2y = 4$ is shown in Figure 2–14. We see that any point in the shaded region of the plane has coordinates which satisfy the inequality $x + 2y > 4$.

Now consider the inequality $x + 2y < 4$ and compare the set of ordered pairs determined with those of the equation $x + 2y = 4$. We see that any point in the shaded region of Figure 2–15 satisfies the relation $x + 2y < 4$.

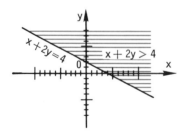

FIGURE 2–14

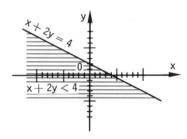

FIGURE 2–15

The graphs of $x + 2y = 4$, $x + 2y > 4$, and $x + 2y < 4$ may be represented simultaneously in the coordinate plane as shown in Figure 2–16. Any point P_1 on the line has coordinates which satisfy the equation $x + 2y = 4$.

Any point P_2 above the line satisfies the inequality $x + 2y > 4$; any point P_3 below the line satisfies the inequality $x + 2y < 4$.

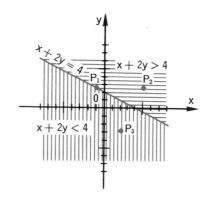

We can summarize these relations by saying that the graph of a linear equation in two variables is a straight line which separates the coordinate plane into three sets of points: (1) the set of points on the line; (2) the set of points on one side of the line; and (3) the set of points

FIGURE 2–16

on the other side of the line. Two points are on opposite sides of a line if the straight line segment joining them has a point in common with the line.

The set of points on one side of a line determines a region which is called an *open half plane*. If the set of points of the line is combined with the points of an open half plane determined by the line, the resulting region is called a *closed half plane*. Note that we have called the half planes *regions* rather than areas. Area implies a function of a surface which can be represented by a finite number. A region may be unbounded or bounded. The quadrants of the coordinate plane are regions but not areas.

Exercises

Graph the following half planes.

1. $\{x \mid x > 5\}$

2. $\{y \mid y > -2\}$

3. $\{(x, y) \mid x + y > 10\}$

4. $\{(x, y) \mid x - y < 5\}$

5. $\{(x, y) \mid 2x + y < 8\}$

6. $\{(x, y) \mid 3x - 6 > 2y + x + 2\}$

7. $\{x \mid x \geq 4\}$

8. $\{(x, y) \mid x + 3y \leq 6\}$

9. $\{(x, y) \mid 3x - 4y \geqq 12\}$

10. $\left\{(x, y) \mid \dfrac{x + 2}{5} < \dfrac{y - 3}{2}\right\}$

2.7 Regions defined by inequalities

On the number line the relation $1 < x < 3$ can be represented by the line segment between $+1$ and $+3$, exclusive. The same relation

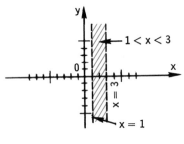

FIGURE 2–17

can be represented on the coordinate plane as the region between the lines $x = 1$ and $x = 3$. The shaded portion of the graph in Figure 2–17 shows the relation $1 < x < 3$. Note that the shaded portion approaches but does not include the lines $x = 1$ and $x = 3$. This is indicated by the dashed appearance of these lines. If they were to be included in the relation, then they would appear solid.

In a similar way we can graph $2 < x + y < 5$. We do this by graphing the lines $x + y = 2$ and $x + y = 5$. These are parallel lines and the region between them represents the relation $2 < x + y < 5$. See Figure 2–18.

Quadratic inequalities may be represented graphically by finding boundaries of the region or regions in which the ordered pairs satisfying the inequality lie. The boundaries are usually the graphs of certain quadratic equations. If we wish to graph $y > x^2$, for example, we can first graph the equation $y = x^2$ as a boundary. This graph is a parabola with its vertex at the origin, as shown in Figure 2–19. An ordered pair which satisfies $y > x^2$ will be found in the shaded region of the plane.

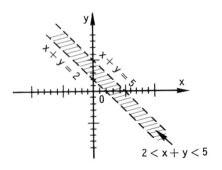

FIGURE 2–18

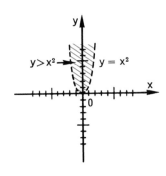

FIGURE 2–19

Other second and third degree inequalities are represented graphically in the figures below.

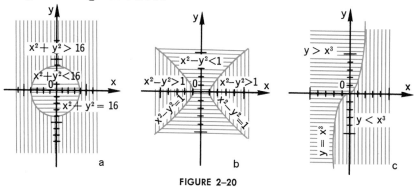

FIGURE 2-20

When two linear equations in two variables are graphed on the same coordinate plane, there is a common solution (if the equations are consistent and independent) represented by the point of intersection of two lines. This is the intersection of the two sets of points determined by the two given linear functions. When a linear equation and a second degree equation are graphed on the same coordinate plane, the number of points in the intersection is 0, 1, or 2 depending upon the relative positions of the line and curve.

In a similar way it is possible to consider the graphs of inequalities on the same coordinate plane. There may be two or more inequalities represented simultaneously on the coordinate plane, and their common solution may be studied. If a system of linear inequalities is graphed so that the intersection set is a convex polygon and its interior, this common solution is called a *polygonal convex set.*

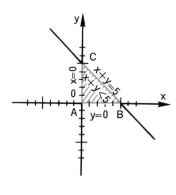

FIGURE 2-21

Consider these three inequalities.

$$x \geq 0,\ y \geq 0,\ x + y \leq 5$$

Note that each inequality determines a closed half plane. The intersection set will be the right triangle with its interior points, as shown in Figure 2-21. The vertices of the triangle are $A(0, 0)$, $B(5, 0)$, $C(0, 5)$. The triangle and its interior represent the polygonal convex set expressed by the three given inequalities.

Exercises

Graph the following inequalities.

1. $\{(x, y) \mid 0 < x - y < 2\}$

2. $\{(x, y) \mid 2 < 2x + y < 8\}$

3. $\{(x, y) \mid -6 < 3x - y < 12\}$

4. $\{(x, y) \mid 0 > x - y > 2\}$

5. $\{(x, y) \mid x^2 + y^2 < 9\}$

6. $\{(x, y) \mid y > x^2 - 1\}$

7. $\{(x, y) \mid y > |x|\}$

8. $\{(x, y) \mid |x + 3| < y - 1\}$

9. $\{(x, y) \mid |y| < |x|\}$

Graph the following polygonal convex sets. Give the coordinates of the vertices of the polygon.

10. $\{(x, y) \mid x \geq 0,\ y \geq 0,\ 2x + y \leq 4\}$

11. $\{(x, y) \mid x \leq 3, y \leq 5, x + y \geq 1, x \geq 0, y \geq 0\}$

12. $\{(x, y) \mid x \leq 0, y + 3 \geq 0, x \geq -5, y \leq x\}$

13. $\{(x, y) \mid 2x + y \leq 6, x - y \leq 2, x \geq 1\}$

14. $\{(x, y) \mid x \geq 1, y \geq 2, y \leq 8, x + y \leq 10, 2x + y \leq 14\}$

2.8 Maximum or minimum of a function for a polygonal convex set

As you have seen in Section 2.7, a system of linear inequalities can determine a polygonal convex set. Now, assume that the linear function $f(x, y) = ax + by + c$ is defined with respect to a given system of linear inequalities, where x and y represent the same variables as considered in the system. If the linear function $f(x, y) = ax + by + c$ is equal to some constant k, then a line is determined by the equation. This line may or may not have a point or points in common with the given polygonal convex set. However, if the value of k is replaced by another value, a line parallel to the first will be determined. Clearly, some values of k will cause the graph of the linear equation $f(x, y) = k$ to intersect the polygon. If k is now considered to represent a variable, there is some maximum value of k which will cause the line $f(x, y) = k$ to intersect the polygonal convex set. To understand this, think of a family of parallel lines and a polygon, as shown in Figure 2–22. The family of lines determined by $f(x, y) = k$, where k is a variable, is shown in the drawing with a representative polygon.

There will be some value of k, say k_1, that will cause the line $f(x, y) = k_1$ to pass through vertex C; any greater value of k will cause the line to be above the polygon. There will be another value of k, say k_2, that will cause the line $f(x, y) = k_2$ to pass through vertex B. The value k_1 is thus a maximum value of $f(x, y)$ with respect to the given polygonal convex set, and the value k_2 is a minimum value of $f(x, y)$ with respect to the set. Should the line $f(x, y) = k$ pass through two consecutive vertices of the polygon, then any point on that side will cause $f(x, y) = k$ to be either a maximum or minimum as the case may be.

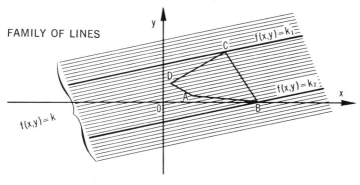

FAMILY OF LINES

FIGURE 2–22

The reasoning above shows that the maximum or minimum value of a linear function defined for a polygonal convex set occurs at a vertex of the polygon. Therefore, to find the maximum and minimum values of $f(x, y) = ax + by + c$, we need only to replace x and y by the coordinates of the vertices of the polygon and choose respectively the largest and smallest values found.

EXAMPLE. Find the maximum and minimum values of $f(x, y) = x + 2y + 1$ for the polygonal convex set determined by this system of inequalities.

$$\{(x, y) \mid x \geq 0, y \geq 0, 2x + y \leq 4, x + y \leq 3\}$$

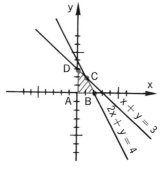

FIGURE 2–23

Solution. First graph the inequalities and find the coordinates of the vertices of the resulting polygon. The coordinates of the vertices are $A(0, 0)$, $B(2, 0)$, $C(1, 2)$, $D(0, 3)$. The shaded portion of the figure is the interior of the polygonal convex set determined by the given inequalities.

To find the maximum and minimum values of the linear

function $f(x, y) = x + 2y + 1$, we evaluate the function at the coordinates of the vertices of the polygon. The function has the following values: at A, $f(0, 0) = 1$; at B, $f(2, 0) = 3$; at C, $f(1, 2) = 6$; at D, $f(0, 3) = 7$. Hence, the maximum value of the function is 7 and the minimum value is 1.

Exercises

1. Graph the system of inequalities $\{(x, y) \mid x \geq 0, y \geq 1, 4x + 5y \leq 20\}$. Find the maximum and minimum values of the function $f(x, y) = 4x + 2y + 7$ defined for the given polygonal convex set.

2. Find the maximum value of $f(x, y) = 2y - 4x + 1$ defined for the same system of inequalities given in Exercise 1.

3. Graph the system of inequalities $\{(x, y) \mid x + 4y \leq 12, 3x - 2y \geq -6, x + y \geq -2, 3x - y \leq 10\}$. Find the coordinates of the vertices of the polygon. Find the maximum and the minimum values of the function $f(x, y) = x - y + 2$ defined for the given system of inequalities.

4. Find the maximum and minimum values of the function $f(x, y) = y + 2x + 7$ defined for the system of inequalities given in Exercise 3.

5. Find the maximum and minimum values of the function $f(x, y) = 2x + 8y + 10$ defined for the system of inequalities given in Exercise 3.

2.9 Linear programming

Linear programming problems are practical problems which can be solved by the application of the methods explained in Section 2.8. These problems are of such a nature that certain limitations exist or are placed upon the variables. Then a maximum or minimum value of some function of these variables can be found. An example will illustrate the method.

EXAMPLE. A farmer has a choice of planting a combination of two different crops on 20 acres of land. For crop A seed costs $30 per acre, and for crop B seed costs $50 per acre. Government restrictions limit acreage of crop A to 15 acres but do not limit crop B. Crop A will take 15 hours of labor per acre at a cost of $1.40 per hour, and crop B will require 10 hours of labor per acre at $1.25 per hour. If the expected income from crop A is $150 per acre, and from crop B is \$130 per acre, how should the 20 acres be apportioned between the two crops to get maximum income? To get maximum profit?

Solution. Let x equal the number of acres of crop A, and y equal the number of acres of crop B. Then we can write

$$x \geq 0, \ y \geq 0, \ x \leq 15, \ x + y \leq 20$$

Next, we can graph the relations and determine the vertices of the polygon. Solving the equations as pairs, we find that the vertices are at $A(0, 0)$, $B(15, 0)$, $C(15, 5)$, $D(0, 20)$. The income function is $I = 150x + 130y$. In order to find a maximum of I, we substitute the coordinates of the vertices of the polygon in the function. Replacing x and y in the income function by the respective values of the coordinates we find

I (at A) $= 0$; I (at B) $= 2250$; I (at C) $= 2900$; I (at D) $= 2600$.

Thus, the minimum is 0 and the maximum is \$2900. Hence, the largest income, \$2900, is to be obtained by planting 15 acres of crop A and 5 acres of crop B.

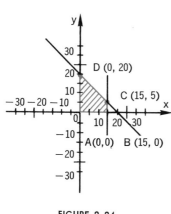

FIGURE 2–24

The profit from any crop equals the income less the costs. The profit from crop A equals $150x - 30x - 15(1.40)x$. The profit from crop B equals $130y - 50y - 10(1.25)y$. Thus the profit function is $P(x, y) = x[150 - 30 - 15(1.40)] + y[130 - 50(1.25)] = 99x + 67.5y$. Substitution of the coordinates of the vertices of the polygon in this function gives P (at A) $= 0$; P (at B) $= 1485$; P (at C) $= 1822.5$; P (at D) $= 1350$. Thus, the maximum profit of \$1822.50 will be obtained by planting 15 acres of crop A and 5 acres of crop B. Notice that the maximum income and the maximum profit both result from the same division of the acreage in this case.

The method of linear programming can be extended to problems which have more than two variables. For example, if three variables are involved, a linear inequality will graph into the points on one side of a plane, and the intersection of all inequalities will be a solid (polyhedron). The function in three variables to be maximized (or minimized) will have its maximum value at a vertex as in two dimensions. Can you extend this concept to more than three dimensions?

Exercises

1. A company is planning to buy new fork hoists for material handling. There are two models that will serve their needs. The warehouse supervisor feels that a minimum of 3 Model M hoists and a minimum of 5 Model R hoists will be needed. The supplier has 8 Model M hoists and 10 Model R hoists on hand for delivery. The company purchasing agent has decided that no more than 14 hoists can be purchased. Model M can handle 24,000 lbs. per hour and Model R can handle 20,000 lbs. per hour. What number of hoists of each model should be purchased for maximum weight-handling capacity? If hoist Model R has an attachment that will enable it to handle 25,000 lbs. per hour, what number of hoists of each model should be purchased for maximum weight-handling capacity if the attachment is used?

2. A manufacturer makes widgets and gadgets. At least 500 widgets and 700 gadgets are needed to meet minimum daily demands. Machines are used to produce the items. Two machines can produce 600 widgets and 700 widgets per day respectively. Two other machines can produce 700 gadgets and 500 gadgets per day respectively. The cost, including materials, of manufacturing a widget is 7 cents and the cost of a gadget is 16 cents. The combined number of widgets and gadgets that the packaging department can handle is 2300 per day. If the company sells widgets for 40 cents each and gadgets for 50 cents each, how many of each item should be produced to have maximum income? How many of each item should be produced for maximum profit? If the cost of producing gadgets goes up to 18 cents each, how many of each item should be produced for maximum profit?

3. A meat packer makes a kind of wurst using beef, pork, cereal, fat, water, and spices. The minimum cereal content is 12%, the minimum fat content is 15%, the minimum water content is 6.5%, and the spices are 0.5%. The remaining constituents are beef and pork, but the proportion may be varied within certain limits. There must be at least 30% beef for good flavor and at

least 20% pork for texture. The beef content must equal or exceed the pork content to satisfy a certain market and for advertising purposes. The cost of all the content except beef and pork is $16.00 per 100 lb. Beef can be bought for $42.00 per 100 lb and pork for $32.00 per 100 lb. Find the combination of beef and pork for the minimum cost. What is the minimum and the maximum cost per 100 lb? If the quality of the wurst is the greatest when there is a minimum of the other materials than beef or pork and a maximum of beef, what combination of beef and pork should be used for highest quality?

Chapter Review

1. Find the numbers in each solution set.

   a. $\{x \mid 3x - 5 = 13\}$　　　　**c.** $\left\{x \mid x - 2 = \dfrac{3}{x}\right\}$

   b. $\{x \mid x^2 - 7x + 10 = 0\}$　　**d.** $\{x \mid \sqrt{x+5} = 3 - \sqrt{x+2}\}$

2. Find $f(0), f(2), f(-3)$ for each of the following functions.

   a $.(x, 3x - 5)$　**b.** $f(x) = 2x^2 - x + 1$　**c.** $\left\{(x, y) \mid \dfrac{5x}{x+3} = y\right\}$

3. Find sample ordered pairs and graph the following equations.

   a. $3x + 8 = y$　　**b.** $x + y = \dfrac{3}{2}$　　**c.** $\{(x, y) \mid y - 7x = -1\}$

4. Find the distance between the given points.

   a. $A(3, 5), B(-1, 4)$　　　　**c.** $E(8, -5), F(-1, 1)$
   b. $C(2, -4), D(0, 3)$　　　　**d.** $G(5, 0), H(-5, 0)$

5. Find the perimeter of the triangle with the vertices at $A(4, -2)$, $B(-1, 5)$, and $C(1, -6)$.

6. Find the slope of each side of the triangle in Exercise 5.

7. Find the slope, the y-intercept, and the x-intercept of each of the following lines.

   a. $4x + y - 3 = 0$　　　　**c.** $2y = 5x + 7$
   b. $4x + 2 = 0$　　　　　　**d.** $7x + 5y - 4 = 0$

8. Write the equations of the lines forming the sides of the triangle in Exercise 5.

9. A point with an abscissa of 2 is at a distance of 5 units from the point $P(-2, 3)$. Find the ordinate of the point.

10. The vertices of a quadrilateral are at $(0, 0)$, $(5, 2)$, $(8, 6)$, and $(3, 4)$. Prove that the figure is a parallelogram.

11. The vertices of a trapezoid are $(1, 3)$, $(-1, -1)$, $(11, -5)$, $(7, 1)$. How far must each of the non-parallel sides be extended in order to intersect?

12. Show that the lines $2x - y + 3 = 0$, $x + 7y + 9 = 0$, and $11x + 2y - 51 = 0$ form the sides of an isosceles triangle.

In Exercises 13–18, find the values of x in each solution set.

13. $\{x \mid 3x - 5 > 7\}$

14. $\{x \mid 6 - 2x < 14\}$

15. $\{x \mid 5x + 7 < 2x + 11\}$

16. $\{x \mid 4x + a < 6b\}$

17. $\left\{x \mid \frac{1}{2}x - 5 > 4 - \frac{1}{4}x\right\}$

18. $\{x \mid x^2 - 10x + 9 > 0\}$

Represent the following inequalities graphically.

19. $\{(x, y) \mid 2x - y < 5\}$

20. $\{(x, y) \mid 3x + y > 4\}$

21. $\{(x, y) \mid 2 < 2x + y < 5\}$

22. $\{(x, y) \mid 2x^2 + 5x - 3 < y\}$

23. Graph this polygonal convex set.

$$\{(x, y) \mid x + 2y \leq 12,\ x \leq 10,\ y \geq 0,\ x - 2 \geq 0\}$$

24. Find the maximum value of the function $f(x, y) = 2x + 8y + 6$ defined for the polygonal convex set in Exercise 23.

CHAPTER OUTLINE

Theory of Equations 3

3.1 Solving higher degree equations

In the previous chapter linear equations and their graphs were studied in considerable detail. You have also had the experience of solving quadratic or second degree equations in prerequisite courses in algebra. One certain method for finding the roots of a quadratic equation is through the application of the quadratic formula. Recall that the formula $x = \dfrac{-b \pm \sqrt{b^2 - 4ac}}{2a}$ will give the roots of the general quadratic equation $ax^2 + bx + c = 0$, $a \neq 0$, where the coefficients are real numbers.

Formulas have long been known for solving any polynomial equation of the third or fourth degree such as

$$2x^3 - 7x^2 + 5x - 7 = 0 \text{ or } -x^4 + 5x^3 - 9x^2 + 8x - 12 = 0$$

The formulas were developed in the Sixteenth Century and are known as the Cardan Formulas. These formulas are quite complex and rarely used; we shall not consider them in this course. However, it is often necessary to solve special equations of higher degree than the second, so we shall study some theorems that make it possible to find real roots of higher degree equations or to approximate them to any desired degree of accuracy.

As we previously mentioned, any number of the domain which results in the value of a function equalling zero when it replaces the variable is a *zero of the function*. For example, if $f(x) = x^2 - x - 6$, then 3 is a zero of $f(x)$ because $f(3) = 3^2 - 3 - 6 = 0$.

In an equation of the form $f(x) = 0$, any zero of $f(x)$ is called a *root* of the equation. Thus, r is a root of $f(x) = 0$ if $f(r) = 0$. The set of all elements in the domain of f which are zeros of $f(x)$ comprise the solution set of $f(x) = 0$. Thus, to solve equations simply means to find zeros of functions.

Exercises

Find the zeros of the given functions.

1. $f(x) = x - 2$

2. $f(a) = 2a + 4$

3. $f(x) = x^2 - 4$

4. $f(t) = t^2 - t$

5. $f(z) = z^2 - z - 2$

6. $f(s) = (s - 2)(s - 5)$

7. $f(u) = (u + 2)(u^2 - 4)$

8. $f(q) = (2q - 3)(3q - 2)$

9. If the domain of $f(x)$ is the set of natural numbers and $f(x) = 3x^2 - 16x + 5 = 0$, give the solution set of the equation.

10. Find the solution set of $(x - 1)(x - 2)(x - 3)(x - 4) = 0$.

11. Find the solution set of $(x - 1)(x - 5) = -3$.

3.2 Synthetic division

Synthetic division is an abbreviated form of division which can be used to perform the division of a polynomial by the linear form $(x - r)$. The method is best explained by means of an example.

EXAMPLE 1. Divide $x^3 + x^2 - 3x - 2$ by $x + 2$.

Solution. Perform the long division in the usual manner. Note that like powers of x are aligned vertically throughout the problem. The method of synthetic division aims to eliminate all needless writing.

$$
\begin{array}{r}
x^2 - x - 1 \\
x + 2\overline{\smash{)}x^3 + x^2 - 3x - 2} \\
\underline{x^3 + 2x^2} \\
-x^2 - 3x \\
\underline{-x^2 - 2x} \\
-x - 2 \\
\underline{-x - 2}
\end{array}
$$

Step 1. Since like powers are in the same column, the coefficients may be detached; that is, the coefficients may be written without the variable. (Remember that the coefficient of any missing term is zero and must be inserted.)

$$\begin{array}{r} 1 - 1 - 1 \\ 1 + 2\overline{)1 + 1 - 3 - 2} \\ \underline{1 + 2} \\ - 1 - 3 \\ \underline{- 1 - 2} \\ - 1 - 2 \\ \underline{- 1 - 2} \end{array}$$

Step 2. Here the products of $+ 2$ and the terms of the quotient are all written in one line. This saves copying the dividend terms.

$$\begin{array}{r} 1 - 1 - 1 \\ 1 + 2\overline{)1 + 1 - 3 - 2} \\ \underline{2 - 2 - 2} \\ 1 - 1 - 1 + 0 \end{array}$$

Step 3. Here we have changed the sign of the constant term of the divisor. This permits us to add rather than subtract in the process of division. We also omit the coefficient of x in the divisor since it is always 1 when synthetic division is used.

$$\begin{array}{r} 1 - 1 - 1 \\ -2\overline{)1 + 1 - 3 - 2} \\ \underline{- 2 + 2 + 2} \\ 1 - 1 - 1 + 0 \end{array}$$

Step 4. Since the first three remainders are the same as the quotient, we may omit the quotient and use the remainders as coefficients of the quotient polynomial. The fourth remainder is the final remainder.

$$\begin{array}{r} -2\overline{)1 + 1 - 3 - 2} \\ \underline{- 2 + 2 + 2} \\ 1 - 1 - 1 + 0 \end{array}$$

The quotient is $x^2 - x - 1$ and the remainder is 0.

SUMMARY OF SYNTHETIC DIVISION

The problem is the same as used in Example 1, on the preceding page.

1. Change the sign of the constant term of the divisor ($+2$ becomes -2). Write detached coefficients of the dividend.

$$-2\overline{)1 + 1 - 3 - 2}$$

2. Bring down the first coefficient of the dividend.

$$\begin{array}{r} -2\overline{)1 + 1 - 3 - 2} \\ \hline 1 \end{array}$$

3. Multiply this coefficient by the divisor (-2), and write the product under the second dividend coefficient. Add.

$$\begin{array}{r} -2/1 + 1 - 3 - 2 \\ -2 \\ \hline 1 - 1 \end{array}$$

4. Repeat step 3 one term at a time until all terms in the dividend have been used.

$$\begin{array}{r} -2/1 + 1 - 3 - 2 \\ -2 + 2 + 2 \\ \hline 1 - 1 - 1 + 0 \end{array}$$

5. Write the quotient with descending powers of the variable. Note that if n is the degree of the dividend, then $n - 1$ is the degree of the quotient. The remainder is the last sum, zero in the example.

$$1x^2 - 1x - 1$$

EXAMPLE 2. Use synthetic division to divide $x^3 - 2x - 21$ by $x - 3$.

Solution. Write the coefficients of the dividend including the zero coefficient of x^2 and divide as follows.

$$\begin{array}{r} 3/1 \quad 0 \; -2 \; -21 \\ 3 \quad 9 \quad 21 \\ \hline 1 \quad 3 \quad 7 \quad 0 \end{array}$$

The quotient is exactly $x^2 + 3x + 7$.

Exercises

Use synthetic division to find the quotients in Exercises 1-8.

1. $(x^2 + 8x + 12) \div (x + 2)$
2. $(x^2 - x - 56) \div (x + 7)$
3. $(x^3 + 2x + 3) \div (x - 2)$
4. $(x^2 - x + 4) \div (x - 2)$
5. $(x^4 - 8x^2 + 16) \div (x + 2)$
6. $(x^3 + x^2 - 17x + 15) \div (x + 5)$
7. $(x^3 - x^2 + 2) \div (x + 1)$
8. $(x^4 + x^3 - 1) \div (x - 2)$

3.3 The remainder theorem—the factor theorem

There are two theorems which are useful in finding zeros of a polynomial function and roots of certain equations. The Remainder Theorem combined with synthetic division provides a convenient means for finding binomial factors of a polynomial. The proof is based upon the familiar relationship between dividend, divisor, quotient, and remainder.

Assume $P(x)$ is any polynomial function of degree n in x, and let $(x - r)$ be its divisor. The quotient, $Q(x)$, will be of degree $n - 1$, and the remainder, R, will be a real number since the divisor is of first degree.

- REMAINDER THEOREM

If $P(x)$ is divided by $(x - r)$ until the remainder is the real number R, then $R = P(r)$.

Proof: The relationship we shall use is
$$P(x) = (x - r) \cdot Q(x) + R$$
Replacing x by r we have
$$P(r) = (r - r) \cdot Q(r) + R$$
$$P(r) = 0 \cdot Q(r) + R$$
$$P(r) = R$$
The theorem is proved.

A corollary to the Remainder Theorem, called the Factor Theorem, is useful when we are searching for the roots of a polynomial equation of the form $P(x) = 0$.

- FACTOR THEOREM

If r is a root of the polynomial equation $P(x) = 0$, that is, if $P(r) = 0$, then $(x - r)$ is a factor of $P(x)$, and conversely.

Proof: If $P(r) = 0$, then from the Remainder Theorem, $P(r) = R = 0$; so we have
$$P(x) = (x - r) \cdot Q(x) + 0$$
$$P(x) = (x - r) \cdot Q(x)$$
Therefore, $(x - r)$ is a factor of $P(x)$ if r is a root of $P(x) = 0$. To prove the converse of the theorem, we assume that $(x - r)$ is a factor of $P(x)$ and write
$$P(x) = (x - r) \cdot Q(x)$$
Replacing x by r we have
$$P(r) = (r - r) \cdot Q(r)$$
$$P(r) = 0 \cdot Q(r)$$
$$P(r) = 0$$
Thus, r is a root of $P(x) = 0$ since replacement of x by r results in r being proved a zero of $P(x)$.

EXAMPLE 1. Find the remainder when $x^3 - 7x - 4$ is divided by $(x + 1)$.

Solution. By the Remainder Theorem it is known that the remainder when $f(x)$ is divided by $(x - r)$ is $f(r)$. Let $f(x) = x^3 -$

$7x - 4$. To find the remainder when $f(x)$ is divided by $(x + 1)$, we compute $f(-1)$.

$$f(-1) = (-1)^3 - 7(-1) - 4 = -1 + 7 - 4 = 2$$

The remainder is 2.

We can also find the remainder in Example 1 by synthetic division as follows.

$$
\begin{array}{r|rrrr}
-1/1 & 0 & -7 & -4 \\
 & -1 & 1 & 6 \\
\hline
1 & -1 & -6 & 2 \\
\end{array}
$$

The final remainder is 2 which confirms the answer found by the Remainder Theorem.

EXAMPLE 2. Find the integral roots of $x^3 - 4x^2 - 7x + 10 = 0$.

Solution. The Factor Theorem states that r is a root of a polynomial equation $f(x) = 0$ if $(x - r)$ is a factor of $f(x)$. To find factors of the given function, we shall use synthetic division in a trial and error manner. Let us divide the given function by $(x - 1)$ and inspect the remainder.

$$
\begin{array}{r|rrrr}
1/1 & -4 & -7 & 10 \\
 & 1 & -3 & -10 \\
\hline
1 & -3 & -10 & 0 \\
\end{array}
$$

Since the remainder is zero, $(x - 1)$ is a factor of $x^3 - 4x^2 - 7x + 10$ and 1 is a root of the given equation.

We can find in a similar way that $f(-2) = 0$ and $f(5) = 0$. The three roots of $x^3 - 4x^2 - 7x + 10 = 0$ are -2, 1, and 5.

A combined and shortened form of synthetic division is shown below for binomial divisors of $x^3 - 4x^2 - 7x + 10$. The value of r in $x - r$ is shown at the left, and beside it is the last line of the synthetic division procedure. The last numeral in each row is the remainder which is the value of $f(r)$.

r	1	-4	-7	10
1	1	-3	-10	0
2	1	-2	-11	-12
3	1	-1	-10	-20
4	1	0	-7	-28
5	1	1	-2	0
-1	1	-5	-2	12
-2	1	-6	5	0

The final remainders which are zero identify zeros of the function and thus, the roots of the equation, 1, 5, and -2.

Exercises

In Exercises 1 through 10 use the Remainder Theorem to find the remainder when the given function is divided by the indicated divisor. Check by synthetic division.

1. $(x^2 - 2) \div (x - 1)$ **6.** $(2x^2 - x + 3) \div (x - 3)$

2. $(x^2 + 1) \div (x + 1)$ **7.** $(x^3 - x + 6) \div (x - 2)$

3. $(x^2 + x - 1) \div (x - 3)$ **8.** $(2x^3 - 3x^2 + x) \div (x - 1)$

4. $(x^2 + 5x - 2) \div (x + 5)$ **9.** $(x^4 + x^2 + 2) \div (x - 3)$

5. $(x^2 - 2x - 63) \div (x + 7)$ **10.** $(2x^4 - x^3 + 1) \div (x + 3)$

Find all integral roots of the following equations.

11. $2x^2 - x = 0$ **16.** $x^3 - 3x^2 + x + 1 = 0$

12. $x^2 + 3x + 2 = 0$ **17.** $2x^3 - 3x^2 - 11x + 6 = 0$

13. $2x^2 + 3x - 20 = 0$ **18.** $x^4 - 10x^2 + 9 = 0$

14. $5x^2 - 14x + 8 = 0$ **19.** $6x^3 + 37x^2 + 32x - 15 = 0$

15. $6x^2 + 7x - 3 = 0$ **20.** $x^5 - 3x + 2 = 0$

3.4 The fundamental theorem of algebra

Early in your study of algebra you learned that every linear equation has exactly one root and every quadratic equation has exactly two roots. You may also have been told that a cubic equation has three roots, a fourth degree equation has four roots, and so on. Intuitively, you may have concluded (correctly) that a polynomial equation of nth degree has exactly n roots. The roots are not necessarily distinct since one real or complex number may appear as a double or other multiple root.

Although mathematicians had believed for some time that an equation of nth degree had n roots, it was not until 1800 that the famous German mathematician, Gauss, developed proof that every polynomial equation has at least one root. The important theorem is stated as follows.

● THE FUNDAMENTAL THEOREM OF ALGEBRA

Every polynomial equation of the form $f(x) = 0$ has at least one root in the field of complex numbers.

We shall accept this theorem without proof, for, as simple as the statement is, it is very difficult to prove. The Fundamental Theorem of Algebra leads us to the following corollary.

> *Corollary:* Every polynomial $f(x)$ of degree n can be transformed into the product of n linear factors, that is, $f(x)$ of degree n equals $k(x - r_1)(x - r_2)(x - r_3) \cdots (x - r_n)$. Hence a polynomial equation of the form $f(x) = 0$ of degree n has exactly n roots, namely, $r_1, r_2, r_3, \cdots r_n$.

This corollary follows from the Fundamental Theorem and the Factor Theorem. The roots are unique for a given function of x. The proof of the theorem will not be given, but you may find it interesting to investigate various proofs which have been made.

It is clear that the Fundamental Theorem of Algebra and the Corollary are existence theorems; that is, they assert that a root exists and that n factors exist. They do not give any method for finding the root or the factors. Much of the history of algebra relates to methods of finding roots of equations. It has been proved that there can be no general method involving radicals for solving a polynomial equation of degree higher than the fourth degree, although several methods of approximating the roots are known.

EXAMPLE. Find roots of the equation $x^3 - 2x^2 - 5x + 6 = 0$.

Solution. The above equation can be factored into the form $(x - r_1)(x - r_2)(x - r_3) = 0$ where the roots are r_1, r_2, and r_3. (*Note:* If the coefficient of x^n is other than 1, the equation can be divided by this coefficient and it becomes 1.) You should see that the product of the roots must be the constant term. If there is an integral root in this example it is a factor of 6. Why? Applying the remainder theorem, we find that $f(1) = 0$. Hence, $r_1 = 1$ and we can write $(x - 1)(x^2 - x - 6) = 0$. The quotient polynomial $q(x) = x^2 - x - 6$ may be found easily by synthetic division of $f(x)$ by $(x - 1)$.

Integral roots of $q(x) = x^2 - x - 6 = 0$ must be factors of -6 and we find $q(-2) = 0$ and $q(3) = 0$. Thus, $(x - 1)(x + 2)(x - 3) = 0$ and the roots are $x = 1$, $x = -2$, and $x = 3$.

3.5 Rational root theorem

In the preceding sections of this chapter we were primarily concerned with integral roots although the theorems are valid for all real roots. Now we shall concern ourselves with the rational roots of a polynomial equation of degree n represented as follows:

$$a_0 x^n + a_1 x^{n-1} + a_2 x^{n-2} + \cdots + a_{n-1} x + a_n = 0$$

where the coefficients are integers, $a_0 \neq 0$, and n is a positive integer. It can be proved that any rational root of the equation can be derived from the fraction $\dfrac{a_n}{a_0}$.

- RATIONAL ROOT THEOREM

If $P(x) = 0$ is a polynomial equation with integral coefficients of degree n in which a_0 is the coefficient of x^n, and a_n is the constant term, then for any rational root $\dfrac{p}{q}$, where p and q are relatively prime integers, p is a factor of a_n and q is a factor of a_0.

Proof: The theorem can be proved by replacing x by the known root $\dfrac{p}{q}$. We have

$$a_0 \frac{p^n}{q^n} + a_1 \frac{p^{n-1}}{q^{n-1}} + \cdots + a_{n-1} \frac{p}{q} + a_n = 0$$

Multiplying both members by q^n gives us

$$a_0 p^n + a_1 p^{n-1} q + \cdots + a_{n-1} p q^{n-1} + a_n q^n = 0$$

Factoring p from the first n terms and subtracting $a_n q^n$ from both members, we have

$$p(a_0 p^{n-1} + a_1 p^{n-2} q + \cdots + a_{n-1} q^{n-1}) = -a_n q^n$$

We observe that p is a factor of the left member and therefore, a factor of the right member. But p and q are relatively prime, and thus, p is a factor of a_n rather than q^n. Using a similar approach but factoring q from the last n terms, we can prove that q is a factor of a_0. We have therefore established the fact that p is a factor of a_n and q is a factor of a_0; the theorem is proved.

EXAMPLE 1. Find the positive rational root of $2x^2 + 5x - 12 = 0$.

Solution. Since $a_0 = 2$ and $a_n = -12$, it is clear from the above theorem that for any rational root the numerator is a factor of -12 and the denominator a factor of 2. By trial and error we find that $f\left(\dfrac{3}{2}\right) = 0$, and thus, the positive rational root is $\dfrac{3}{2}$. The other root is negative.

An important corollary that pertains to integral roots of polynomial equations follows.

- THEOREM

    If a polynomial equation with integers as coefficients has 1 as the leading coefficient, that is,

    $$a_0x^n + a_1x^{n-1} + \cdots + a_{n-1}x + a_n = 0, \; a_0 = 1$$

    then any rational roots which are integers are factors of a_n.

    Proof: The proof of the theorem follows directly from the Rational Root Theorem. For any rational root $\dfrac{p}{q}$, q is a factor of the leading coefficient 1, and hence $\dfrac{p}{q}$ is an integer.

    EXAMPLE 2. Find integral roots of $x^3 - x^2 - x - 2 = 0$.

Solution. The possible integral roots are factors of -2, namely, $\pm 2, \pm 1$. Either by direct substitution or by synthetic division, we find that $f(2) = 0$. The only rational root is the integer 2.

Exercises

Find rational roots of the following equations.

1. $x^3 - 4x^2 + x + 2 = 0$

2. $x^3 + 2x^2 - 5x - 6 = 0$

3. $x^4 + 5x^3 + 5x^2 - 5x - 6 = 0$

4. $x^3 - 5x^2 - 4x + 20 = 0$

5. $x^3 + 2x^2 + x + 18 = 0$

6. $x^4 - 5x^3 + 9x^2 - 7x + 2 = 0$

7. $2x^3 + 3x^2 - 8x + 3 = 0$

8. $6x^3 - 11x^2 - 24x + 9 = 0$

9. $4x^3 + 5x^2 + 2x - 6 = 0$

10. $2x^4 - x^3 - 6x + 3 = 0$

3.6   Descartes rule of signs

A famous theorem first proved by the French mathematician and philosopher René Descartes provides a convenient test for the existence of real roots of a polynomial equation. We shall state the theorem without proof. Assume that the terms of a polynomial equation with real coefficients are arranged in descending order of powers of the variable.

- THEOREM: DESCARTES RULE OF SIGNS

    The number of positive roots of a polynomial equation $P(x) = 0$ is no greater than the number of variations in sign, and, if not equal to the number of variations in sign, then less than this by a positive even number.

A variation in sign is counted whenever successive coefficients have different signs, zero coefficients being ignored. The number of variations for $x^4 + 3x^3 - 2x^2 - 3x + 8 = 0$ is two since there is a sign change from the second to the third term and another sign change from the fourth to the fifth term. Thus, the Rule of Signs would require that there be either two or zero positive real roots. Why must $x^3 - x^2 + x - 1 = 0$ have at least one positive real root?

We can apply Descartes Rule of Signs to find a limit on the number of negative real roots, but first we need to state a theorem about an equation with roots which are the negatives of the roots of a given equation. Let $P(x) = 0$ have real roots $r_1, r_2, r_3, \cdots r_n$. The following theorem enables us to write the equation with the roots $-r_1, -r_2, -r_3, \cdots -r_n$.

• THEOREM

If $P(x) = 0$ has the roots $r_1, r_2, r_3, \cdots r_n$, then the equation $P(-x) = 0$ has the roots $-r_1, -r_2, -r_3, \cdots -r_n$.

$P(-x) = 0$ can easily be formed from $P(x) = 0$ by changing the sign of each odd power term of $P(x)$.

EXAMPLE. Write the equation that has roots which are the negatives of the roots of $x^4 - 3x^3 - 2x^2 - 3x + 8 = 0$.

Solution. The required equation is $x^4 + 3x^3 - 2x^2 + 3x + 8 = 0$.

Descartes Rule of Signs can now be applied to find a limit on the number of negative roots of $P(x) = 0$. If we find $P(-x) = 0$ and apply the Rule, we conclude that the number of negative real roots of $P(x) = 0$ is the number of variations in sign of $P(-x)$ or less than this by an even number.

The number of negative real roots in the previous example is either two or zero since there are two variations in sign for $P(-x)$.

Zero is a root of $P(x) = 0$ if $a_n = 0$. Why?

Exercises

1 – 10. Find the maximum number of positive real roots for each equation in the exercises following Section 3.5.

11 – 20. Write the equation which has real roots that are the negatives of each equation in the exercises following Section 3.5. Find the maximum number of negative real roots for each equation.

3.7   Other theorems about roots

It is easily seen from Descartes Rule of Signs that there can be no positive real roots of $P(x) = 0$ if there is no variation in sign of $P(x)$. Likewise, there are no negative real roots of $P(x) = 0$ if there is no variation in sign of $P(-x)$. Combining this observation with the Remainder Theorem, we are able to establish upper and lower limits for real roots of a polynomial equation with real coefficients.

For example, we can show that there are no real roots of $x^3 - 2x^2 - 3x - 4 = 0$ greater than 4. Using synthetic division, we shall divide the polynomial in the left member of the equation by $x - 1$, $x - 2$, etc., successively.

r	1	-2	-3	-4
1	1	-1	-4	-8
2	1	0	-3	-10
3	1	1	0	-4
4	1	2	5	16

From the preceding divisions and previous theorems we can make several statements about the positive real roots of $x^3 - 2x^2 - 3x - 4 = 0$.

a. There is exactly one positive real root (by Descartes Rule of Signs).

b. Since $P(1) = -8$, $P(2) = -10$, $P(3) = -4$ and $P(4) = 16$, we conclude that the positive real root lies between 3 and 4.

c. Observing that $P(4) > 0$ and there are no variations in signs in the last row of the synthetic division of $P(x)$ by $(x - 4)$, we conclude that there are no positive real roots greater than 4.

The following theorems can now be stated without proof.

• THEOREM

If a is any integer and the signs of $P(a)$ and $P(a + 1)$ are different, at least one real root lies between a and $a + 1$.

The theorem is intuitively clear since a polynomial function is continuous, and points $[a, P(a)]$ and $[a + 1, P(a + 1)]$ lie on opposite sides of the x-axis. There must be at least one point (possibly an odd number of points) on the graph of $P(x)$ between $x = a$ and

$x = a + 1$ which coincides with the x-axis. We say that we *isolate* a real root if we find two consecutive integers which bound the root.

EXAMPLE 1. Isolate the real roots of $x^3 - x - 1 = 0$.

Solution. Using synthetic division we can isolate the one positive real root as follows.

r	1	0	-1	-1
1	1	1	0	-1
2	1	2	3	5

There is a real root between 1 and 2.

Since $P(-x) = -x^3 + x - 1 = 0$, we see that there are either two or zero negative roots. By synthetic division again we have

r	-1	0	1	-1
1	-1	-1	0	-1
2	-1	-2	-3	-7

Therefore, there is no real root less than -1 since any value of r greater than 1 will not result in a change in the sign of the last numeral. Points on the graph are $(-1, -1)$, $(0, -1)$ and $(1, -1)$ which indicate that the curve has no real roots in the interval $-1 < x < 1$. The graph shown in Figure 3–1 confirms this.

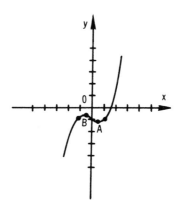

FIGURE 3–1

• THEOREM

> If c is a positive number and $P(x)$ is divided by $(x - c)$ (using synthetic division) resulting in a quotient and remainder having no changes in sign (zero coefficients ignored), then $P(x) = 0$ has no real root greater than c.

We call c an upper limit of the real roots of $P(x) = 0$. Similarly, a lower limit d can be found by dividing $P(-x)$ by $(x - d)$. If the resulting quotient and remainder have no changes in sign, then $-d$ is a lower limit of the real roots of $P(x) = 0$.

EXAMPLE 2. Find the least positive integer which is an upper limit, and the greatest negative integer which is a lower limit, of the real roots of $x^4 - 3x^3 - 2x^2 + 3x - 5 = 0$.

Solution.

r	1	-3	-2	3	-5
1	1	-2	-4	-1	-6
2	1	-1	-4	-5	-15
3	1	0	-2	-3	-14
4	1	1	2	11	39

Thus, 4 is the least integral upper limit.

r	1	3	-2	-3	-5
1	1	4	2	-1	-6
2	1	5	8	13	21

The greatest integral lower limit of the real roots is -2.

It is desirable at times to write an equation which has roots that are less than the roots of a given equation by a constant amount. For example, we might wish to write the equation with roots which are 2 less than those of $x^2 - 8x + 15 = 0$. The direct way to accomplish this is to find the roots of the given equation, subtract 2 from each root, and then form the new equation by multiplying the appropriate linear factors together. In this example the roots of $x^2 = 8x + 15 = 0$ are 3 and 5. The desired equation has the roots 1 and 3 and may be formed as follows.

$$(x - 1)(x - 3) = 0$$

$$x^2 - 4x + 3 = 0$$

A more convenient method has been found. It is especially useful for equations of higher degree where the real roots may be more difficult to identify. By successively dividing $P(x)$ and the resulting quotients by $x - h$, where h is the constant by which we wish to decrease the roots, we can obtain the coefficients of the desired equation. An example will illustrate the method.

EXAMPLE 3. Write the equation with roots which are two less than those of $2x^3 - x^2 - 13x - 6 = 0$.

Solution. By repeated synthetic division we have

2/2	-1	-13	-6
	4	6	-14
2/2	3	-7	(-20)
	4	14	
2/2	7	(7)	
	4		
2	(11)		

Using the final quotient and the remainders in parentheses as coefficients, the desired equation is $2x^3 + 11x^2 + 7x - 20 = 0$. You should verify that the roots of the given equation are 3, -2, $-\frac{1}{2}$, and those of the derived equation are 1, -4, $-2\frac{1}{2}$.

Exercises

Isolate the real roots of each equation.

1. $x^2 + 3x + 1 = 0$
2. $x^2 - x - 1 = 0$
3. $x^2 - 4x - 2 = 0$
4. $2x^2 - 5x + 1 = 0$
5. $x^3 - 2 = 0$
6. $x^3 - 3x + 1 = 0$
7. $x^4 - 2x^3 + x - 2 = 0$
8. $2x^4 + x^2 - 3x + 5 = 0$

Find the integers that are the least upper limit and the greatest lower limit of the roots in the following equations.

9. $x^3 + 3x^2 - 5x - 10 = 0$
10. $x^4 - 8x + 2 = 0$
11. $3x^3 - 2x^2 + 5x - 1 = 0$
12. $x^5 + 5x^4 - 3x^3 + 20x^2 - 15 = 0$

13. Write an equation with real roots that are one less than the roots of $x^3 - 4x^2 + x - 2 = 0$.

14. Write an equation with real roots that are two less than the roots of $x^3 + 2x^2 - 5x - 6 = 0$.

15. Write an equation with real roots that are one more than the roots of $x^4 - 5x^3 + 9x^2 - 7x + 2 = 0$.

3.8 Imaginary roots

A corollary to the Fundamental Theorem of Algebra asserts that a polynomial equation of degree n has exactly n roots, but it neither reveals any method for finding the roots nor states whether the roots are real or imaginary. As you know from the quadratic formula, the roots of a second degree equation are imaginary if the value of the discriminant, $b^2 - 4ac$, is negative. Such roots always occur as conjugate pairs as an inspection of the formula $x = \dfrac{-b \pm \sqrt{b^2 - 4ac}}{2a}$ will show, providing a, b and c are rational numbers.

It can be proved that the roots of higher degree polynomial equations, when imaginary, occur as conjugate pairs of complex numbers. The following theorem concerns the polynomial equation

$$a_0x^n + a_1x^{n-1} + a_2x^{n-2} + \cdots + a_{n-1}x + a_n = 0$$

where $a_0 \neq 0$ and the coefficients are real numbers.

● THEOREM

If $f(x) = 0$, where $f(x)$ is a polynomial of degree n with real coefficients, and if $a + bi$ is a root of $f(x) = 0$, $b \neq 0$, then $a - bi$ is also a root.

Proof: If $a + bi$ is a root of $f(x) = 0$, then $f(a + bi) = 0$. When the expansion of $f(a + bi)$ is carried out, there will be terms containing powers of a and no powers of b, assuming $a \neq 0$. Since the coefficients of $f(x)$ are real, these terms represent real numbers and their value is $f(a)$. There will also be terms in the expansion containing powers of bi, sometimes involving a and sometimes not. Those terms which contain *even* powers of i are real, and those which contain *odd* powers of i are imaginary. Thus, the expansion of $f(a + bi)$ is of the form $P_1(a,b) + P_2(a,b)i$ where $P_1(a,b)$ and $P_2(a,b)$ are functions of a and b. Since $P_1(a,b) + P_2(a,b)i = 0$, it is clear from the definition of a zero complex number that $P_1(a,b) = 0$ and $P_2(a,b) = 0$.

Now consider $f(a - bi)$; we can rewrite this function in the form $f[a + b(-i)]$. Observe that $P_1(a,b)$ contains only even powers of bi and odd or even powers of a; thus, $P_1(a,b)$ will be the real part of $f[a + b(-i)]$. Similarly, we observe that $P_2(a,b)$ contains only odd powers of $b(-i)$, and thus, $-P_2(a,b)$ is the imaginary part of $f[a + b(-i)]$. Therefore, $f[a + b(-i)] = P_1(a,b) - P_2(a,b)i$. But $P_1(a,b) = 0$ and $P_2(a,b) = 0$, and so we conclude that $a - bi$ is a root of $f(x) = 0$ because $f(a - bi) = f[a + b(-i)] = 0$.

Exercises

1. Prove that if a quadratic equation has one real root, the other root is also real.

2. Prove that if an equation is of the third degree and has an imaginary root, then it has two and only two imaginary roots.

3. One root of an equation is $-2i$. Give another root.

4. One root of an equation is $-\dfrac{1}{2} + \dfrac{1}{2}i$. Give another root.

5. Show that the graph of every third degree function of x must intersect the x-axis at least once.

In the following exercises express the answer as a polynomial equation with integral coefficients.

6. Form the cubic equation with the roots 2, $1 + i$, $1 - i$.

7. Form the quartic equation with the roots ± 1, $1 \pm i$.

8. Form the cubic equation with the roots 1, $\dfrac{-1 \pm i \sqrt{3}}{2}$.

9. Form the polynomial equation of lowest degree with the roots $-2 + i$ and $1 - 3i$.

10. Form the simplest equation with 3 as a double root and $2i$ as another root.

3.9 Slope of a tangent at a point on a curve—$D_x y$

In Chapter 2 you studied the graphs of linear equations in some detail and learned that the slope of a line is constant. In elementary and intermediate algebra you have had the experience of graphing equations of second and possibly higher degree. The graphs of these equations were curves such as parabolas, circles, ellipses, and so forth. We cannot speak of the slope of a curve in the same way as we can that of a straight line; we can consider, however, the slope of a tangent line to a curve at a point on the curve. The meaning of a tangent line to a curve should be intuitively clear if you think of such examples as a wheel of a train resting on the track or a ladder leaning against a dome or other curved surface. Later in this section a more careful definition of a tangent to a curve will be made.

We shall now assume that a graph of the equation $y = f(x)$ has been drawn in the coordinate plane. Let A and B be two points near each other on the continuous curve, and let the coordinates of A be (x, y). The coordinates of B differ from those of A by amounts we shall call Δx and Δy (delta x and delta y) where $\Delta x \neq 0$ and Δy may be positive or negative or zero. (The symbol Δx is not Δ times x, but is a single symbol indicating an increment in x.) Then the coordinates of B are $(x + \Delta x, y + \Delta y)$.

A straight line that passes through A and B is a secant line to the curve. Its slope is $\dfrac{\overrightarrow{CB}}{\overrightarrow{AC}} = \dfrac{\Delta y}{\Delta x}$.

Now suppose that A remains fixed while B moves along the curve toward A. Then the absolute

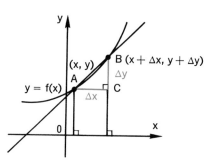

FIGURE 3–2

values of Δx and Δy will become smaller and smaller, each approaching zero. Thus, we can consider Δx as a variable which approaches zero as B approaches A. Likewise, Δy approaches zero as B approaches A. If B is made to coincide with A, then the secant line becomes a *tangent line* to the curve at point A.

Under these conditions what happens to the slope of the secant line? We see that $\frac{\Delta y}{\Delta x}$ takes the indeterminate form $\frac{0}{0}$ when the secant becomes a tangent. An *indeterminate form* is a meaningless symbol, one that cannot be evaluated, such as $\frac{0}{0}$ (zero divided by zero) or 0^0 (zero to the zero power). If we are to evaluate the slope of the tangent line, we must have a special way of defining the ratio $\frac{\Delta y}{\Delta x}$ when B coincides with A. We can define this ratio by examining a function to which it is equal. When will the slope of a secant line be approximately equal to the slope of a tangent line at a point on the curve? Before reading the solution of Example 1, see if you can find a function equal to $\frac{\Delta y}{\Delta x}$.

EXAMPLE 1. Find the slope of the tangent to the graph of $y = 2x^2 - 3x + 1$ at any point (x, y) on the curve. Find the slope of the tangent at the point $(2, 3)$ on the curve.

Solution. First let us consider the secant through two general points $A(x, y)$ and $B(x + \Delta x, y + \Delta y)$ near to each other on the curve. The coordinates of both A and B must satisfy the given equation so we can write

at B: $(y + \Delta y) = 2(x + \Delta x)^2 - 3(x + \Delta x) + 1$

or $y + \Delta y = 2x^2 + 4x\Delta x + 2\overline{\Delta x}^2 - 3x - 3\Delta x + 1$

at A: $\underline{y \qquad\qquad = 2x^2 \qquad\qquad\qquad\qquad\quad - 3x \qquad\qquad + 1}$

Subtracting A from B we get

$$\Delta y = 4x\Delta x + 2\overline{\Delta x}^2 - 3\Delta x$$

Now divide both members by Δx. There is no difficulty in dividing by Δx since it is a non-zero real number. We get

$$\frac{\Delta y}{\Delta x} = 4x + 2\Delta x - 3$$

If the ratio $\frac{\Delta y}{\Delta x}$ is the slope of the secant AB for two points A and B on the curve, then $4x + 2\Delta x - 3$ is also the slope of the secant.

Consider now what happens as Δx approaches zero. We see that Δy also approaches zero as point B approaches A on the curve. What is the limiting value of the ratio $\dfrac{\Delta y}{\Delta x}$ as Δx approaches zero? Although the ratio itself becomes indeterminate, the function to which it is equal does not. What does $4x + 2\Delta x - 3$ equal if Δx is zero? It is easy to see that the middle term $2\Delta x$ vanishes as Δx approaches zero and the function approaches $4x - 3$. We therefore assign to the ratio $\dfrac{\Delta y}{\Delta x}$ the limiting value $4x - 3$ when Δx approaches zero.

The symbol $\dot{D}_x y$ is defined as follows.

$$D_x y = \lim_{\Delta x \to 0} \frac{\Delta y}{\Delta x}$$

$D_x y$ is read "the derivative of y with respect to x." The *derivative* is seen to be the rate of change of the function with respect to the independent variable. It is, in effect, a *slope function* which will give us the slope of a tangent line to a curve at any point where the abscissa is known. In our example, where $y = 2x^2 - 3x + 1$, $D_x y = 4x - 3$. This function, studied in differential calculus, can be interpreted as the slope of the tangent at any point (x, y) on the graph of $y = 2x^2 - 3x + 1$.

We can now proceed to find the slope of the tangent at the point $(2, 3)$. If we replace x by 2 in the equation $D_x y = 4x - 3$, we get

$$D_x y = 4(2) - 3 = 5$$

The value of the slope of the tangent at $(2, 3)$ is 5. The student should make a sketch of the curve and examine the apparent slope of the tangent line at the point $(2, 3)$.

EXAMPLE 2. Find the slope of the tangent to the graph of $y = 5x^3 - 2x^2 + x - 1$ at the point on the curve where the abscissa is -1.

Solution. Let $A(x, y)$ and $B(x + \Delta x, y + \Delta y)$ be two points on the curve near to each other. Then we can write

B: $\quad y + \Delta y = 5(x + \Delta x)^3 - 2(x + \Delta x)^2 + (x + \Delta x) - 1$

or, $\quad y + \Delta y = 5x^3 + 15x^2\Delta x + 15x\overset{2}{\Delta x} + 5\overset{3}{\Delta x} - 2x^2 - 4x\Delta x - 2\overset{2}{\Delta x} + x + \Delta x - 1$

A: $\quad y \qquad = 5x^3 \qquad\qquad\qquad\qquad\quad - 2x^2 \qquad\qquad\quad + x \qquad - 1$

by subtraction:

$\qquad \Delta y = \qquad\quad 15x^2\Delta x + 15x\overset{2}{\Delta x} + 5\overset{3}{\Delta x} \qquad - 4x\Delta x - 2\overset{2}{\Delta x} \qquad + \Delta x$

$\qquad \dfrac{\Delta y}{\Delta x} = \qquad\quad 15x^2 \quad + 15x\Delta x + 5\overset{2}{\Delta x} - 4x - 2\Delta x + 1$

Then, $\lim\limits_{\Delta x \to 0} \dfrac{\Delta y}{\Delta x} = 15x^2 - 4x + 1$

Thus, $D_x y = 15x^2 - 4x + 1$ and the slope of the tangent line to the curve is given by this derivative function at any point (x, y). At the point on the curve where $x = -1$, the slope of the tangent is

$$D_x y = 15(-1)^2 - 4(-1) + 1 = 20$$

The slope of the tangent line at the point $(-1, -9)$ is 20.

Exercises

Find the slope of the tangent to the graph of the given functions at the indicated points.

1. $y = x^2$; **(a)** $(1, 1)$; **(b)** $(0, 0)$

2. $y = x^2 + 1$; **(a)** $(2, 5)$; **(b)** $(0, 1)$

3. $y = 2x^2$; **(a)** $(2, 8)$; **(b)** $(-1, 2)$

4. $y = \dfrac{1}{2}x^2$; **(a)** $(2, 2)$; **(b)** $(-3, 4\frac{1}{2})$

5. $y = -2x^2 + 3x + 1$; **(a)** $(0, 1)$; **(b)** $(1, 2)$

6. $y = .5x^2 - .4x - .3$; **(a)** $(1, -.2)$; **(b)** $(-1, .6)$

7. $y = 2x^2 - 3x - 4$ at the point whose abscissa is -2.

8. $y = \dfrac{1}{2}x^2 + \dfrac{1}{4}x + \dfrac{1}{8}$ at the point whose abscissa is $\dfrac{1}{2}$.

9. $y = x^2 + \dfrac{1}{6}x - \dfrac{1}{3}$ at the point $\left(\dfrac{1}{2}, 0\right)$.

10. $y = \dfrac{x^3 - 1}{8}$ at the point $\left(2, \dfrac{7}{8}\right)$.

3.10   Tangent to a curve at a point on it

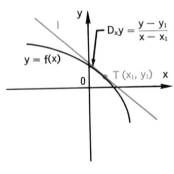

FIGURE 3–3

The definition of the slope of a line given in Formula (II), Chapter 2, enables us to write the equation of a tangent line at a point on a curve. If $T(x_1, y_1)$ is the point of tangency of line l to the graph of $f(x)$, and $D_x y$ is the slope of the tangent line l, then

$$D_x y = \frac{y - y_1}{x - x_1}$$

is the equation of the tangent line, $D_x y$ evaluated at $x = x_1$. See Figure 3–3.

EXAMPLE. Find the equation of the tangent to the curve whose equation is $y = 2x^3 - x^2 + 3x - 1$ at the point where the abscissa is -2.

Solution. Find $D_x y$.

$$y + \Delta y = 2(x + \Delta x)^3 - (x + \Delta x)^2 + 3(x + \Delta x) - 1$$

or

$$y + \Delta y = 2x^3 + 6x^2 \Delta x + 6x\overset{-2}{\Delta x} + 2\overset{-3}{\Delta x} - x^2 - 2x\Delta x - \overset{-2}{\Delta x} + 3x + 3\Delta x - 1$$
$$y \quad\quad = 2x^3 \quad\quad\quad\quad\quad\quad\quad\quad\quad - x^2 \quad\quad\quad\quad\quad\quad + 3x \quad\quad\quad - 1$$

Thus, $\quad \Delta y = \quad\quad 6x^2 \Delta x + 6x\overset{-2}{\Delta x} + 2\overset{-3}{\Delta x} \quad\quad - 2x\Delta x - \overset{-2}{\Delta x} \quad\quad + 3\Delta x$

and $\quad \dfrac{\Delta y}{\Delta x} = 6x^2 + 6x\Delta x + 2\overset{-2}{\Delta x} - 2x - \Delta x + 3$

$$D_x y = \lim_{\Delta x \to 0} \frac{\Delta y}{\Delta x} = 6x^2 - 2x + 3$$

the slope of the tangent at any point (x, y) on the curve. If $x = -2$, then the $f(-2) = -27$ and the value of $D_x y$ at the point $(-2, -27)$ is given by $6(-2)^2 - 2(-2) + 3 = 31$. Thus, the slope of the tangent at $(-2, -27)$ is 31. The equation of the tangent is

$$D_x y = \frac{y - y_1}{x - x_1}$$

If (x_1, y_1) is $(-2, -27)$, then

$$31 = \frac{y - (-27)}{x - (-2)} = \frac{y + 27}{x + 2}$$

or, $31x - y + 35 = 0$, is the equation of the tangent to the curve at $(-2, -27)$.

Exercises

Find the equation of the tangent to the graph of the given functions at the designated point.

1. $y = x^2$; $(2, 4)$
2. $y = x^2 - 3$; $(3, 6)$
3. $y = 2x^2 - 3x$; $(-1, 5)$
4. $y = x^2 - 3x + 2$; $(1, 0)$
5. $y = x^2 - 5x + 6$; $(2\frac{1}{2}, -\frac{1}{4})$
6. $y = -x^2 - x + 2$; $(\frac{1}{2}, 1\frac{1}{4})$
7. $y = -3x^2 + 5$; $(-2, -7)$
8. $y = \frac{1}{2}x^2 + x - 1$; $(-4, 3)$

3.11　Tangent line parallel to x-axis—maxima—minima

If a line in the coordinate plane is parallel to the x-axis, its slope is zero because $\Delta y = 0$ for any $\Delta x \neq 0$. If the line is tangent to a curve,

$y = f(x)$, at a point (x, y), then $D_x y = 0$ when the derivative is evaluated at x. There are three possible forms a curve may have in the neighborhood of a point where the derivative is zero. See Figure 3–4.

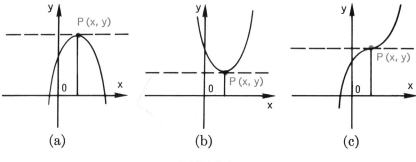

(a)   (b)   (c)

FIGURE 3–4

In (a) the curve has a *maximum* point where $D_x y = 0$. In (b) the curve has a *minimum* point where the tangent line is parallel to the x-axis making the derivative zero at that point. In (c) the tangent line intersects the curve; the point where the derivative is zero in this case is called a *point of inflection*. Points on the curve which are maxima or minima are collectively called *extrema*.

When we say that the point on the curve is a maximum point, we do not necessarily mean that the function does not have a greater value than the ordinate at this point. Similarly, the minimum point is not necessarily the least value that a function may have. See Figure 3–5. Sometimes such points as A and B in the figure are called a *relative maximum* and a *relative minimum*, respectively.

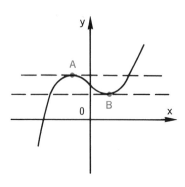

FIGURE 3–5

Suppose the derivative of a function has been found and a value of x has been determined such that $D_x y = 0$. The question arises, is the point a maximum, a minimum, or a point of inflection? One method of determining this is by finding values of ordinates sufficiently close to the ordinate of the point to be tested. If these ordinates are *both less* than the ordinate at the point where $D_x y = 0$, then the curve has a *maximum* value at the point. If the ordinates are *both greater* than the ordinate of the point, the curve is at a *minimum*. If one of the two ordinates is greater and the other is less than the ordinate of the point being tested, the tangent line intersects the curve and there is no maximum or minimum at that point.

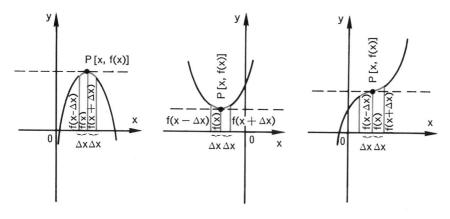

FIGURE 3–6

Let $P[x, f(x)]$ be a point on the graph of $f(x)$ such that $D_x f(x) = 0$, and let Δx be a deviation from x with some small positive value. Evaluate $f(x + \Delta x)$ and $f(x - \Delta x)$. If both $f(x + \Delta x)$ and $f(x - \Delta x) < f(x)$, then $P[x, f(x)]$ is a maximum point. If both $f(x + \Delta x)$ and $f(x - \Delta x) > f(x)$, then $P[x, f(x)]$ is a minimum point. If $f(x - \Delta x) < f(x) < f(x + \Delta x)$ or $f(x - \Delta x) > f(x) > f(x + \Delta x)$, then $P[x, f(x)]$ is neither a maximum nor a minimum; it is a point of inflection. One danger in using this method is that Δx must be chosen sufficiently small; otherwise the situation shown in Figure 3–7 could result.

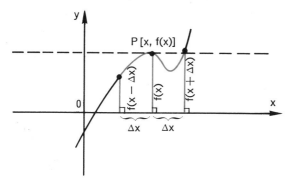

FIGURE 3–7

EXAMPLE 1. Find the extreme point of the graph of $y = x^2 + 4x - 12$ and determine whether the point is a maximum or a minimum.

Solution. Find $D_x y$.

$$y + \Delta y = (x + \Delta x)^2 + 4(x + \Delta x) - 12$$
$$y + \Delta y = x^2 + 2x\Delta x + \overline{\Delta x}^2 + 4x + 4\Delta x - 12$$
$$\underline{y \qquad\quad = x^2 \qquad\qquad\qquad + 4x \qquad\qquad - 12}$$
$$\Delta y = \qquad 2x\Delta x + \overline{\Delta x}^2 \qquad + 4\Delta x$$

$$\frac{\Delta y}{\Delta x} = 2x + \Delta x + 4$$

$$D_x y = \lim_{\Delta x \to 0} \frac{\Delta y}{\Delta x} = 2x + 4$$

At the minimum or maximum point $D_x y = 0$. Thus, $2x + 4 = 0$ and $x = -2$. The point to be tested is $(-2, -16)$, since $f(-2) = -16$. Let Δx be .1 and find $f(-2.1)$ and $f(-1.9)$. We get $f(-2.1) = -15.99$ and $f(-1.9) = -15.99$. Each of these values is greater than -16, so the point $(-2, -16)$ is a minimum point.

EXAMPLE 2. Examine the equation $y = x^3 - x^2 + 1$ for maxima and minima and give the equations of horizontal tangents.

Solution. $D_x y = 3x^2 - 2x$. Setting $D_x y = 0$ we have $3x^2 - 2x = 0$. Hence, $x = 0$ or $x = \dfrac{2}{3}$. The corresponding values of y are 1 and $\dfrac{23}{27}$. Therefore the maximum or minimum points on the curve are $(0, 1)$ and $\left(\dfrac{2}{3}, \dfrac{23}{27}\right)$. To determine whether the value of $f(x)$ at $(0, 1)$ is a minimum or maximum, we shall find $f(-.1)$ and $f(+.1)$. We get $f(-.1) = +.989$ and $f(+.1) = +.991$. Since both $f(-.1)$ and $f(+.1)$ are less than $f(0)$, the point $(0, 1)$ is a maximum. By a like process, we find that $\left(\dfrac{2}{3}, \dfrac{23}{27}\right)$ is a minimum. The equations of the horizontal tangents are $y = 1$ and $y = \dfrac{23}{27}$.

Exercises

1. Locate the minimum point of $y = x^2 - x - 6$. Draw the figure.

2. Locate the extreme point of $y = 8 - 2x - x^2$, and tell whether it is a maximum or a minimum. Draw the figure.

3. Locate the extreme point of $y = x^2 + 2x - 15$ and tell whether it is a maximum or a minimum. Draw the figure.

4. Find the equation of the horizontal tangent of $y = 2x^2 - 3x + 1$. Draw the figure.

5. Find the equations of the horizontal tangents of $y = x^3 - x^2 + 3$. Draw the figure.

6. Find the equations of the horizontal tangents of $y = x^4 - 8x^2 + 16$. Draw the figure.

3.12 Curve sketching

If we know the extrema of a curve, $y = f(x)$, we not only know certain important points on it; we also know something about the configuration of the curve near these points. These facts enable us to sketch the curve with some degree of accuracy. If, in addition to these facts, we know the real roots of the equation $f(x) = 0$ (either exactly or approximately), then we know where the graph crosses the x-axis and can fill in with any needed accuracy by finding additional ordered pairs satisfying the function.

EXAMPLE. Sketch the graph of $y = x^3 + 2x^2 - 4x - 5$.

Solution. $D_x y = 3x^2 + 4x - 4$. Maximum or minimum points are at the points whose abscissas are roots of $3x^2 + 4x - 4 = 0$; that is, at $x = -2$, and $x = \dfrac{2}{3}$. Hence $A(-2, 3)$ and $B\left(\dfrac{2}{3}, -\dfrac{175}{27}\right)$ or, approximately, $B(.67, -6.5)$, are the extrema (maximum and minimum). The tests show that A is a maximum and B is a minimum. By using the factor theorem, we find that -1, $\dfrac{-1 + \sqrt{21}}{2}$, and $\dfrac{-1 - \sqrt{21}}{2}$ are roots of $x^3 + 2x^2 - 4x - 5 = 0$. Approximate values of the roots are -1, 1.8, -2.8. The figure shows a sketch of the curve.

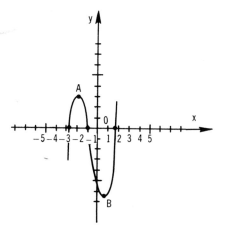

FIGURE 3–8

There are other features which often facilitate sketching the graph of an equation in two variables. We shall take up some of these tests in the following paragraphs.

Intercepts: An intercept is a point on the curve which coincides with an axis. Given $f(x, y) = 0$, if y is replaced by zero and the resulting equation solved for values of x, these values are the x-intercepts. Similarly, if x is replaced by zero in $f(x, y) = 0$, the resulting values of y are the y-intercepts.

Symmetries: Given $f(x, y) = 0$ if, when x is replaced by $-x$, the equation is unchanged, then the graph is symmetric with respect to the y-axis. Similarly, if the equation is unchanged when y is replaced by $-y$, the graph is symmetric with respect to the x-axis. Furthermore, if the equation is unchanged when both $-x$ replaces x and $-y$ replaces y, the graph is symmetric with respect to the origin. Finally, if x and y are interchanged and the equation is unchanged, the graph is symmetric with respect to the line $y = x$.

Excluded points or intervals: If it is possible to express $f(x, y) = 0$ in the form $y = F(x)$, then any real number x_1 for which $F(x_1)$ reduces to $\frac{k}{0}$, $k \neq 0$, is excluded from the domain of F. This means that there is no point on the graph with the abscissa x_1. For example, given $xy - y + 2 = 0$, we can express the equation in the form $y = \frac{2}{1 - x}$. Thus, there is no point on the graph for $x = 1$. The line $x - 1 = 0$ is an *asymptote* of the curve. An asymptote is a line which is approached by a graph. The x- and y-axes are asymptotes of the graph of $y = \frac{k}{x}$, a curve with which you are familiar. Similarly, if $f(x, y) = 0$ is transformed into $x = G(y)$, excluded points are easily found for G. How are these excluded values interpreted?

There are often excluded *intervals* which can aid in sketching the graph of an equation. For example, if $x^2 - y = 0$, it is obvious that there are no points on the graph for $y < 0$. In general, if a real number replaces one of the variables, and this results in an imaginary value of the other variable, there is no point on the graph corresponding to that real number. In $x^2 - y^2 = 4$ we find that $y = \pm \sqrt{x^2 - 4}$. Any real replacement of x between -2 and $+2$ results in an imaginary value of y. Therefore, there is the excluded interval $-2 < x < 2$ for which there are no points on the graph.

Exercises

Sketch the curve for each of the following equations.

1. $y = x^3 - 2x^2 - 5x + 6$

2. $y = x^3 + x$

3. $y = x^4 - 2x^2 - 8$

4. $y = x^3 - 7x - 6$

5. $y = x^4 + x^2$

6. $y = \sqrt{2x^2 - 1}$

7. $xy - x - 4 = 0$

8. $4x^2 - 9y^2 - 36 = 0$

9. $x^2 - 2xy = 0$

10. $\dfrac{x}{y} + \dfrac{y}{x} = 1$

3.13   Approximate value of a real root

When a real root of an equation $f(x) = 0$ has been isolated between consecutive integers a and $a + 1$, it is possible to find a decimal approximation of the root as near as desired by numerous methods. In this section we shall explain one such method, and in the following section we shall demonstrate a method often used with electronic digital computers.

The method in this section involves finding a series of values such that each succeeding value is a better approximation of a real root than the preceding one. If $f(a) < 0$ and $f(a + 1) > 0$, then at least one real root exists between $x = a$ and $x = a + 1$. This is also true if $f(a) > 0$ and $f(a + 1) < 0$. Let $a + h$ be one of these roots such that $f(a + h) = 0$, where $0 < h < 1$. Our goal is to find a value that is nearly equal to h, which we shall call h_1. Then $a + h_1$ is a number nearer to the root than a. Repeating the process using the result of the preceding computation, we can arrive at closer and closer approximations of the root $a + h$. An example will illustrate the procedure.

EXAMPLE. Find an approximate value of the real root of $x^3 - 2x^2 + x + 1 = 0$.

Solution. First we shall isolate the real root by synthetic division.

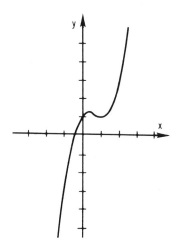

r	1	-2	1	1
1	1	-1	0	1
2	1	0	1	3

There are no positive real roots.

FIGURE 3-9

$$\begin{array}{c|cccc}
r & -1 & -2 & -1 & 1 \\
\hline
1 & -1 & -3 & -4 & -3
\end{array}$$

A real root exists between 0 and -1, so we shall let $a = -1$. A graph of $y = f(x) = x^3 - 2x^2 + x + 1$ is shown in Figure 3–9. Let the root be $a + h$ or $-1 + h$ where $0 < h < 1$. Therefore, $f(-1 + h) = 0$. Expanding we have

$$\begin{aligned}
f(-1 + h) &= (-1 + h)^3 - 2(-1 + h)^2 + (-1 + h) + 1 \\
&= -1 + 3h - 3h^2 + h^3 - 2 + 4h - 2h^2 - 1 + h + 1 \\
&= h^3 - 5h^2 + 8h - 3
\end{aligned}$$

The solution of $f(-1 + h) = 0$, that is, $h^3 - 5h^2 + 8h - 3 = 0$, appears to be as difficult as the solution of the given equation. Observe, however, that h^3 and $-5h^2$ are small compared to h since $0 < h < 1$. Therefore, the linear equation $8h_1 - 3 = 0$ has a root which is very close to a real root of $h^3 - 5h^2 + 8h - 3 = 0$. Solving $8h_1 - 3 = 0$ for h_1, we get $h_1 = \dfrac{3}{8}$ or .4 approximately.

Thus, $-1 + .4$, or $-.6$, is a closer approximation of the real root $-1 + h$ than is -1. Now we can repeat the process with a new value of h and find a closer approximation than $-.6$ as follows.

$$\begin{aligned}
f(-.6 + h) &= (-.6 + h)^3 - 2(-.6 + h)^2 + (-.6 + h) + 1 \\
&= -.216 + 1.08h - 1.8h^2 + h^3 - .72 + 2.4h - 2h^2 - \\
&\quad .6 + h + 1 \\
&= h^3 - 3.8h^2 + 4.48h - .536
\end{aligned}$$

If we drop the terms containing h^3 and h^2, which are much less than h, we can find a value close to h by solving the equation $4.48h_2 - .536 = 0$. This gives us $h_2 = .12$ approximately. The real root is approximately $-.6 + .12$ or $-.48$. Repeating the process will give us an approximation which will be still closer to the real root. In practice we can avoid the calculation of the terms containing h^3 and h^2 entirely.

Exercises

Find approximate values to the nearest tenth of the real roots of each given equation.

1. $x^2 - x - 5 = 0$

2. $2x^2 + x - 1 = 0$

3. $x^2 + 3x + 2 = 0$

4. $2x^3 - 4x^2 - 3 = 0$

5. $x^3 - 4x + 6 = 0$

6. $3x^4 + x^2 - 1 = 0$

7. $2x^4 - x^3 + x - 2 = 0$

8. $-x^3 + x^2 - x + 1 = 0$

3.14 Iteration

Any succession of computations which produce a sequence of numbers that converge on a desired number as a limit may be called *iteration*. Of particular interest to us is the iterative method of approximating an irrational real root of a higher degree equation. Generally such processes are tedious and the time and effort required to perform them have restricted their usefulness. However, the capability of modern electronic computers to handle data and perform computations at great speed has made iteration a very practical method of solving certain problems. Although we shall illustrate the method as one of approximating real roots of a polynomial function, iteration can be used in many other approximations.

Iteration involves transforming the given equation $f(x) = 0$ into the form of a function of the variable equal to the variable, that is, $x = F(x)$. If an estimate of the root is evaluated in the function $F(x)$, the value of the function is a closer approximation of the value of the root than the estimate if iteration succeeds. This closer approximation to the desired number is fed back into the function resulting in a still closer approximation. The process of iteration is characterized by the repetitive application of a function resulting in a convergent sequence of numbers. *Feedback* is a term that can be applied to such a process.

An example will illustrate a method of forming a function such that the iterative process can be applied: Given $f(x) = 0$, transform the equation into the form $x = F(x)$, where $F(x)$ will be called the *iteration function*. Successive values of $F(x)$ form a convergent sequence if iteration is to be successful. $8 + 8 + 20 - 20 = +16$

$1 + 2 + 10 - 20 = -7$

EXAMPLE 1. Solve $f(x) = x^3 + 2x^2 + 10x - 20 = 0$ for a real root by the method of iteration.

Solution. Since $f(1) = -7$ and $f(2) = +16$, a real root lies between 1 and 2. Let us write the given equation $x^3 + 2x^2 + 10x - 20 = 0$ in the form $x = F(x)$. We shall transform the equation as follows.

$$x(x^2 + 2x + 10) = 20$$

or
$$x = \frac{20}{x^2 + 2x + 10}$$

We shall designate $\dfrac{20}{x^2 + 2x + 10}$ as $F(x)$, the iteration function.

Such a function can be formed from the equation in many ways; experience will indicate the most useful forms.

Starting with an estimate of the root of $f(x) = 0$, such as $x_0 = 1$, let us find $F(x_0)$. The subscript of x_0 indicates that this is the original estimate of the real root near to 1.

$$F(x_0) = F(1) = \frac{20}{(1)^2 + 2(1) + 10} = 1.54 \text{ approximately}$$

Suppose $x_1 = 1.54$, where the subscript indicates the first approximation of x by the iteration function $F(x)$.

Now find $F(x_1)$ and designate the result as x_2, and so on. The following sequence can be written.

$$F(x_0) = 1.54 = x_1$$
$$F(x_1) = 1.30 = x_2$$
$$F(x_2) = 1.40 = x_3$$
$$F(x_3) = 1.35 = x_4$$
$$F(x_4) = 1.38 = x_5$$
$$F(x_5) = 1.37 = x_6$$
$$F(x_6) = 1.37 = x_7$$

The sequence converges at a limit near 1.37 which is an approximation of the real root desired. When you consider that an electronic computer can perform tens of thousands of computations per second and give the result accurate to ten digits, you can see that the iterative process is a most useful one for such machines.

A very important difficulty can arise, however, which is sometimes not easily surmounted. This is the case when the sequence does not converge to a limit but rather diverges and the iterative process fails. You may have noted the rather unusual form in which we obtained the iteration function $F(x)$ in the example. We might have transformed $x^3 + 2x^2 + 10x - 20 = 0$ into the form:

$x = \dfrac{20 - 2x^2 - x^3}{10}$. Let $F'(x)$, another iterative function, equal the right member. Now if we find the sequence, $F'(x_1)$, $F'(x_2)$, $F'(x_3)$, $\cdots$, will this sequence converge on the approximate root 1.37? If $x_0 = 1$, we get

$$F'(x_0) = 1.7 = x_1$$
$$F'(x_1) = .93 = x_2$$
$$F'(x_2) = 1.75 = x_3$$
$$F'(x_3) = .85 = x_4, \text{ etc.}$$

It is seen that the successive values of $F'(x)$ are alternately greater and less than the root, as in the first example for $F(x)$, but do not converge. How, then, can we find a transformation of a given equation so that we can be assured that iteration will succeed?

It can be proved that the sequence of numbers resulting from iteration will converge if the *absolute value* of the derivative of the iteration function, $D_x F(x)$, is less than 1 for values of x near the root.

It frequently happens that the derivative of $F(x)$ is difficult to find and as an approximation we may consider a secant line in the neighborhood of the root. If the root has been isolated between two consecutive integers, a and $a + 1$, then $| F(a + 1) - F(a) |$ is frequently a satisfactory approximation of $| D_x F(x) |$ for our purposes.

Returning to our original example, you recall that the root is between 1 and 2. Then $F(1) = 1.54$ and $F(2) = 1.11$, and we have

$$| F(2) - F(1) | = | 1.11 - 1.54 | = .43$$

Since $.43 < 1$, the method of iteration will probably succeed.

Now let us test $F'(x) = \dfrac{20 - 2x^2 - x^3}{10}$ to see if the expression $|F'(a + 1) - F'(a) | < 1$.

$$| F'(2) - F'(1) | = | 0.4 - 1.7 | = 1.3$$

Since $1.3 > 1$, the iteration process with $F'(x)$ may fail. A closer first approximation to the root might indicate that iteration should be attempted with $F'(x)$. That is, we might test $| F'(1.4) - F'(1.3) |$. In this case iteration fails since $| D_x F'(x) | > 1$ in the vicinity of the root.

It can further be shown that if $D_x F(x)$ is negative, the successive values of $F(x)$ will lie alternately above and below the root, but if $D_x F(x)$ is positive the sequence will approach the limit from one direction (depending on the estimate). The estimate does not need to be one of the integral values found when the root is isolated; it may be any estimate. The closer the estimate to the root, however, the more rapidly a desired degree of accuracy in the result will be reached. Also note that minor computational inaccuracies tend to be insignificant.

EXAMPLE 2. Solve $x^4 - 4x^2 + 1 = 0$ by iteration for the smallest positive real root.

Solution. Since $f(0) = 1$, $f(1) = -2$, $f(2) = 1$, there are two positive real roots, one between 0 and 1 and the other between 1 and 2. Transform $x^4 - 4x^2 + 1 = 0$ as follows.

$$x^2(x^2 - 4) = -1$$

$$x^2 = \frac{1}{4 - x^2}$$

$$x = \frac{1}{\sqrt{4 - x^2}} \quad \text{(Only positive roots are desired.)}$$

$$\text{Let } F(x) = \frac{1}{\sqrt{4 - x^2}} \text{ and } x_0 = 0$$

$$F(0) = \frac{1}{\sqrt{4}} = .5$$

$$F(.5) = \frac{1}{\sqrt{3.75}} = .516$$

$$F(.516) = \frac{1}{\sqrt{3.736}} = .517$$

Note how rapidly the sequence converges on the approximate root .517. Can you find the second positive real root?

EXAMPLE 3. Solve $3^x - 4x = 0$ by iteration for the smallest positive root.

Solution. If $f(x) = 3^x - 4x$, then $f(0) = 1$, $f(1) = -1$, $f(2) = 1$. There is one root between 0 and 1 and another between 1 and 2. Transform $3^x - 4x = 0$ into $x = \frac{3^x}{4}$. Let $F(x) = \frac{3^x}{4}$ and $x_0 = 0$.

$$F(0) = .25$$
$$F(.25) = .33 \text{ (by logarithms)}$$
$$F(.33) = .36$$
$$F(.36) = .37$$
$$F(.37) = .375$$
$$F(.375) = .377$$
$$F(.377) = .378$$

A root is approximately .378.

Exercises

Find an approximate real root of the given equations by iteration.

1. $x^2 + 2x - 1 = 0$ 5. $x^4 - 2x^2 - 2 = 0$

2. $x^2 - x - 3 = 0$ 6. $2x^3 - 6x^2 - x + 7 = 0$

3. $x^3 - x^2 - 3 = 0$ 7. $2^x + x = 4$

4. $x^3 + 2x^2 - 5 = 0$ 8. $x^2 - \log x = 4$

3.15   Cube roots and fourth roots of 1

How many roots exist for the equation $x^n - 1 = 0$? How many values of $\sqrt[n]{1}$ are there? You know that the two square roots of 1 are $+1$ and -1. What are the three cube roots of 1? the four fourth roots?

Assume $x^3 = 1$. Then $x^3 - 1 = 0$. Factoring, we have

$$(x - 1)(x^2 + x + 1) = 0$$

If $x - 1 = 0$, then $x = 1$. Let x_1 designate the positive real cube root of 1, and let x_2, x_3 be the other two roots. We call x_1 the principal cube root of 1; $x_1 = 1$. If $x^2 + x + 1 = 0$, then $x_2 = \dfrac{-1 + i\sqrt{3}}{2}$ and $x_3 = \dfrac{-1 - i\sqrt{3}}{2}$.

Thus, it is seen that the cube roots of 1 other than x_1 are complex numbers. The student should check x_2 and x_3 in the equation $x^3 = 1$.

Assume $x^4 = 1$. Then $x^4 - 1 = 0$. Factoring, we have

$$(x - 1)(x + 1)(x^2 + 1) = 0$$

Hence, $x_1 = 1$, $x_2 = -1$, $x_3 = i$, $x_4 = -i$.

The fourth roots of 1 are a pair of real numbers and a pair of imaginary numbers. The student should check x_2, x_3, and x_4 in the equation $x^4 = 1$.

The figures below show the three cube roots of 1 graphed on the complex plane, and the four fourth roots of 1 also graphed on

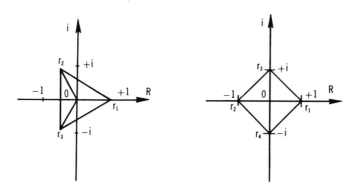

THE CUBE ROOTS OF 1   THE FOURTH ROOTS OF 1

FIGURE 3–10   FIGURE 3–11

the complex plane. A study of the figures formed by joining the points will be an aid in remembering them.

All the roots including the fifth and higher roots of 1 can be found graphically by drawing a unit circle on the complex plane with its center at the origin. The positive real root, or principal root, is at $+1$ on the real axis. If the circumference of the circle is divided into n equal arcs beginning at $+1$, the points of division determine the n nth roots of 1. Note that -1 is an nth root whenever n is even. The complex roots can be found by trigonometry for $n \geq 5$.

Exercises

1. Find the five fifth roots of 1 graphically.
2. Find the cube roots of -1 graphically and check by solving $x^3 + 1 = 0$ algebraically.
3. Find the five fifth roots of -1 graphically.
4. Find the three cube roots of 8.

Chapter Review

Estimate answers to the nearest tenth or use trigonometry for more accuracy.

1. Find all rational numbers which are zeros of the following functions by synthetic division.
   a. $f(x) = x^2 - 5x + 4$ **c.** $\{(a, b) \mid b = a^4 - 13a^2 + 36\}$
   b. $(t, t^3 + 2t^2 - 1)$ **d.** $\{(x, y) \mid y = 2x^2 - 7x + 3\}$

2. Find quotients by synthetic division.
   a. $(2x^3 - x^2 - 10x + 8) \div (x - 2)$
   b. $(x^4 + x^2 - 5) \div (x + 3)$

3. Find all integral roots of the following equations.
   a. $x^3 - 2x^2 - 13x - 10 = 0$
   b. $x^4 - 6x^2 + 8 = 0$

4. Find all roots of the equation $x^3 - 2x^2 - 2x - 3 = 0$.

5. Find $D_x y$ for the following equations.
   a. $y = 3x - 4$ **c.** $y = 2x^3 - x$
   b. $y = 2x^2 + 3x - 1$ **d.** $y = x^4 + 7$

6. Find the slope of the tangent line to the curve $y = x^2 - 4x + 1$ at the point $(1, -2)$. Find the equation of this tangent line.

7. Write the equation of the tangent line to $y = 3x^2 - 2x + 1$ at the point on the curve $(2, 9)$.

8. Find the extreme points of the following curves. Test for maximum or minimum values. Sketch the graph.
a. $y = x^2 - 8x + 4$
b. $y = 3 - 2x - x^2$
c. $y = x^3 - 27x + 1$

9. Isolate the roots and find an approximate value of each root to the nearest tenth by the method of Section 3.13.
a. $x^2 - 3x - 3 = 0$ **b.** $x^3 - x + 1 = 0$

10. Find approximate values of all positive real roots by iteration to the nearest tenth.
a. $2x^2 + 3x - 8 = 0$ **b.** $x^3 - 2x^2 + 3x - 8 = 0$

CHAPTER OUTLINE

Matrices and Vectors

4

4.1 Introduction

In this chapter we shall study the algebra of matrices. The development of an algebra of matrices involves two operations, addition and multiplication, and in many ways is similar to the development of the set of real numbers. We shall investigate the properties of matrices and compare them with the properties of real numbers.

It is assumed that you have a working knowledge of determinants as you begin the study of matrices. Briefly, these are the concepts about determinants which you are expected to know. First of all, you should be able to evaluate determinants of second and third order. The following definitions are given to refresh your memory.

The value of a second order determinant is defined as follows.

$$D = \begin{vmatrix} a_1 & b_1 \\ a_2 & b_2 \end{vmatrix} = a_1 b_2 - a_2 b_1$$

The value of a third order determinant is defined as follows.

$$D = \begin{vmatrix} a_1 & b_1 & c_1 \\ a_2 & b_2 & c_2 \\ a_3 & b_3 & c_3 \end{vmatrix} = a_1 \begin{vmatrix} b_2 & c_2 \\ b_3 & c_3 \end{vmatrix} - b_1 \begin{vmatrix} a_2 & c_2 \\ a_3 & c_3 \end{vmatrix} + c_1 \begin{vmatrix} a_2 & b_2 \\ a_3 & b_3 \end{vmatrix}$$

or $\quad D = a_1 b_2 c_3 + a_2 b_3 c_1 + a_3 b_1 c_2 - a_1 b_3 c_2 - a_2 b_1 c_3 - a_3 b_2 c_1$

Determinants of higher order may be more easily evaluated by expanding by minors. You are urged to review the method at this time if it is unfamiliar to you.

Secondly, you should know that a principal application of determinants is in the solution of systems of linear equations. If a system of two equations in two variables is given, the solution set, if it exists as a single ordered pair, can be found as shown below.

EXAMPLE 1. Solve the general system of two equations in two variables by determinants.

$$a_1 x + b_1 y = c_1$$
$$a_2 x + b_2 y = c_2$$

Solution.

$$x = \frac{\begin{vmatrix} c_1 & b_1 \\ c_2 & b_2 \end{vmatrix}}{\begin{vmatrix} a_1 & b_1 \\ a_2 & b_2 \end{vmatrix}} \; ; y = \frac{\begin{vmatrix} a_1 & c_1 \\ a_2 & c_2 \end{vmatrix}}{\begin{vmatrix} a_1 & b_1 \\ a_2 & b_2 \end{vmatrix}} \quad (a_1 b_2 \neq a_2 b_1)$$

The common solution of a system of three linear equations in three variables is illustrated by the following example.

EXAMPLE 2. Solve:
$$a_1 x + b_1 y + c_1 z = d_1$$
$$a_2 x + b_2 y + c_2 z = d_2$$
$$a_3 x + b_3 y + c_3 z = d_3$$

Solution.

$$x = \frac{\begin{vmatrix} d_1 & b_1 & c_1 \\ d_2 & b_2 & c_2 \\ d_3 & b_3 & c_3 \end{vmatrix}}{\begin{vmatrix} a_1 & b_1 & c_1 \\ a_2 & b_2 & c_2 \\ a_3 & b_3 & c_3 \end{vmatrix}} \; ; y = \frac{\begin{vmatrix} a_1 & d_1 & c_1 \\ a_2 & d_2 & c_2 \\ a_3 & d_3 & c_3 \end{vmatrix}}{\begin{vmatrix} a_1 & b_1 & c_1 \\ a_2 & b_2 & c_2 \\ a_3 & b_3 & c_3 \end{vmatrix}} \; ; z = \frac{\begin{vmatrix} a_1 & b_1 & d_1 \\ a_2 & b_2 & d_2 \\ a_3 & b_3 & d_3 \end{vmatrix}}{\begin{vmatrix} a_1 & b_1 & c_1 \\ a_2 & b_2 & c_2 \\ a_3 & b_3 & c_3 \end{vmatrix}}$$

The method used in the two examples is known as *Cramer's Rule.* This method can be extended to solve a system of n linear equations in n variables. The determinant in the denominator of each value is simply the coefficients of the variables arranged in order and is called the *determinant of the system.* If the determinant of the system is equal to zero, there is no unique common solution. Why?

In the preceding paragraphs we have summarized the basic knowledge that you need to know about determinants. If your background in this area has been slighted, or if you need additional review of this topic, you should refer to a second year algebra text and bolster your knowledge by working a number of exercises involving determinants.

4.2   Definition of matrix

The concept of matrix arose as a convenient way of writing the coefficients in a system of linear equations. Matrices (plural of matrix) are also widely used in science and business where masses of information can be organized into rectangular form. In recent years a number of new uses for this important mathematical tool have been developed.

A *matrix* is any rectangular array of numbers. The numbers in a table of values of trigonometric functions can be considered as a matrix. The numbers in a magic square form a matrix. The price quotations for a number of items may form a matrix if they are arranged in some rectangular manner. Large parentheses are commonly used to identify a matrix although brackets or double vertical bars are sometimes found.

The matrix associated with the coefficients and constants of the system of linear equations

$$2x - 3y = 7$$
$$3x + y = 16$$

can be written in the form

$$\begin{pmatrix} 2 & -3 & 7 \\ 3 & 1 & 16 \end{pmatrix}$$

Alternate forms are

$$\begin{bmatrix} 2 & -3 & 7 \\ 3 & 1 & 16 \end{bmatrix} \text{ or } \begin{Vmatrix} 2 & -3 & 7 \\ 3 & 1 & 16 \end{Vmatrix}$$

Each number in a matrix is an *element* of the matrix. The example given above has six elements arranged into two rows and three columns. The rows are the horizontal lines and the columns are the vertical lines of numbers.

A matrix which has the same number of columns as it has rows is called a *square matrix*. In our study we shall be concerned primarily with square matrices. A matrix with m rows and n columns is an $m \times n$ matrix (read "m by n"). We say that the dimensions of the matrix are m and n. The matrix in the preceding example is a 2×3 matrix.

A square matrix with n rows and n columns is defined as a matrix of *nth order*. We cannot assign an order to a non-square matrix although it may contain square matrices of various orders.

The general matrices of second order and of third order are, respectively

$$\begin{pmatrix} a_1 & b_1 \\ a_2 & b_2 \end{pmatrix} \qquad \begin{pmatrix} a_1 & b_1 & c_1 \\ a_2 & b_2 & c_2 \\ a_3 & b_3 & c_3 \end{pmatrix}$$

The subscripts identify the row in which the element occurs. In matrices with a large number of rows and columns, it is often convenient to use double subscripts, the first designating the row and the second designating the column. A square matrix of nth order may be represented in this way as follows.

$$\begin{pmatrix} a_{11} & a_{12} & a_{13} & \cdot & \cdot & \cdot & a_{1n} \\ a_{21} & a_{22} & a_{23} & \cdot & \cdot & \cdot & a_{2n} \\ \cdot & \cdot & \cdot & \cdot & \cdot & \cdot & \cdot \\ a_{n1} & a_{n2} & a_{n3} & \cdot & \cdot & \cdot & a_{nn} \end{pmatrix}$$

In this representation a_{ij} would be the element in the ith row and the jth column.

There is a determinant associated with every square matrix. The determinant can be evaluated and expressed as a real number; the matrix is simply the rectangular array of numbers and does not have a numerical value. Can you predict the determinant which is associated with the general 2×2 matrix $\begin{pmatrix} a_1 & b_1 \\ a_2 & b_2 \end{pmatrix}$? Very likely, you might hope that the determinant would be expressed by replacing the parentheses with vertical bars. This is exactly what is done. Do you think the same method of association will follow for all square matrices? Once again, your hopes are correct.

In general, the determinant of a square matrix is defined by specifying a certain function of the elements of the matrix. Thus, the determinant of $\begin{pmatrix} a_1 & b_1 \\ a_2 & b_2 \end{pmatrix}$ is $a_1b_2 - a_2b_1$ and is written as $\begin{vmatrix} a_1 & b_1 \\ a_2 & b_2 \end{vmatrix}$.

A matrix which has only one row or one column is called a *vector*. This algebraic concept of a vector is very useful for studying the same properties that are often represented as directed line segments. In physics we study forces, velocities, and other directed quantities by means of vectors, but these are normally represented geometrically as directed line segments. An algebraic vector can represent these and other vector quantities which possess the properties of magnitude and direction. In mathematics we can study complex numbers as well as other topics of mathematics by means of vectors.

A two-dimensional vector is an ordered pair such as (x,y); a three-dimensional vector is an ordered triple such as (x,y,z). These examples are *row vectors* but we can also write *column vectors* if there is a reason to do so. No physical interpretation is required of a vector by the algebraic definition given. It is fortunate, however, that there are so many useful applications of vectors.

We shall now turn our attention to square matrices of the second order and develop some of their properties and the algebraic combinations which are possible. The examples can be extended to include square matrices of any order.

Two matrices are *equal* if and only if they have the same dimensions and are identical, element by element. For example, $\begin{pmatrix} a_1 & b_1 \\ a_2 & b_2 \end{pmatrix} = \begin{pmatrix} r_1 & s_1 \\ r_2 & s_2 \end{pmatrix}$ if and only if $a_1 = r_1, b_1 = s_1, a_2 = r_2,$ and $b_2 = s_2$.

We often identify a vector or matrix by a capital letter. If $A = \begin{pmatrix} a_{11} & a_{12} \\ a_{21} & a_{22} \end{pmatrix}$ and $B = \begin{pmatrix} b_{11} & b_{12} \\ b_{21} & b_{22} \end{pmatrix}$, then $A = B$ if and only if $a_{ij} = b_{ij}$, where $i = 1, 2,$ and $j = 1, 2$. This is a symbolic way of stating that two matrices are equal if and only if elements in corresponding positions are equal.

4.3   Addition of matrices

It is possible to define the fundamental operations of addition and multiplication of matrices so that they become useful. Let us first consider addition. The definition of addition of matrices states that the sum of two $m \times n$ matrices is an $m \times n$ matrix in which the elements are the sum of the corresponding elements of the given matrices. The ijth element of the sum of A and B is $a_{ij} + b_{ij}$. This definition is meaningful only if the matrices to be added have the same dimensions, that is, an $m \times n$ matrix can be added only to an $m \times n$ matrix.

EXAMPLE.   Find the sum of the matrices (vectors): $(1, 3, -2) + (-5, 1, 3)$.

Solution. $(1, 3, -2) + (-5, 1, 3) = (1 - 5, 3 + 1, -2 + 3) = (-4, 4, 1)$.

Note that the definition given above and the definition of equal matrices apply to matrices of any dimensions and are not restricted to square matrices.

Exercises

1. Write the general 3×5 matrix using double subscript notation.

2. Write a matrix giving the age, height, and weight of five persons whom you know.

3. How many second order square matrices can be constructed from the general third order matrix $\begin{pmatrix} a_1 & b_1 & c_1 \\ a_2 & b_2 & c_2 \\ a_3 & b_3 & c_3 \end{pmatrix}$ if we assume that elements must retain their relative positions, but the structure may be "condensed"? For example, $\begin{pmatrix} b_1 & c_1 \\ b_3 & c_3 \end{pmatrix}$ is one of the required matrices. Write all of the second order matrices that are possible.

4. Show that there is a parallel between the sum of two vectors, $(a,b) + (c,d)$, and the sum of two complex numbers, $(a + bi) + (c + di)$.

5. If $(x,2y) = (y + 5, x - 3)$, find values of x and y.

6. Find the sum $A + B$ if $A = \begin{pmatrix} a_{11} & a_{12} & a_{13} \\ a_{21} & a_{22} & a_{23} \\ a_{31} & a_{32} & a_{33} \end{pmatrix}$ and

$$B = \begin{pmatrix} b_{11} & b_{12} & b_{13} \\ b_{21} & b_{22} & b_{23} \\ b_{31} & b_{32} & b_{33} \end{pmatrix}$$

7. Using general second order matrices, show that addition is commutative.

8. Show that addition of second order matrices is associative.

4.4 Multiplication of matrices

Matrices may be involved in products in two different ways. It may be desirable to multiply a matrix by a constant (sometimes called a "scalar") or we may need to find the product of two matrices. We shall first define the product of a scalar k and matrix A, where $A = \begin{pmatrix} a_1 & b_1 \\ a_2 & b_2 \end{pmatrix}$, as follows.

$$kA = k \begin{pmatrix} a_1 & b_1 \\ a_2 & b_2 \end{pmatrix} = \begin{pmatrix} ka_1 & kb_1 \\ ka_2 & kb_2 \end{pmatrix}$$

It is seen that each element of A is multiplied by the constant k to find the product kA.

The product of a two-dimensional row vector and a two-dimensional column vector is defined as $(a \quad b) \begin{pmatrix} x \\ y \end{pmatrix} = ax + by$. Note that the product is the real number $ax + by$. It is clear that the second vector must have as many elements in the column as the first vector has in the row.

Now we shall define the product of matrix $A = \begin{pmatrix} a_1 & b_1 \\ a_2 & b_2 \end{pmatrix}$ and

matrix $X = \begin{pmatrix} x_1 & y_1 \\ x_2 & y_2 \end{pmatrix}$ as

$$A \cdot X = \begin{pmatrix} a_1 & b_1 \\ a_2 & b_2 \end{pmatrix} \begin{pmatrix} x_1 & y_1 \\ x_2 & y_2 \end{pmatrix} = \begin{pmatrix} a_1 x_1 + b_1 x_2 & a_1 y_1 + b_1 y_2 \\ a_2 x_1 + b_2 x_2 & a_2 y_1 + b_2 y_2 \end{pmatrix}$$

We find each element of the product matrix from one *row* of the first matrix and one *column* of the second matrix. *The element in the ith row and jth column of the product matrix is the product of the ith row vector of A with the jth column vector of X.*

EXAMPLE. $\begin{pmatrix} 1 & 2 & 3 \\ 5 & -1 & 2 \end{pmatrix} \begin{pmatrix} x \\ y \\ z \end{pmatrix} = \begin{pmatrix} 1x + 2y + 3z \\ 5x - y + 2z \end{pmatrix}$

Note that the product matrix has as many rows as the first matrix and as many columns as the second matrix. In this example, the product of a 2×3 matrix and a 3×1 matrix is a 2×1 matrix. In general, the product of an $m \times n$ matrix and an $n \times r$ matrix is an $m \times r$ matrix.

Exercises

1. Find the product of the scalar 3 with the matrix $\begin{pmatrix} 2 & 1 & -3 \\ -4 & 0 & 7 \end{pmatrix}$.

2. Find $2A - 3B$ if $A = \begin{pmatrix} 1 & -7 \\ 3 & 2 \end{pmatrix}$ and $B = \begin{pmatrix} -4 & 5 \\ 1 & -1 \end{pmatrix}$.

3. Write the following equation as a set of 3 equations in 3 variables.

$$\begin{pmatrix} a_1 & b_1 & c_1 \\ a_2 & b_2 & c_2 \\ a_3 & b_3 & c_3 \end{pmatrix} \begin{pmatrix} x \\ y \\ z \end{pmatrix} = \begin{pmatrix} d_1 \\ d_2 \\ d_3 \end{pmatrix}$$

4. Let $A = \begin{pmatrix} a_{11} & a_{12} \\ a_{21} & a_{22} \end{pmatrix}$, $X = \begin{pmatrix} x \\ y \end{pmatrix}$, $Z = \begin{pmatrix} 0 \\ 0 \end{pmatrix}$ and $B = \begin{pmatrix} b_1 \\ b_2 \end{pmatrix}$. Write $AX + B = Z$ in the form of a system of linear equations.

5. If the product of a 3×5 matrix and another matrix is a 3×2 matrix, what are the dimensions of the second matrix?

6. Multiply.

  a. $\begin{pmatrix} 1 & 3 \\ -2 & 2 \end{pmatrix} \begin{pmatrix} 5 & 1 \\ 3 & -2 \end{pmatrix}$ **b.** $\begin{pmatrix} 7 & 6 \\ 2 & -5 \end{pmatrix} \begin{pmatrix} -1 & 3 \\ -7 & -2 \end{pmatrix}$

  c. $\begin{pmatrix} 5 & 1 & 1 \\ 3 & 2 & 4 \end{pmatrix} \begin{pmatrix} 2 & 1 \\ 5 & 6 \\ 1 & 3 \end{pmatrix}$ **d.** $\begin{pmatrix} 2 & 3 & -2 \\ 1 & 5 & -3 \\ -1 & 7 & 2 \end{pmatrix} \begin{pmatrix} 1 & 0 & 1 \\ 0 & 1 & 0 \\ 1 & 0 & 1 \end{pmatrix}$

7. Prove that the product of two general second order matrices is not commutative.

8. Prove that $(AB)C = A(BC)$, the associative property, holds for matrices of second order where $A = \begin{pmatrix} a_{11} & a_{12} \\ a_{21} & a_{22} \end{pmatrix}$, $B = \begin{pmatrix} b_{11} & b_{12} \\ b_{21} & b_{22} \end{pmatrix}$ and $C = \begin{pmatrix} c_{11} & c_{12} \\ c_{21} & c_{22} \end{pmatrix}$.

4.5   Inverses of a matrix

In the set of real numbers identity elements and inverses exist for the operations of addition and multiplication, except that there is no multiplicative inverse of zero. Recall these properties of real numbers as summarized below.

For every real number a: 1. $a + 0 = a$

2. $a \cdot 1 = a$

3. $a + (-a) = 0$

4. $a\left(\dfrac{1}{a}\right) = 1$ if $a \neq 0$

The question naturally arises, "Is it possible to define identity matrices and inverse matrices for the operations of addition and multiplication in a similar manner?" First, a zero matrix must be defined. A *zero matrix* is a matrix in which each element is zero; for example, $\begin{pmatrix} 0 & 0 \\ 0 & 0 \end{pmatrix}$ is the second order zero matrix. Now let us investigate to see if we can find a matrix such that its sum with matrix A is A. If $A = \begin{pmatrix} a_1 & b_1 \\ a_1 & b_1 \end{pmatrix}$, it is clear that $\begin{pmatrix} a_1 & b_1 \\ a_2 & b_2 \end{pmatrix} + \begin{pmatrix} 0 & 0 \\ 0 & 0 \end{pmatrix} = \begin{pmatrix} a_1 & b_1 \\ a_2 & b_2 \end{pmatrix}$. We can now define an $m \times n$ zero matrix as the *identity matrix under addition* for any $m \times n$ matrix.

Now that the identity matrix under addition has been defined, we can investigate the existence of an inverse of any matrix A. Is there a matrix which can be added to A such that the sum is the corresponding zero matrix? By "corresponding" we mean a matrix with the same dimensions as A. What elements can be used to correctly fill the blanks below?

$$\begin{pmatrix} a_1 & b_1 \\ a_2 & b_2 \end{pmatrix} + \begin{pmatrix} - & - \\ - & - \end{pmatrix} = \begin{pmatrix} 0 & 0 \\ 0 & 0 \end{pmatrix}$$

It is clear from the definition of addition of matrices that the *additive inverse* of A is $\begin{pmatrix} -a_1 & -b_1 \\ -a_2 & -b_2 \end{pmatrix}$. Thus far, the set of 2×2

matrices, and, in general, all $m \times n$ matrices, have the same properties with respect to addition as the set of real numbers.

Next we can try to find an *identity matrix under multiplication* for matrix A. Does there exist a matrix, say I, such that $A \cdot I = A$? What elements can be used to correctly fill the blanks below?

$$A \cdot I = \begin{pmatrix} a_1 & b_1 \\ a_2 & b_2 \end{pmatrix}\begin{pmatrix} - & - \\ - & - \end{pmatrix} = \begin{pmatrix} a_1 & b_1 \\ a_2 & b_2 \end{pmatrix} = A$$

Experimentally you can find that the matrix which satisfies the requirement is $\begin{pmatrix} 1 & 0 \\ 0 & 1 \end{pmatrix}$. Can you prove this by letting $I = \begin{pmatrix} x_1 & y_1 \\ x_2 & y_2 \end{pmatrix}$ and solving for values of x_1, y_1, x_2, y_2?

Furthermore, it can be shown similarly that the third order identity matrix under multiplication is $\begin{pmatrix} 1 & 0 & 0 \\ 0 & 1 & 0 \\ 0 & 0 & 1 \end{pmatrix}$. Only square matrices have identity matrices defined for multiplication. Why?

Finally, we shall attempt to find an *inverse under multiplication* for matrix A, where A is any non-zero matrix of second order. Does there exist a matrix, A^{-1}, such that $A \cdot A^{-1} = I$? What elements can be used to correctly fill the blanks below?

$$A \cdot A^{-1} = \begin{pmatrix} a_1 & b_1 \\ a_2 & b_2 \end{pmatrix}\begin{pmatrix} - & - \\ - & - \end{pmatrix} = \begin{pmatrix} 1 & 0 \\ 0 & 1 \end{pmatrix} = I$$

How will the elements required for the blanks compare with the elements of A?

Let us designate the elements of A^{-1} by x_1, y_1, x_2, y_2 so that

$$A^{-1} = \begin{pmatrix} x_1 & y_1 \\ x_2 & y_2 \end{pmatrix}$$

We can write the equation $A \cdot A^{-1} = I$ as follows.

$$\begin{pmatrix} a_1 & b_1 \\ a_2 & b_2 \end{pmatrix}\begin{pmatrix} x_1 & y_1 \\ x_2 & y_2 \end{pmatrix} = \begin{pmatrix} 1 & 0 \\ 0 & 1 \end{pmatrix}$$

From the definition of the product of two matrices, we have

$$\begin{pmatrix} a_1x_1 + b_1x_2 & a_1y_1 + b_1y_2 \\ a_2x_1 + b_2x_2 & a_2y_1 + b_2y_2 \end{pmatrix} = \begin{pmatrix} 1 & 0 \\ 0 & 1 \end{pmatrix}$$

The definition of equality of matrices requires that the following equations be satisfied.

$$a_1x_1 + b_1x_2 = 1; \ a_1y_1 + b_1y_2 = 0; \ a_2x_1 + b_2x_2 = 0; \ a_2y_1 + b_2y_2 = 1$$

Solving these equations simultaneously, we find that

$$x_1 = \frac{b_2}{a_1b_2 - a_2b_1} \qquad\qquad y_1 = \frac{-b_1}{a_1b_2 - a_2b_1}$$

$$x_2 = \frac{-a_2}{a_1b_2 - a_2b_1} \qquad\qquad y_2 = \frac{a_1}{a_1b_2 - a_2b_1}$$

Since the denominator $a_1b_2 - a_2b_1$ (assumed to be a non-zero number) is a constant (scalar) in each solution, we can write A^{-1} as follows.

$$A^{-1} = \frac{1}{a_1b_2 - a_2b_1} \begin{pmatrix} b_2 & -b_1 \\ -a_2 & a_1 \end{pmatrix} \text{ or } \frac{1}{\begin{vmatrix} a_1 & b_1 \\ a_2 & b_2 \end{vmatrix}} \begin{pmatrix} b_2 & -b_1 \\ -a_2 & a_1 \end{pmatrix}$$

Note that $\begin{vmatrix} a_1 & b_1 \\ a_2 & b_2 \end{vmatrix}$ is the determinant derived from the given square matrix. The inverse of A exists only when the determinant of A is non-zero. Why? A matrix for which the value of the corresponding determinant is not zero is called a *non-singular* matrix. Only non-singular matrices possess an inverse under multiplication.

EXAMPLE 1. Find the inverse under multiplication of the matrix $\begin{pmatrix} 3 & -1 \\ 4 & 2 \end{pmatrix}$.

Solution. The inverse exists since the value of the determinant is not zero. $\begin{vmatrix} 3 & -1 \\ 4 & 2 \end{vmatrix} = 3 \cdot 2 - 4(-1) = 10$. The inverse of the matrix

is $\frac{1}{10} \begin{pmatrix} 2 & 1 \\ -4 & 3 \end{pmatrix}$ or $\begin{pmatrix} \frac{1}{5} & \frac{1}{10} \\ -\frac{2}{5} & \frac{3}{10} \end{pmatrix}$ which can be verified by showing

that
$$\begin{pmatrix} 3 & -1 \\ 4 & 2 \end{pmatrix} \begin{pmatrix} \frac{1}{5} & \frac{1}{10} \\ -\frac{2}{5} & \frac{3}{10} \end{pmatrix} = \begin{pmatrix} 1 & 0 \\ 0 & 1 \end{pmatrix}$$

It can also be proved that the product of a matrix and its inverse is commutative. Thus, $A \cdot A^{-1} = A^{-1} \cdot A = I$.

In summary, we see that square matrices have identity elements and inverses under addition and multiplication (with exceptions) as do the real numbers. There are some very important exceptions, however, that should be noted. First, only non-singular matrices have inverses. Second, multiplication of matrices is non-commutative, in general. And third, it is possible for the product of two matrices to be the zero matrix without either of the given matrices being a zero matrix; that is, if $A \cdot B = 0$, it is not necessarily true that A or B be a zero matrix. See Exercise 4 in the list following this section.

You may wish to investigate the algebra of matrices further. For example, you could solve the equation $AX + B = C$ for matrix X where A, B, and C are matrices of the same order. How is this done?

EXAMPLE 2. Solve for matrix X : $\begin{pmatrix} 2 & 1 \\ -3 & 2 \end{pmatrix} X + \begin{pmatrix} -5 & 0 \\ 2 & 4 \end{pmatrix} = \begin{pmatrix} 3 & -9 \\ 7 & 1 \end{pmatrix}$

Solution.

$$\begin{pmatrix} 2 & 1 \\ -3 & 2 \end{pmatrix} X + \begin{pmatrix} -5 & 0 \\ 2 & 4 \end{pmatrix} + \begin{pmatrix} 5 & 0 \\ -2 & -4 \end{pmatrix} = \begin{pmatrix} 3 & -9 \\ 7 & 1 \end{pmatrix} + \begin{pmatrix} 5 & 0 \\ -2 & -4 \end{pmatrix}$$

$$\begin{pmatrix} 2 & 1 \\ -3 & 2 \end{pmatrix} X + \begin{pmatrix} 0 & 0 \\ 0 & 0 \end{pmatrix} = \begin{pmatrix} 8 & -9 \\ 5 & -3 \end{pmatrix} \text{ or } \begin{pmatrix} 2 & 1 \\ -3 & 2 \end{pmatrix} X = \begin{pmatrix} 8 & -9 \\ 5 & -3 \end{pmatrix}$$

$$\frac{1}{\begin{vmatrix} 2 & 1 \\ -3 & 2 \end{vmatrix}} \begin{pmatrix} 2 & -1 \\ 3 & 2 \end{pmatrix} \begin{pmatrix} 2 & 1 \\ -3 & 2 \end{pmatrix} X = \frac{1}{\begin{vmatrix} 2 & 1 \\ -3 & 2 \end{vmatrix}} \begin{pmatrix} 2 & -1 \\ 3 & 2 \end{pmatrix} \begin{pmatrix} 8 & -9 \\ 5 & -3 \end{pmatrix}$$

$$\frac{1}{7} \begin{pmatrix} 7 & 0 \\ 0 & 7 \end{pmatrix} X = \frac{1}{7} \begin{pmatrix} 11 & -15 \\ 34 & -33 \end{pmatrix}$$

$$\begin{pmatrix} 1 & 0 \\ 0 & 1 \end{pmatrix} X = \begin{pmatrix} \frac{11}{7} & -\frac{15}{7} \\ \frac{34}{7} & -\frac{33}{7} \end{pmatrix} \text{ or } X = \begin{pmatrix} \frac{11}{7} & -\frac{15}{7} \\ \frac{34}{7} & -\frac{33}{7} \end{pmatrix}$$

Check. $\begin{pmatrix} 2 & 1 \\ -3 & 2 \end{pmatrix} \begin{pmatrix} \frac{11}{7} & -\frac{15}{7} \\ \frac{34}{7} & -\frac{33}{7} \end{pmatrix} + \begin{pmatrix} -5 & 0 \\ 2 & 4 \end{pmatrix} \overset{?}{=} \begin{pmatrix} 3 & -9 \\ 7 & 1 \end{pmatrix}$

$$\begin{pmatrix} \frac{56}{7} & -\frac{63}{7} \\ \frac{35}{7} & -\frac{21}{7} \end{pmatrix} + \begin{pmatrix} -5 & 0 \\ 2 & 4 \end{pmatrix} \overset{?}{=} \begin{pmatrix} 3 & -9 \\ 7 & 1 \end{pmatrix}$$

$$\begin{pmatrix} 8 & -9 \\ 5 & -3 \end{pmatrix} + \begin{pmatrix} -5 & 0 \\ 2 & 4 \end{pmatrix} \overset{?}{=} \begin{pmatrix} 3 & -9 \\ 7 & 1 \end{pmatrix}$$

$$\begin{pmatrix} 3 & -9 \\ 7 & 1 \end{pmatrix} = \begin{pmatrix} 3 & -9 \\ 7 & 1 \end{pmatrix}$$

Exercises

1. Prove: $AI = IA = A$ for second order matrices.

2. Prove: $AA^{-1} = A^{-1}A = I$ for second order matrices.

$6)$ 9

3. Referring to the properties of real numbers as listed in Section 1.7, which of these properties hold for the set of all matrices of second order? Verify your answer. (Previous exercises may be cited in some cases.)

4. Find the product $\begin{pmatrix} 1 & 2 \\ 3 & 6 \end{pmatrix}\begin{pmatrix} 2 & 2 \\ -1 & -1 \end{pmatrix}$. How does this result compare with the product of real numbers?

5. If $AB = 0$ and $A = \begin{pmatrix} 1 & 1 \\ 1 & 1 \end{pmatrix}$, find a matrix B where B is not the zero matrix. How many different solutions are possible?

6. Find the inverse matrix of each of the following matrices, if it exists.

　a. $\begin{pmatrix} 1 & 3 \\ 2 & 5 \end{pmatrix}$　**b.** $\begin{pmatrix} -1 & -2 \\ 3 & -6 \end{pmatrix}$　**c.** $\begin{pmatrix} 4 & 3 \\ 8 & 6 \end{pmatrix}$　**d.** $\begin{pmatrix} 7 & 40 \\ 2 & 12 \end{pmatrix}$

7. If $\begin{pmatrix} a_1 & b_1 \\ a_2 & b_2 \end{pmatrix}$ is non-singular, show that neither of the following conditions is possible. (k is any non-zero real number.)
　a. $a_1 = ka_2$ and $b_1 = kb_2$
　b. $a_1 = kb_1$ and $a_2 = kb_2$

8. Find matrix X if $\begin{pmatrix} 2 & -1 \\ 3 & 5 \end{pmatrix} X = \begin{pmatrix} 4 & 3 \\ 1 & -2 \end{pmatrix}$.

9. Find matrix X if $\begin{pmatrix} 5 & 1 \\ -2 & 2 \end{pmatrix} X + \begin{pmatrix} 3 & -2 \\ 4 & 6 \end{pmatrix} = \begin{pmatrix} 4 & 3 \\ 10 & 2 \end{pmatrix}$.

10. If $AB = C$, where A, B and C are second order matrices, prove that the product of the determinants of A and B is the determinant of C.

4.6　Matrix solution of systems of linear equations

It is possible to operate with matrices so that the solution set of a system of linear equations is systematically achieved. We shall illustrate this for two variables by the following example.

EXAMPLE 1. Find the solution set using matrices.

$$\begin{aligned} x - y &= 2 \\ 2x + 5y &= 11 \end{aligned}$$

Solution. The coefficients and constants may be written in the form of a 2×3 matrix as follows.

$$\begin{pmatrix} 1 & -1 & 2 \\ 2 & 5 & 11 \end{pmatrix}$$

We can modify this matrix by transforming *rows* since each row represents an equation. Any operation which will result in an equivalent system of equations is permitted for the matrix. We shall mentally multiply the elements of the first row by 2 and subtract the result, element by element, from the second row. The objective is to obtain a zero in the a_{21} position. We get the following matrix which represents a system of equations equivalent to the given system.

$$\begin{pmatrix} 1 & -1 & 2 \\ 0 & 7 & 7 \end{pmatrix}$$

Each term of the last row can be divided by 7 (or any other non-zero real number) and we get an equivalent system expressed by

$$\begin{pmatrix} 1 & -1 & 2 \\ 0 & 1 & 1 \end{pmatrix}$$

Next we shall add the second row to the first row and obtain the matrix

$$\begin{pmatrix} 1 & 0 & 3 \\ 0 & 1 & 1 \end{pmatrix}$$

This produces a zero in the a_{12} position. Writing this matrix as a system of equations we have: $x = 3$, $y = 1$. Therefore, the solution set is $\{(3, 1)\}$.

In general, if we have the system of equations

$$a_1 x + b_1 y = c_1$$
$$a_2 x + b_2 y = c_2$$

we can write the matrix which describes the system as follows.

$$\begin{pmatrix} a_1 & b_1 & c_1 \\ a_2 & b_2 & c_2 \end{pmatrix}$$

By operating from row one to row two, we can obtain a zero in position a_2. Then by operating from row two to row one, we can obtain a zero in position b_1. The result is a matrix in the form

$$\begin{pmatrix} a_1 & 0 & c_1' \\ 0 & b_2' & c_2' \end{pmatrix}$$

The solution set of the system of equations is $\left\{ \left(\dfrac{c_1'}{a_1'}, \dfrac{c_2'}{b_2'} \right) \right\}$.

The method of matrices under row transformations can be adapted to systems of equations of higher order. For example, the general system of three equations in three variables

$$a_1 x + b_1 y + c_1 z = d_1$$
$$a_2 x + b_2 y + c_2 z = d_2$$
$$a_3 x + b_3 y + c_3 z = d_3$$

can be expressed by the matrix

$$\begin{pmatrix} a_1 & b_1 & c_1 & d_1 \\ a_2 & b_2 & c_2 & d_2 \\ a_3 & b_3 & c_3 & d_3 \end{pmatrix}$$

By operating with row one, we can obtain zeros in the positions a_2 and a_3. Then by operating from row two to row three, we can obtain a zero in position b_3. The matrix is now of the form

$$\begin{pmatrix} a_1 & b_1 & c_1 & d_1 \\ 0 & b_2' & c_2' & d_2' \\ 0 & 0 & c_3' & d_3' \end{pmatrix}$$

It is now possible to find the solution set. We see that $z = \dfrac{d_3'}{c_3'}$, and by replacing z in the second equation, we find the value of y. Then, replacing y and z by the values already found, we can find the value of x.

However, it may be desirable to obtain zeros in the position of c_2', c_1, and b_1. This can be done by operating from row three to row two and row one and from row two to row one.

Let us continue to transform the matrix by rows until the matrix is of the form

$$\begin{pmatrix} a_1 & 0 & 0 & d_1'' \\ 0 & b_2' & 0 & d_2'' \\ 0 & 0 & c_3' & d_3' \end{pmatrix}$$

It is now obvious that $\left\{\left(\dfrac{d_1''}{a_1}, \dfrac{d_2''}{b_2'}, \dfrac{d_3'}{c_3'}\right)\right\}$ is the solution set.

Do you see that it is possible to obtain zero in any desired position, regardless of the numbers in each position, except when zero occurs in the principal diagonal? The *principal diagonal* is the diagonal from the upper left corner to the lower right corner. If there is a zero in the principal diagonal, we may interchange the rows since the order of equations in a system of equations is immaterial.

EXAMPLE 2. Solve the system of equations by matrices using row transformations.

$$\begin{array}{rrrr} x & - 2y & + z & = 7 \\ 3x & + y & - z & = 2 \\ 2x & + 3y & + 2z & = 7 \end{array}$$

Solution. The following sequence of matrices represents equivalent systems of equations.

$$\begin{pmatrix} 1 & -2 & 1 & 7 \\ 3 & 1 & -1 & 2 \\ 2 & 3 & 2 & 7 \end{pmatrix}$$

Multiply row one by 3 and subtract the result from row two. Also, multiply row one by 2 and subtract the result from row three.

$$\begin{pmatrix} 1 & -2 & 1 & 7 \\ 0 & 7 & -4 & -19 \\ 0 & 7 & 0 & -7 \end{pmatrix}$$

Subtract row two from row three.

$$\begin{pmatrix} 1 & -2 & 1 & 7 \\ 0 & 7 & -4 & -19 \\ 0 & 0 & 4 & 12 \end{pmatrix}$$

Divide row three by 4.

$$\begin{pmatrix} 1 & -2 & 1 & 7 \\ 0 & 7 & -4 & -19 \\ 0 & 0 & 1 & 3 \end{pmatrix}$$

Multiply row three by 4 and add the result to row two. Subtract row three from row one.

$$\begin{pmatrix} 1 & -2 & 0 & 4 \\ 0 & 7 & 0 & -7 \\ 0 & 0 & 1 & 3 \end{pmatrix}$$

Divide row two by 7.

$$\begin{pmatrix} 1 & -2 & 0 & 4 \\ 0 & 1 & 0 & -1 \\ 0 & 0 & 1 & 3 \end{pmatrix}$$

Multiply row two by 2 and add the result to row one.

$$\begin{pmatrix} 1 & 0 & 0 & 2 \\ 0 & 1 & 0 & -1 \\ 0 & 0 & 1 & 3 \end{pmatrix}$$

Thus, $x = 2$, $y = -1$, $z = 3$. The solution set is $\{(2, -1, 3)\}$.

Exercises

Solve the following systems of linear equations using matrices with row transformations.

1. $3x + 5y = 7$
     $6x - y = -8$

2. $4x - 7y + 2 = 0$ (*Hint:* Interchange
     $x + 2y - 7 = 0$ the equations.)

3. $5x = 7y - 50$
     $2y = 1 - 3x$

4. $x - y + z = 3$
     $2y - z = 1$
     $2y - x + 1 = 0$

5. $2x + y - 2z - 7 = 0$
     $x - 2y - 5z + 1 = 0$
     $4x + y + z + 1 = 0$

6. $x + 2y = 5$
     $3x + 4z = 2$
     $2y + 3w = -2$
     $3z - 2w = 1$

4.7   Geometrical vectors

Many applications of mathematics, to science in particular, require solutions which are often best achieved by means of geometrical vectors. A *vector* may be defined as a quantity which possesses both magnitude and direction. Geometrically, a vector is represented as a directed line segment. Physically, quantities such as velocity and voltage possess the attributes of magnitude and direction and may therefore be represented as vectors.

The magnitude of a vector is given by the length of the line segment, and the direction is indicated by an arrowhead placed on one end of the line segment. A *scalar* is a number or quantity possessing only magnitude. Real numbers are scalars.

It is customary to place a small arrow above each letter or letters used to designate a vector. Thus $\vec{A}$ means a vector with magnitude A. Two parallel vectors with arrowheads similarly placed have the same direction. Two vectors which are represented by equal line segments in the same unit of measure have the same magnitude. Two vectors are equal if and only if they have the same direction and the same magnitude. The negative of a vector is another vector of equal magnitude but with opposite direction.

The sum of two or more vectors is called the *resultant* of the vectors. In Figure 4–1, the sum of $\vec{P}$ and $\vec{Q}$ is shown as it may be found geometrically by two methods. Vector $\vec{R}$ is the resultant, that is, $\vec{R} = \vec{P} + \vec{Q}$. The construction is known as *vectorial addition*. Both direction and magnitude are involved in the sum of the vectors.

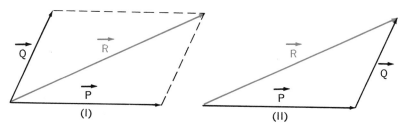

FIGURE 4–1

If the sum of two vectors is vector $\vec{A}$, then the two vectors are called *components* of $\vec{A}$. In Figure 4–2, $\vec{X}$ and $\vec{Y}$ are components of $\vec{A}$. Components of a vector are often perpendicular to each other, but this arrangement is not required. One may choose to find the component of a vector in any direction to suit the situation.

The product of a scalar k and a vector $\vec{A}$ is a vector with the same direction as $\vec{A}$ and with the magnitude kA.

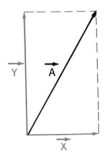

FIGURE 4-2

Exercises

Let O, A, B, C be points in the plane with the given coordinates; $O(0, 0)$, $A(2, 1)$, $B(-1, 3)$, $C(-4, -8)$.

1. Find the magnitude of $\overrightarrow{OA} + \overrightarrow{OB}$.

2. Find the coordinates of X, where $\overrightarrow{OX} = 3 \cdot \overrightarrow{OA}$.

3. Find the magnitude of $\overrightarrow{OX}$, where $\overrightarrow{OX} = \overrightarrow{OA} + \overrightarrow{OB} + \overrightarrow{OC}$.

4. Is vector addition a commutative operation? Is it associative? Does every vector have an additive inverse?

Given vectors $\vec{A}$, $\vec{B}$, $\vec{C}$, $\vec{D}$, *and* $\vec{E}$, *perform the indicated vectorial additions.*

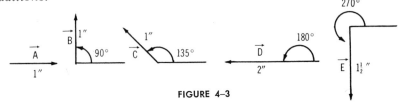

FIGURE 4-3

5. $\vec{A} + \vec{B}$ **7.** $\vec{A} + \vec{E}$ **9.** $\vec{A} + \vec{C}$ **11.** $\vec{A} + \vec{B} + \vec{D}$

6. $\vec{C} + \vec{D}$ **8.** $\vec{C} + \vec{E}$ **10.** $\vec{A} + \vec{D}$ **12.** $\vec{B} + \vec{D} + \vec{E}$

13. Subtraction of vectors is defined by the equation $\vec{A} - \vec{B} = \vec{A} + (-\vec{B})$. Perform the subtraction of $\vec{A} - \vec{B}$ by construction.

14. Add: $2\vec{A} + 3\vec{B}$.

15. Subtract: $\vec{B} - 2\vec{E}$.

16. Find the components of $\vec{C}$ which are parallel to $\vec{A}$ and $\vec{B}$.

17. Show that $2\vec{A} + \vec{D} = 0$.

18. Find a component of $\vec{D}$ parallel to $\vec{C}$.

19. Find the magnitude of the resultant of $3\vec{A} + 4\vec{B}$.

4.8 Algebraic vectors

In this section we shall relate the algebraic and geometric concepts of vectors in two dimensions. In the following section the same concepts will be extended to three dimensions.

In the previous section we defined and applied vectors and vector relationships in the form of directed line segments. The topics which were covered included equality of vectors, vector addition, and multiplication of a vector and a scalar (real number).

The purpose of that section was to give you an intuitive feeling for the concept of geometrical vectors. Now we will explore the concept of algebraic vectors and tie the two together. Note again that throughout this earlier treatment we restricted ourselves to the geometric interpretation of vectors as directed line segments.

The magnitude of a vector was interpreted as the length of the line segment representing it in an appropriate unit. The amplitude was defined as the directed angle between the positive x-axis and the line segment.

EXAMPLE 1. Represent vector $\vec{V}$ with a magnitude V of 4 and an amplitude θ of 45°. What are the x- and y-components?

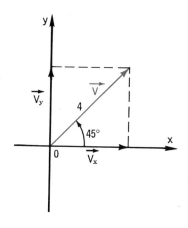

Solution. Figure 4–4 illustrates vector $\vec{V}$. The x-component, $\vec{V_x}$, has a magnitude of $\dfrac{4}{\sqrt{2}}$, and the y-component, $\vec{V_v}$, also has a magnitude of $\dfrac{4}{\sqrt{2}}$. The coordinates of the endpoint of $\vec{V}$ are $(2\sqrt{2},\ 2\sqrt{2})$.

FIGURE 4–4

You should also recall the method of adding or subtracting two vectors graphically. See Sections 4.7, 8.5.

In Section 4.2 we introduced the idea of a vector as an ordered pair of real numbers. Although we have considered both row and column vectors earlier, we shall now confine our attention to row vectors in two dimensions of the form $(x,\ y)$. How can we relate this algebraic concept of vector with that of a directed line segment?

If a vector has its initial point at O, the origin, we can identify the vector (x, y) with the vector $\overrightarrow{OP}$, where P is the point with coordinates (x, y). Sometimes an alternate notation using brackets is employed to distinguish a vector $[x, y]$ from the coordinates of a point (x, y), but we shall rely on the context to provide this distinction. Thus, there is a vector in the form of a directed line segment which can be associated with every point of the plane. What would be the point associated with the zero vector? If two vectors have the same magnitude, is it true that the algebraic vectors corresponding to them are necessarily identical? If two vectors have the same amplitude, will the corresponding algebraic vectors be the same ordered pair of numbers? Under what conditions will two geometric vectors be represented by the same ordered pair?

We have defined the addition of two vectors (as special matrices) in Section 4.3. The sum of vector $\overrightarrow{A}$, or (a_1, a_2), and vector $\overrightarrow{B}$, or (b_1, b_2), is defined by the equation

$$\overrightarrow{A} + \overrightarrow{B} = (a_1, a_2) + (b_1, b_2) = (a_1 + b_1, a_2 + b_2)$$

Can you show that this is equivalent to the addition of vectors represented by line segments involving a parallelogram or triangle? The difference $\overrightarrow{A} - \overrightarrow{B}$ is defined to be $\overrightarrow{A} + (-\overrightarrow{B})$ where $-\overrightarrow{B} = (-b_1, -b_2)$.

An extension of the vector concept to include directed line segments between any two points in the plane is often convenient and useful. Suppose $P_1 (x_1, y_1)$ is the initial point of a vector, and $P_2 (x_2, y_2)$ is the terminal point. How can $\overrightarrow{P_1P_2}$ be represented as an ordered pair of real numbers? If P_1 happens to be the origin, there is no problem since $\overrightarrow{OP_2}$ is represented by (x_2, y_2).

In Fig. 4–5, right triangle P_1QP_2 has $\overrightarrow{P_1P_2}$ as the hypotenuse. This is the same sort of triangle we used to define the slope of line P_1P_2 and the distance between P_1 and P_2. See Sections 2.2 and 2.3. We shall now define the ordered pair of numbers (algebraic vector) asso-

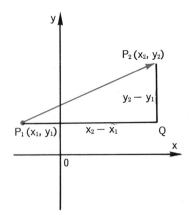

FIGURE 4–5

ciated with directed line segment $\overrightarrow{P_1 P}$ (geometric vector) as

$$\overrightarrow{P_1 P_2} = (x_2 - x_1,\ y_2 - y_1)$$

Note that the first real number is the difference of the abscissas and the second is the difference of the ordinates. Also observe that the order of the coordinates of the points is important. For example, vector $\overrightarrow{P_2 P_1}$ is given by $\overrightarrow{P_2 P_1} = (x_1 - x_2,\ y_1 - y_2)$.

Two vectors are equal if they have the same magnitude and the same direction. Likewise, if two vectors are represented by the same ordered pair, the magnitudes and directions can be proved equal. The magnitude of $\overrightarrow{P_1 P_2}$ is given by $|\overrightarrow{P_1 P_2}| = \sqrt{(x_2 - x_1)^2 + (y_2 - y_1)^2}$. Two vectors are equal in magnitude if the absolute values of the difference of the abscissas are equal and the absolute values of the difference of the ordinates are equal. Two vectors have the same direction if the slopes are equal and the amplitudes are the same. If magnitude and direction remain unchanged, a vector may be represented with its initial point at any point in the plane.

EXAMPLE 2. What relationships can be written if it is given that $(a_1,\ a_2)$ and $(b_1,\ b_2)$ are equal vectors?

Solution. The magnitudes are equal. Thus, we can write

$$\sqrt{a_1{}^2 + a_2{}^2} = \sqrt{b_1{}^2 + b_2{}^2}$$

The slopes are also equal; this gives us

$$\frac{a_2}{a_1} = \frac{b_2}{b_1},\ a_1 \neq 0 \text{ and } b_1 \neq 0$$

And, finally, $a_1 = b_1$ and $a_2 = b_2$.

A vector may be involved in a product in several ways. We may have the product of a vector with a scalar, the "dot" or "inner" product of two vectors, and the "cross" or "outer" product of two vectors. The latter cannot be defined until we introduce 3 dimensions in the next section. The scope of this text does not permit us to investigate these products fully. Perhaps in later courses in mathematics you will have the opportunity to explore this interesting and useful topic.

Definitions of the two types of products involving vectors in two dimensions are as follows.

- *Scalar-Vector Product:* If k is any scalar, and $\vec{A}$ is any vector given by $(a_1,\ a_2)$, then $k\vec{A} = k(a_1,\ a_2) = (ka_1,\ ka_2)$.

What is the geometrical effect of multiplying a vector by a scalar?
Make a sketch to illustrate your answer and check the results with
the definition.

- *Inner or Dot Product:* If $\vec{A}$ and $\vec{B}$ are two vectors given by
  (a_1, a_2) and (b_1, b_2), respectively, then $\vec{A} \cdot \vec{B}$, read "A dot B"
  is defined by the equation

$$\vec{A} \cdot \vec{B} = (a_1, a_2) \cdot (b_1, b_2) = a_1 b_1 + a_2 b_2$$

Note that the inner product of two vectors is a scalar. Compare
with Section 4.4.

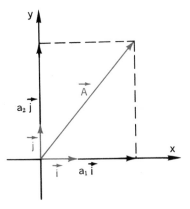

We shall introduce one more concept about vectors in two dimensions before moving on to three
dimensions. Let us call a vector of
unit length in the direction of the
positive x-axis by the symbol $\vec{i}$ (not
to be confused with the imaginary
unit i). Further, let $\vec{j}$ be a vector
of unit length in the positive direction of the y-axis. These units, $\vec{i}$
and $\vec{j}$, are called *basic vectors.* Do
you see that $\vec{i} = (1, 0)$ and $\vec{j} = (0, 1)$?

FIGURE 4–6

If components of vector $\vec{A}$, that
is, (a_1, a_2), shown in Figure 4–6 are
found, they can be expressed as
$a_1\vec{i}$ and $a_2\vec{j}$. Why? It can be proved that $\vec{A} = a_1\vec{i} + a_2\vec{j}$ as follows.

$$\begin{aligned}
a_1\vec{i} + a_2\vec{j} &= a_1 (1, 0) + a_2 (0, 1) \\
&= (a_1, 0) + (0, a_2) && \text{Scalar product} \\
&= (a_1 + 0, 0 + a_2) && \text{Addition of vectors} \\
&= (a_1, a_2) && \text{Zero is the identity element} \\
& && \text{for real numbers.}
\end{aligned}$$

But $(a_1, a_2) = \vec{A}$ and so we have proved that $\vec{A} = a_1\vec{i} + a_2\vec{j}$.

Exercises

*In Exercises 1-4 find the sum of the given vectors algebraically and
graphically.*

1. $(3, 5) + (-1, 2)$ **3.** $(-5, 2) + (1, -8)$

2. $(-2, -3) + (2, 4)$ **4.** $\vec{i} + \vec{j}$

5. Prove that $\vec{A} + \vec{B} = \vec{B} + \vec{A}$.

6. Find the zero vector in two dimensions. By definition this is the vector which does not alter any vector upon addition.

In Exercises 7-10 the initial and terminal points of a vector are given. Express the vector as an ordered pair of real numbers.

7. $(1, 3)$; $(-2, 5)$ **9.** $(7, 7)$; $(-2, -2)$

8. $(0, 5)$; $(-5, 0)$ **10.** $(5, -6)$; $(6, -5)$

11. Find the magnitude (length) of each of the vectors in Exercises 7-10.

12. Find the following inner products.

    a. $\vec{i} \cdot \vec{i}$ **b.** $\vec{j} \cdot \vec{j}$ **c.** $\vec{i} \cdot \vec{j}$ **d.** $\vec{j} \cdot \vec{i}$

13. Find the inner product: $(4, -2) \cdot (3, 5)$.

14. Prove $\vec{A} \cdot \vec{B} = \vec{B} \cdot \vec{A}$.

15. If it is given that $\vec{A} \cdot \vec{B} = AB \cos \theta$, where A is the magnitude of $\vec{A}$, and B is the magnitude of $\vec{B}$, and θ is the angle from $\vec{B}$ to $\vec{A}$, show that $\vec{A} \cdot \vec{B} = 0$ if the vectors are perpendicular.

16. Let p be the length of the projection of $\vec{A}$ on $\vec{B}$. See Figure 4-7. Show that $\vec{A} \cdot \vec{B} = pB$. Make a similar drawing to show that $\vec{A} \cdot \vec{B} = qA$ if q is the projection of $\vec{B}$ on $\vec{A}$.

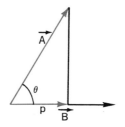

FIGURE 4-7

4.9   Vectors in three dimensions

In the previous section concerning vectors in two dimensions, it was not necessary to discuss the very familiar coordinate plane. However, it is not likely that many of you have had experience with a three-dimensional coordinate system, even though we live in a tangible space of three dimensions. Therefore, our first task is to set up an appropriate system to study three-dimensional space.

Let us imagine three real number lines intersecting at the zero point of each in a manner such that each line is perpendicular to the plane determined by the other two. In an effort to depict this arrangement on a plane, we resort to a figure which is intended to convey the feeling of depth, a 3-*d* effect. (We shall use 2-*d* and 3-*d* as abbreviations for "two-dimensional" and "three-dimensional", respectively.) The designation of the axes is purely arbitrary. We shall call the axes by the names x-axis, y-axis, and z-axis. There are only two really distinct orientations possible; Fig. 4–8 shows the accepted convention, where the x-axis emanates from the plane of the paper at the origin 0.

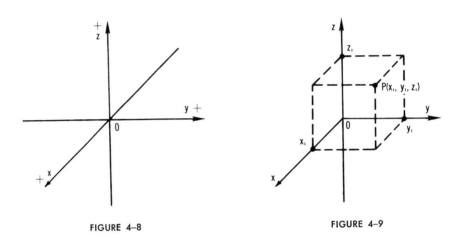

FIGURE 4–8   FIGURE 4–9

In order to completely locate a point in 3-d space, we shall need an ordered triple of real numbers. How can we locate a point P which has the coordinates (x_1, y_1, z_1)? See Fig. 4–9. The first step is to find x_1 on the x-axis, y_1 on the y-axis, and z_1 on the z-axis. Construct (in your imagination) a plane perpendicular to the x-axis at x_1, and construct planes in a similar manner to the y-axis and z-axis at y_1 and z_1, respectively. The three planes intersect in the point P which is the only point in 3-d space with the coordinates (x_1, y_1, z_1).

For clarification, imagine yourself in a rectangular room. Let the front wall be the y-z plane, the floor the x-y plane, and the left wall the x-z plane. The origin will be in the lower left corner. How can we find a point in the room which corresponds to (5, 3, 2), if the units are in feet? Measure 5 feet from the origin along the base of the left wall. A plane through this point perpendicular to the x-axis will be parallel to the front wall. Then measure 3 feet from the origin along the base of the front wall and imagine a plane perpendicular to the y-axis, or parallel to the left wall at this point. Finally, measure 2 feet from the origin along the z-axis which is the line of intersection of the front and left walls. An imaginary plane through this point and parallel to the floor will intersect the other two planes at a point somewhere in the room with the coordinates (5, 3, 2). The situation is more difficult to visualize if one or more of the numbers in the ordered triple are negative, but in the abstract sense the situation should be equally understandable. For example, the point (−5, 3, 2) would be *behind* the front wall.

Can you use a similar illustration to show that there is a unique ordered triple of real numbers which corresponds to a point in 3-*d* space with a given coordinate system? (*Hint:* Find the distance from the point to the *y-z* plane, the *x-z* plane, and the *x-y* plane.) *There is a one-to-one correspondence between the set of all points in 3-d space and the set of all ordered triples of real numbers.* Can you make analogous statements for 2-*d* and 1-*d* space? For *n-d* space?

We shall now define an ordered triple as a vector in 3-*d* vector space. The geometric interpretation is basically the same as that for 2-*d* space because a directed line segment from the origin O to point $P(x, y, z)$ is called the vector $\overrightarrow{OP}$ corresponding to vector (x, y, z). All vectors have both magnitude and direction except the zero vector $(0, 0, 0)$ which has no direction. Its magnitude is zero.

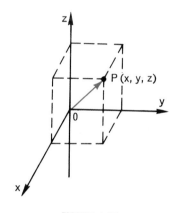

FIGURE 4–10

The operation of addition for 3-*d* vectors is merely an extension of the definition for 2-*d* vectors. If vector $\overrightarrow{A}$, represented by (a_1, a_2, a_3), is added to vector $\overrightarrow{B}$, represented by (b_1, b_2, b_3), the sum is defined by the equation

$$\overrightarrow{A} + \overrightarrow{B} = (a_1, a_2, a_3) + (b_1, b_2, b_3) = (a_1 + b_1, a_2 + b_2, a_3 + b_3)$$

A vector from $P_1 (x_1, y_1, z_1)$ to $P_2 (x_2, y_2, z_2)$ in 3-*d* space can also be represented by an ordered triple as follows.

$$\overrightarrow{P_1 P_2} = (x_2 - x_1, y_2 - y_1, z_2 - z_1)$$

Compare with the vector $\overrightarrow{P_1 P_2}$ in 2-*d* space. When are two vectors in 3-*d* space equal?

The distance between two points in 3-d space is found by a formula which is an extension of that used in 2-d space. Let us return to our example of the point $(5, 3, 2)$ in the coordinate system determined in the room. What is the distance of this point from the origin? Let us first locate a point P' on the floor directly under the given point. The distance, $|OP'|$, of this point from the origin is $\sqrt{5^2 + 3^2}$. Why? Then, from right triangle $OP'P$, we find that the distance $|OP|$ is given by $\sqrt{5^2 + 3^2 + 2^2}$ or $\sqrt{38}$.

In general, the distance of $P(x, y, z)$ from the origin $O(0, 0, 0)$ is

$$|OP| = \sqrt{x^2 + y^2 + z^2}$$

Or, using vectors, the magnitude of vector $\overrightarrow{OP}$ is

$$|\overrightarrow{OP}| = \sqrt{x^2 + y^2 + z^2}$$

The distance from $P_1 (x_1, y_1, z_1)$ to $P_2 (x_2, y_2, z_2)$ is similarly given by

$$|P_1 P_2| = \sqrt{(x_2 - x_1)^2 + (y_2 - y_1)^2 + (z_2 - z_1)^2}$$

In vector notation, the magnitude of vector $\overrightarrow{P_1 P_2}$ is

$$|\overrightarrow{P_1 P_2}| = \sqrt{(x_2 - x_1)^2 + (y_2 - y_1)^2 + (z_2 - z_1)^2}$$

Now let us investigate the product of a scalar k and a 3-d vector $\overrightarrow{A} = (a_1, a_2, a_3)$. By definition, $k\overrightarrow{A} = k(a_1, a_2, a_3) = (ka_1, ka_2, ka_3)$. Note the similarity to scalar multiplication by a vector in two dimensions. What do you think the definition of scalar-vector multiplication would be for n-dimensional space?

The "dot" product is one way to multiply two vectors and is useful for certain applications. In 3-d space the inner or dot product $\overrightarrow{A} \cdot \overrightarrow{B}$, where $\overrightarrow{A} = (a_1, a_2, a_3)$ and $\overrightarrow{B} = (b_1, b_2, b_3)$, is defined by the equation

$$\overrightarrow{A} \cdot \overrightarrow{B} = (a_1, a_2, a_3) \cdot (b_1, b_2, b_3) = a_1 b_1 + a_2 b_2 + a_3 b_3$$

Note again that this product is a scalar.

Example 1. Find the inner product of $(2, -1, 3)$ and $(5, 2, -1)$.

Solution. $(2, -1, 3) \cdot (5, 2, -1) = (2)(5) + (-1)(2) + (3)(-1) = 10 - 2 - 3 = 5$.

There are three basic vectors, called $\overrightarrow{i}, \overrightarrow{j}, \overrightarrow{k}$, which are required for a 3-d coordinate system. We shall specify that $\overrightarrow{i}$ is the basic vector on the x-axis, $\overrightarrow{j}$ is the basic vector on the y-axis, and $\overrightarrow{k}$ is the basic vector on the z-axis. You should verify that $\overrightarrow{i} = (1, 0, 0)$,

$\vec{j} = (0, 1, 0)$, and $\vec{k} = (0, 0, 1)$. These basic vectors are shown with a representation of vector $\vec{A} = (a_1, a_2, a_3)$ in Fig. 4–11. Do you see that $a_1\vec{i}$, $a_2\vec{j}$, $a_3\vec{k}$ are the *component* vectors of vector $\vec{A}$ along the three axes? Thus, we can write vector $\vec{A}$ in the form

$$\vec{A} = (a_1, a_2, a_3) = a_1\vec{i} + a_2\vec{j} + a_3\vec{k}$$

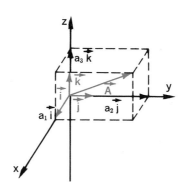

FIGURE 4–11

The proof is similar to that given in Section 4.8 for 2-*d* vectors. Can you state the proof for 3-*d* vectors?

An important product of vectors, useful in science, is called the outer or "cross" product. In this case, as contrasted with the inner or "dot" product, the result is a vector and not a scalar. Furthermore, it is a vector which does not lie in the plane of the given vectors but is perpendicular to each. The scope of this text does not permit a full consideration of the cross product of two vectors, but the definition will be given for you to study. We shall define the cross product of $\vec{A} = (a_1, a_2, a_3)$ and $\vec{B} = (b_1, b_2, b_3)$, using determinants, as follows.

$$\vec{A} \times \vec{B} = \begin{vmatrix} a_2 & a_3 \\ b_2 & b_3 \end{vmatrix} \vec{i} - \begin{vmatrix} a_1 & a_3 \\ b_1 & b_3 \end{vmatrix} \vec{j} + \begin{vmatrix} a_1 & a_2 \\ b_1 & b_2 \end{vmatrix} \vec{k}$$

In expanded form this becomes

$$\vec{A} \times \vec{B} = (a_2 b_3 - a_3 b_2) \vec{i} - (a_1 b_3 - a_3 b_1) \vec{j} + (a_1 b_2 - a_2 b_1) \vec{k}$$

An easy way to remember the coefficients is to set up the determinant

$$\begin{vmatrix} \vec{i} & \vec{j} & \vec{k} \\ a_1 & a_2 & a_3 \\ b_1 & b_2 & b_3 \end{vmatrix}$$

and expand by minors using the first row.

EXAMPLE 2. Find the cross product of $(2, 4, -3)$ and $(-1, 5, 2)$.

Solution.

$$\begin{vmatrix} \vec{i} & \vec{j} & \vec{k} \\ 2 & 4 & -3 \\ -1 & 5 & 2 \end{vmatrix} = \begin{vmatrix} 4 & -3 \\ 5 & 2 \end{vmatrix} \vec{i} - \begin{vmatrix} 2 & -3 \\ -1 & 2 \end{vmatrix} \vec{j} + \begin{vmatrix} 2 & 4 \\ -1 & 5 \end{vmatrix} \vec{k} =$$

$23\vec{i} - 1\vec{j} + 14\vec{k}$ or $(23, -1, 14)$

Exercises

Find the magnitude of the vectors in Exercises 1 − 4.

1. $(2, 1, 3)$ **3.** $(-1, 0, 1)$

2. $(3, -4, 12)$ **4.** $(5, -2, -3)$

Find the distance between the two points in 3-d space in Exercises 5 − 8.

5. $(3, 3, -1)$; $(5, 3, 2)$ **7.** $(8, 1, 1)$; $(4, 0, 1)$

6. $(-2, 4, 7)$; $(-3, 5, 2)$ **8.** $(23, 17, 56)$; $(20, 21, 44)$

Find the inner or "dot" product in Exercises 9 − 12.

9. $(7, -2, 4) \cdot (3, 8, 1)$ **11.** $(5, 5, 5) \cdot (2, 2, 2)$

10. $(-6, 2, 10) \cdot (4, 1, 9)$ **12.** $(-4, 9, -8) \cdot (3, 2, -2)$

13. Show that $\vec{A} \cdot \vec{B} = \vec{B} \cdot \vec{A}$ for 3-d vectors.

14. Show that $\vec{A} \times \vec{B} = -(\vec{B} \times \vec{A})$.

15. Show that $|\overrightarrow{P_1 P_2}| = |\overrightarrow{P_2 P_1}|$.

16. If $\vec{A} = (a_1, a_2, a_3)$, then $-\vec{A}$ is defined to be $(-a_1, -a_2, -a_3)$. Show that $|-\vec{A}| = |\vec{A}|$.

17. Prove that $\vec{i} \cdot \vec{i} = 1$; $\vec{j} \cdot \vec{j} = 1$; $\vec{k} \cdot \vec{k} = 1$.

18. Let $\vec{A} = (1, -3, 2)$ and $\vec{B} = (5, 1, -2)$. Find the cross product $\vec{A} \times \vec{B}$.

Chapter Review

1. Solve the equation $X + \begin{pmatrix} 3 & 0 & 4 \\ 1 & 2 & -3 \\ 2 & -5 & 1 \end{pmatrix} = \begin{pmatrix} 6 & -1 & 5 \\ 2 & 1 & 3 \\ -4 & -3 & 3 \end{pmatrix}$ for the matrix X.

2. If $A = \begin{pmatrix} 2 & 3 & -1 \\ 0 & 4 & 3 \\ 1 & 1 & 0 \end{pmatrix}$ and $B = \begin{pmatrix} 1 & 0 & 6 \\ 2 & -3 & 5 \\ -1 & 4 & 1 \end{pmatrix}$, find

    a. $A \cdot B$ **b.** $B \cdot A$ **c.** $3A - 2B$

3. Solve the matrix equation $X \cdot \begin{pmatrix} 2 & 5 \\ -1 & -3 \end{pmatrix} = \begin{pmatrix} 1 & -3 \\ 2 & -1 \end{pmatrix}$.

4. Solve by using row transformations on the matrix representing the system

$$x - 2y - 3z = 2$$
$$x - 4y + 3z = 14$$
$$-3x + 5y + 4z = 0$$

5. Consider the points $O, P, Q, R,$ and S with coordinates as follows: $O(0, 0), P(2, 3), Q(8, 1), R(-2, 5), S(-1, 7)$.

   a. Find the coordinates of V, where $\overrightarrow{PQ} + \overrightarrow{RS} = \overrightarrow{OV}$.

   b. If X has coordinates $(-1, -3)$ and $\overrightarrow{PQ} + \overrightarrow{RS} = \overrightarrow{XY}$, find the coordinates of Y.

6. Find the magnitude of $-2 \cdot \overrightarrow{AB}$ if A has coordinates $(2, 3)$ and B has coordinates $(7, 15)$.

7. Find the following sums.

   a. $(8, 7) + (9, -3)$ **b.** $2(3, 1, -2) - 7(1, 4, -3)$

8. Let $\vec{i}$ and $\vec{j}$ be the basic vectors in two dimensions, where $\vec{i} = (1, 0)$ and $\vec{j} = (0, 1)$. Find scalars $a, b, c,$ and d such that $\vec{i} = a(1, 1) + b(1, -1)$ and $\vec{j} = c(1, 1) + d(1, -1)$. Using these results, show that any vector (x, y) can be expressed as a linear combination of the vectors $(1, 1)$ and $(1, -1)$. That is, if (x, y) is any vector, then there exist scalars m and n such that $(x, y) = m(1, 1) + n(1, -1)$.

9. Find the following dot products.

   a. $(5, -1) \cdot (-2, 6)$

   b. $(3\vec{i} + 4\vec{j}) \cdot (-\vec{i} + 2\vec{j})$, where $\vec{i}$ and $\vec{j}$ are the basic vectors $(1, 0)$ and $(0, 1)$, respectively.

10. Let $\vec{A} = (2, -1, 4)$ and $\vec{B} = (6, -2, 1)$.

    a. Find the magnitude of $\vec{A}$.

    b. Find the magnitude of $\vec{B}$.

    c. Find $|\overrightarrow{AB}|$.

    d. Find the cross product $\vec{A} \times \vec{B}$.

CHAPTER OUTLINE

The Circular Functions   5

5.1   Introduction

There exists a class of functions which has the special property of repetitiveness. Graphically the functions have a cyclical or periodic character. The graph of one of the best known of these periodic functions is shown in Figure 5–1; it represents simple wave motion.

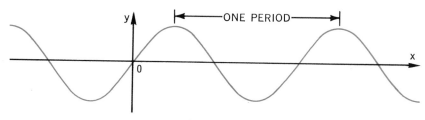

FIGURE 5–1

The interval on the *x*-axis from any point on the graph to another point which is similarly placed in the cycle is called a *period*. A formal definition of period will be presented later.

This periodic character of the values of the functions, as represented by the graph, is a distinguishing characteristic of the class of *circular functions*. The repetitive nature of these functions provides many useful applications of the circular functions to physics and to other scientific areas. Electronics and circular or cyclical motions obviously involve periodic mathematical models.

127

5.2   The unit circle

In algebra you had occasion to draw a circle on a coordinate plane with its center at the origin and with a radius length one unit. This circle is called the *unit circle*. It is possible to associate the set of real numbers with points on the unit circle to form a function. For each real number there corresponds *exactly one* point on the circle under the mapping we shall describe. However, the inverse relation is not a function since each point on the circle will be paired with an unlimited number of real numbers.

The simplest way to establish the association of real numbers with points of the circle is to establish first the well-known one-to-one correspondence of the set of real numbers with points of a scaled number line. Let the length of the unit of the number line be the same as the length of the radius of the unit circle we will use.

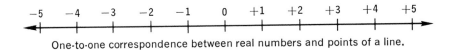

One-to-one correspondence between real numbers and points of a line.

FIGURE 5–2

Now we shall orient the number line so that it is tangent to the unit circle at the point (1, 0). The zero point on the line is the point of tangency. In this position the number line is parallel to the *y*-axis.

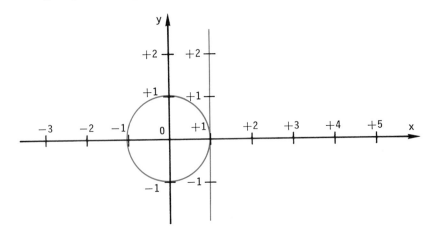

FIGURE 5–3

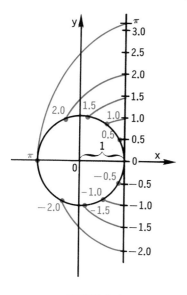

FIGURE 5–4

Imagine both rays of the number line from the zero point being *wrapped* around the unit circle so that each point of the number line coincides with a point of the circle. This establishes the correspondence such that the real number associated with any point on the number line is now associated with a point on the unit circle. This represents a *mapping*, first from the set of real numbers to the set of points on the number line, then to the set of points on the unit circle. It is not a one-to-one correspondence. Why?

Consider an arc from the point $A(1, 0)$ to the point $P(x, y)$ on the unit circle. The real number s is the measure of the arc length in the same units as the number line. Let a function C be determined so that for each real number s there corresponds exactly one ordered pair of real numbers, (x, y), which are coordinates of a point on the unit circle.

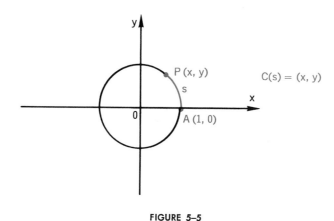

FIGURE 5–5

If $s < 0$, the arc is measured clockwise along the circle, according to custom, from the point $(1, 0)$.

Some sample ordered pairs, $(s, (x, y))$, in the function C are given as examples. Since the circumference of the circle is 2π, key values of s are often given as fractions or multiples of π. You should verify each pair of values in the following table from known geometrical relationships.

Function C

s	0	$\frac{\pi}{2}$ or 1.5708	π or 3.1416	$\frac{3\pi}{2}$ or 4.7124	$-\frac{\pi}{2}$ or -1.5708	$\frac{\pi}{3}$ or 1.0472	$\frac{\pi}{4}$ or .7854	$\frac{\pi}{6}$ or .5236
(x, y)	$(1, 0)$	$(0, 1)$	$(-1, 0)$	$(0, -1)$	$(0, -1)$	$\left(\frac{1}{2}, \frac{\sqrt{3}}{2}\right)$	$\left(\frac{\sqrt{2}}{2}, \frac{\sqrt{2}}{2}\right)$	$\left(\frac{\sqrt{3}}{2}, \frac{1}{2}\right)$

Definition: A function is *periodic* if, for some real number α, $f(x + \alpha) = f(x)$ where $x + \alpha$ and $x - \alpha$ are in the domain of f for each x in the domain of f.

The *period* of f is α, and the smallest positive value of α for which the definition holds is the *fundamental period*. In this text, "period" of a function will always mean "fundamental period" unless otherwise stated.

Exercises

1. Show that $C(-s) = (x, -y)$. (*Hint:* Reflect $P(x, y)$ on the x-axis.)

2. For each real number s given, find the pair (x, y) determined by $C(s) = (x, y)$. Make a sketch of a unit circle and locate the approximate position of the point corresponding to s in each case. One circle is sufficient for all points.

   a. $s = -\pi$
   b. $s = \frac{5\pi}{4}$
   c. $s = 4\pi$
   d. $s = \frac{3\pi}{4}$
   e. $s = \frac{-2\pi}{3}$
   f. $s = 15\pi$
   g. $s = -1.4$
   h. $s = 2.4$
   i. $s = -5.8$

3. Show graphically that 2π is a period, not necessarily the fundamental period, of C where $C(s) = (x, y)$ according to the definition given in this section. Investigate $C(s + 2\pi n)$ where $n \in N$, the set of natural numbers. Give several examples.

4. Starting with the point (1, 0) on the unit circle, divide the circle into eight congruent arcs. What is the smallest positive arc length s from (1, 0) to each of the other points of division? Find the coordinates of each of these points. (*Hint:* Use the equation $x^2 + y^2 = 1$ and the fact that $|x| = |y|$ for some points.)

5. Starting with the point (1, 0), divide the unit circle into six congruent arcs. Find the smallest positive arc length s from (1, 0) to each point of division. Find the coordinates of these points, in radical form if necessary.

6. Estimate the least positive value of s (to hundredths) in function C for which (x, y) is given. ($\pi \approx 3.14$)

   a. (0, 1)   c. (.97, .25)   e. (.45, $-$.89)
   b. (-1, 0)   d. (.60, .80)   f. ($-$.79, $-$.61)

7. Estimate the negative value of s which has the least absolute value for each part of Exercise 6.

8. Estimate a positive number $s > 2\pi$ for each part of Exercise 6.

5.3   The sine function and the cosine function

In the previous section, we associated each real number s with a certain point on the unit circle having coordinates (x, y) by a function we called C. Now let us examine the nature of the elements x and y.

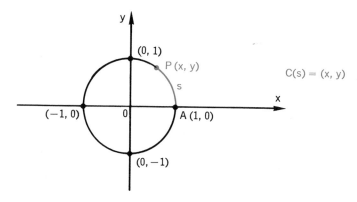

FIGURE 5–6

Imagine that s assumes a sequence of values increasing from 0 to $\dfrac{\pi}{2}$. Intuitively you can see that the value of x decreases from 1 to 0, but not linearly, as this happens. Similarly, as s varies from 0 to $\frac{\pi}{2}$, the value of y increases from 0 to 1. As s changes from $\frac{\pi}{2}$ to π, can you describe generally how values of x and y change? How do x and y behave as s increases from π to 2π? For $s \geqq 2\pi$, do you see that (x, y) assumes values that repeat those for $0 \leqq s < 2\pi$?

We shall now define x and y for a given real number s as the circular functions cosine and sine of s, respectively.

> **Definition:** For any real number s, where $C(s) = (x, y)$ such that $x^2 + y^2 = 1$, let $x = $ *cosine* of s and $y = $ *sine* of s. In abbreviated form, $x = \cos s$ and $y = \sin s$.

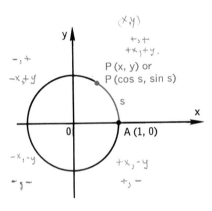

FIGURE 5–7

The cosine function assigns a real number x to any real number s such that $-1 \leqq x \leqq 1$ or $|x| \leqq 1$. The sine function assigns a real number y to s such that $-1 \leqq y \leqq 1$ or $|y| \leqq 1$. The domain of each of these circular functions is the set of all real numbers, and the range of each consists of the set of real numbers between -1 and $+1$, inclusive.

Exercises

1. Determine the signs of x and y (and thus the signs of $\cos s$ and $\sin s$) for points on the unit circle in the first quadrant measured by s. Determine the signs of the two circular functions for points on the unit circle in the second, third, and fourth quadrants. Make a table representing these conditions.

2. Make a sketch and determine the quadrant of the point on the unit circle for each of the following conditions. Let $n \in W$, the set of whole numbers.

   a. $0 < (s \pm 2\pi n) < \frac{\pi}{2}$ c. $\pi < (s \pm 2\pi n) < \frac{3\pi}{2}$

   b. $\frac{3\pi}{2} < (s \pm 2\pi n) < 2\pi$ d. $\frac{\pi}{2} < (s \pm 2\pi n) < \pi$

3. Examine cos $(s + \alpha)$ and sin $(s + \alpha)$ where the domain of α is the set of real numbers. Find at least three different values of α so that cos $(s + \alpha) =$ cos s and sin $(s + \alpha) =$ sin s for any real replacement of s. What is the least positive value of α such that these equations are true? What is the fundamental period of each of the two circular functions?

(handwritten margin notes)
$cos\ s = cos\ (s + \alpha)$
$cos\ \alpha = 0$
$sin\ s = sin\ (s + \alpha)$
$sin\ \alpha = 0$

4. Show that sin $(-s) = -$sin s and cos $(-s) =$ cos s. (*Hint:* Use the graph of a unit circle and the concept of reflection.)

> If $f(-x) = f(x)$, f is called an *even function*.
> If $f(-x) = -f(x)$, f is called an *odd function*.

Which of the two circular functions is odd and which is even? Which has a graph symmetrical about the y-axis? Are all even functions symmetrical in this way?

5. Draw a unit circle in which the radius is 10 cm. Devise a means for measuring an arc s on the circle to the nearest millimeter. Locate at least three points in each quadrant, and give ordered pairs $(s,$ (cos s, sin s)) in function C for these points by making estimates to the nearest hundredth of a unit (in this case the radius).

5.4   Other circular functions

There exist still other periodic functions in the class of circular functions. For example, the ratios $\dfrac{\sin s}{\cos s}$ and $\dfrac{\cos s}{\sin s}$, and the reciprocals of the sine and cosine functions also determine periodic functions. These other circular functions have well established names and their definitions are given.

> **Definition 1:** *The Tangent Function.* The *tangent* of s, symbolized tan s, is defined as follows: For all real numbers s such that cos $s \neq 0$, $\tan s = \dfrac{\sin s}{\cos s}$.

> **Definition 2:** *The Cotangent Function.* The *cotangent* of s, symbolized cot s, is defined as follows: For all real numbers s such that sin $s \neq 0$, $\cot s = \dfrac{\cos s}{\sin s}$.

> **Definition 3:** *The Secant Function.* The *secant* of s, symbolized sec s, is defined as follows: For all real numbers s such that cos $s \neq 0$, $\sec s = \dfrac{1}{\cos s}$.

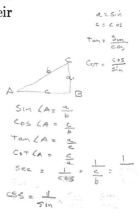

Definition 4: *The Cosecant Function.* The *cosecant* of s, symbolized csc s, is defined as follows: For all real numbers s such that sin $s \neq 0$, csc $s = \dfrac{1}{\sin s}$.

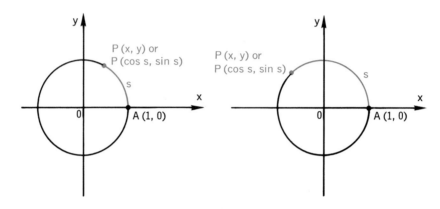

FIGURE 5–8

Definition 1 can be illustrated by referring to Figure 5–8. Since $\tan s = \dfrac{\sin s}{\cos s}$, it is obvious that $\tan s = \dfrac{y}{x}$. What restrictions must be placed on x? For which points on the unit circle is the tangent function not defined? What numbers are not in the domain of $\tan s$?

Similar questions are appropriate for the remaining circular functions.

Exercises

1. Show that $\tan (-s) = -\tan s$. Is tangent an odd or an even function?

2. Show that the domain of $\tan s$ is $\{s | s \in R, s \neq \dfrac{\pi}{2} + \pi n, n$ is an integer$\}$.

3. Show that $\tan (s + \alpha) = \tan s$ for $\alpha = \pi n$ where n is an integer. What is the fundamental period of tangent?

4. Verify each of the following statements.

   a. $\cot(-s) = -\cot s$
   b. $\sec(-s) = \sec s$
   c. $\csc(-s) = -\csc s$

   Which are odd and which are even functions?

5. Prove each of the following statements assuming that n is an integer.

   a. The domain of $\cot s$ is the set of all real numbers s such that $s \neq \pi n$.
   b. The domain of $\sec s$ is the set of all real numbers s such that $s \neq \left(\dfrac{2n-1}{2}\right)\pi$.
   c. The domain of $\csc s$ is the set of all real numbers s such that $s \neq \pi n$.

6. Prove each of the following statements.

   a. The fundamental period of cotangent function is π.
   b. The fundamental period of secant function is 2π.
   c. The fundamental period of cosecant function is 2π.

7. Draw a unit circle on graph paper so that the radius is ten graph units in length. Select a point on the circle in each quadrant and estimate the value of s and the coordinates (x, y) in function C. Calculate the values of each of the six circular functions for each s from the definitions.

Eq of a Circle
$x^2 + y^2 = 1$ ← Learn

5.5 Equations involving circular functions

Any point on the unit circle satisfies the equation $x^2 + y^2 = 1$. From this equation, we immediately can write the following relation where $\cos^2 s$ means $(\cos s)^2$.

$$\cos^2 s + \sin^2 s = 1$$

Here are two alternate forms of the relation.

$$\cos^2 s = 1 - \sin^2 s$$
$$\sin^2 s = 1 - \cos^2 s$$

Since, by definition, $\tan s = \dfrac{\sin s}{\cos s}$ and $\cot s = \dfrac{\cos s}{\sin s}$, we can write two additional relations.

$$\sin s = \tan s \cos s \quad \text{or} \quad \cos s = \frac{\sin s}{\tan s}$$

$$\cos s = \cot s \sin s \quad \text{or} \quad \sin s = \frac{\cos s}{\cot s}$$

Given two real numbers, s_1 and s_2, and the corresponding arcs and points, $(\cos s_1, \sin s_1)$ and $(\cos s_2, \sin s_2)$, on the unit circle, find the real number $s_1 + s_2$ and the corresponding arc and point $(\cos (s_1 + s_2), \sin (s_1 + s_2))$. Are there expressions equivalent to $\cos (s_1 + s_2)$ and $\sin (s_1 + s_2)$ in terms of functions of s_1 and s_2? Let us recall some relations from geometry.

Consider Figure 5–9 with s_1, s_2, $s_1 + s_2$, and $-s_2$ as shown. P_1 is the terminal point of s_1; P_2 is the terminal point of s_2; P_3 is the terminal point of $s_1 + s_2$; and P_4 is the terminal point of $-s_2$. Draw chords AP_3 and P_4P_1.

Note that arc P_4P_1 is congruent to arc AP_3 since each is measured by the sum of s_1 and s_2. From geometry, congruent arcs in the same circle have congruent chords so that $P_4P_1 \cong AP_3$. Congruent line segments have the same measure so, by the distance formula, we can write the following equations.

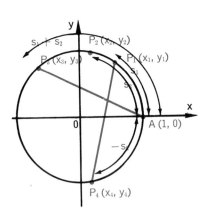

FIGURE 5–9

$$\sqrt{(x_3 - 1)^2 + (y_3 - 0)^2} = \sqrt{(x_1 - x_4)^2 + (y_1 - y_4)^2}$$

$$x_3{}^2 - 2x_3 + 1 + y_3{}^2 = x_1{}^2 - 2x_1x_4 + x_4{}^2 + y_1{}^2 - 2y_1y_4 + y_4{}^2$$

Since $x^2 + y^2 = 1$ for all points on the circle, from

$$(x_3{}^2 + y_3{}^2) - 2x_3 + 1 = (x_1{}^2 + y_1{}^2) + (x_4{}^2 + y_4{}^2) - 2x_1x_4 - 2y_1y_4$$

we have the following result by substitution.

$$1 - 2x_3 + 1 = 1 + 1 - 2x_1x_4 - 2y_1y_4$$

Simplifying, we get the following equation.

$$x_3 = x_1 x_4 + y_1 y_4$$

Substituting the appropriate functions of s and using the fact that cosine is an even function and sine is an odd function, we obtain the following important formulas.

$$\cos (s_1 + s_2) = \cos s_1 \cos (-s_2) + \sin s_1 \sin (-s_2)$$

or $\cos (s_1 + s_2) = \cos s_1 \cos s_2 - \sin s_1 \sin s_2$ (I)

Replacing s_2 with $-s_2$ in Formula (I), we get Formula (II).

$$\cos (s_1 - s_2) = \cos s_1 \cos (-s_2) - \sin s_1 \sin (-s_2)$$

or $\cos (s_1 - s_2) = \cos s_1 \cos s_2 + \sin s_1 \sin s_2$ (II)

In the special case where we replace s_1 with $\dfrac{\pi}{2}$ and s_2 with s, from Formulas (I) and (II) we have the following formulas.

$$\cos \left(\frac{\pi}{2} + s \right) = -\sin s$$

$$\cos \left(\frac{\pi}{2} - s \right) = \sin s$$

Replacing s with $\dfrac{\pi}{2} + s$ in the last equation, we have the following formula.

$$\cos s = \sin \left(\frac{\pi}{2} + s \right)$$

Replacing s with $\dfrac{\pi}{2} - s$ in the same equation, we have the following formula.

$$\cos s = \sin \left(\frac{\pi}{2} - s \right)$$

In the formula $\cos \left(\dfrac{\pi}{2} - s \right) = \sin s$, we replace s with $s_1 + s_2$.

$$\cos \left[\frac{\pi}{2} - (s_1 + s_2) \right] = \sin (s_1 + s_2)$$

or

$$\cos \left[\left(\frac{\pi}{2} - s_1 \right) - s_2 \right] = \sin (s_1 + s_2)$$

Applying Formula (II) to the previous equation results in Formula (III).

$$\cos\left(\frac{\pi}{2} - s_1\right)\cos s_2 + \sin\left(\frac{\pi}{2} - s_1\right)\sin s_2 = \sin(s_1 + s_2)$$

or $\qquad \sin(s_1 + s_2) = \sin s_1 \cos s_2 + \cos s_1 \sin s_2 \qquad$ (III)

To obtain Formula (IV), we replace s_2 with $-s_2$ in Formula (III).

$$\sin(s_1 - s_2) = \sin s_1 \cos s_2 - \cos s_1 \sin s_2 \qquad \text{(IV)}$$

Formulas (I), (II), (III), and (IV) are called the *sum and difference formulas of sine and cosine*. Similar formulas exist for other circular functions.

Exercises

1. Verify Formulas (I), (II), (III), and (IV) for $s_1 = \frac{\pi}{2}$ and $s_2 = \frac{\pi}{2}$.

2. Verify Formulas (I), (II), (III), and (IV) for $s_1 = 0$ and $s_2 = \frac{\pi}{3}$;

for $s_1 = \frac{2\pi}{3}$ and $s_2 = \frac{\pi}{3}$.

3. Develop formulas for each of the following sums or differences.

a. $\sin(\pi + s)$ **e.** $\sin(2\pi + s)$
b. $\sin(\pi - s)$ **f.** $\sin(2\pi - s)$
c. $\cos(\pi + s)$ **g.** $\cos(2\pi + s)$
d. $\cos(\pi - s)$ **h.** $\cos(2\pi - s)$

4. Develop formulas for $\tan(s_1 + s_2)$, $\tan(s_1 - s_2)$, $\cot(s_1 + s_2)$, and $\cot(s_1 - s_2)$.

5. Verify the following equations using the formulas developed in the preceding section and in the previous exercises.

a. $\cos\left(\frac{\pi}{6} + s\right) + \sin\left(\frac{\pi}{3} + s\right) = \sqrt{3}\cos s$

b. $\sin\left(\frac{3\pi}{2} + s\right) - \cos\left(\frac{\pi}{2} - s\right) = -(\cos s + \sin s)$

c. $\tan(\pi + s)\cos s = -\cos\left(\frac{3\pi}{2} - s\right)$

d. $\cos\left(\frac{\pi}{3} - s_1\right)\cos\left(\frac{5\pi}{3} + s_2\right) - \sin\left(\frac{\pi}{3} - s_1\right)\sin\left(\frac{5\pi}{3} + s_2\right) =$

$\cos(s_2 - s_1)$

5.6 Evaluating circular functions when $s < 0$ or $s > \dfrac{\pi}{2}$

When s is a negative number, or a positive number greater than $\dfrac{\pi}{2}$, complications can arise in evaluating sin s, cos s, and the other circular functions. As you have seen, tables of values of circular functions are ordinarily given only for $0 \leqq s \leqq \dfrac{\pi}{2}$ where s is represented to four decimal places. Obviously there is a need for means of developing relationships to permit use of the tables when s is outside the range of the table.

It is possible to find an arc measured by s', where $0 < s' < \dfrac{\pi}{2}$, which is related to values of s outside the tabular range of values. Notice that multiples of $\dfrac{\pi}{2}$ are excluded in this development.

If s is the measure of an arc such that $\dfrac{\pi}{2} < s < \pi$, the terminal point of the *related arc* with measure s' has the same ordinate, y, and an abscissa which is the negative of x. This is equivalent to finding the image of $P\,(x, y)$ transformed by a reflection on the y-axis. Thus $P'(-x, y)$ determines s', the measure of the related arc for s. (See Figure 5–10.)

For $\dfrac{3\pi}{2} < s < 2\pi$, the image of $P(x, y)$ under a re-

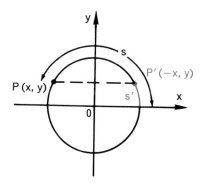

FIGURE 5–10

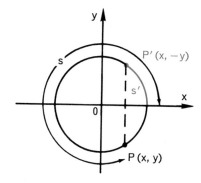

FIGURE 5–11

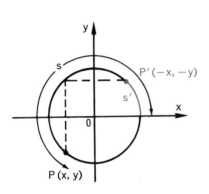

FIGURE 5–12

flection on the x-axis is $P'(x, -y)$. The sign of the ordinate is reversed. (See Figure 5–11.)

A double reflection, one on the x-axis and one on the y-axis, produces point $P'(-x, -y)$ which is the image of $P(x, y)$ where $\pi < s < \dfrac{3\pi}{2}$. (See Figure 5–12.)

In all three cases the arc measured by s' has a length greater than zero and less than $\dfrac{\pi}{2}$. Thus s' is a real number such that $0 < s' < \dfrac{\pi}{2}$. For all other positive and negative numbers s such that the end point of the corresponding arc falls in the second, third, or fourth quadrants, the appropriate transformations can be stated.

COL   SUMMARY

When the arc measured by s terminates in Quadrant I, every circular function $f(s) = f(s')$ where $s' = 2\pi n - s$ for n an integer.

When the arc measured by s terminates in Quadrant II, we have the following equations and related conditions. Recall that R represents the set of real numbers, and Z represents the set of integers.

Equations	*Conditions*
1. $\sin s = \sin s'$	
2. $\cos s = -\cos s'$	
3. $\tan s = -\tan s'$	$s \in R;\ 0 < s' < \dfrac{\pi}{2}\ ;$
4. $\cot s = -\cot s'$	$s' = (2n - 1)\pi - s,\ n \in Z$
5. $\sec s = -\sec s'$	
6. $\csc s = \csc s'$	

When the arc measured by s terminates in Quadrant III, we have the following equations and related conditions.

Equations	*Conditions*
1. $\sin s = -\sin s'$	
2. $\cos s = -\cos s'$	
3. $\tan s = \tan s'$	$s \in R; 0 < s' < \dfrac{\pi}{2};$
4. $\cot s = \cot s'$	$s' = s - (2n - 1)\pi, \ n \in Z$
5. $\sec s = -\sec s'$	
6. $\csc s = -\csc s'$	

When the arc measured by s terminates in Quadrant IV, we have the following equations and related conditions.

Equations	*Conditions*
1. $\sin s = -\sin s'$	
2. $\cos s = \cos s'$	
3. $\tan s = -\tan s'$	$s \in R; 0 < s' < \dfrac{\pi}{2};$
4. $\cot s = -\cot s'$	$s' = 2\pi n - s, \ n \in Z$
5. $\sec s = \sec s'$	
6. $\csc s = -\csc s'$	

By using the relations presented in this section, it is possible to use tables of values of the circular (or trigonometric) functions for any real number s such that the number is in the domain of the function. If s is expressed in terms of π, convert to approximate decimal notation by replacing π with 3.1416.

EXAMPLE. Evaluate the following functions to the nearest hundredth using Table 2, page 459.

(a) $\sin .60$ (c) $\tan \dfrac{3\pi}{5}$ (e) $\cot (-1.86)$

(b) $\cos \dfrac{\pi}{6}$ (d) $\sin 4.40$ (f) $\cos 5.04$

Solution.

(a) If $s = .60$, the arc terminates in Quadrant I and $\sin .60 \approx .56$.

(b) If $s = \dfrac{\pi}{6}$, the arc terminates in Quadrant I. Therefore $\cos \dfrac{\pi}{6} \approx$ $\cos .52 \approx .87$.

(c) If $s = \dfrac{3\pi}{5}$, the arc terminates in Quadrant II. Thus $\tan \dfrac{3\pi}{5} =$

$-\tan\left(\pi - \dfrac{3\pi}{5}\right) \approx -\tan 1.26 \approx -3.11$.

(d) If $s = 4.40$, the arc terminates in Quadrant III. Therefore $\sin 4.40 = -\sin (4.40 - 3.14) = -\sin 1.26 \approx -.95$.

(e) If $s = -1.86$, the arc terminates in Quadrant III. Therefore $\cot (-1.86) = -\cot 1.86 = -\cot (3.14 - 1.86) = -\cot 1.28$ $\approx -.30$.

(f) If $s = 5.04$, the arc terminates in Quadrant IV. Therefore $\cos 5.04 = \cos (6.28 - 5.04) = \cos 1.24 \approx .33$.

Exercises

Use Table 2, page 459 to evaluate Exercises 1–12. Find each value to the nearest hundredth.

1. $\sin .175$

2. $\cos \dfrac{1}{3}$

3. $\tan \dfrac{\pi}{7}$

4. $\cos \dfrac{2\pi}{5}$

5. $\tan\left(-\dfrac{\pi}{10}\right)$

6. $\cos 4$

7. $\sin 32$

8. $\tan 6$

9. $\sin (-13.25)$

10. $\cos (3\pi - 2)$

11. $\cot (-3\pi)$

12. $\sin\left(\dfrac{5\pi}{12} + 1.46\right)$

Name the quadrant(s) in which the arc measured by s terminates if the following conditions are true.

13. $\sin s < 0, \tan s < 0$

14. $\cos s > 0, \csc s < 0$

15. $\tan s < 0, \cos s < 0$

16. $\sin s > 0, \cot s < 0$

17. $\cos s < 0, \sin s < 0$

18. $\sec s > 0, \cos s > 0$

19. Prepare a table of ordered pairs for $(x, \sin x)$ where x is an element of $\{0, .1, .2, .3, \cdots, 6.3\}$. Plot the points.

20. Prepare a table of ordered pairs for $(x, \cos x)$ where x is an element of $\{0, .1, .2, .3, \cdots, 6.3\}$. Plot the points.

5.7 Graphs of the circular functions

A table of values for $0 \leqq s \leqq \dfrac{\pi}{2}$ immediately determines the set of ordered pairs $(s, f(s))$ for any circular function f. Since a real number s', such that $0 \leqq s' \leqq \dfrac{\pi}{2}$, can be associated with any real number s, a set of ordered pairs for any s in the domain of f is determined. The graphs of the six circular functions for $-2\pi \leqq s \leqq 2\pi$ are shown below. Appropriate limitations of the domains, consistent with the definitions, are understood.

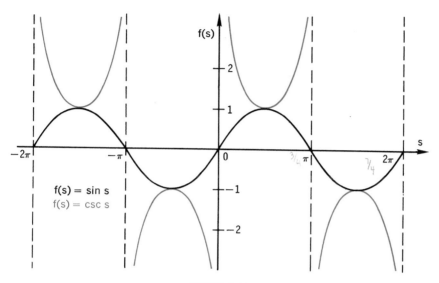

$f(s) = \sin s$
$f(s) = \csc s$

FIGURE 5–13

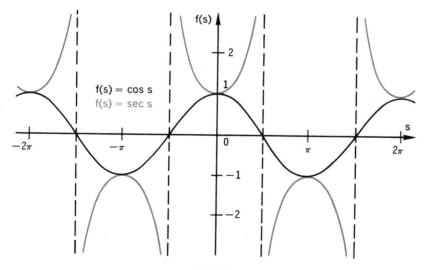

$f(s) = \cos s$
$f(s) = \sec s$

FIGURE 5–14

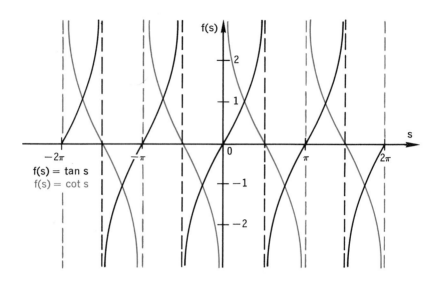

FIGURE 5–15

Now we shall investigate the graphs of circular functions modified by constants. Consider the function $f(s) = A \sin (ks + c)$ where A, k, and c are real constants. Figures 5–13, 5–14, and 5–15 are graphs of the special cases where $A = 1$, $k = 1$, and $c = 0$. From your knowledge of graphing, you can see that A affects only the ordinate for a given replacement of s.

> **Definition:** The *amplitude* of the sine function, $f(s) = A \sin s$, or the cosine function, $f(s) = A \cos s$, is the absolute value of A, or $|A|$.

A change in A tends to *stretch* or *shrink* the curve vertically. An oscilloscope is ideal for demonstrating this variation. If $A < 0$, the curve is a reflection of the graph of the function on the x-axis for the coefficient having the same absolute value but opposite sign.

Assume $A = 1$ and $c = 0$ and consider variations in k for the function $f(s) = A \sin (ks + c)$. Note that a full period exists between $s = 0$ and $s = \dfrac{2\pi}{k}$.

Definition: The fundamental period of the function $f(s) = A \sin (ks + c)$ is $\dfrac{2\pi}{k}$. The fundamental period of the function $f(s) = A \cos (ks + c)$ is $\dfrac{2\pi}{k}$. The fundamental period of the function $f(s) = A \tan (ks + c)$ is $\dfrac{\pi}{k}$.

Now consider $f(s) = A \sin (ks + c)$ where $A = 1$, $k = 1$, and c is any value other than zero. For example, if $c = \pi$, the graph of $f(s) = \sin (s + \pi)$ is shifted π units to the left. This is true because the curve "starts" at $s = -\pi$ since $\sin (-\pi + \pi) = \sin 0 = 0$. If $c > 0$, the shift is $\dfrac{c}{k}$ units to the left, and if $c < 0$, the shift is $\dfrac{c}{k}$ units to the right. The amount of shift is $\left| \dfrac{c}{k} \right|$ in each case.

Definition: In the function $f(s) = A \sin (ks + c)$, $\left| \dfrac{c}{k} \right|$ is called the *phase shift* of the curve and of the function f.

Note: This definition applies to all circular functions.

The definition above can be clarified by writing the function in the form $f(s) = A \sin k \left(s + \dfrac{c}{k} \right)$ and replacing s by $\dfrac{-c}{k}$ to obtain a zero of the function.

Combining these three effects, changes in amplitude, in period, and in phase shift, we are able to sketch the graph of a more complex circular function. Note that amplitude is defined only for the sine and cosine functions, and that the fundamental period is either $\dfrac{2\pi}{k}$ or $\dfrac{\pi}{k}$ depending upon the selected function.

EXAMPLE. Graph $f(s) = 3 \sin \left(2s + \dfrac{\pi}{2} \right)$ for two periods or "cycles."

Solution. The amplitude is 3, the period is $\dfrac{2\pi}{2}$ or π, and the phase shift is $\dfrac{\pi}{4}$ units to the left.

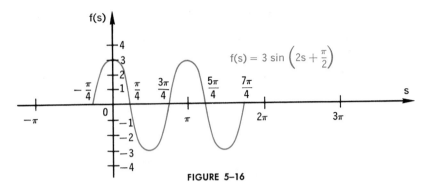

FIGURE 5–16

Exercises

1. Prepare a table of values for the six circular functions consisting of at least ten points for each function.

2. From the table in Exercise 1, graph the basic curves of the six circular functions for at least one period.

3. Graph $f(s) = \sin s$, $g(s) = \sin 2s$, and $h(s) = 2 \sin s$ on the same set of axes.

4. Give the amplitude, period, and phase shift for each function if such numbers exist.

   a. $f(s) = 2 \sin 5s$ \qquad\qquad e. $f(s) = 243 \sin (15s - 40)$

   b. $f(s) = 3 \cos \left(s - \dfrac{\pi}{2} \right)$ \qquad f. $f(s) = -6 \cos (\pi - s)$

   c. $f(s) = \tan (2s - \pi)$ \qquad g. $f(x) = 12 \cot 3\left(x - \dfrac{\pi}{2} \right)$

   d. $f(s) = \tan 2(s - \pi)$ \qquad h. $f(t) = 10 \sin \left(\dfrac{1}{3} t - \dfrac{5\pi}{3} \right)$

5. Construct the graphs of the following functions.

   a. $f(s) = 2 \sin \left(s + \dfrac{\pi}{2} \right)$

   b. $f(s) = 5 \cos (2s + \pi)$

   c. $f(s) = -\sin \left(s - \dfrac{\pi}{4} \right)$

5.8   Additional formulas relating the circular functions

Recall Formula (I) from Section 5.5.

$$\cos (s_1 + s_2) = \cos s_1 \cos s_2 - \sin s_1 \sin s_2$$

When $s_1 = s_2 = s$, we obtain the following formula.

$$\cos 2s = \cos^2 s - \sin^2 s \tag{V}$$

Alternately, from the formulas $\cos^2 s = 1 - \sin^2 s$ and $\sin^2 s = 1 - \cos^2 s$, we have the following formulas.

$$\cos 2s = 2\cos^2 s - 1 \tag{VI}$$

$$\cos 2s = 1 - 2\sin^2 s \tag{VII}$$

Now solve Formulas (VI) and (VII) for cos s and sin s, respectively.

$$\cos s = \pm\sqrt{\frac{1 + \cos 2s}{2}}$$

$$\sin s = \pm\sqrt{\frac{1 - \cos 2s}{2}}$$

The sign is chosen according to the quadrant in which the point determined by $C(s)$ is located.

Since s is a real number, we can replace $2s$ with r and thus s with $\frac{r}{2}$ to get the *formulas for half any real number* r.

$$\cos\frac{r}{2} = \pm\sqrt{\frac{1 + \cos r}{2}} \tag{VIII}$$

$$\sin\frac{r}{2} = \pm\sqrt{\frac{1 - \cos r}{2}} \tag{IX}$$

Formulas for tangent and cotangent of double and half of real numbers will be derived in the exercises.

Exercises

1. Derive a formula for tan $2s$ in terms of sin s and cos s. Change the formula to one in terms of tan s.

2. Derive a formula for $\tan\frac{r}{2}$ in terms of sin r and cos r.

3. Evaluate $\cos\frac{\pi}{4}$ using the value of $\cos\frac{\pi}{2}$.

4. Find the value of $\sin\frac{\pi}{3}$ using the values of $\sin\frac{\pi}{6}$ and $\cos\frac{\pi}{6}$.

5. Verify that $\dfrac{1 - \tan^2 s}{1 + \tan^2 s} = \cos 2s$.

6. Evaluate $\sin \dfrac{\pi}{12}$ and $\cos \dfrac{\pi}{12}$ to the nearest hundredth without tables.

7. Show that $\tan \dfrac{s}{2} = \dfrac{\sin s}{1 + \cos s} = \dfrac{1 - \cos s}{\sin s}$.

8. Prove that $\sin 3s = 3 \sin s - 4 \sin^3 s$.

5.9   Inverses of the circular functions

The *inverse* of any function is obtained by interchanging the elements of each ordered pair in the function. Thus the inverse of the function with ordered pairs $(s, \sin s)$ is the set of all ordered pairs $(\sin s, s)$. In other words, the domain of a function becomes the range of the inverse of the function, and the range of the function becomes the domain of the inverse. We shall call the inverse of the sine function the *arcsine relation*. You will soon see why the arcsine relation is not a function.

The inverse of any function may be produced graphically by reflecting the graph of the given function on the line $y = x$, the line which bisects the first and third quadrants.

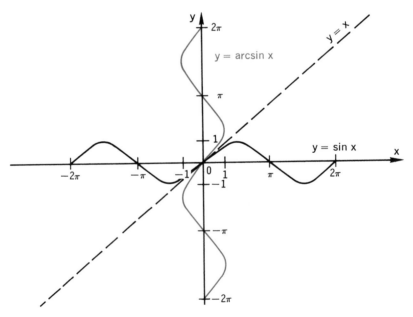

FIGURE 5–17

Note that $\{(x, y) \mid y = \arcsin x\}$ and $\{(x, y) \mid x = \sin y\}$ generate the same set of ordered pairs and, therefore, describe the same relation. The domain of $y = \arcsin x$ is $-1 \leq x \leq 1$ or $|x| \leq 1$, and the range of the relation is the set of real numbers.

Corresponding inverses for the remaining circular functions exist. The most used inverses are the *arccosine*, the *arctangent*, and the *arccotangent relations*.

Inverse of $\cos x$: $\{(x, y) \mid y = \arccos x\}$ or $\{(x, y) \mid x = \cos y\}$
Inverse of $\tan x$: $\{(x, y) \mid y = \arctan x\}$ or $\{(x, y) \mid x = \tan y\}$
Inverse of $\cot x$: $\{(x, y) \mid y = \text{arccot } x\}$ or $\{(x, y) \mid x = \cot y\}$

Are any of the inverse relations functions? What restrictions are required for the domain of each?

We may limit the ranges of the inverses of the circular functions so that the inverse relations *become* functions. We capitalize the first letter in this case so that $y = \text{Arcsin } x$, for example, is a function. An alternate form of Arcsin x is $\text{Sin}^{-1} x$.

Function	*Domain*	*Range*
$y = \text{Arcsin } x$ or $y = \text{Sin}^{-1} x$	$-1 \leq x \leq 1$ or $|x| \leq 1$	$-\dfrac{\pi}{2} \leq \text{Arcsin } x \leq \dfrac{\pi}{2}$
$y = \text{Arccos } x$ or $y = \text{Cos}^{-1} x$	$-1 \leq x \leq 1$	$0 \leq \text{Arccos } x \leq \pi$
$y = \text{Arctan } x$ or $y = \text{Tan}^{-1} x$	$x \in R$	$-\dfrac{\pi}{2} < \text{Arctan } x < \dfrac{\pi}{2}$
$y = \text{Arccot } x$ or $y = \text{Cot}^{-1} x$	$x \in R$	$0 < \text{Arccot } x < \pi$

Values of the Arcfunctions are called *principal values*. *General values* include all replacements which satisfy the arcfunctions. For example, the general values of $\arcsin \dfrac{1}{2}$ are $\dfrac{\pi}{6} + 2\pi n$ and $\dfrac{5\pi}{6} + 2\pi n$ where n is an element of the set of integers. The principal value, designated by Arcsin $\dfrac{1}{2}$, is $\dfrac{\pi}{6}$.

EXAMPLE 1. Find the value of each of the following Arcfunctions.

(a) $\text{Arcsin } \dfrac{\sqrt{2}}{2}$ (b) $\text{Arccos } \left(-\dfrac{1}{2}\right)$ (c) $\text{Arctan } (-1)$

Solution.

(a) Let $s = \text{Arcsin } \dfrac{\sqrt{2}}{2}$; then $\sin s = \dfrac{\sqrt{2}}{2}$ where $|s| \leq \dfrac{\pi}{2}$. $s = \dfrac{\pi}{4}$

(b) Let $s = \text{Arccos}\left(-\frac{1}{2}\right)$; then $\cos s = -\frac{1}{2}$ where $0 \leq s \leq \pi$.

$$s = \frac{2\pi}{3}$$

(c) Let $s = \text{Arctan}\,(-1)$; then $\tan s = -1$ where $|s| < \frac{\pi}{2}$. $s = -\frac{\pi}{4}$

EXAMPLE 2. Evaluate $\sin\,(\text{Arctan}\,1)$.

Solution. Let $r = \text{Arctan}\,1$; then $r = \frac{\pi}{4}$ and $\sin r = \sin\frac{\pi}{4} = \frac{\sqrt{2}}{2}$.

Exercises

1. Sketch the graph of $\{(x, y) \mid y = \text{Arccos}\,x\}$.
2. Sketch the graph of $\{(x, y) \mid y = \text{Arctan}\,x\}$.
3. Sketch the graph of $\{(x, y) \mid y = \text{Cot}^{-1}x\}$.
4. Find the general values of each of the following arcfunctions.

   a. $\arcsin\left(-\frac{1}{2}\right)$　　　　　c. $\arctan .7$

   b. $\arccos\left(\frac{\sqrt{3}}{2}\right)$　　　　　d. $\arcsin .3090$

5. Find each principal value without using tables.

   a. $\text{Arccos}\,\frac{1}{2}$　　　　　e. $\text{Sin}^{-1}\,\frac{\sqrt{3}}{2}$

   b. $\text{Arctan}\,\frac{\sqrt{3}}{3}$　　　　　f. $\text{Tan}^{-1}\,(-\sqrt{3})$

   c. $\text{Arccot}\,(-1)$　　　　　g. $\text{Arccos}\,0$

   d. $\text{Arcsin}\left(-\frac{1}{2}\right)$　　　　　h. $\text{Cos}^{-1}\left(-\frac{\sqrt{3}}{2}\right)$

6. Use tables to evaluate each of the following to the nearest hundredth.

   a. $\text{Arctan}\,1.234$　　　　　e. $\text{Sin}^{-1}\,(-.9555)$

   b. $\text{Arcsin}\,.2250$　　　　　f. $\text{Cos}^{-1}\,(-.1330)$

   c. $\text{Arccos}\,.2756$　　　　　g. $\text{Tan}^{-1}\,(-31.24)$

   d. $\text{Arccot}\,3.34$　　　　　h. $\text{Sin}^{-1}\,(-.9825)$

7. Evaluate.

a. $\sin\left(\text{Arcsin } \dfrac{1}{2}\right)$

b. $\sin\left(\text{Arccos } \dfrac{1}{2}\right)$

c. $\cos\left(\text{Arctan } 1\right)$

d. $\tan\left[\text{Arcsin}\left(-\dfrac{\sqrt{2}}{2}\right)\right]$

e. $\sin 2\left(\text{Arcsin } \dfrac{1}{2}\right)$

f. $\cos\left(\dfrac{\pi}{2} - \text{Arccos } \dfrac{\sqrt{2}}{2}\right)$

8. Express each of the following in terms of u and v.

a. $\sin\left(\text{Arcsin } u - \text{Arccos } v\right)$

b. $\cos\left(\text{Arcsin } u + \text{Arccos } v\right)$

5.10   Relating the circular functions to trigonometry

In this chapter you have considered the class of circular functions as an abstract study of periodic functions resulting from the "wrapping function" C. The function C associates the set of real numbers with the set of points on a unit circle. The coordinates of each point are the basis for the definitions of the sine and cosine functions with real numbers as the domain.

An area of mathematics called trigonometry also involves the sine and cosine functions. In trigonometry the domain of each function is the set of real numbers, but each real number is the measure of an angle. Thus trigonometry is really an extension of the study of geometry with emphasis on angles, triangles, and similarity. You probably already know the classical definitions of the sine, cosine, and other trigonometric functions in terms of the ratios of measures of sides of a right triangle.

The four chapters which follow present a standard treatment of trigonometry. There are numerous ideas and many difficult problems contained in these chapters which will challenge your abilities regardless of your background.

In Chapters 6–9, you will find developments of many of the same formulas and relations found in this chapter, but they are approached from the viewpoint of trigonometry of angles and triangles. There is an advantage in considering the same topics from two contrasting viewpoints. This approach should give you a broader perspective of mathematics.

Chapter Review

1. Find the ordered pair (x, y) for each given real number s as determined by the function $C(s) = (x, y)$. Use tables only as required.

   a. $\dfrac{\pi}{2}$ **d.** $-\dfrac{5\pi}{6}$ **g.** 2.344

   b. $\dfrac{3\pi}{4}$ **e.** $\dfrac{11\pi}{6}$ **h.** 8.15

   c. $\dfrac{\pi}{6}$ **f.** -23.5π **i.** -4.66

2. If $0 < s < 2\pi$, find a value of s to the nearest hundredth for each given ordered pair (x, y) in the function $C(s) = (x, y)$.

   a. $(.17, .99)$ **d.** $(-.71, .71)$ **g.** $(.60, .80)$
   b. $(.73, .68)$ **e.** $(.88, -.47)$ **h.** $(-.94, .34)$
   c. $(.93, .36)$ **f.** $(-.37, -.93)$ **i.** $(-.060, .998)$

3. Evaluate after simplifying.

   a. $\sin\dfrac{1}{2}\cos 1 + \cos\dfrac{1}{2}\sin 1$ **d.** $2\sin .6\cos .6$

   b. $\cos .2\cos .5 - \sin .2\sin .5$ **e.** $\cos^2\dfrac{\pi}{4} - \sin^2\dfrac{\pi}{4}$

   c. $\sin\dfrac{\pi}{3}\cos\dfrac{\pi}{6} - \cos\dfrac{\pi}{3}\sin\dfrac{\pi}{6}$ **f.** $\dfrac{1 + \cos .44}{2}$

4. Simplify.

   a. $\sin^2 2s - \cos^2 2s$ **b.** $(\cos r + \sin r)^2 - \sin 2r$

5. Graph the function $f(s) = 2\sin 2\left(s - \dfrac{\pi}{2}\right)$ for the domain $-\pi \leq s \leq 3\pi$.

6. State the amplitude, period, and phase shift for each function.

   a. $f(s) = 3\cos\dfrac{s}{3}$ **c.** $f(s) = \tan(\pi s - \pi)$

   b. $f(s) = -6\sin(3s + 4)$

7. Evaluate.

   a. $\text{Arctan }\sqrt{3}$ **c.** $\text{Sin}^{-1} 1 + \text{Cos}^{-1} 1$
   b. $\text{Arccos}\left(-\tfrac{1}{2}\right)$ **d.** $\text{Arccos}(-.66)$

8. Evaluate after simplifying.

    a. sin (Arccos .8)   **c.** $\sin\left(\text{Sin}^{-1}\dfrac{1}{2}\right)$

    b. cos (Arctan 1)   **d.** $\sin\left(2\text{ Arccos }\dfrac{1}{2}\right)$

9. Verify the following identities.

    a. $|\sin s + \cos s| = \sqrt{1 + \sin 2s}$
    b. $\text{Arctan }(0 - s) = -\text{Arctan } s$

10. Simplify $\dfrac{\cos 2r}{(\sin r + \cos r)}$ and evaluate this expression for $r = \dfrac{\pi}{6}$.

CHAPTER OUTLINE

The Trigonometric Functions 6

6.1 The meaning of angle

Trigonometry is that branch of mathematics which deals with functions of angles. The functions are useful in many kinds of computations relating to lengths, sizes of angles, areas, and so on; they are also very useful in many phases of analysis that are not directly related to geometrical problems.

In previous courses in mathematics you learned that an angle is a figure that is the union of two rays that have the same initial point. An angle is often regarded as being generated by the rotation of a ray that has its initial point fixed. The starting position of the ray is called the *initial side* of the angle and the final position is called the *terminal side* of the angle. If rotation is counterclockwise, the angle is measured by a positive number. If rotation is clockwise, the measure of the angle is a negative number.

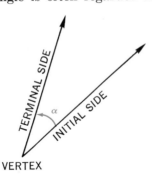

FIGURE 6–1

154

6.2   The trigonometric functions of an angle

Let the positive x-axis of a coordinate system be the initial side of α (Greek letter ăl'pha) and let $P(x, y)$ be some point on its terminal side. Then $OM = x$ is the abscissa of P, $MP = y$

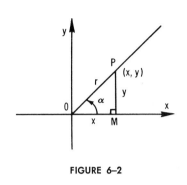

is its ordinate, and $OP = r$ is its distance from the origin. The distance r is defined to be positive. By the Pythagorean Theorem $r = \sqrt{x^2 + y^2}$. An angle such as the one described is in standard position.

The three quantities x, y, and r can be combined into six ratios:

FIGURE 6–2

$\dfrac{x}{y}; \dfrac{y}{x}; \dfrac{x}{r}; \dfrac{r}{x}; \dfrac{y}{r}; \dfrac{r}{y}.$ The values of

these ratios depend upon the measure of angle α; they are functions of α.

Before you learned about a system of coordinates, you had experience with angles in triangles which were not related to axes. In particular, you studied triangles in which one angle was a

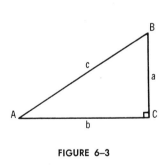

FIGURE 6–3

right angle. We shall often use such triangles and we shall usu- ally letter them as shown in the figure using A, B, and C to desig- nate the vertices (and the angle at that vertex), and a, b, and c to designate the lengths of the opposite sides. The ratios of

the sides are $\dfrac{b}{a}, \dfrac{a}{b}, \dfrac{a}{c}, \dfrac{c}{a}, \dfrac{b}{c}, \dfrac{c}{b}.$ All

right triangles containing acute angles congruent to A and B are similar and thus have equal ratios between their corresponding sides. Therefore, these ratios are determined by the measures of the acute angles and any two congruent angles will have the same ratios as- sociated with them. We can let A and B designate either the angle itself or its measure for the purpose of defining the trigonometric functions. The context in which A or B appears will determine whether we are referring to the angle or its measure.

The values of the preceding ratios are functions of A or of B. Each of the six functions is identified by a name.

$$\text{sine of } A = \sin A$$
$$\text{cosine of } A = \cos A$$
$$\text{tangent of } A = \tan A$$
$$\text{cotangent of } A = \cot A$$
$$\text{secant of } A = \sec A$$
$$\text{cosecant of } A = \csc A$$

Their definitions in terms of α are as follows.

$$\sin \alpha = \frac{\text{ordinate}}{\text{distance}} = \frac{y}{r} \qquad \cos \alpha = \frac{\text{abscissa}}{\text{distance}} = \frac{x}{r}$$

$$\tan \alpha = \frac{\text{ordinate}}{\text{abscissa}} = \frac{y}{x} \qquad \cot \alpha = \frac{\text{abscissa}}{\text{ordinate}} = \frac{x}{y}$$

$$\sec \alpha = \frac{\text{distance}}{\text{abscissa}} = \frac{r}{x} \qquad \csc \alpha = \frac{\text{distance}}{\text{ordinate}} = \frac{r}{y}$$

In terms of acute angle A in a right triangle the above definitions can be interpreted as follows.

$$\sin A = \frac{\text{side opposite}}{\text{hypotenuse}} = \frac{a}{c} \qquad \cos A = \frac{\text{side adjacent}}{\text{hypotenuse}} = \frac{b}{c}$$

$$\tan A = \frac{\text{side opposite}}{\text{side adjacent}} = \frac{a}{b} \qquad \cot A = \frac{\text{side adjacent}}{\text{side opposite}} = \frac{b}{a}$$

$$\sec A = \frac{\text{hypotenuse}}{\text{side adjacent}} = \frac{c}{b} \qquad \csc A = \frac{\text{hypotenuse}}{\text{side opposite}} = \frac{c}{a}$$

The above definitions should be learned in both forms. There is an advantage to the graphical form when studying relations between the functions and in generalizing the functions to study angles of any size. The definitions as applied to the right triangle are helpful in making applications to practical problems.

In right triangle ABC, the functions of B can be readily given and the student should be able to state the functions of B as ratios. Furthermore, the student should recognize the functions with the triangle in any position and with letters other than A, B, and C naming the vertices.

The functions defined above are elementary trigonometric functions, and it is possible to define the following additional functions.

$$\text{versed sine } A = 1 - \cos A$$

$$\text{haversine } A = \frac{1 - \cos A}{2}$$

$$\text{coversed sine } A = 1 - \sin A$$

We do not deal with these special functions in this course since they have very limited application.

Exercises

In the following exercises all angles are in standard position.

1. The point (4, 3) lies on the terminal side of angle α. Write the numerical values of the six trigonometric functions of α. (*Hint:* First find the value of r.)

2. The point (5, 12) lies on the terminal side of β (Greek letter beta). Write the values of the six trigonometric functions of β.

3. A right triangle has sides that are 7 inches, 24 inches, and 25 inches. Write the six trigonometric functions of the angle opposite the shorter leg. Write the functions of the angle opposite the longer leg.

4. The point (15, 8) is on the terminal side of an angle. Write the values of the six functions of the angle.

5. The point (3, 4) lies on the terminal side of X. The point (6, 8) lies on the terminal side of Y. Compare the six trigonometric ratios of X and Y.

6. The altitude to the hypotenuse of a right triangle is 6 inches long. If the hypotenuse is divided into segments 4 inches and 9 inches long by the altitude, find the values of the trigonometric functions of the acute angles of the right triangle.

6.3   Functions of the special angles: $0°$, $30°$, $45°$, $60°$, $90°$

It is possible to find numerical values of the trigonometric functions of certain angles from relationships learned in geometry. You will recall that the hypotenuse of a $30°$–$60°$ right triangle is twice the length of the shorter leg. This fact enables us to draw such a triangle and read the ratios directly. If A is $30°$ and C is the right angle, then the hypotenuse c can be set equal to 2 units and the side opposite angle A has measure 1.

The adjacent side b has measure $\sqrt{3}$ units, found by applying the Pythagorean Theorem. We can thus write the values of the six trigonometric functions of 30° directly. Since B is 60°, we can also write the values for 60°.

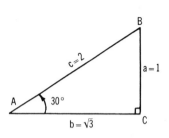

FIGURE 6–4

In an isosceles right triangle A and B are 45° angles. The ratio of the sides is $1 : 1 : \sqrt{2}$. Once again the six ratios may be read directly from the figure.

In finding the values of functions of 0° and 90° it is convenient to use the graph. It is assumed that the positive x-axis is the initial side. An angle of 0° has point $P(1, 0)$ on the terminal side. Since $r = \sqrt{x^2 + y^2}$, we find for 0° that $r = 1$. Referring to the definitions in terms of the graph, values of the six trigonometric functions may be found directly.

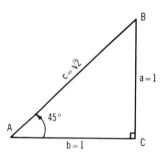

FIGURE 6–5

Similarly, point $P'(0, 1)$ lies on the terminal side of 90° and the values of the functions are immediately determined. Since division by zero is impossible, certain functions are undefined for 0° and 90°.

The following table summarizes the values of the trigonometric functions of 0°, 30°, 45°, 60°, and 90°. The values should be studied and you should be able to give any value either from memory or by making a quick sketch.

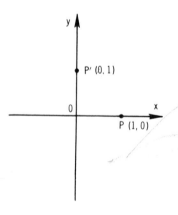

FIGURE 6–6

A	$\sin A$	$\cos A$	$\tan A$	$\cot A$	$\sec A$	$\csc A$
0°	0	1	0	—	1	—
30°	$\dfrac{1}{2}$	$\dfrac{\sqrt{3}}{2}$	$\dfrac{\sqrt{3}}{3}$	$\sqrt{3}$	$\dfrac{2\sqrt{3}}{3}$	2
45°	$\dfrac{\sqrt{2}}{2}$	$\dfrac{\sqrt{2}}{2}$	1	1	$\sqrt{2}$	$\sqrt{2}$
60°	$\dfrac{\sqrt{3}}{2}$	$\dfrac{1}{2}$	$\sqrt{3}$	$\dfrac{\sqrt{3}}{3}$	2	$\dfrac{2\sqrt{3}}{3}$
90°	1	0	—	0	—	1

Exercises

Find numerical values in simplest radical form.

1. $\sin 30° + \cos 30°$

2. $\sin 45° + \cos 45°$

3. $\sin 45° + \cos 60°$

4. $\sin 60° - \cos 60°$

5. $\sin 45° - \sin 90°$

6. $2 \sin 45° - \cos 30°$

7. $\sin 60° + \cos 30° - \tan 45°$

8. $\sin 45° \cos 60° - \tan 30° \sin 90°$

6.4   Line representation of the trigonometric functions

Let a circle be drawn with its center at the origin of a coordinate system and with a radius of 1 unit (perhaps 10 graph units). Then let α be an acute angle in standard position. Then $ON = OP = OR = 1.$

The values of the six trigonometric functions of α can be measured directly from the drawing.

Note that as α changes, the lengths of the following line segments change.

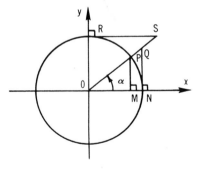

FIGURE 6–7

$$\sin \alpha = \frac{MP}{OP} = \frac{MP}{1} = MP$$

$$\cos \alpha = \frac{OM}{OP} = \frac{OM}{1} = OM$$

$$\tan \alpha = \frac{NQ}{ON} = \frac{NQ}{1} = NQ$$

$$\sec \alpha = \frac{OQ}{ON} = \frac{OQ}{1} = OQ$$

Since $\angle RSO \cong \alpha$, we have

$$\cot \alpha = \frac{RS}{OR} = \frac{RS}{1} = RS$$

$$\csc \alpha = \frac{OS}{OR} = \frac{OS}{1} = OS$$

You can study the variation of the functions by letting α increase from $0°$ to $90°$ and examining the line segments. Approximate values of the functions can be found if a careful drawing is made for any given angle. A comparable drawing can be made if the angle is greater than $90°$.

A study of the cyclic nature of the functions can be made by considering the drawing above as radius OP rotates from $\alpha = 0°$ to $\alpha = 360°$, and beyond.

Exercises

1. Find the approximate value of each of the functions of $30°$ by direct measurement on a drawing.

2. Find the approximate value of each of the functions of $53°$ by direct measurement on a drawing.

3. If $\tan x = \frac{7}{11}$, find the number of degrees in angle x to the nearest degree by graphing.

4. Construct angle T if $\cos T = \frac{3}{5}$.

5. Construct angle H if $\tan H = \frac{7}{4}$.

6. Sin $y = \frac{15}{17}$. Find the value of each of the other functions of y.

7. If $\sin x = \frac{\sqrt{3}}{2}$, find $\tan x$.

8. If $\cot y = 1$, find $\sin y$.

9. Construct an angle whose tangent is 3 and give the remaining values of the functions of the angle.

10. Find the size of angle R if sin R = .56. (Nearest degree.)

6.5   Table of natural values of the functions

You have seen that approximations of the values of the functions of a given acute angle can be found by drawing the angle in a right triangle, measuring the sides, and computing their ratio. Also, the angle may be drawn as a central angle in a unit circle (with radius 1) and the lengths of certain line segments associated with the angle measured to give approximate values of the functions. There are other more accurate ways to find numerical values of the functions. (See Section 11.6.) These values are frequently needed and hence they have been computed carefully and tabulated. Table 2 gives values of the sine, cosine, tangent, and cotangent of acute angles for every ten minutes from 0° to 90°, accurate to four decimal places.

You should learn to read this table in two ways. First, when an acute angle is designated, you should be able to find any one of the values of the four given functions from the table. Second, you should be able to find the angle, to the nearest ten minutes, corresponding to any given function value. Notice that the table is arranged so that angles from 0° to 45° are read down, on the left-hand side; the headings at the top of each page are used for these values. The angles from 45° to 90° are read up, on the right-hand side of the table; the headings at the bottom of each page are used for these values. The secant and cosecant functions are not tabulated in this book because it is seldom necessary to use them. Their values may be calculated if necessary.

EXAMPLE 1. Find the value of cos 19° 30′.

Solution. In the left-hand column find 19° 30′. Under the heading *cosine* we find .9426 opposite 19° 30′. Hence, cos 19° 30′ = .9426.

EXAMPLE 2. Find the natural value of tan 72° 12′.

Solution. Since the values in Table 2 are given to the nearest ten minutes, interpolation procedures will be required. (See Appendix, A.7.) The following form is suggested.

$$10'\left[\,_{2'}\left[\begin{array}{l} \tan 72° 20' = 3.1397 \\ \tan 72° 12' = \underline{\quad\quad} \\ \tan 72° 10' = 3.1084 \end{array}\right]x\,\right].0313$$

The unknown difference (x) may be easily found by solving the following proportion.

$$\frac{2}{10} = \frac{x}{.0313}$$

Working entirely in decimals

.0313
$\times$ .2
———
.00626 = .0063 (correct to 4 decimal places)

or $x = .0063$ approximately

Thus, $\tan 72° 12' = 3.1084 + .0063 = 3.1147$.

EXAMPLE 3. In the equation $\sin x = .2672$ solve for x.

Solution. We look down the column under the heading *sine* until we come to the value .2672. Opposite this number in the left-hand column we find 15° 30'. Hence, $x = 15° 30'$.

EXAMPLE 4. If $\sin x = .5525$, find x to the nearest minute.

Solution. Interpolation will be required.

$$10'\left[\,_{y'}\left[\begin{array}{l} \sin 33° 40' = .5544 \\ \sin x \quad\quad = .5525 \\ \sin 33° 30' = .5519 \end{array}\right]\begin{array}{l}.0025 \\ .0006\end{array}\,\right]$$

The proportion can be written

$$\frac{y}{10'} = \frac{.0006}{.0025} \quad \text{or} \quad y = \frac{.0006}{.0025} \times 10' = 2.4'$$

$$y = 2.4'$$

Hence, $x = 33° 30' + 2' = 33° 32'$.

Exercises

Find values of the indicated functions in Exercises 1–9.

1. $\sin 26°$
2. $\cos 17° 30'$
3. $\tan 39°$
4. $\cot 11° 40'$
5. $\sin 56° 25'$
6. $\cos 72° 53'$
7. $\sin 86° 27'$
8. $\cos 47° 14'$
9. $\tan 88° 39'$

Give the acute angle value of x to the nearest minute in Exercises 10–18.

10. $\sin x = .0872$
11. $\tan x = .3153$
12. $\cos x = .8601$

13. $\cot x = 2.300$ **15.** $\sin x = .9219$ **17.** $\cot x = 1.2555$

14. $\tan x = 2.300$ **16.** $\cos x = .0562$ **18.** $\sin x = .7224$

6.6   Fundamental identities—cofunctions

As you have no doubt noticed, the six trigonometric functions can be paired so that a function is associated with a cofunction, that is, the prefix *co-* is found in three of the functions. The pairs are

sine	tangent	secant
and	and	and
cosine	cotangent	cosecant

We shall investigate the relation of a cofunction to the corresponding function.

An inspection of the drawing of a right triangle reveals that

$$\sin A = \cos B = \frac{a}{c}$$

$$\tan A = \cot B = \frac{a}{b}$$

$$\sec A = \csc B = \frac{c}{b}$$

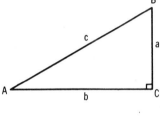

FIGURE 6–8

Angle A is the complement of angle B and the prefix *co-* comes from the first two letters of the word complement. Since $B = (90° - A)$ we can write

$$\sin A = \cos (90° - A) \qquad \cos A = \sin (90° - A)$$
$$\tan A = \cot (90° - A) \qquad \cot A = \tan (90° - A)$$
$$\sec A = \csc (90° - A) \qquad \csc A = \sec (90° - A)$$

> **Principle:** *Any function of an acute angle is equal to the cofunction of the complement of the angle.*

Exercises

Exercises 1–3 refer to the drawing in Figure 6–8.

1. If $\sin A = \dfrac{\sqrt{3}}{3}$, what is the value of $\cos B$?

2. If $\tan B = 1.7$, what is $\cot A$?

3. If $\cos A = .109$, what is $\sin (90° - A)$?

4. Given $\tan 30° = \dfrac{\sqrt{3}}{3}$, what is $\cot 60°$?

5. Given $\sin 45° = \dfrac{\sqrt{2}}{2}$, find $\cos 45°$.

6. If $\tan 69° = 2.605$, what is $\cot 21°$?

7. If $\cos 11° = .9816$, what is $\sin 79°$?

8. If $\tan 84° = 9.514$, find $\cot 6°$.

6.7   Fundamental identities—reciprocally related functions

Inspection of the definitions of the trigonometric functions shows the following important reciprocal relations.

$$(1) \quad \sin A = \frac{1}{\csc A} \qquad \csc A = \frac{1}{\sin A} \qquad \sin A \csc A = 1$$

$$(2) \quad \cos A = \frac{1}{\sec A} \qquad \sec A = \frac{1}{\cos A} \qquad \cos A \sec A = 1$$

$$(3) \quad \tan A = \frac{1}{\cot A} \qquad \cot A = \frac{1}{\tan A} \qquad \tan A \cot A = 1$$

These relations should be recognized in any of the above forms.

Exercises

1. Given $\sin A = \dfrac{1}{2}$, find $\csc A$.

2. If $\cos B = \dfrac{\sqrt{3}}{2}$, find $\sec B$.

3. If $\tan C = \dfrac{\sqrt{2}}{5}$, find $\cot C$.

4. Find $\sin X$ if $\csc X = 3$.

5. Find $\cos Y$ if $\sec Y = 1.7$.

6. What is $\cot M$ if $\tan M = 1$?

7. What is $\cos A$ if $\sec A = 1.3$?

In Exercises 8-13 use Table 2.

8. Show that $\sin 30° \csc 30° = 1$.

9. Show that $\cos 45° \sec 45° = 1$.

10. Show that $\tan 60° \cot 60° = 1$.

11. Find $\sin 30° \cos 60°$.

12. Find $\cos 50° \sec 40°$.

13. Find $\tan 15° \cos 15° \csc 15°$.

6.8   Fundamental identities—quotient and Pythagorean relations

From the definitions, we know

that $\sin A = \dfrac{a}{c}$ and $\cos A = \dfrac{b}{c}$.

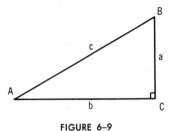

FIGURE 6–9

The quotient $\dfrac{\sin A}{\cos A} = \dfrac{\dfrac{a}{c}}{\dfrac{b}{c}} = \dfrac{a}{b}$.

But $\tan A = \dfrac{a}{b}$. Thus,

$$\frac{\sin A}{\cos A} = \tan A \quad \text{or} \quad \sin A = \cos A \tan A$$

Similarly,

$$\frac{\cos A}{\sin A} = \cot A \quad \text{or} \quad \cos A = \sin A \cot A$$

The above are known as the quotient relations of the trigonometric functions.

In a right triangle (see Figure 6–9), we know that $a^2 + b^2 = c^2$. We can transform this formula by dividing each member by c^2. We get

$$\frac{a^2}{c^2} + \frac{b^2}{c^2} = 1 \quad \text{or} \quad \left(\frac{a}{c}\right)^2 + \left(\frac{b}{c}\right)^2 = 1$$

Replacing the ratios by the proper functions, we have

(1) $$\sin^2 A + \cos^2 A = 1$$

If we transform the Pythagorean Formula by dividing by b^2, we get

$$\frac{a^2}{b^2} + 1 = \frac{c^2}{b^2} \quad \text{or} \quad \left(\frac{a}{b}\right)^2 + 1 = \left(\frac{c}{b}\right)^2$$

Replacing the ratios by the proper functions, we have

(2) $$\tan^2 A + 1 = \sec^2 A$$

If we divide by a^2, we get

$$1 + \frac{b^2}{a^2} = \frac{c^2}{a^2} \quad \text{or} \quad 1 + \left(\frac{b}{a}\right)^2 = \left(\frac{c}{a}\right)^2$$

Replacing the ratios by the proper functions, we have

(3) $$1 + \cot^2 A = \csc^2 A$$

The last three identities are known as the Pythagorean relations. The first of these should be memorized; the other two should become familiar as they are used. Each of the equations may be transformed algebraically into alternate forms.

EXAMPLE 1. If $\sin A = .5$, find $\cos A$.

Solution. $\sin^2 A + \cos^2 A = 1$. Thus, $\cos A = \sqrt{1 - \sin^2 A}$. Replacing $\sin A$ by $.5$, we get $\cos A = \sqrt{1 - (.5)^2} = \sqrt{1 - .25} = \sqrt{.75}$. An approximate value of $\cos A$ is $.87$.

EXAMPLE 2. If $\tan A = \dfrac{3}{4}$, find $\sec A$.

Solution. The identity we shall use is $\tan^2 A + 1 = \sec^2 A$.

$$\sec A = \sqrt{\tan^2 + 1} = \sqrt{\left(\frac{3}{4}\right)^2 + 1} = \sqrt{\frac{25}{16}} = \frac{5}{4} \quad \text{or} \quad 1.25.$$

LIST OF FUNDAMENTAL IDENTITIES

Cofunction Relations:

$$\sin A = \cos (90° - A) ; \quad \cos A = \sin (90° - A)$$
$$\tan A = \cot (90° - A) ; \quad \cot A = \tan (90° - A)$$
$$\sec A = \csc (90° - A) ; \quad \csc A = \sec (90° - A)$$

Reciprocal Relations:

$$\sin A = \frac{1}{\csc A} ; \quad \csc A = \frac{1}{\sin A}$$

$$\cos A = \frac{1}{\sec A} ; \quad \sec A = \frac{1}{\cos A}$$

$$\tan A = \frac{1}{\cot A} ; \quad \cot A = \frac{1}{\tan A}$$

Quotient Relations:

$$\tan A = \frac{\sin A}{\cos A} ; \quad \cot A = \frac{\cos A}{\sin A}$$

Pythagorean Relations:

$$\sin^2 A + \cos^2 A = 1$$
$$\tan^2 A + 1 = \sec^2 A$$
$$\cot^2 A + 1 = \csc^2 A$$

Exercises

1. If $\sin A = \dfrac{4}{5}$, find $\cos A$.

2. If $\cos B = \dfrac{3}{5}$, find $\sin B$.

3. If $\tan A = \dfrac{7}{2}$, find $\sec A$.

4. If $\sec T = \dfrac{5}{3}$, find $\tan T$.

5. Given $\cot X = .8$, find $\csc X$.

6. Given $\cos W = \dfrac{\sqrt{2}}{3}$, find $\sin W$.

7. Given $\tan N = \dfrac{\sqrt{11}}{2}$, find $\sec N$.

8. Given $\cos A = .32$, find $\sin A$. Find $\tan A$. Find $\sec A$.
9. Find $\tan A$ in terms of $\sin A$.
10. Find $\sec A$ in terms of $\cot A$.
11. Find all functions in terms of $\sin A$.
12. Find all functions in terms of $\tan A$.

6.9   Transformation of identities

It may happen that two expressions involving trigonometric functions are equal. As elsewhere in algebra, an equation that is true for all permissible values of the variable is called an *identity*. The identities listed in the preceding section will be accepted as a basis for proving that certain other equations are identities.

Verifying stated relations as identities involves transforming one member of the equation by means of the fundamental identities and the principles of algebra into the same form as the other member. You may transform the left member into the same form as the right member; you may transform the right member into the same form as the left member; or you may transform each member separately into two other forms which are identical. It is important that you *do not* apply an operation that affects both members. For example, you are not permitted to multiply both members by the same quantity. Do you see why?

Sometimes it is advisable to transform each member into one function—sine or tangent, for example—and simplify. Often the simplified forms are identical and the identity has been verified.

EXAMPLE 1. Is the equation $\dfrac{\cos A}{\cot^2 A} = \sin A \tan A$ consistent with the fundamental identities?

Solution. Let us transform the left member by replacing $\cot^2 A$ with $\dfrac{\cos^2 A}{\sin^2 A}$.

Note: There are advantages in arranging the work so that there is a vertical sequence of steps in the transformation of a member. Only one member at a time should be transformed, to avoid confusion of operations.

$$\frac{\cos A}{\cot^2 A} = \sin A \tan A$$

$$\frac{\cos A}{\dfrac{\cos^2 A}{\sin^2 A}} = \sin A \tan A$$

$$\frac{\cos A \, \sin^2 A}{\cos^2 A} = \sin A \tan A$$

$$\frac{\sin^2 A}{\cos A} = \sin A \tan A$$

$$\sin A \left(\frac{\sin A}{\cos A}\right) = \sin A \tan A$$

$$\sin A \tan A = \sin A \tan A$$

The transformation of the left member has produced an expression identical with the given right member and so the given statement is consistent with the fundamental identities. With experience you may be able to condense the steps somewhat. Also, you may omit the member which is not transformed in any step (except the final one) with the understanding that this indicates no change.

EXAMPLE 2. Verify that $\dfrac{\tan A - \sin A}{\tan A + \sin A} = \dfrac{\sec A - 1}{\sec A + 1}$.

Solution. We can transform the left member by replacing $\tan A$ with $\dfrac{\sin A}{\cos A}$ and factoring out $\sin A$ in both the numerator and denominator.

To prove:

$$\frac{\tan A - \sin A}{\tan A + \sin A} = \frac{\sec A - 1}{\sec A + 1}$$

$$\frac{\dfrac{\sin A}{\cos A} - \sin A}{\dfrac{\sin A}{\cos A} + \sin A} =$$

$$\frac{\sin A \left(\dfrac{1}{\cos A} - 1 \right)}{\sin A \left(\dfrac{1}{\cos A} + 1 \right)} =$$

$$\frac{\dfrac{1}{\cos A} - 1}{\dfrac{1}{\cos A} + 1} =$$

$$\frac{\sec A - 1}{\sec A + 1} = \frac{\sec A - 1}{\sec A + 1}$$

Thus the identity has been verified.

EXAMPLE 3. Find a numerical value of some function of S such that $\tan S \cos S = \dfrac{1}{2}$.

Solution. In this case we are not to verify an identity. We can use the fundamental identities to transform the left member, however, so that a solution can be reached.

$$\tan S \cos S = \frac{1}{2}$$

$$\left(\frac{\sin S}{\cos S} \right) \cos S = \frac{1}{2}$$

$$\sin S = \frac{1}{2}$$

At this point we could refer to the tables to find a value of S, but this was not called for in the problem.

Exercises

1. Is the equation $\dfrac{\sin A}{\tan A} = \cos A$ consistent with accepted identities?

2. Is $\sec A \tan A = \sin A$ consistent with accepted identities?

Verify the identities in Exercises 3–20.

3. $\sin^2 A \cot^2 A = (1 - \sin A)(1 + \sin A)$

4. $\tan B = \dfrac{\cos B}{\sin B \cot^2 B}$

5. $\dfrac{\tan V \cos V}{\sin V} = 1$

6. $\sin E \cot E + \cos E \tan E = \sin E + \cos E$

7. $\dfrac{1}{\sec^2 X} + \dfrac{1}{\csc^2 X} - 1 = 0$

8. $\dfrac{\sec A - 1}{\sec A + 1} + \dfrac{\cos A - 1}{\cos A + 1} = 0$

9. $\sin V(1 + \cot^2 V) = \csc V$

10. $\dfrac{\sin (90° - w)}{\cos (90° - w)} = \cot w$

11. $\sec (90° - z) = \dfrac{1}{\sin z}$

12. $1 + \tan^2 (90° - x) = \dfrac{1}{\cos^2 (90° - x)}$

13. $\dfrac{\sin A}{\csc A} + \dfrac{\cos A}{\sec A} = 1$

14. $\dfrac{\sec B}{\cos B} - \dfrac{\tan B}{\cot B} = 1$

15. $\dfrac{1}{\csc^2 w} + \sec^2 w + \dfrac{1}{\sec^2 w} = 2 + \dfrac{\sec^2 w}{\csc^2 w}$

16. $\sec^4 v - \sec^2 v = \dfrac{1}{\cot^4 v} + \dfrac{1}{\cot^2 v}$

17. $\sin^4 X + \cos^2 X = \cos^4 X + \sin^2 X$

18. If $x = r \cos \alpha$, and $y = r \sin \alpha$, show that $x^2 + y^2 = r^2$.

19. If $x = a \cos \theta$ and $y = b \sin \theta$, show that $\dfrac{x^2}{a^2} + \dfrac{y^2}{b^2} = 1$.

20. If $x = a \sec \theta$ and $y = b \tan \theta$, show that $\dfrac{x^2}{a^2} - \dfrac{y^2}{b^2} = 1$.

Find a numerical value of one function of x in Exercises 21–28.

21. $\sin x \sec x = 1$

22. $\sin x = \tan x$

23. $\sin x = 2 \cos x$

24. $\dfrac{\tan x}{\sin x} = \sqrt{2}$

25. $2 \tan x = \cot x$

26. $2 \sin^2 x = 3 \cos^2 x$

27. $1 - \sin^2 x = \dfrac{1}{9}$

28. $1 + \tan^2 x = \sin^2 x + \dfrac{1}{\sec^2 x}$

29. If $\sin \alpha = \dfrac{1}{3}$, find the value of $\dfrac{\cos \alpha \tan \alpha}{\csc \alpha}$.

30. If $\tan \beta = \dfrac{3}{4}$, find the value of $\dfrac{\sin \beta \sec \beta}{\cot \beta}$.

31. Prove that $\sin x + \cos x \geq 1$ if $0° \leq x \leq 90°$.

32. Prove that $\tan x + \cot x \geq 2$ if $0° \leq x \leq 90°$.

6.10   Definition of radian measure

A *radian* is a central angle whose sides intercept an arc equal in length to a radius of the circle. In nearly all mathematics, except where computation based upon the results of measurement by certain instruments is involved, sizes of angles and arcs are expressed in radian measure. If a central angle is measured in radians, the number of linear units in the inter-cepted arc on a unit circle is equal to the number of radians.

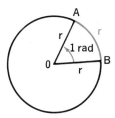

FIGURE 6–10

Since the ratio of the circumference of a circle to its diameter is π, it follows that the central angle of a semicircle is π radians. (The formula for the circumference is derived from this relation; if $\pi = \dfrac{C}{d}$, then $C = \pi d$ or $2\pi r$.) In other words, π radians is equivalent to 180°. It is customary to omit the word "radians" when giving the size of an angle in these units; this is because the ratio $\dfrac{C}{d}$ and all other such ratios are dimensionless (without units).

The proportion relating R radians to D degrees is

$$\frac{R}{\pi} = \frac{D}{180°}$$

If either R or D is known, it is easy to solve the equation for the other. Frequently, angles in radians are left in terms of π.

A conversion factor can be derived for changing from radian measure to degrees. Assume $R = 1$; we then have

$$1 \text{ radian} = \frac{180°}{\pi} = \frac{180°}{3.1416} = 57° \ 17' \ 44.8''$$

Thus, 1 radian = 57.29578 degrees, approximately.

We can also derive a conversion factor to change from degree measure to radians. Suppose $D = 1$; we then have

$$1° = \frac{\pi}{180°} = .01745 \text{ radians, approximately}$$

Formulas for conversion are as follows.

$$D = 57.29578 \, R \quad \text{and} \quad R = .01745 \, D$$

EXAMPLE 1. Transform 78° to radians.

Solution. $R = .01745 \, D$
$\qquad R = .01745 \, (78) = 1.36 \text{ radians}$

EXAMPLE 2. Transform .445 radians to degrees.

Solution. $D = 57.296 \, R$
$\qquad D = 57.296 \, (.445) = 25.5° \text{ or } 25° \ 30', \text{ approximately}$

EXAMPLE 3. Change 60° to radian measure; leave in terms of π.

Solution. $\dfrac{R}{\pi} = \dfrac{60°}{180°}$

$\qquad R = \dfrac{\pi}{3}$

EXAMPLE 4. Convert $\dfrac{5\pi}{6}$ radians to degrees.

Solution.

$$\dfrac{\dfrac{5\pi}{6}}{\pi} = \dfrac{D}{180°}$$

$$D = 180° \frac{5\pi}{6\pi} = 150°$$

Exercises

1. Convert the following degree measures to radian measure. Leave the result in terms of π.

a. 30°	**c.** 270°	**e.** 210°	**g.** 75°
b. 90°	**d.** 135°	**f.** 300°	**h.** 120°

2. Convert the following radian measures to the nearest degree.

    a. $\dfrac{\pi}{4}$　 **b.** $\dfrac{5\pi}{4}$　 **c.** $\dfrac{7\pi}{8}$　 **d.** $\dfrac{11\pi}{6}$　 **e.** $\dfrac{3\pi}{5}$　 **f.** 2　 **g.** .75

3. Convert to radians to the nearest hundredth.

    a. 24°　 **b.** 140°　 **c.** 315°　 **d.** 200°　 **e.** 3.25°　 **f.** 41° 10′

4. Convert to degrees to the nearest 10′.

    a. .50　 **b.** 1.50　 **c.** .62　 **d.** 3.5　 **e.** 10　 **f.** 1.0647

5. Find the number of degrees in

    a. $1 + \pi$　 **b.** $\pi - 2$　 **c.** $2\pi - 5$

6. Find the number of radians in

    a. The sum of the interior angles of a pentagon.
    b. The sum of the interior angles of an octagon.
    c. The sum of the exterior angles of an equilateral triangle.

6.11　Length of an arc

From your study of geometry you know that if two central angles in different circles are congruent, the ratio of the lengths of their arcs equals the ratio of their radii. For example,

if $\angle O \cong \angle Q$, then $\dfrac{\text{arc } AB}{\text{arc } CD} = \dfrac{OA}{QC}$.

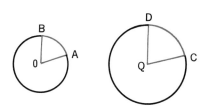

FIGURE 6–11

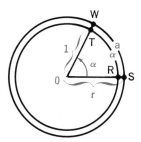

FIGURE 6–12

Now let O be the center of two concentric circles. Let r be the radius of the larger circle, and let the smaller circle be a unit circle with the radius equal to 1. In our derivation it is equally possible for r to be less than 1. If a central angle α is drawn in the two circles it will intercept arc RT on the unit circle and arc SW on the other circle. Suppose arc SW contains a linear units. Arc RT contains α linear units since it is an arc of a unit circle intercepted by central angle α measured in radians. We can write the proportion

$$\frac{a}{\alpha} = \frac{r}{1}$$

or
$$a = r\alpha$$

Hence, $a = r\alpha$, where a is an arc in linear units, r is the radius in the same linear units, and α is the central angle in radians.

The length of any circular arc equals the product of the radius of the circle and the radian measure of the central angle it subtends.

EXAMPLE. Find the length of an arc that subtends a central angle of $32°$ in a circle whose radius is 11.0 inches.

Solution. $32° = .558$ radians, approximately.

Arc $a = r\,\alpha$
$$a = 11.0 \cdot (.558) = 6.14 \text{ inches, approximately}$$

Exercises

1. Find the length of arc in a circle of radius 10 inches if the central angle subtended is

   a. $30°$ **b.** $45°$ **c.** $120°$ **d.** $57° \, 18'$ **e.** $5°$ **f.** $77°$

2. Find the length of an arc whose central angle is $79°$ in a circle whose diameter is 31 inches.

3. If the radius of a circle is 10 inches, what is the central angle in degrees subtended by an arc of 5 inches?

4. The diameter of a circle is 8 inches. Find the central angle in radians and in degrees for each of the following lengths of arc.

   a. 4 inches **b.** 1 inch **c.** 10 inches **d.** 21 inches **e.** 3.25 inches

5. An arc is 6.5 inches long and it subtends a central angle of $\frac{\pi}{4}$. Find the diameter of the circle.

6.12   Functions of angles of any size

Until now we have not considered trigonometric functions of angles greater than $90°$. The definitions in terms of the coordinates of a point on the terminal side of an angle in standard position provide a basis for finding functions of angles of any size, positive or negative. Let $P_1(x_1, y_1)$ be a point in the first quadrant on the terminal side of angle A_1 ; let $P_2(x_2, y_2)$ be a point in the second quadrant on the terminal side of angle A_2 ; let $P_3(x_3, y_3)$ be a

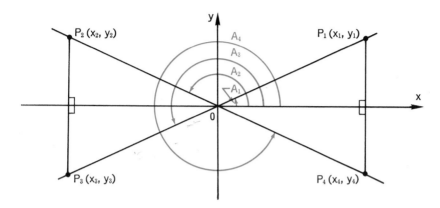

FIGURE 6–13

point in the third quadrant on the terminal side of angle A_3; and let $P_4(x_4, y_4)$ be a point in the fourth quadrant on the terminal side of angle A_4. With each angle in standard position, recall the following ratios.

$$\sin A = \frac{y}{r} \qquad\qquad \csc A = \frac{r}{y}$$

$$\cos A = \frac{x}{r} \qquad\qquad \sec A = \frac{r}{x}$$

$$\tan A = \frac{y}{x} \qquad\qquad \cot A = \frac{x}{y}$$

These definitions apply regardless of the quadrant in which the terminal side lies, or if it lies on a branch of the axes. Since r is defined to be positive, the signs of the functions in each quadrant will be determined by the signs of the coordinates x and y. The following table shows the signs of the six functions in each quadrant. You should verify each sign by considering the signs of the coordinates of a point in each quadrant.

SIGNS OF THE TRIGONOMETRIC FUNCTIONS

| | | Quadrant | | |
Function	First	Second	Third	Fourth
sin A	+	+	−	−
cos A	+	−	−	+
tan A	+	−	+	−
csc A	+	+	−	−
sec A	+	−	−	+
cot A	+	−	+	−

Note that the signs of reciprocally related functions are alike. It is not necessary to memorize this table. When you need to know the sign of a function of any angle, consider the quadrant in which its terminal side lies, recall the signs of the abscissa and ordinate for points in that quadrant, and thus determine the sign of the function.

You will note that a right triangle is formed when a line is drawn from each of the points P_1, P_2, P_3, P_4 perpendicular to the x-axis. The acute angle in this right triangle with its vertex at the origin we shall call the *related angle* α. (Exceptions are quadrantal angles which must be handled in special ways since no right triangle is

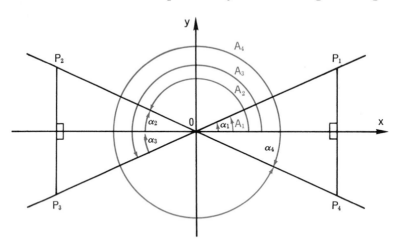

FIGURE 6–14

formed.) For each angle A there is a related angle α. In the first quadrant, $\alpha_1 = A_1$; in the second quadrant, $\alpha_2 = 180° - A_2$ or $\pi - A_2$; in the third quadrant, $\alpha_3 = A_3 - 180°$ or $A_3 - \pi$; in the fourth quadrant, $\alpha_4 = 360° - A_4$ or $2\pi - A_4$.

We can now state: *any trigonometric function, F, of any angle A is equal to the same function of its related angle α with the proper sign prefixed.* In mathematical symbols we have

$$F\ (A)\ =\ \pm\ F\ (\alpha)$$

Since α is a positive angle less than 90° (except for certain quadrantal angles which are considered in the next section), any function of an angle of any size may be reduced to a function of an acute angle and the value found in Table 2. The proper sign for the given function can be selected from the table on page 176 or can be determined by the signs of the coordinates in the quadrant where the terminal side of the angle lies.

EXAMPLE 1. Find sin 120° in terms of the sine of an acute angle.

Solution. Since the terminal side of 120° is in the second quadrant, the related angle $\alpha = 180° - 120° = 60°$. Therefore, sin 120° = +sin 60°, the plus sign being used because the ratio of the ordinate y to the distance r of a point in the second quadrant is positive.

EXAMPLE 2. Find cos 220° in terms of the cosine of an acute angle.

Solution. 220° terminates in the third quadrant; therefore, the related angle $\alpha = 220° - 180° = 40°$. Hence, cos 220° = −cos 40°. The result is negative because we have seen that the cosine is negative if the terminal side of the angle is in the third quadrant.

EXAMPLE 3. Find tan 307° in terms of a function of an acute angle.

Solution. $\alpha = 360° - 307° = 53°$
tan 307° = −tan 53°

EXAMPLE 4. Find sin (−60°) in terms of the sine of a positive acute angle.

Solution. The terminal side of −60° lies in the fourth quadrant and the angle is equivalent to 300°. Thus $\alpha = 360° - 300° = 60°$ and we have

$$\sin\ (-60°)\ =\ -\sin 60°$$

The student should investigate the signs of other functions of negative angles. Can you show that sin (−A) = − sin A and cos (−A) = cos A for all angles A? The sine is an odd function and the cosine is an even function.

EXAMPLE 5. Find $\cos \frac{3\pi}{4}$ in terms of a function of an acute angle.

Solution. $\frac{3\pi}{4}$ terminates in the second quadrant; thus,

$\alpha = \pi - \frac{3\pi}{4} = \frac{\pi}{4}$. Hence, $\cos \frac{3\pi}{4} = -\cos \frac{\pi}{4}$ or $-\cos 45°$.

Exercises

Express Exercises 1–12 in terms of the same function of an angle less than 90°.

1. sin 135°	**5.** sin 340°	**9.** csc 311°
2. cos 210°	**6.** cos 175°	**10.** sin 195°
3. tan 320°	**7.** tan 204°	**11.** cos 351°
4. cot 260°	**8.** sec 142°	**12.** cot 96°

Express Exercises 13–21 in terms of a function of an angle less than 45°. (Hint: *Use cofunctions when necessary.*)

13. cot 310°	**16.** cos 310°	**19.** cos 355°
14. cos 100°	**17.** sec 125°	**20.** tan 262°
15. tan 240°	**18.** sin 305°	**21.** csc 73°

Express Exercises 22–30 in terms of functions of positive angles less than 90°.

22. sin (−30°)	**25.** cot (−80°)	**28.** tan (−200°)
23. tan (−50°)	**26.** sin (−100°)	**29.** sec (−135°)
24. cos (−20°)	**27.** cos (−150°)	**30.** sin (−300°)

31. Evaluate the functions in Exercises 1–30 by referring to the table of values of the natural functions.

6.13   Values of functions of quadrantal angles: 0°, 90°, 180°, 270°, 360°

We have already determined the special values of functions of 0° and 90°. (See Section 6.3.) In a like manner, we can find values of functions of other quadrantal angles. We can omit special consideration of 360° because it is equivalent to 0°. A point (−1, 0)

on the terminal side of a 180° angle gives the values $x = -1$, $y = 0$, $r = +1$. Thus,

$$\sin 180° = \frac{0}{+1} = 0$$

$$\cos 180° = \frac{-1}{+1} = -1$$

$$\tan 180° = \frac{0}{-1} = 0$$

$$\sec 180° = \frac{+1}{-1} = -1$$

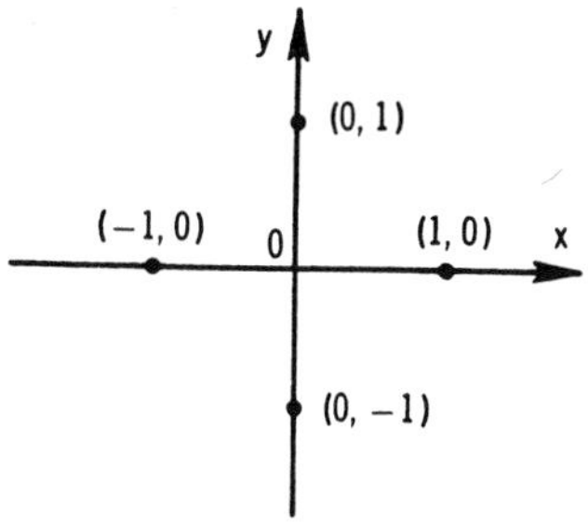

FIGURE 6–15

The cot 180° and csc 180° are not defined because division by zero is impossible.

Similarly,

$$\sin 270° = \frac{-1}{+1} = -1$$

$$\cos 270° = \frac{0}{+1} = 0$$

$$\cot 270° = \frac{0}{-1} = 0$$

$$\csc 270° = \frac{+1}{-1} = -1$$

The tan 270° and sec 270° are not defined.

The following table summarizes values of the functions of quadrantal angles.

VALUES OF FUNCTIONS OF QUADRANTAL ANGLES

Angle	sin	cos	tan	csc	sec	cot
0	0	1	0	—	1	—
90° or $\frac{\pi}{2}$	1	0	—	1	—	0
180° or π	0	-1	0	—	-1	—
270° or $\frac{3\pi}{2}$	-1	0	—	-1	—	0
360° or 2π	0	1	0	—	1	—

Exercises

1. Prove that $\sin (k \cdot 90°) = 0$ if k is any even integer.

2. Prove that $\cos(k\ 90°) = 0$ if k is any odd integer.

3. For what values of k does $\tan(k\ 90°) = 0$? For what values of k is $\tan(k\ 90°)$ undefined?

4. For what values of k is $\sin(k\ 90°) = 1$? $\cos(k\ 90°) = 1$?

5. For what values of k is $\sin(k\ 90°) = \csc(k\ 90°)$?

6.14 Functions of angles in the form ($k\ 90° \pm a$)

Every non-quadrantal angle can be expressed in the form $(k\ 90° \pm a)$ where k is an integer and a is a positive angle less than 90°. For example, $210° = 2 \cdot 90° + 30°$ in which $k = 2$ and $a = 30°$. We could also write $210° = 3 \cdot 90° - 60°$ in which $k = 3$ and $a = 60°$. It is clear that if k is an even integer, then a is the related angle defined in Section 6.12. If k is an odd integer, then a is the *complement* of the related angle. These relations enable us to simplify functions of angles which are in the form $(k\ 90° \pm a)$ or that are put in this form.

Rule I. Given $F(k\ 90° \pm a)$, if k is an *even* integer, then the given function equals $\pm$ the *same function* of a.

Rule II. Given $F(k\ 90° \pm a)$, if k is an *odd* integer, then the given function equals $\pm$ the *cofunction* of a.

In each rule the sign of the result is determined by the quadrant in which the terminal side lies. The given function F, not the cofunction if Rule II is applied, determines the sign of the simplified form.

EXAMPLE 1. Simplify $\sin 250°$.

Solution. (a) $\sin 250° = \sin(2 \cdot 90° + 70°) = -\sin 70°$
(b) $\sin 250° = \sin(3 \cdot 90° - 20°) = -\cos 20°$

Are the results equivalent?

EXAMPLE 2. Simplify $\cos(270° - x)$.

Solution. $\cos(270° - x) = \cos(3 \cdot 90° - x) = -\sin x$

EXAMPLE 3. Simplify $\tan(2\pi - \alpha)$. (It is assumed here that α is expressed in radians.)

Solution. $\tan(2\pi - \alpha) = -\tan \alpha$

EXAMPLE 4. Simplify $\sin(x - 180°)$.

Solution. $\sin (x - 180°) = \sin (-2 \cdot 90° + x) = -\sin x$

The negative sign is chosen because the terminal side lies in the third quadrant if x is acute.

Note: It is assumed in the development of the rules in this section that a is a positive acute angle. The rules hold, however, regardless of the magnitude or sign of a.

Exercises

In Exercises 1–12 simplify by changing the given angle into the form $(k \, 90° \pm a)$ and expressing the result as a function of a.

1. $\sin 100°$	**5.** $\sec 195°$	**9.** $\cos 850°$
2. $\cos 300°$	**6.** $\csc 345°$	**10.** $\cot (-120°)$
3. $\tan 240°$	**7.** $\sin 390°$	**11.** $\sin (-400°)$
4. $\cot 165°$	**8.** $\tan 520°$	**12.** $\tan (-1000°)$

In Exercises 13–21 simplify, using the rules of Section 6.14.

13. $\cos (180° + x)$	**16.** $\cot (90° + x)$	**19.** $\sin (540° - x)$
14. $\tan (270° - x)$	**17.** $\cot (90° - x)$	**20.** $\tan (\pi - x)$
15. $\sin (360° - x)$	**18.** $\cos (450° + x)$	**21.** $\sin (x - 270°)$

6.15   Functions of $(\alpha + \beta)$

Let α be an angle in standard position and let β be an angle adjacent to it as shown in the figure. Then $\angle MOB$ is equal to

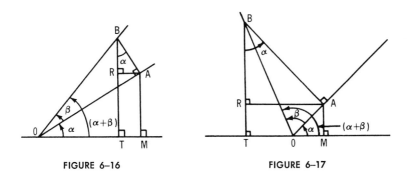

FIGURE 6–16   FIGURE 6–17

$\alpha + \beta$. Figure 6–16 shows the case where $\alpha + \beta < 90°$ and Figure 6–17 shows the case where $\alpha + \beta > 90°$. Select any point B on the terminal side of β and draw perpendiculars to the initial and terminal sides of α at T and A, respectively. From A draw perpendiculars to BT and OT determining points R and M, respectively.

Other cases can be similarly illustrated; the formulas developed are general. Since their sides are respectively perpendicular, $\angle ABR \cong \alpha$.

$$\sin (\alpha + \beta) = \frac{BT}{OB}$$

$$= \frac{BR + RT}{OB} = \frac{BR + AM}{OB} = \frac{BR}{OB} + \frac{AM}{OB}$$

$$= \frac{BR}{OB} \cdot \frac{BA}{BA} + \frac{AM}{OB} \cdot \frac{OA}{OA} = \frac{BR}{BA} \cdot \frac{BA}{OB} + \frac{AM}{OA} \cdot \frac{OA}{OB}$$

$$= \frac{AM}{OA} \cdot \frac{OA}{OB} + \frac{BR}{BA} \cdot \frac{BA}{OB}$$

$$\sin (\alpha + \beta) = \sin \alpha \cos \beta + \cos \alpha \sin \beta \qquad (I)$$

From the same figures

$$\cos (\alpha + \beta) = \frac{OT}{OB}$$

$$= \frac{OM - TM}{OB} = \frac{OM}{OB} - \frac{TM}{OB} = \frac{OM}{OB} - \frac{AR}{OB}$$

$$= \frac{OM}{OB} \cdot \frac{OA}{OA} - \frac{AR}{OB} \cdot \frac{AB}{AB}$$

$$= \frac{OM}{OA} \cdot \frac{OA}{OB} - \frac{AR}{AB} \cdot \frac{AB}{OB}$$

$$\cos (\alpha + \beta) = \cos \alpha \cos \beta - \sin \alpha \sin \beta \qquad (II)$$

Let β be replaced by $-\beta$ in the above formulas. Then $\sin \beta$ must be replaced by $-\sin \beta$. We get

$$\sin (\alpha - \beta) = \sin \alpha \cos \beta - \cos \alpha \sin \beta \qquad (III)$$

$$\cos (\alpha - \beta) = \cos \alpha \cos \beta + \sin \alpha \sin \beta \qquad (IV)$$

EXAMPLE 1. Find sin 75° and cos 75° from the functions of 30° and 45°.

Solution. $\sin 75° = \sin (45° + 30°)$

$$= \sin 45° \cos 30° + \cos 45° \sin 30°$$

$$= \frac{\sqrt{2}}{2} \cdot \frac{\sqrt{3}}{2} + \frac{\sqrt{2}}{2} \cdot \frac{1}{2} = \frac{\sqrt{6} + \sqrt{2}}{4}$$

$$= \frac{2.449 + 1.414}{4} = .966$$

$$\cos 75° = \cos (45° + 30°)$$
$$= \cos 45° \cos 30° - \sin 45° \sin 30°$$
$$= \frac{\sqrt{2}}{2} \cdot \frac{\sqrt{3}}{2} - \frac{\sqrt{2}}{2} \cdot \frac{1}{2} = \frac{\sqrt{6} - \sqrt{2}}{4}$$
$$= \frac{2.449 - 1.414}{4} = .259$$

These values agree with those found in Table 2.

Since $\tan x = \dfrac{\sin x}{\cos x}$, we can develop formulas for $\tan (\alpha \pm \beta)$.

$$\tan (\alpha + \beta) = \frac{\sin (\alpha + \beta)}{\cos (\alpha + \beta)}$$

$$\tan (\alpha + \beta) = \frac{\sin \alpha \cos \beta + \cos \alpha \sin \beta}{\cos \alpha \cos \beta - \sin \alpha \sin \beta}$$

Dividing both numerator and denominator by $\cos \alpha \cos \beta$, assuming $\cos \alpha \neq 0$ and $\cos \beta \neq 0$, we get

$$= \frac{\dfrac{\sin \alpha \cos \beta}{\cos \alpha \cos \beta} + \dfrac{\cos \alpha \sin \beta}{\cos \alpha \cos \beta}}{\dfrac{\cos \alpha \cos \beta}{\cos \alpha \cos \beta} - \dfrac{\sin \alpha \sin \beta}{\cos \alpha \cos \beta}}$$

Thus, $\tan (\alpha + \beta) = \dfrac{\tan \alpha + \tan \beta}{1 - \tan \alpha \cdot \tan \beta}$ (V)

Replacing β by $-\beta$, we get

$$\tan (\alpha - \beta) = \frac{\tan \alpha - \tan \beta}{1 + \tan \alpha \cdot \tan \beta} \tag{VI}$$

EXAMPLE 2. Find $\tan 105°$ from functions of $60°$ and $45°$.

Solution. $\tan 105° = \tan (60° + 45°)$

$$= \frac{\tan 60° + \tan 45°}{1 - \tan 60° \tan 45°}$$

$$= \frac{\sqrt{3} + 1}{1 - \sqrt{3} \cdot 1}$$

$$\tan 105° = -2 - \sqrt{3} = -3.732$$

Exercises

1. Find $\sin 105°$ and $\cos 105°$ from functions of $60°$ and $45°$.
2. Find $\tan 75°$ from functions of $45°$ and $30°$.

3. Find sin 15° and cos 15° from functions of 45° and 30°. Find the same values using functions of 60° and 45°.

4. Find tan 15° by means of Formula VI and compare it with the result obtained by dividing sin 15° by cos 15° found in Exercise 3.

5. Find sin 75° and cos 75° without tables.

6. Find the sine, cosine and tangent of 150° by using the fact that $150° = 180° - 30°$.

7. If $\sin \alpha = \dfrac{4}{5}$ and $\sin \beta = \dfrac{3}{5}$, find $\sin(\alpha + \beta)$. (*Hint:* Draw a right triangle with α as an acute angle and find the length of the adjacent side. Draw a right triangle containing β and find the length of the adjacent side.)

8. If $\sin \alpha = \dfrac{5}{13}$ and $\cos \beta = \dfrac{4}{5}$, find $\cos(\alpha - \beta)$. Find the tan $(\alpha + \beta)$.

9. Show that $\cos(30° - x) + \cos(30° + x) = \sqrt{3} \cos x$.

10. Derive a formula for $\cot(\alpha + \beta)$ in terms of $\cot \alpha$ and $\cot \beta$.

11. Derive a formula for $\sin(\alpha + \beta + \gamma)$ in terms of the functions of α, β, and γ.

12. Show that $\sin(\alpha + \beta) \sin(\alpha - \beta) = \sin^2\alpha - \sin^2\beta$.

6.16   Functions of 2α and $\dfrac{\alpha}{2}$

Formulas may be developed for functions of the double angle 2α and for the half angle $\dfrac{\alpha}{2}$ where α is the measure of any angle. Algebraic substitution is required to find $\sin 2\alpha$, $\cos 2\alpha$, and $\tan 2\alpha$.

If $\alpha = \beta$, Formula (I) becomes

$$\sin(\alpha + \alpha) = \sin \alpha \cos \alpha + \sin \alpha \cos \alpha$$

Thus, $\sin 2\alpha = 2 \sin \alpha \cos \alpha$ (VII)

Formula (II) becomes

$$\cos(\alpha + \alpha) = \cos \alpha \cos \alpha - \sin \alpha \sin \alpha$$

Thus, $\cos 2\alpha = \cos^2 \alpha - \sin^2 \alpha$ (VIII)

or $\cos 2\alpha = 2 \cos^2 \alpha - 1$ (IX)

or $\cos 2\alpha = 1 - 2 \sin^2 \alpha$ (X)

Formula (V) becomes

$$\tan(\alpha + \alpha) = \frac{\tan\alpha + \tan\alpha}{1 - \tan\alpha\,\tan\alpha}$$

Thus, $$\tan 2\alpha = \frac{2\tan\alpha}{1 - \tan^2\alpha} \qquad \text{(XI)}$$

If we let $\alpha = \frac{x}{2}$, then Formula (X) becomes

$$\cos x = 1 - 2\sin^2\frac{x}{2}$$

Solving for $\sin\frac{x}{2}$, we get

$$\sin\frac{x}{2} = \pm\sqrt{\frac{1 - \cos x}{2}} \qquad \text{(XII)}$$

If we let $\alpha = \frac{x}{2}$, Formula (IX) becomes

$$\cos x = 2\cos^2\frac{x}{2} - 1$$

Solving for $\cos\frac{x}{2}$, we get

$$\cos\frac{x}{2} = \pm\sqrt{\frac{1 + \cos x}{2}} \qquad \text{(XIII)}$$

Dividing (XII) by (XIII), we have

$$\tan\frac{x}{2} = \pm\sqrt{\frac{1 - \cos x}{1 + \cos x}} \qquad \text{(XIV)}$$

In applying Formulas (XII), (XIII), and (XIV), the sign of the radical is chosen according to the quadrant in which the terminal side of $\frac{x}{2}$ lies.

It can be shown that alternate forms of (XIV) are

$$\tan\frac{x}{2} = \frac{1 - \cos x}{\sin x} \qquad \text{(XV)}$$

or

$$\tan\frac{x}{2} = \frac{\sin x}{1 + \cos x} \qquad \text{(XVI)}$$

The student should verify that the double sign is not required in (XV) and (XVI).

EXAMPLE 1. Find sin 60° from functions of 30°.

Solution. sin 60° = sin (2 · 30°)

$$= 2 \sin 30° \cos 30° = 2 \cdot \frac{1}{2} \cdot \frac{\sqrt{3}}{2} = \frac{\sqrt{3}}{2}$$

$$= .866$$

The result can be checked by referring to the table of natural values.

EXAMPLE 2. Find cos 15° from functions of 30°.

Solution. $\cos 15° = \cos \dfrac{30°}{2}$

$$= \sqrt{\frac{1 + \cos 30°}{2}} = +\sqrt{\frac{1 + \dfrac{\sqrt{3}}{2}}{2}}$$

$$= \frac{1}{2} \sqrt{2 + \sqrt{3}}$$

$$= .966$$

Exercises

1. Find cos 60° from functions of 30°.
2. Find tan 60° from functions of 30°.
3. Find sin 45° from functions of 90°.
4. Find sin 120°, cos 120° and tan 120° from functions of 60°.
5. Find sin 90°, cos 90° and tan 90° from functions of 45°.
6. If $\sin r = \dfrac{3}{5}$, find sin 2r. Find cos 2r. Find $\sin \dfrac{r}{2}$.
7. If $\tan y = \dfrac{5}{12}$, find tan 2y. Find $\tan \dfrac{y}{2}$.
8. Find sin 22° 30′, cos 22° 30′ and tan 22° 30′ from functions of 45°.
9. Find sin 7° 30′ without tables.
10. Develop a formula for sin 3α in terms of sin α. (*Hint:* 3α = 2α + α.)
11. Develop a formula for cos 3α in terms of cos α.
12. Develop a formula for tan 3α in terms of tan α.
13. Prove that $\tan 3\alpha = \dfrac{3 \tan\alpha - \tan^3\alpha}{1 - 3 \tan^2\alpha}$.
14. Prove formulas XV and XVI from formula XIV.
15. Prove that $\cot \dfrac{\alpha}{2} = \dfrac{\sin\alpha}{1 - \cos\alpha}$.

6.17   Transforming sum or difference of functions to products

If Formulas (I) and (III) of Section 6.15 are added, the sum is

$$\sin (\alpha + \beta) + \sin (\alpha - \beta) = 2 \sin \alpha \cos \beta$$

If we assume $\alpha + \beta = x$ and $\alpha - \beta = y$, then $x + y = 2\alpha$, and $x - y = 2\beta$. Substituting these variables in the above equation, we have

$$\sin x + \sin y = 2 \sin \frac{x + y}{2} \cos \frac{x - y}{2} \qquad \text{(XVII)}$$

If (III) is subtracted from (I), we can write

$$\sin x - \sin y = 2 \cos \frac{x + y}{2} \sin \frac{x - y}{2} \qquad \text{(XVIII)}$$

If (II) and (IV) are added, we can write

$$\cos x + \cos y = 2 \cos \frac{x + y}{2} \cos \frac{x - y}{2} \qquad \text{(XIX)}$$

If (IV) is subtracted from (II), we can write

$$\cos x - \cos y = -2 \sin \frac{x + y}{2} \sin \frac{x - y}{2} \qquad \text{(XX)}$$

The above formulas enable us to transform a sum or difference of functions into a product of functions.

EXAMPLE.   Show that $\cos (60° + x) + \cos (60° - x) = \cos x$.

Solution. By Formula (XIX) we have

$\cos (60° + x) + \cos (60° - x)$

$$= 2 \cos \left(\frac{60° + x + 60° - x}{2} \right) \cos \left(\frac{60° + x - 60° + x}{2} \right)$$

$$= 2 \cos 60° \cos x$$

$$= 2 \cdot \frac{1}{2} \cdot \cos x = \cos x$$

Exercises

1. Show that $\sin (60° + x) + \sin (60° - x) = \sqrt{3} \cos x$.

2. Show that $\cos (45° + x) - \cos (45° - x) = - \sqrt{2} \sin x$.

3. Given $\cos 20 = .9397$, find $\sin 50° + \sin 10°$.

4. Given $\sin 10° = .1736$, find $\cos 40° - \cos 20°$.

5. Simplify $\sin 3A - \sin A$ by one of the formulas in Section 6.17.

6. Express as a product $\sin(-10°) + \sin 20°$.

7. Find the numerical value of $\sin 40° + \sin 20°$ by reading the value of only one function.

8. Express as a sum or a difference of functions.
   a. $2 \sin 40° \sin 20°$ **b.** $2 \sin 40° \cos 20°$

9. Express as a product of two functions.
   a. $\sin 10° + \sin 6°$ **b.** $\cos 10° - \cos 6°$

10. Express as a product of two functions. $\cos 40° + \cos 70°$.

11. From Formula XVII, prove that $2 \sin \alpha \cos \beta = \sin(\alpha + \beta) + \sin(\alpha - \beta)$.

12. Prove that $2 \sin \alpha \sin \beta = \cos(\alpha - \beta) - \cos(\alpha + \beta)$.

13. Prove that $\cos 2\theta = 2 \sin(45° + \theta) \sin(45° - \theta)$.

14. Express $2 \sin 5\alpha \cos 3\alpha$ as the sum of sines.

15. Express $2 \cos 5\alpha \cos 3\alpha$ as the sum of cosines.

6.18   Verification of identities

Now that we have added a number of formulas to the list of fundamental identities, we are able to verify identities that are much more complex.

EXAMPLE. Verify that $\cot A = \dfrac{\sin 2A}{1 - \cos 2A}$.

Solution.

$$\cot A = \frac{\sin 2A}{1 - \cos 2A}$$

$$= \frac{2 \sin A \cos A}{1 - (2 \cos^2 A - 1)}$$

$$= \frac{2 \sin A \cos A}{2 - 2 \cos^2 A}$$

$$= \frac{2 \sin A \cos A}{2(1 - \cos^2 A)}$$

$$= \frac{\sin A \cos A}{\sin^2 A}$$

$$= \frac{\cos A}{\sin A}$$

$$\cot A = \cot A$$

An alternate verification can be easily made if it is recognized that the right member is a reciprocal form of (XV) making the right member equal to $\dfrac{1}{\tan A}$. The equality of the members is then evident.

Exercises

Verify each of the following identities.

1. $\dfrac{1}{2} \sin 2A = \dfrac{\tan A}{1 + \tan^2 A}$

5. $1 + \cos 2A = \dfrac{2}{1 + \tan^2 A}$

2. $\cot \dfrac{x}{2} = \dfrac{1 + \cos x}{\sin x}$

6. $\tan 2x \tan x + 2 = \dfrac{\tan 2x}{\tan x}$

3. $\sin 2B (\cot B + \tan B) = 2$

7. $\csc A \sec A = 2 \csc 2A$

4. $\dfrac{1 - \tan^2 \theta}{1 + \tan^2 \theta} = \cos 2\theta$

8. $\cot X = \dfrac{\sin 2X}{1 - \cos 2X}$

9. $1 - \sin A = \left(\sin \dfrac{A}{2} - \cos \dfrac{A}{2} \right)^2$

10. $\cos^4 A = \dfrac{2 \cos 2A + \cos^2 2A + 1}{4}$

11. $\dfrac{\sin A + \sin B}{\sin A - \sin B} = \dfrac{\tan \dfrac{A + B}{2}}{\tan \dfrac{A - B}{2}}$

12. $\dfrac{\sin \alpha + \sin 3\alpha}{\cos \alpha + \cos 3\alpha} = \tan 2\alpha$

13. $\dfrac{\cos 2A}{1 + \sin 2A} = \dfrac{\cot A - 1}{\cot A + 1}$

14. $\dfrac{\cos A + \sin A}{\cos A - \sin A} = \dfrac{1 + \sin 2A}{\cos 2A}$

15. Show that $a \cos A + b \cos B = c \cos (A - B)$ for any triangle ABC.

16. Prove that $\cot \alpha - \cot \beta = \dfrac{\sin (\beta - \alpha)}{\sin \alpha \sin \beta}$.

Chapter Review

1. Describe the variation of $\sin \theta$ as θ varies from $0°$ to $90°$; from $90°$ to $180°$; from $180°$ to $270°$; from $270°$ to $360°$.

2. Describe the variation of $\cos \theta$ as θ varies in the manner described in Exercise 1.

3. Describe the variation of $\tan \theta$ as θ varies in the manner described in Exercise 1.

4. Express all trigonometric functions of x in terms of $\cos x$.

5. Express each of the following functions in terms of functions of θ .

    a. $\cos (\theta + 180°)$ **c.** $\tan (540° - \theta)$

    b. $\sin (270° - \theta)$ **d.** $\cos (630° + \theta)$

6. If $\sin A = \dfrac{5}{13}$ and A is an acute angle, find the value of each remaining trigonometric function of A.

7. Find numerical values of the following functions.

    a. $\cos 157°$ **e.** $\sin 312° 52'$

    b. $\sin 198°$ **f.** $\tan 95° 14'$

    c. $\tan 315°$ **g.** $\sin (-143° 20')$

    d. $\cos 262° 40'$ **h.** $\cot (-423° 10')$

8. Prove $\tan (\theta + 45°) = \dfrac{1 + \tan \theta}{1 - \tan \theta}$.

9. If $\sin A = \dfrac{12}{13}$ and $\sin B = \dfrac{3}{5}$, find values of the following functions.

    a. $\sin (A + B)$ **d.** $\sin (A - B)$

    b. $\cos (A + B)$ **e.** $\cos (A - B)$

    c. $\tan (A + B)$ **f.** $\cot (A + B)$

10. Find the numerical value of $\sin \dfrac{7\pi}{12}$ without tables.

11. Show that $\sin x < \tan x$ for $0° < x < 90°$ by means of a drawing of angle x in a unit circle.

12. Verify the following identities.

    a. $\tan \theta \csc \theta \cos \theta = 1$

    b. $\cos^2 \theta = \dfrac{\cot^2 \theta}{1 + \cot^2 \theta}$

    c. $\dfrac{1 - \sin A}{1 + \sin A} = (\sec A - \tan A)^2$

    d. $(\tan A - \cot A)^2 + 4 = \sec^2 A + \csc^2 A$

    e. $\cos B \cos (A + B) + \sin B \sin (A + B) = \cos A$

    f. $\dfrac{\tan A - \sin A}{\sec A} = \dfrac{\sin^3 A}{1 + \cos A}$

g. $\dfrac{2 \tan^2 A}{1 + \tan^2 A} = 1 - \cos 2A$

h. $\tan 2A = \tan A + \dfrac{\tan A}{\cos 2A}$

i. $\sin 2A = \dfrac{2 \tan A}{1 + \tan^2 A}$

j. $\dfrac{4 \sin A}{1 - \sin^2 A} = \dfrac{1 + \sin A}{1 - \sin A} - \dfrac{1 - \sin A}{1 + \sin A}$

k. $\tan A + \sin A = \dfrac{\csc A + \cot A}{\csc A \cot A}$

CHAPTER OUTLINE

Graphical Representation of Trigonometric Functions

7

7.1 The graph of the sine function

The sine function generates ordered pairs of numbers of the form $(x, \sin x)$. If x is any angle (or number), then $\sin x$ is a number such that $-1 \leqq \sin x \leqq +1$. We can read directly from Table 2 the ordered pairs for values of x between $0°$ and $90°$. By means of the related angle concept we can easily find ordered pairs for any value of x. Below is a graph of the equation $y = \sin x$. You should find a number of values of $\sin x$ from the graph and compare them with corresponding tabular values.

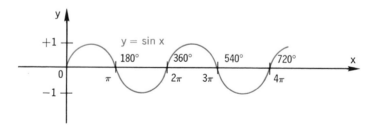

FIGURE 7–1

192

The periodic nature of the function is evident. By *periodic* we mean that values of the function repeat in a fixed cycle, much as a pendulum or clock mechanism repeats its movement.

There are many wave forms that are *sinusoidal;* that is, they are curves that resemble the sine curve. If waves on the surface of a liquid are examined in cross section they exhibit the sine wave form for the simplest case. When a vibrating tuning fork is moved at a uniform velocity, each tip follows the path of a sine wave. If a stylus is attached to a tip, the wave may be traced on paper or on a coated strip of glass. This experiment is sometimes performed in physics classes.

In radiated energy, whether it be sound, light, electricity, heat, or other energy, the wave form is frequently sinusoidal. For example, a pure middle C tone of the musical scale will generate waves in the air at a frequency of 256 cycles (or waves) per second; if the energy of the sound wave is plotted against time, the resulting curve is a sine wave form. Another example is the voltage of the electric current in your home. This voltage (alternating current) is a sine wave form repeated 60 cycles per second in most parts of America. The wave form may be observed directly by means of an electronics instrument called an oscilloscope. If such an instrument is available, a very interesting experiment can be made by examining various wave forms, including the sine wave.

7.2 The graph of the cosine function

The cosine function generates ordered pairs that are of the form $(x, \cos x)$; these pairs can be read directly from the table of natural values for x between $0°$ and $90°$. Note that in the first quadrant the cosine of x decreases as x increases. As for the sine function, by means of the related angle we can find ordered pairs of the cosine function for any value of x. These may be graphed as shown below.

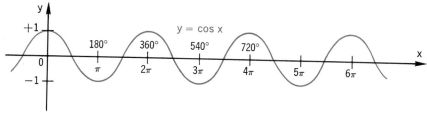

FIGURE 7–2

You should compare values of cos x found in the table with values obtained from a number of points on the graph.

You will note the resemblance of the cosine curve to the sine curve. Actually, since sin $x =$ cos $(90° - x)$, the cosine curve is said to be 90° out of phase with the sine curve; that is, it is a sine curve displaced 90° to the left along the x-axis.

7.3 The graph of the tangent function

The graph of the ordered pairs of the form $(x,$ tan $x)$ increases from 0 to an unlimited positive value as x takes on values from 0° to 90°. The sign of the tangent function is positive in the first quadrant, negative in the second, positive in the third, alternating in successive quadrants in this pattern. This is clear from the graph of $y =$ tan x shown in Figure 7–3. You should compare values of the tangent found from the graph with tabular values for a number of angles.

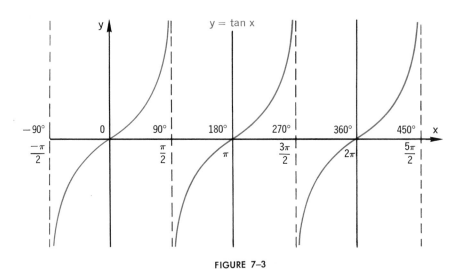

FIGURE 7–3

The vertical lines at $x =$ 90°, 270°, and so on are called *asymptotes*. The tangent function is not defined for $x =$ 90°, but the graph of tan x approaches the asymptote as x approaches 90° from either side.

The graphs of the sine, cosine, and tangent functions are very useful in determining the sign of each function in the various quadrants. A mental picture of the sine curve, for example, makes it very clear that sin x is positive if x is an angle terminating in the first or second quadrants, but negative if x terminates in the third or fourth quadrants. Similarly, a mental picture of the cosine curve shows that the cosine function is positive for angles terminating in the first and fourth quadrants, and negative in the second and third quadrants. The sign of the tangent function alternates from positive to negative in the first and second quadrants and this alternation is repeated in the third and fourth quadrants.

Knowledge of the characteristics of the graphs of the functions is useful also in enabling one to determine quickly the quadrantal values of the functions. At a glance it is obvious that the sine function is zero at $0°$, $180°$, $360°$, and at every integral multiple of $180°$. The maximum value of the sine function is $+1$ at $x = 90°$, and the minimum is -1 at $x = 270°$. Since the graph is periodic and repeats itself every $360°$, other zero, maximum, and minimum points can be readily found. Similar special values of the cosine and tangent functions may be determined by an inspection of the graph. You are encouraged to study the curve forms so that you can picture mentally the shape and critical points of each curve.

Exercises

1. Sketch the graph of the sine function from $x = 0°$ to $x = 360°$. Extend the sketch from $x = 0°$ to $x = -360°$. At what negative value of x is the sine function at a minimum? At a maximum? By examining the curve, give the sign of the value of the function in each quadrant.

2. Sketch the graph of the cosine function from $x = 0°$ to $x = 360°$. Extend the sketch from $x = 0°$ to $x = -360°$. At what negative value of x is the cosine function at a minimum? At a maximum? By examining the curve, give the sign of the value of the function in each quadrant.

3. Sketch the graph of the tangent function from $x = 0°$ to $x = 360°$. How do the first quadrant and the third quadrant compare? Describe the variation of the tangent function in each quadrant. Do the sine and tangent curves coincide at any points when graphed on the same coordinate axes?

4. Sketch the sine and cosine functions on the same axes for values of x from $0°$ to $360°$. At what points do the curves intersect? For what values of x does $\sin x = \cos x$?

5. Sketch the graph of $y = \csc x$ by graphing reciprocal values of $\sin x$. Does the graph exist for $-1 < y < +1$? What are minimum points? What are maximum points? (These are relative maxima and minima.)

6. Sketch the graph of $y = \sec x$ by graphing reciprocal values of $\cos x$. How does the graph of $\sec x$ compare with the graph of $\csc x$? (See Exercise 5.)

7. Sketch the graph of $y = \cot x$ by graphing reciprocal values of $\tan x$. Check by referring to values of $\cot x$ in the table of natural values. Are the signs of the two functions always the same for any given value of x ? For what values of x between $0°$ and $360°$ do the curves of $\cot x$ and $\tan x$ intersect?

8. As a special project, graph the six trigonometric functions on the same axes for values of x from $0°$ to $360°$. It is suggested that different colors for each of the functions will be helpful in distinguishing curves.

7.4 Amplitude and period

You have seen that the maximum absolute value of $\sin x$ or $\cos x$ is $+1$. If we consider an equation of the form $y = A \sin x$, it is clear that every value of $\sin x$ is multiplied by A and hence the maximum value of y is $|A|$, the absolute value of A. Similarly, for $y = A \cos x$, the maximum value of y is $|A|$. We define $|A|$ to be the *amplitude* of each curve. It is a *peak* value.

In the case of $y = A \tan x$, we cannot call $|A|$ the amplitude, for this implies a maximum value and $\tan x$ increases without limit as x approaches values such as $\frac{\pi}{2}$. Therefore the amplitude is defined only for $\sin x$ and $\cos x$ and for no other function.

You have noticed that the graphs of all the trigonometric functions repeat themselves. The sine and cosine functions repeat every $360°$ or 2π radians; the tangent function repeats every $180°$ or π radians. It is more advantageous to express angles in radian measure when dealing with the periodic nature of the functions.

Any function is said to be periodic if, for all x in the domain and for some constant P not equal to zero, $f(x + P) = f(x)$.

The *fundamental period* of the function is the smallest positive value of P for which the relation is true. When we use the term period we shall always mean fundamental period unless otherwise stated.

Now observe that

$$\sin{(x + 2\pi)} = \sin x \text{ for all values of } x$$

Since 2π is the smallest positive real number for which this is true, the fundamental period of the sine function is 2π. Similarly, we note that

$$\cos{(x + 2\pi)} = \cos x \text{ for all values of } x$$

and

$$\tan{(x + \pi)} = \tan x \text{ for all values of } x$$

Thus, the fundamental period of the cosine function is 2π, and the fundamental period of the tangent function is π.

Let us now consider an equation of the form $y = \sin kx$, where k is a constant. Since the fundamental period of the sine function is 2π, we can write

$$y = \sin kx = \sin{(kx + 2\pi)}$$

or

$$y = \sin k\left(x + \frac{2\pi}{k}\right)$$

Thus, the period of $y = \sin kx$ is $\dfrac{2\pi}{k}$. If P represents the fundamental period, we have

$$P = \frac{2\pi}{k} \quad \text{for an equation of the form } y = \sin kx$$

The period of the cosine function is given by the same formula. The period of the tangent function is given by this formula:

$$P = \frac{\pi}{k} \quad \text{for an equation of the form } y = \tan kx$$

EXAMPLE 1. Find the amplitude and period of $y = 3 \sin 2x$.

Solution. $|A| = |3| = 3$. The amplitude is 3.

The period $P = \dfrac{2\pi}{k} = \dfrac{2\pi}{2} = \pi$.

EXAMPLE 2. Find the amplitude and period of $y = -5 \sin \dfrac{x}{4}$.

Solution. $|A| = |-5| = 5$. The amplitude is 5.

$$P = \frac{2\pi}{k} = \frac{2\pi}{\frac{1}{4}} = 8\pi$$

Exercises

1. Show that the period of $y = \cos kx$ is $\dfrac{2\pi}{k}$.

2. Show that the period of $y = \tan kx$ is $\dfrac{\pi}{k}$.

Give the amplitude and period of the equations in Exercises 3–10.

3. $y = 4 \sin x$

4. $y = 2 \cos 2x$

5. $y = 10 \tan 4x$

6. $y = 110 \sin 20x$

7. $y = \dfrac{1}{4} \cos \dfrac{x}{2}$

8. $y = -7 \sin 6x$

9. $y = 2 \sin \pi x$

10. $y = .75 \cos \dfrac{\pi x}{2}$

11. Show that the fundamental period of $y = \cot kx$ is $\dfrac{\pi}{k}$.

12. Show that the fundamental period of $y = \sec kx$ and $y = \csc kx$ is $\dfrac{2\pi}{k}$.

7.5 Sketching graphs of the trigonometric functions

It is a simple task to make a rough sketch of the graph of $y = A \sin kx$ for one complete period by determining five key points. These five points include the three zero points, the maximum point, and the minimum point. A general knowledge of the configuration of the sine curve permits easy roughing in of the curve once these points have been plotted. If greater accuracy is demanded, additional points can be plotted by finding ordered pairs with abscissas lying between the five key points. In a similar manner, the graph of $y = A \cos kx$ and $y = A \tan kx$ may be sketched.

EXAMPLE 1. Sketch one period of the graph of $y = 4 \sin 2x$.

Solution. Compute the amplitude and the period. $|A| = 4$;

$P = \pi$. The five key points are $(0, 0)$, $\left(\dfrac{\pi}{4}, 4\right)$, $\left(\dfrac{\pi}{2}, 0\right)$, $\left(\dfrac{3\pi}{4}, -4\right)$, and $(\pi, 0)$. The sketch is shown below.

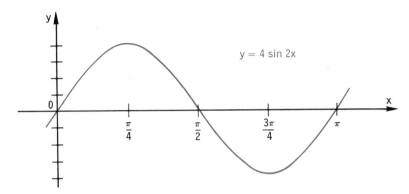

FIGURE 7–4

EXAMPLE 2. Sketch one period of the graph of $y = 3 \cos \dfrac{x}{2}$.

Solution. $|A| = 3$; $P = 4\pi$.

Key points are: $(0, 3)$, $(\pi, 0)$, $(2\pi, -3)$, $(3\pi, 0)$, $(4\pi, 3)$. The sketch is shown below.

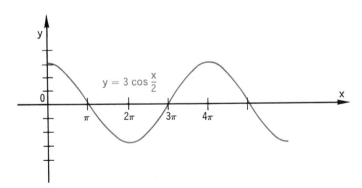

FIGURE 7–5

EXAMPLE 3. Sketch two periods of the graph of $y = 3 \tan 2x$.

Solution. $P = \dfrac{\pi}{2}$. Asymptotes are at $x = \dfrac{\pi}{4}$ and $\dfrac{3\pi}{4}$. Zero points are at $x = 0$, $x = \dfrac{\pi}{2}$, and $x = \pi$. At $x = \dfrac{\pi}{8}$, $y = 3$; and at $x = \dfrac{3\pi}{8}$, $y = -3$, and so on.

The sketch is shown below.

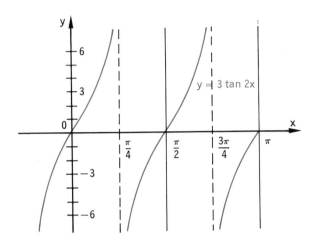

FIGURE 7–6

Exercises

1. Sketch two periods of the graph of $y = 3 \sin x$.

2. Sketch two periods of the graph of $y = \dfrac{1}{2} \cos 2x$.

3. Sketch two periods of the graph of $y = \tan \dfrac{x}{2}$.

4. Sketch the graphs of $y = \sin x$, $y = 2 \sin x$, and $y = \sin 2x$ on the same coordinate axes.

5. Sketch the graph of $y = -\sin x$.

6. Sketch the graph of $y = 6 \sin 4x$.

7. Sketch the graph of $y = -2 \cos x$.

8. Sketch the graph of $y = \sin \left(x + \dfrac{\pi}{2} \right)$.

9. Sketch the graph of $y = \sin \dfrac{1}{x}$. (*Hint:* Start with values of x greater than 2π and decrease the values.)

7.6   Sketching compound functions

Compound functions may be composed of sums or products of trigonometric functions and sometimes sums or products of the trigonometric functions with other function forms. A simple example is $x + \sin x$. If we assume $y = x + \sin x$, then y is a compound function, the sum of a linear and a trigonometric function. If $f(x) = x$ and $g(x) = \sin x$, then $y = f(x) + g(x)$.

We can make a sketch of compound functions such as the above example by sketching $f(x)$ and $g(x)$ on the same coordinate axes and adding the ordinates geometrically. It is necessary only to determine a few critical points and the remainder of the curve of the compound function can be filled in with any desired degree of accuracy by finding additional ordered pairs.

Let us sketch the graph of $y = x + \sin x$. First sketch $y_1 = f(x) = x$ and $y_2 = g(x) = \sin x$ on the same axes.

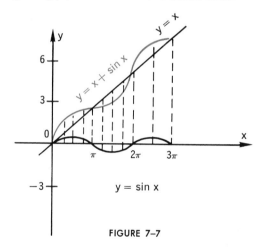

FIGURE 7–7

A pair of drawing compasses can be very helpful in adding the ordinates geometrically. We shall illustrate the sum of two trigonometric functions by means of another example.

EXAMPLE. Sketch the graph of $y = \sin x + \cos x$.

Solution. Suppose $f(x) = \sin x$ and $g(x) = \cos x$. Then $y = f(x) + g(x)$. Sketch the graph of $y_1 = f(x)$ and $y_2 = g(x)$ on the same coordinate axes. Add the ordinates of special values (such as zeros for one of the functions, or the points of intersection) and fill in the graph with a smooth curve. Tables of values may be used to find ordered pairs of the compound function as a check on geometric methods.

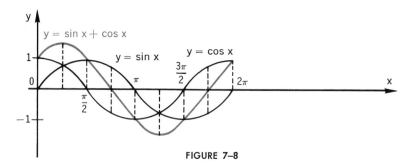

FIGURE 7–8

Functions which have different periods, amplitudes, or phase relationships offer additional difficulties, but the methods remain essentially as outlined above.

Products of functions also increase the difficulty of graphing. A product such as that found in the equation $y = x \sin x$ can be sketched if we consider x as a variable coefficient of $\sin x$. The lines $y = \pm x$ will serve as boundaries for maximum and minimum values of the compound function as shown in Figure 7–9.

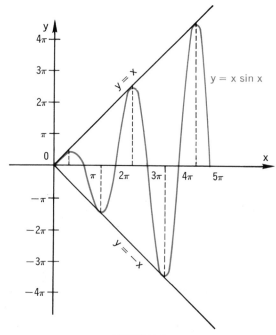

FIGURE 7–9

At a maximum or minimum point $y = \pm\, x$ because these are values of y where $\sin x = \pm\, 1$. At a point where $\sin x = 0$, of course $y = 0$. Knowing these key points enables us to sketch an approximate graph of the compound function.

Exercises

Graph the curves of the compound functions in Exercises 1–8.

1. $y = x + \cos x$ **5.** $y = 2 \sin x + 3 \cos x$

2. $y = x - \sin x$ **6.** $y = \sin x + \sin \left(x + \dfrac{\pi}{2} \right)$

3. $y = 2x + 2 \sin x$ **7.** $y = x \cos x$

4. $y = \cos x - \sin x$ **8.** $y = 2x \sin 2x$

Chapter Review

Find the period and amplitude (where it is defined) for each of the following functions.

1. $y = 4 \cos 2x$ **4.** $y = 15 \sin \dfrac{3}{2} x$

2. $y = -7 \sin 5x$ **5.** $y = -\sqrt{3} \cos (x - \pi)$

3. $y = 2 \tan .5x$ **6.** $y = 5 \cot \dfrac{x}{2}$

Sketch the graph of each function for at least two periods.

7. $y = \dfrac{1}{2} \sin 2x$ **10.** $y = -3 \sin x$

8. $y = 3 \cos \dfrac{x}{2}$ **11.** $y = 2 \sin x - \cos x$

9. $y = 2 \tan 2x$ **12.** $y = x + 2 \sin 2x$

CHAPTER OUTLINE

7.1   The graph of the sine function

7.2   The graph of the cosine function

7.3   The graph of the tangent function

7.4   Amplitude and period

7.5   Sketching graphs of the trigonometric functions

7.6   Sketching compound functions

Applications of Trigonometry   8

8.1   Right triangles

Let us suppose that a civil engineer is given the job of laying out a cloverleaf intersection between two major highways. He must design the grade so that one highway will pass over the other at the proper elevation. The radii of the interchange loops, the transition curves to the highways, and the bank of the curves must all be designed so that a certain speed will be safe. If the highways do not intersect at right angles the problem is further complicated. The engineer must make use of many branches of mathematics in solving such a problem, but applications of the trigonometric functions will play a prominent part.

There are numerous problems more or less difficult than that facing the engineer that can be represented by geometrical drawings in which certain line segments and angles are known and other line segments and angles are desired. Many of these problems can be solved by means of the trigonometric functions. We shall first consider the applications of trigonometry to right triangles and later to any triangle and other more complex figures.

Since the functions were defined in a manner adaptable to angles and sides of a right triangle, the application of trigonometry to such situations is quite direct. Generally two elements are known (a side and an angle, or two sides); the length of a side or the size of an angle is desired. Some examples will illustrate the application of trigonometry to simple practical situations.

EXAMPLE 1. A utility pole is supported by a cable attached to it at the top and anchored in a concrete block at ground level a distance of 12 feet from the base of the pole. If the angle between the cable and the ground is 73° find the height of the pole and the length of the cable.

Solution. Make a sketch to represent the geometric relations in the problem. Identify the vertices of the triangle with the letters *A*, *B*, and *C*. Place the known values on the figure in the proper positions and then represent the lengths to be found. Let the height of the pole be *h* and the length of the cable be *l*. Write the ratio of the unknown height *h* to the known distance 12 feet and set it equal to the corresponding trigonometric function. The known angle 73° is

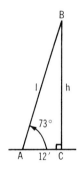

FIGURE 8–1

at *A*. The ratio $\frac{h}{12}$ is equal to $\frac{side\ opposite}{side\ adjacent}$ with respect to $\angle A$, or tangent *A*, or tan 73°. We then have the following result.

$$\frac{h}{12} = \tan 73°$$

$$\frac{h}{12} = 3.2709$$

$$h = 12\ (3.2709)$$

$$h = 39 \text{ feet, approximately}$$

Similarly, we can find the length of the cable by writing the equation:

$$\frac{12}{l} = \cos 73°$$

$$\frac{12}{l} = .2924$$

$$l = \frac{12}{.2924}$$

$$l = 41 \text{ feet, approximately}$$

EXAMPLE 2. A 22-foot ladder leans against a vertical wall of a building making an angle of 16° with the wall. Assuming level ground, how far from the base of the building is the foot of the ladder? How high does the ladder reach on the wall?

Solution. Make a drawing and place known values in the proper locations. Let x be the distance from the foot of the ladder to the base of the wall and let y be the height that the ladder reaches on the wall. We can write the ratio as follows.

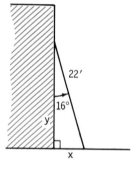

$$\frac{x}{22} = \sin 16°$$

$$x = 22 \, (.2756)$$

$$x = 6.06 \text{ feet} \quad \text{or} \quad 6 \text{ ft. } 1 \text{ in., approximately}$$

Also, $\dfrac{y}{22} = \cos 16°$

$$y = 22 \, (.9613)$$

$$y = 21.1 \text{ ft.} \quad \text{or} \quad 21 \text{ ft. } 1 \text{ in., approximately}$$

FIGURE 8–2

In problems where an observer is involved there is frequently given an *angle of elevation* or an *angle of depression*.

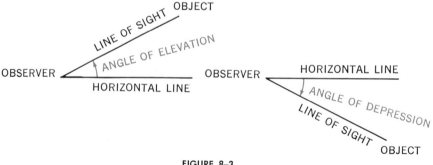

FIGURE 8–3

The figures show that an angle of elevation is the angle between a horizontal line and the line of sight from the observer to an object at a higher level. An angle of depression is the angle between a horizontal line and the line of sight from the observer to an object at a lower level.

EXAMPLE 3. When the angle of elevation of the sun is 27° the shadow of a tree is 75 feet long. How tall is the tree?

Solution. Make a sketch. Let h be the height of the tree.

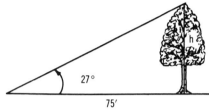

$$\frac{h}{75} = \tan 27°$$
$$h = 75 \,(.5095)$$
$$h = 38 \text{ feet approximately}$$

FIGURE 8–4

EXAMPLE 4. A picture frame is 32 inches long and 20 inches wide. What angle does the diagonal make with the longer side?

Solution. Make a sketch. Let A be the angle to be found.

Then $\tan A = \dfrac{20}{32}$
$$\tan A = .6250$$
$$A = 32° \, 0' \text{ approximately}$$

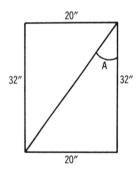

FIGURE 8–5

In a trigonometry problem you may be asked to "solve the triangle." By this we mean you are to find the sides or angles that are unknown. For example, in a right triangle, if one acute angle and a side are given, when you are asked to solve the triangle, the remaining two sides and the other acute angle are to be found.

Exercises

In Exercises 1–3 assume that C is the right angle.

1. Solve right triangle ABC, given $a = 21.0$ cm. and $c = 30.0$ cm.

2. Solve right triangle ABC, given $A = 41°\ 0'$ and $b = 7.44$ inches.

3. In right triangle ABC, $a = 31.2$ inches and $c = 42.4$ inches. Find the angle at A to the nearest minute.

4. A ladder is 16.0 feet long, stands on level ground, and rests against a wall at a point 12.0 feet from the ground. How far from the wall is the foot of the ladder, and what angle does the ladder make with the ground?

5. The base angles of an isosceles triangle are $57°\ 30'$, and the base is 7.50 inches long. Find the equal sides and the altitude to the base.

6. A regular hexagon is inscribed in a circle whose diameter is 7.52 inches. Find the length of its apothem (the distance from the center to the midpoint of a side).

7. A regular pentagon has an apothem of 7.43 centimeters. Find the length of a side, and find the radius.

8. A TV tower is 750.0 feet high and casts a shadow 476.0 feet long. Find the angle of elevation of the sun to the nearest minute.

9. A monument is 112.5 feet high and casts a shadow 201.2 feet long. What is the angle of elevation of the sun?

10. A mountain peak is known to be 1826 feet high above the level of a plain. When the angle of elevation of the sun is $27°\ 10'$, the shadow of the mountain just reaches a village on the plain. How far is the village from a point directly beneath the peak and on the level of the plain?

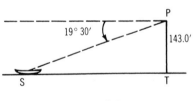

FIGURE 8–6

11. From a point P on a cliff by a lake the angle of depression of a boat is $19°\ 30'$. If the edge of the cliff is 143.0 feet above the lake, how far is the boat from the cliff if the cliff is vertical?

12. Find the bearing of a road that runs directly from A to B, B being 3.0 miles north and 1.7 miles east of A. (The *bearing* of B from A is the positive angle with vertex at A measured clockwise from north to B.)

13. Find the bearing of a road that runs directly from C to D, D being 8.5 miles south and 1.8 miles west of C.

14. A rectangle is 17.5 cm. by 26.2 cm. Find the angle made by the longer side and a diagonal.

15. A 7.4 inch chord subtends a central angle of 41° 0′ in a circle. What is the radius of the circle?

16. The diameter of a circle is 13.4 inches. Find the length of a chord that subtends a central angle of 26° 20′.

17. Find the radius of a circle that is inscribed in an equilateral triangle each of whose sides is 12.6 cm.

18. Find the area of a regular pentagon that is inscribed in a circle whose diameter is 7.3 inches.

19. To find the height of a mountain peak two points, A and B, were located on a plain in line with the peak and the angles of elevation were measured from each point. The angle at A was 36° 40′ and the angle at B was 21° 10′. The distance from A to B was 570 feet. How high is the peak above the level of the plain?

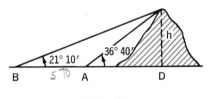

FIGURE 8–7

20. A mountain peak stands near a level plain on which are two farm houses C and D that are in a straight line from the peak. The angle of depression from the peak to C is 49° 42′, and the angle of depression to D is 26° 27′. The peak is known to be 1004 feet above the level of the plain. What is the distance from C to D?

21. A flagpole 40.0 feet high stands on top of a building. From a point P on the street, the angle of elevation of the top of the pole is 54° 54′ and the angle of elevation of the bottom of the pole is 47° 30′. How high is the building?

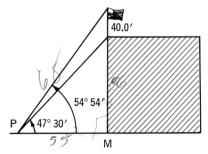

FIGURE 8–8

22. In order to find the height of a chimney CT, the angle of elevation of the top T is measured by means of a transit from point A, whose distance from the chimney is not known. Then

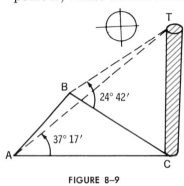

the transit is turned through a horizontal angle of 90° and point B is located. At B the angle of elevation of the top of the chimney is measured again. Find the height of the chimney if CAT is a 37° 17′ angle, CBT is a 24° 42′ angle, and $AB = 173.0$ feet.

FIGURE 8–9

8.2   The Law of Sines

It often happens that the triangle we wish to solve is not a right triangle. Three elements of a triangle (sides or angles) are required to determine a triangle, and to "solve" the triangle means to find the three remaining elements. Of course, three angles do not determine a plane triangle and there are other possible combinations of three elements that do not determine a unique triangle.

Two laws can be developed which will solve any triangle if it is solvable. These are the Law of Sines and the Law of Cosines. There are in existence other trigonometric laws and formulas for solving triangles but these are not required. The other formulas sometimes have certain computational advantages over the Law of Sines or the Law of Cosines.

We shall state and prove the Law of Sines.

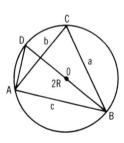

FIGURE 8–10

The ratio of the sines of any two angles of a triangle equals the ratio of the sides opposite them.

For the proof we circumscribe a circle about triangle ABC and draw a diameter through one vertex, vertex B. Let $2R$ be the length of the diameter. Draw AD. Then $\angle D \cong \angle C$, and the measure of $\angle BAD$ is

$90°$. Why? Hence, $\sin C = \sin D = \dfrac{c}{2R}$. Then $\dfrac{c}{\sin C} = 2R$. By drawing diameters from A and C we can likewise show that $\dfrac{b}{\sin B} = 2R$ and $\dfrac{a}{\sin A} = 2R$. Hence

$$\frac{a}{\sin A} = \frac{b}{\sin B} = \frac{c}{\sin C} \qquad \text{(I)}$$

or

$$\frac{a}{b} = \frac{\sin A}{\sin B}, \quad \frac{a}{c} = \frac{\sin A}{\sin C}, \quad \frac{b}{c} = \frac{\sin B}{\sin C}$$

An alternate statement of the Law of Sines is that *the ratio of any side of a triangle to the sine of the opposite angle is a constant.* For example, in a $30°$–$60°$ right triangle with sides 1, $\sqrt{3}$, and 2, the ratios are $\dfrac{1}{\sin 30°} = \dfrac{\sqrt{3}}{\sin 60°} = \dfrac{2}{\sin 90°}.$ (In this case each ratio is equal to 2.)

The Law of Sines can be applied to solve a triangle when any side, the opposite angle, and any other element are known or can be found.

EXAMPLE 1. In triangle ABC it is found that $A = 27° \ 20'$, $B = 64° \ 30'$, and side $c = 320$ centimeters. Find C, a, and b.

Solution. Make a sketch of the triangle.

$C = 180° - 27° \ 20' - 64° \ 30'$
$\quad = 180° - 91° \ 50'$
$\quad = 88° \ 10'$

We can now apply the Law of Sines.

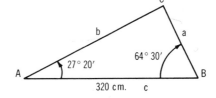

FIGURE 8–11

$$\frac{c}{\sin C} = \frac{a}{\sin A}$$

$$\frac{320}{\sin 88° \ 10'} = \frac{a}{\sin 27° \ 20'}$$

$$a = \frac{320 \sin 27° \ 20'}{\sin 88° \ 10'}$$

$$= \frac{320 \, (.4592)}{.9995}$$

$a = 147$ cm., approximately

Also,
$$\frac{c}{\sin C} = \frac{b}{\sin B}$$

$$\frac{320}{\sin 88° 10'} = \frac{b}{\sin 64° 30'}$$

$$b = \frac{320 \sin 64° 30'}{\sin 88° 10'} = \frac{320 \ (.9026)}{.9995}$$

$$b = 289 \text{ cm. approximately}$$

The above computations may be performed by longhand methods, by logarithms, or by slide rule.

EXAMPLE 2. In triangle ABC it is known that side $c = 17.0$ inches, side $a = 18.0$ inches, and $C = 63° 10'$. Solve the triangle for the remaining elements.

Solution. This is known in geometry as the ambiguous case because, depending upon the values given, there can be no solution, one solution, or two solutions. Fig. 8–12 shows how this construction would be made if $\angle C$ and sides a and c are known. It can happen as in case 1 that the given length c_1 is not long enough to form a triangle. Case 2 shows that a certain length c_2 will form a right triangle with only one solution possible. Case 3 shows that two triangles can be constructed ($\triangle CBA$ and $\triangle CBA'$). Case 4 shows that only one triangle containing C is possible if $c \geqq a$. In a practical situation there may be enough information to tell which of the two solutions are desired in case 3, the ambiguous case.

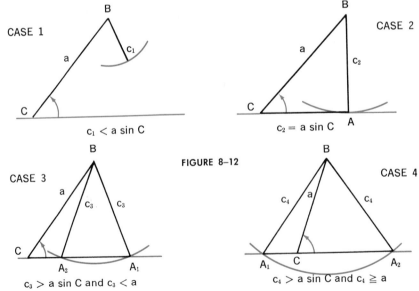

FIGURE 8–12

A test can be performed to determine which case applies. If the measures of two sides, a and c, and the measure of angle C are known, then if

$a \sin C > c$, no triangle is possible;

$a \sin C = c$, one solution is possible—a right triangle;

$a \sin C < c$, two solutions are possible, one with $\angle A$ acute and the other obtuse unless $c \geqq a$, in which case only one triangle is possible.

Now, to continue with EXAMPLE 2, we perform the test: $a \sin C$ is compared to c. We find that $a \sin C = 18 \sin 63° 10' = 18(.8923) = 16.1$, which is less than $c = 17$ inches. Hence, since $c < a$, two solutions are possible. We shall give both solutions.

$$\frac{a}{\sin A} = \frac{c}{\sin C}$$

$$\frac{18}{\tilde{\sin} A} = \frac{17}{\sin 63° 10'}$$

$$\sin A = \frac{18 \sin 63° 10'}{17}$$

$$= \frac{18 \,(.8923)}{17}$$

$$\sin A = .9448$$

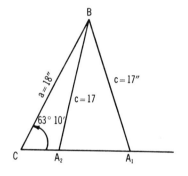

FIGURE 8–13

$A_1 = 70° 50'$ to the nearest $10'$. (Subscripts denote the first solution.)

Then $B_1 = 180° - (63° 10' + 70° 50')$

$B_1 = 46° 0'$

We can then repeat the Law of Sines to solve for b.

$$\frac{c}{\sin C} = \frac{b}{\sin B}$$

$$\frac{17}{\sin 63° 10'} = \frac{b_1}{\sin 46° 0'}$$

$$b_1 = \frac{17 \sin 46° 0'}{\sin 63° 10'} = \frac{17 \,(.7193)}{.8923}$$

$$b_1 = 13.7 \text{ in.}$$

If $\angle A$ is an obtuse angle and $\sin A = .9448$, then

$A_2 = 109° 10'$, the supplement of A_1

and $\qquad B_2 = 7° 40'$

Solving for b_2 we find $b_2 = 2.54$ inches.

In summary, the two possible triangles have sides and angles as follows:

(1) $a = 18, b = 13.7, c = 17, A = 70° 50', B = 46° 0', C = 63° 10'$.
(2) $a = 18, b = 2.54, c = 17, A = 109° 10', B = 7° 40', C = 63° 10'$.

Exercises

1. In triangle ABC, $A = 37° 20'$, $B = 51° 30'$, $c = 125$ cm. Find C, a, b.

2. In triangle RST, $R = 29° 10'$, $S = 62° 20'$, $t = 11.5$ in. Find T, r, s.

3. In triangle HJK, $H = 38° 42'$, $h = 172$ yd, $k = 203$ yd. Find J, K, j.

4. In triangle DEF, $D = 107° 13'$, $d = 17.2$ cm., $f = 12.2$ cm. Find E, F, e.

5. Use the Law of Sines to prove that the bisector of an interior angle of a triangle divides the opposite side into parts that have the same ratio as the sides adjacent to the angle bisected.

6. A flower bed is in the shape of an obtuse triangle. One angle is $45°$, the side opposite is 28 feet, and another side is 36 feet. Find the remaining angles and side.

7. A triangular piece of sheet metal has sides 23.4 inches and 29.6 inches long with the angle opposite the shorter side $47° 15'$. Find the length of the third side.

8. A 35.0 foot pole stands vertically on a uniformly sloped hillside. At a time when the angle of elevation of the sun is $37° 12'$ the shadow of the pole extends directly down the slope. If the hillside has an angle of inclination of $6° 40'$, find the length of the shadow.

8.3   The Law of Cosines

The Law of Cosines may be applied to solve a triangle whenever two sides and the included angle (SAS) are known or when the three sides (SSS) are known. The Law is stated as follows.

In any triangle the square of a side equals the sum of the squares of the other two sides decreased by twice the product of those sides and the cosine of the included angle.

The proof can be made with either an acute triangle or an obtuse triangle, as shown in Figure 8–14.

In Figure 8–14A, $c^2 = h^2 + (a - x)^2 = h^2 + a^2 - 2ax + x^2$
$$b^2 = h^2 + x^2$$

Subtracting: $c^2 - b^2 = a^2 - 2ax$

But, $x = b \cos C$

Hence, $c^2 = a^2 + b^2 - 2ab \cos C$

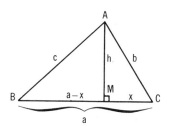

FIGURE 8–14A

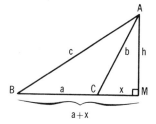

FIGURE 8–14B

In Figure 8–14B, $c^2 = h^2 + a^2 + 2ax + x^2$
$$b^2 = h^2 + x^2$$

Subtracting: $c^2 - b^2 = a^2 + 2ax$

But, $x = b \cos(180° - C) = -b \cos C$

Hence, $c^2 = a^2 + b^2 - 2ab \cos C$ (II)

By drawing altitudes from B and C, similar formulas for a^2 and b^2 can be proved. These formulas are

$$a^2 = b^2 + c^2 - 2bc \cos A$$
$$b^2 = a^2 + c^2 - 2ac \cos B$$

EXAMPLE 1. In triangle RST, $S = 48° 40'$, $r = 32.4$ inches, and $t = 26.7$ inches. Solve the triangle.

Solution. The Law of Cosines enables us to write

$$s^2 = r^2 + t^2 - 2rt \cos S$$
$$s^2 = 32.4^2 + 26.7^2 - 2(32.4)(26.7)(.6604)$$
$$s^2 = 1050 + 713 - 1143$$
$$s^2 = 620$$
$$s = 24.9 \text{ inches, approximately}$$

By the Law of Sines, $\dfrac{s}{\sin S} = \dfrac{r}{\sin R} = \dfrac{t}{\sin T}$

$$\frac{24.9}{\sin 48° 40'} = \frac{32.4}{\sin R}$$

$$\sin R = \frac{32.4 \sin 48° 40'}{24.9} = \frac{32.4 \,(.7509)}{24.9}$$

$$\sin R = .9771$$
$$R = 77° 40' \text{ to the nearest 10 minutes}$$

Similarly, $\quad \sin T = \dfrac{26.7 \sin 48° 40'}{24.9} = \dfrac{26.7 \,(.7509)}{24.9}$

$$\sin T = .8052$$
$$T = 53° 40' \text{ to the nearest 10 minutes}$$

Check: $R + S + T = 77° 40' + 48° 40' + 53° 40' = 180° 0'.$

EXAMPLE 2. The sides of a triangle are 7.23 cm., 5.81 cm., and 4.93 cm. Find the size of each angle of the triangle.

Solution. The Law of Cosines can be solved for the cosine of the angle. If $a^2 = b^2 + c^2 - 2bc \cos A$, then

$$\cos A = \frac{b^2 + c^2 - a^2}{2bc}$$

In the given triangle, assume $a = 7.23$, $b = 5.81$ and $c = 4.93$.

We then have $\quad \cos A = \dfrac{5.81^2 + 4.93^2 - 7.23^2}{2(5.81)(4.93)}$

$$\cos A = .1011$$
$$A = 84° 12'$$

Similarly, $\quad \cos B = \dfrac{a^2 + c^2 - b^2}{2ac}$

$$\cos B = \frac{7.23^2 + 4.93^2 - 5.81^2}{2(7.23)(4.93)}$$

$$\cos B = .6007$$
$$B = 53° 5'$$

And $\quad \cos C = \dfrac{a^2 + b^2 - c^2}{2ab}$

$$\cos C = \frac{7.23^2 + 5.81^2 - 4.93^2}{2(7.23)(5.81)}$$

$$\cos C = .7347$$
$$C = 42° 43'$$

Check: $A + B + C = 84° 12' + 53° 5' + 42° 43' = 180° 0'.$

Exercises

1. In triangle PQR, $P = 52° \, 10'$, $q = 6.0$ cm., and $r = 8.0$ cm. Find Q, R, and p.

2. In triangle DEF, $d = 4.0$ in., $e = 5.0$ in., and $f = 7.0$ in. Find each angle correct to the nearest degree.

3. Given triangle ABC with $A = 52° \, 40'$, $b = 540$ ft., and $c = 490$ ft., find B, C, and a.

4. In triangle RST, $R = 61° \, 25'$, $s = 191$ cm., and $t = 205$ cm. Find S, T, and r.

5. In triangle HJK, $K = 105° \, 18'$, $h = 6.11$ in., and $j = 5.84$ in. Find H, J, and k.

6. In triangle ABC, $a = 11.4$ cm., $b = 13.7$ cm., and $c = 12.2$ cm. Find each angle correct to the nearest 10 minutes.

7. Find a formula for $\cos C$ in terms of sides a, b, and c of triangle ABC.

8. The sides of a triangle are 6.8 in., 8.4 in., and 4.9 in. Find the size of the smallest angle.

9. The sides of a parallelogram are 55 in. and 71 in. Find the length of each diagonal if the larger angle is 106°.

10. From a point of observation on a level plain the distance to one of two houses is 253 yards and to the other house is 319 yards. What is the distance between the houses if the angle subtended by them at the point of observation is $42° \, 12'$?

8.4   Area of a triangle

We shall prove that

> *The area of any triangle equals half the product of two sides and the sine of the included angle.*

Let K represent the area of triangle ABC, and let h be the altitude on AC. Then $K = \dfrac{1}{2}\,bh$. But $h = c \sin A$.

Thus, $K = \dfrac{1}{2}\,bc \sin A$ (III)

By drawing altitudes from A and C, we can also prove

$$K = \frac{1}{2}\,ab \sin C$$

and, $$K = \frac{1}{2}\,ac \sin B$$

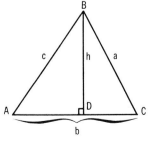

FIGURE 8–15

If two angles and a side are known and it is required to find the area, first use the Law of Sines to find another side and then apply the formula just derived.

EXAMPLE. Find the area of triangle ABC if $a = 17.7$ cm., $b = 21.0$ cm., and $C = 78°\ 10'$.

Solution. Select the formula

$$K = \frac{1}{2}\ ab \sin C$$

Then,　　　　　　$$K = \frac{1}{2}\ (17.7)(21.0) \sin 78°\ 10'$$

$$K = 182 \text{ sq. cm.}$$

Exercises

Find the area of each triangle.

1. $a = 7.5$ inches, $b = 9.0$ inches, $C = 100°\ 0'$.
2. $a = 11.7$ cm., $b = 13.5$ cm., $C = 81°\ 20'$.
3. $b = 146.2$ in., $c = 209.3$ in., $A = 61°\ 12'$.
4. $a = 19.42$ ft., $c = 19.42$ ft., $B = 31°\ 16'$.
5. $a = 200.0$ cm., $c = 203.0$ cm., $B = 94°\ 16'$.
6. Find the area of triangle RST if $r = 165.5$ cm., $s = 180.3$ cm., $T = 74°\ 5'$.
7. Find the area of triangle DEF if $D = 70°\ 11'$, $E = 43°\ 55'$, $e = 16.7$ cm.
8. Find the area of triangle ABC if $a = 174$ in., $b = 138$ in. and $c = 188$ in. (*Hint*: Find one angle by the Law of Cosines). Check by using Hero's formula for the area of a triangle from geometry.　　$K = \sqrt{s(s-a)(s-b)(s-c)}$, 　　where　　$s = \dfrac{a+b+c}{2}$.

8.5　Vector triangles

Vectors were discussed in Section 4.7. You will recall that vectors possess the qualities of magnitude and direction. Graphical addition of vectors involves forming a triangle with the given vectors as sides. The vector sum of two or more vectors is called the resultant. Trigonometric solutions of vector addition or subtraction are usually more accurate than graphical methods which must be considered as rough approximations unless carefully done with precision drawing instruments.

Common measures which can be represented by vectors are velocity, acceleration, weight, forces of all kinds, electric voltages, and numerous other natural measures. We shall illustrate trigonometric solutions of problems where vector addition is involved.

EXAMPLE 1. Two forces, one of 30.0 pounds and the other of 50.0 pounds act on an object. If the angle between the forces is 40° 0′ find the magnitude and the direction of the resultant force. Give the direction as the angle between the resultant and the 50.0 pound force.

Note: A resultant force in such a situation may replace the two given forces and produce the same effect on the object.

Solution. Make a sketch showing the given vector quantities and the resultant as the diagonal of a parallelogram. Call the resultant force $\vec{R}$ and the angle it makes with the 50.0 pound force vector θ. Since $OACB$ is a parallelogram, $\vec{OB} = \vec{AC}$. Therefore we know two sides and the included angle in triangle OAC

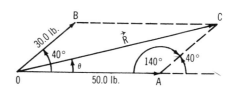

FIGURE 8–16

because angle OAC is 140°, the supplement of 40°. Let R represent the magnitude of $\vec{R}$. The Law of Cosines gives us

$$R^2 = 50.0^2 + 30.0^2 - 2\,(50.0)(30.0)\,\cos 140°$$
$$R^2 = 2500 + 900 - 3000(-.7660)$$
$$R^2 = 5698$$
$$R\ = 75.5 \text{ pounds}$$

By the Law of Sines,

$$\frac{75.5}{\sin 140°} = \frac{30.0}{\sin \theta}$$

$$\sin \theta = \frac{30.0 \sin 140°}{75.5} = \frac{30.0\,(.6428)}{75.5}$$

$$\sin \theta = .2554$$
$$\theta = 14° 48′$$

EXAMPLE 2. The air speed of a plane is 245 miles per hour. There is a 22 mile per hour wind from the northeast at a time when the heading of the plane is due east. Find the ground speed and the direction of the path of the plane.

Note: Air speed is the velocity of the plane in motionless air; ground speed is the velocity of the plane with respect to an observer on the ground. Air speed exceeds ground speed in a headwind; air speed is less than ground speed in a tailwind.

Solution. The figure shows the two vectors which determine the velocity and the direction of the plane. The bearing B of the plane is $90° + \theta$. The Law of Cosines gives

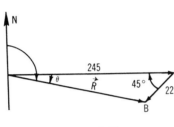

FIGURE 8-17

$$R^2 = 245^2 + 22^2 - 2\,(245)(22)\cos 45°$$
$$R^2 = 52886$$
$$R = 230 \text{ miles per hour}$$

By the Law of Sines, we get

$$\frac{230}{\sin 45°} = \frac{22}{\sin \theta}$$
$$\sin \theta = \frac{22 \sin 45°}{230} = .0676$$
$$\theta = 3° 50'$$
$$B = 93° 50'$$

EXAMPLE 3. A 320 pound crate is pushed up a loading ramp inclined at an angle of 16° 30'. Find the component of the weight acting down the plane (parallel to the ramp); find the component perpendicular to the surface of the ramp. If it requires 42 pounds to overcome the force of friction (force applied parallel to the ramp) what is the total force required to move the crate?

Solution. The drawing shows the forces acting on the crate in the form of vectors. Let $\overrightarrow{W}_d$ represent the component of the weight down the plane and $\overrightarrow{W}_p$ the component perpendicular to

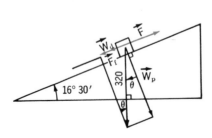

FIGURE 8-18

the plane. Let $\overrightarrow{F}_f$ be the force of friction and $\overrightarrow{F}$ the force required to move the crate up the ramp. A principle of physics states that forces are balanced when no acceleration takes place. Thus, $\overrightarrow{F} = \overrightarrow{W}_d + \overrightarrow{F}_f$ and $F = W_d + F_f$ since the force $\overrightarrow{F}$ must equal the sum of the two forces acting down the plane $\overrightarrow{W}_d$ and $\overrightarrow{F}_f$. It can be shown from geometry that $\theta = 16° 30'$.

We can write

$$\frac{W_d}{320} = \sin 16° 30'$$

Then, $W_d = 320 \sin 16° 30' = 320 (.2840)$

$W_d = 91$ pounds

Also, $$\frac{W_p}{320} = \cos 16° 30'$$

$W_p = 320 \cos 16° 30' = 320 (.9588)$

$W_p = 307$ pounds

And $F = F_f + W_d = 42 + 91 = 133$ pounds

The computation above may be summarized as follows: The component of the weight parallel to the surface of the ramp is 91 pounds; the component perpendicular to the ramp is 307 pounds. The total force required to move the crate up the plane is 133 pounds.

EXAMPLE 4. An object which weighs 30 grams is attached to a length of string and whirled around in a circle. Centrifugal force causes the object to pull the string outward, so that as the velocity is increased, the angle which the string makes with a vertical line is increased. If the magnitude of the centrifugal force is 50 grams find the angle which the string makes with a vertical line. What is the force pulling on the string?

Solution. It can be shown in physics that the string will form a line that is an extension of the resultant of the weight and the centrifugal force. See Figure 8–19. In rectangle $OABC$, $\overrightarrow{R}$ is the

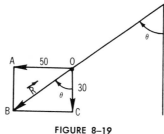

FIGURE 8–19

force on the string, and θ is the angle that the string makes with a vertical line.

$$\tan \theta = \frac{50}{30} = 1.6667$$

$$\theta = 59°, \text{ approximately}$$

$$R = \frac{30}{\cos 59°}$$

$$R = 58 \text{ grams}$$

Exercises

1. The air speed of a plane headed due north is 260 miles per hour. A wind from the east is 16 miles per hour. Find the velocity and direction of the plane. If the wind shifts so that it blows from an angle of 110° clockwise from north, what is the ground speed and the direction of the plane if no correction in heading is made by the pilot.

2. A boat that travels at 16 knots (nautical miles per hour) in calm water is moving across a current of 3 knots in a river. If the axis of the boat makes an angle of 35° with the current (heading into the current) what is the effective velocity? What is the angle between the direction of motion and the heading?

3. One force of 125 pounds acts on an object; another force of 85 pounds acts on the same object at an angle of 72° from the first. Find the magnitude and direction of the resultant force.

4. An object weighing 734 pounds is pushed up a loading ramp which is inclined at an angle of 12° with the level ground. Find the force required to move the object up the ramp if the force of friction is 63 pounds.

5. A metal ball weighing 115 grams is attached to the end of a string and whirled in a circle. If the centrifugal force at a given velocity is 290 grams, find the angle which the string makes with a vertical line. What is the force on the string (tension)?

6. An object resting on an inclined plane will slide down at a uniform velocity when the plane is inclined at a certain angle. If the force of friction is 12 grams and the weight of the object is 75 grams, what is the angle of the inclined plane? (*Hint:* The force of friction opposes the motion and hence the force of friction equals the component of the weight parallel to the inclined plane in this situation.)

7. Points C and D are directly across from each other on the opposite banks of a river. A boat that travels at a velocity of 12 miles per hour crosses the river from C to D. If the current of the river has a velocity of 4 miles per hour, at what angle must the skipper head in order to travel directly from C to D?

8. Three forces in a horizontal plane act on an object. The forces are 7 lb., 11 lb., and 15 lb. The angle between the 7 lb. and 11 lb. forces is 105°, between the 11 lb. and the 15 lb. forces is 147°, and between the 15 lb. and the 7 lb. forces is 108°. What is the magnitude and direction of the resultant force? (Find the angle between the 15 lb. force and the resultant force.)

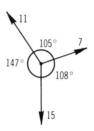

FIGURE 8–20

8.6   Area of a circular sector and segment

The figure $OACB$ is a *sector* of a circle. The ratio of its area to the area of the circle equals the ratio of its arc to the circumference. That is, if A is the area of the sector,

$$\frac{A}{\pi r^2} = \frac{\text{arc } BCA}{2\pi r}$$

From Section 6.11 we know that the length of arc BCA is $r \cdot \alpha$. Thus, the area of a circular sector is given by the following formula.

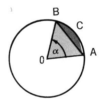

FIGURE 8–21

$$A = \frac{1}{2} r^2 \alpha \qquad \text{(IV)}$$

The area between chord AB and arc ACB is a circular *segment*. Its area can be found by subtracting the area of triangle OAB from the area of sector $OACB$. Since the area of a triangle is given by the formula $K = \frac{1}{2} ab \sin C$, we find the area of triangle OAB to be $\frac{1}{2} r^2 \sin \alpha$. Thus the area of the circular segment is

$$\text{Area of segment } ACB = \frac{1}{2} r^2 \alpha - \frac{1}{2} r^2 \sin \alpha$$

or

$$\text{Area} = \frac{1}{2} r^2 (\alpha - \sin \alpha) \qquad \text{(V)}$$

You are reminded that α in these formulas must be expressed in radian measure.

EXAMPLE. A sector has a central angle of 100° in a circle whose radius is 3.0 inches. Find the area of the circular sector and the area of the corresponding circular segment.

Solution. Converting 100° to radian measure, we find

$$100° = 1.745 \text{ radians}$$

$$\text{Area of the sector} = \frac{1}{2} \cdot 3.0^2 (1.745) = 7.9 \text{ sq. in.}$$

$$\text{Area of the segment} = \frac{1}{2} \cdot 3.0^2 (1.745 - .985) = 3.4 \text{ square inches.}$$

Exercises

1. A sector has a central angle of 82° 0′ in a circle with a diameter of 14.6 cm. Find the area of the sector and of the segment.

2. A sector has a central angle of $\frac{2\pi}{3}$ in a circle whose radius is 1.36 inches. Find the area of the sector and the segment.

3. The radius of a circle is 20.4 cm. In the circle is inscribed a polygon of five sides. Four of the central angles subtended by the sides are $\frac{\pi}{6}, \frac{\pi}{4}, \frac{2\pi}{3}, \frac{2\pi}{5}$. Find the area of the polygon.

4. Find the area swept over by the spoke of a wheel of radius 15 inches as the wheel rotates through an angle of 270°.

5. Find the area of the circular segment between a 4.8 inch chord and its arc if the diameter of the circle is 7.2 inches.

Miscellaneous Exercises

Find angles and sides whose measures are not given in Exercises 1–8. Each exercise refers to a given triangle ABC with angles and sides lettered according to the usual convention.

1. $A = 61° 15′$, $B = 42° 12′$, $a = 14.2$ in.

2. $B = 26° 48′$, $C = 83° 0′$, $c = 82.3$ yd.

3. $a = 9.36$ cm., $b = 1.40$ cm., $C = 60° 42′$.

4. $b = 46.2$ cm., $c = 53.1$ cm., $A = 103° 7′$.

5. $A = 27° 49′$, $b = 52.7$ ft., $c = 47.2$ ft.

6. $B = 83° 1′$, $a = .193$ mi., $c = .201$ mi.

7. $a = 21.4$ cm., $b = 30.2$ cm., $c = 27.0$ cm.

8. $a = 1015$ yd., $b = 987.0$ yd., $c = 1232$ yd.

Find the area of each triangle in Exercises 9–12.

9. $A = 77° \ 14'$, $B = 58° \ 11'$, $c = 42.5$ cm.

10. $C = 112° \ 15'$, $a = 491$ ft., $b = 344$ ft.

11. $A = 50° \ 4'$, $a = 67.1$ cm., $c = 80.3$ cm.

12. $a = 85.07$ ft., $b = 63.21$ ft., $c = 70.04$ ft.

13. Point B is across a lake from point A, and the distance AB is to be found. Point C is on the same level as A, and B is visible from C. The distance AC is measured and found to be 1341 ft. $A = 73° \ 11'$, and $C = 52° \ 4'$. Find the distance AB.

14. A ship is traveling at 19.5 knots due N.E. At 8:22 A.M. a mountain peak has a bearing of 149° 48′, and at 9:05 A.M. it has a bearing of 154° 21′. How far is the ship from the mountain peak at the time of the second observation? (A knot is one nautical mile per hour; a nautical mile is approximately 6080 feet.)

15. A triangular lot has sides which are 162.5 ft., 183.0 ft., and 211.3 ft. long. Find the area of the lot.

16. Circles whose radii are 7.4 in., 8.1 in., and 9.7 in., respectively, are mutually externally tangent. Find the area enclosed by arcs of the circles.

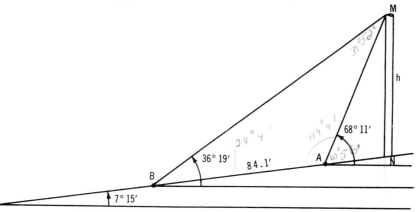

FIGURE 8–22

17. A hill is inclined at a uniform angle of 7° 15′. The angle of elevation of the top of a chimney standing on top of the hill from point A down the hill is 68° 11′, and from point B farther down the hill is 36° 19′. B, A, and the base of the chimney are in a straight line directly up the hill. If the distance AB is 84.1 ft., find the height of the chimney.

18. The diagonal of a parallelogram is 42.21 yards and makes angles of 26° 11′ and 49° 51′ respectively with the sides. Find the lengths of the sides.

19. The distance between villages A and B situated on a plain is 4.20 miles. Point C is on the same plain, and at C the straight road from A to B subtends an angle of 86° 12′. C is 3.75 miles from B. Find the distance from C to A.

20. In order to find the distance from H to K a point M is selected from which both H and K can be seen. HM is measured and found to be 76.42 yards. KM is found to be 90.65 yards. Angle HMK is 81° 14′. If H, K, and M are on a level plain, find HK.

21. An inaccessible distance RS is to be determined, R and S being on level ground. Points T and W are selected and TW is measured and found to be 807 yards. Four angles are measured as follows: $RSW = 77°$ 17′, $RTW = 84°$ 46′, $SWR = 39°$ 7′, $SWT = 101° 51′$. Find RS.

22. Two planes leave the same airport at the same time. One plane flies on a bearing of 10° 12′ at 235 miles per hour, and the other flies on a bearing of 121° 15′ at 305 miles per hour. How far apart are the planes at the end of 1 hour and 20 minutes of flying time?

23. An airplane was flying on a straight line toward a landing field. The pilot observed that the angle of depression of the field was 11° 15′. One minute later he observed that the angle of depression was 16° 30′. Assuming that the plane was flying at an altitude of 5800 feet, at what speed was it flying?

Chapter Review

1. In right triangle ABC, find B if $a = 31.2$ cm. and $c = 47.1$ cm.

2. The longest side of a triangle is 7.6 cm. long and the two angles adjacent to this side are 23° 10′ and 34° 40′. Find the lengths of the other two sides of the triangle.

3. The base angles of an isosceles trapezoid are 72° each. If the parallel sides are 4.21 inches and 2.78 inches long, find the area of the trapezoid.

4. The three sides of a triangle are in the ratio 2:3:4. If the perimeter of the triangle is 23.4 inches, find the size of each angle.

5. Find the area of the triangle in Exercise 4.

6. The angle of elevation of the top of a microwave relay tower from point R on the ground is 41° 13′. From point S, which is in a direct line between point R and the base of the tower, the angle of elevation is 64° 56′. Find the height of the tower if the distance between points R and S is 71.3 feet, assuming level ground.

7. Find the area of a regular decagon if each side is 16.9 inches long.

8. A room in the shape of a rectangular solid is 32 feet by 16 feet by 9 feet high. What is the length of a diagonal from one corner to the opposite corner of the room? What is the angle between a diagonal of the room and the floor? What is the angle between a diagonal of the room and a diagonal of the longer wall?

9. A straight walk 4 feet wide is constructed across a circular grass plaza so that the center of the walk is 22 feet from the center of the circle. The diameter of the plaza is 100 feet. Find the area of the walk that is within the plaza.

10. From point A, one of two points 200 yards apart on the rim of Grand Canyon, the angle of depression to a small pinnacle is found to be 37° 42′. From point A, the horizontal angle between point B and a vertical line through the pinnacle is 78° 35′. From point B, the horizontal angle between point A and a vertical line through the pinnacle is 24° 53′. Find the angle of depression from point B to the pinnacle.

CHAPTER OUTLINE

Inverses of
Trigonometric Functions
and Trigonometric Equations 9

9.1 Meaning of inverse of a function

You are familiar with a number of inverse operations. Examples are square and square root with nonnegative numbers, and cube and cube root. The inverse of the logarithm of a number is the antilogarithm of the number. It is clear that the application of two inverse operations to a number leaves the number unchanged.

Given $y = f(x)$, if $x = g(y)$ states the same relation between x and y, then g is said to be the *inverse function* of f. For example, if $y = 2x + 5$, then $x = \frac{1}{2}y - 2\frac{1}{2}$ where the second function is the inverse of the first and *vice versa*. The inverse of a function may be formed by interchanging the elements of the ordered pairs of the function. The inverse may be a function or it may be a non-functional relation. For example, if $f(x) = x^2$, the ordered pairs of f are of the form (x, x^2) and the inverse of f is given by (x^2, x), which is not a function.

In trigonometry we are concerned primarily with six special functions and their inverses. You have already solved many equations like $\sin x = .3393$ by finding $x = 19° \ 50'$ in the table of natural values. In the ambiguous case of the Law of Sines you found two possible values of x for a given value of $\sin x$. In Section 9.2 we

228

shall distinguish between principal values, in which a unique value of x is determined, and general values.

We shall define the inverse of the trigonometric functions as follows.

> The inverse of sin x is arcsin x.
> The inverse of cos x is arccos x.
> The inverse of tan x is arctan x.

There are corresponding relations for the sec x, csc x, and cot x, but they are infrequently used. Why are the inverses not functions?

We can write an equation such as sin x = .3393 in the form x = arcsin .3393 where the second equation is read "x is an angle whose sine is .3393," or "x equals the arcsine of .3393." The solution for x will give all angles that have as the value of their sine the number .3393. An infinite number of such angles exists, but we are primarily interested in positive angles less than 360°.

An alternate notation for the inverse function is illustrated by this example: arcsin x = $\sin^{-1} x$. The $^{-1}$ written in the position of an exponent *does not mean* that $\sin^{-1} x = \dfrac{1}{\sin x}$; it indicates the inverse sine function, the arcsine. Sometimes the notation $\sin^{-1}x$ is read "the anti-sine of x." $\sin^{-1}x$ = arcsin x.

EXAMPLE 1. Find x if sin x = .5.

Solution. If sin x = .5, then x = arcsin .5. Hence, x = 30°, 150°, 390°, 510°, and so on.

EXAMPLE 2. Give all positive values of x less than 360° which satisfy the equation tan x = −1.

Solution. x = arctan (−1)
x = 135°, 315°

EXAMPLE 3. Evaluate sin (arcsin .8660).

Solution. Assume A = arcsin .8660.
Then sin A = .8660, and
sin (arcsin .8660) = .8660.

EXAMPLE 4. Evaluate $\tan\left(\arccos \dfrac{3}{5}\right)$.

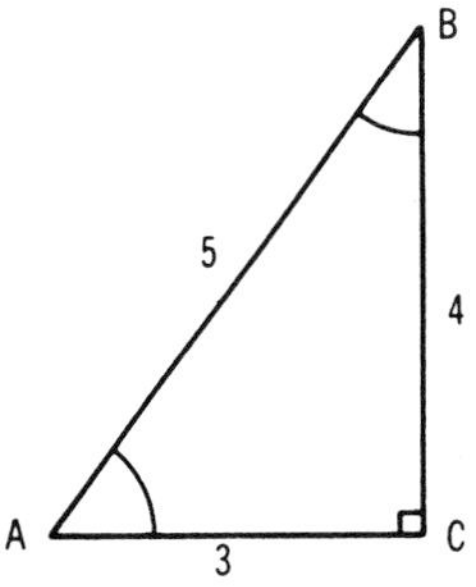

FIGURE 9–1

Solution. Assume A = arccos $\dfrac{3}{5}$.

Then cos A = $\dfrac{3}{5}$. Draw a right triangle and call one acute angle A.

Since $\cos A = \dfrac{3}{5}$, the adjacent side can be set equal to 3 and the hypotenuse equal to 5. The opposite side can be computed to be 4. Thus, $\tan \left(\arccos \dfrac{3}{5} \right) = \tan A = \dfrac{4}{3}$.

Exercises

In Exercises 1–10 find values of x such that $0° \leqq x < 360°$.

1. $x = \arcsin 0$

2. $x = \arccos 0$

3. $x = \arctan 1$

4. $x = \arcsin \dfrac{\sqrt{3}}{2}$

5. $x = \arctan 2$

6. $x = \arcsin \dfrac{1}{\sqrt{2}}$

7. $x = \operatorname{arcsec} 2$

8. $x = \arccos .6428$

9. $x = \operatorname{arccot} 2.1445$

10. $x = \arcsin (-.5)$

In Exercises 11–20 find numerical values of the given expressions. Assume that angles are acute.

11. $\sin \left(\arcsin \dfrac{1}{2} \right)$

12. $\cot \left(\arctan \dfrac{4}{5} \right)$

13. $\cos \left(\arcsin \dfrac{\sqrt{3}}{2} \right)$

14. $\tan \left(\arcsin \dfrac{5}{13} \right)$

15. $\sec \left(\arccos \dfrac{1}{2} \right)$

16. $\sin (\arctan 1) + \cos (\arccos .5)$

17. $\cos \left(\operatorname{arccot} \dfrac{4}{3} \right)$

18. $\tan \left(\arcsin \dfrac{\sqrt{2}}{2} \right) - \cot \left(\arccos \dfrac{\sqrt{2}}{2} \right)$

19. $\sin (\arctan \sqrt{3} + \operatorname{arccot} \sqrt{3})$ (*Hint:* Assume $A = \arctan \sqrt{3}$ and $B = \operatorname{arccot} \sqrt{3}$.)

20. $\tan \left(\arcsin \dfrac{\sqrt{3}}{2} - \arccos \dfrac{\sqrt{3}}{2} \right)$

Verify the following equations without tables.

21. $\arcsin \dfrac{\sqrt{2}}{2} + \arccos \dfrac{\sqrt{2}}{2} = \dfrac{\pi}{2}$

22. $\arccos \dfrac{\sqrt{3}}{2} + \arcsin \dfrac{\sqrt{3}}{2} = \dfrac{\pi}{2}$

23. $\arcsin \dfrac{2}{5} + \arccos \dfrac{2}{5} = \dfrac{\pi}{2}$

24. $\arctan 1 + \arccos \dfrac{\sqrt{3}}{2} = \arcsin \dfrac{1}{2} + \operatorname{arcsec} \sqrt{2}$

25. $\arctan \dfrac{3}{4} + \arctan \dfrac{5}{12} = \arctan \dfrac{56}{33}$ (*Hint*: Take the tangent of both members.)

26. $\arcsin \dfrac{3}{5} + \arccos \dfrac{15}{17} = \arctan \dfrac{77}{36}$

9.2   Principal and general values of the inverses of the trigonometric functions

An inverse of a trigonometric function will determine a relation that is not a function since one value in the domain corresponds to more than one value in the range. The inverse of a trigonometric function is a function only if we impose certain restrictions on the value of the variable, that is, if for each element in the domain we assign one and only one element in the range. The result of these restrictions is the *principal value* of the inverse trigonometric relations. By principal value we mean that we select *one* range (interval) of the values of the inverse of the function. In order to distinguish the principal value, we shall capitalize the "A" as in $y = \operatorname{Arcsin} x$.

If x is a positive number, the principal value of any inverse function is defined as an angle between $0°$ and $90°$, inclusive. In each of the following equations, y is an angle such that $0° \leqq y \leqq 90°$. $y = \operatorname{Arcsin} x$; $y = \operatorname{Arccos} x$; $y = \operatorname{Arctan} x$; $y = \operatorname{Arccot} x$; $y = \operatorname{Arcsec} x$; $y = \operatorname{Arccsc} x$.

The definition of the principal value of an inverse of a trigonometric function is not so simple if x is a negative number. The following definitions will be made for $x < 0$.

$$\text{If } y = \operatorname{Arcsin} x, \text{ then } 0° > y \geqq -90°.$$
$$\text{If } y = \operatorname{Arccos} x, \text{ then } 90° < y \leqq 180°.$$
$$\text{If } y = \operatorname{Arctan} x, \text{ then } 0° > y > -90°.$$

Thus, for negative values of x, Arcsin x is a negative angle greater than or equal to $-90°$; Arccos x is a positive angle greater than $90°$ but less than or equal to $180°$; Arctan x is a negative angle greater than $-90°$. Arccot x, Arcsec x, and Arccsc x will not be defined here for negative values of x. The range of the inverse is appropriately restricted so that it is a function rather than a non-functional relation.

EXAMPLE 1. Find the principal value of $\operatorname{Arcsin}\left(-\dfrac{1}{2}\right)$.

Solution. $\text{Arcsin} \left(+ \frac{1}{2} \right) = 30°$; hence, $\text{Arcsin} \left(- \frac{1}{2} \right) = -30°$.

EXAMPLE 2. Find the principal value of $\text{Arccos} \left(- \frac{\sqrt{3}}{2} \right)$.

Solution. $\text{Arccos} \left(\frac{\sqrt{3}}{2} \right) = 30°$; hence, $\text{Arccos} \left(- \frac{\sqrt{3}}{2} \right) = 180° -$ $30° = 150°$. Here $30°$ is the related angle.

EXAMPLE 3. Find the principal value of $\text{Arctan}\,(-1)$.

Solution. $\text{Arctan}\,1 = 45°$; hence, $\text{Arctan}\,(-1) = -45°$.

Sometimes it is desirable to give *general values* of the inverse of a trigonometric function. To do this we first find all values between $0°$ and $360°$, inclusive. In order to give general values, we then add $n\,360°$ to each value less than $360°$ where n is any integer. Radian notation may also be used. If values repeat every $180°$, it is convenient to add $n\,180°$ to the first such value.

Note: If "a" is not capitalized (as in arcsin y), it will be understood that general values are intended unless otherwise specified.

EXAMPLE 4. Give general values of x if $x = \text{arcsin}\,\frac{1}{2}$.

Solution. $x = 30°$ and $x = 150°$ are the positive angles less than $360°$ whose sine equals $\frac{1}{2}$. Therefore, general values are

$$x = 30° + n\,360°; x = 150° + n\,360°$$

Exercises

Give principal values in Exercises 1-10.

1. $\text{Arcsin}\,\frac{\sqrt{3}}{2}$
2. $\text{Arccos}\,\frac{1}{2}$
3. $\text{Arctan}\,.8693$
4. $\text{Arccos}\,.8910$
5. $\text{Arcsin}\left(- \frac{\sqrt{2}}{2} \right)$

6. $\text{Arcsin}\,1$
7. $\text{Arctan}\,\frac{3}{4}$
8. $\text{Arctan}\,(-.3443)$
9. $\text{Arccos}\left(- \frac{\sqrt{2}}{2} \right)$
10. $\text{Arccos}\,(- .5746)$

Give general values in Exercises 11–20.

11. arcsin $\dfrac{\sqrt{3}}{2}$ **16.** arctan (-1)

12. arctan .5095   **17.** arcsin (-1)

13. arccos $\dfrac{\sqrt{2}}{2}$ **18.** arccos $\left(-\dfrac{1}{2}\right)$

14. arcsin $\dfrac{3}{4}$ **19.** arctan $\dfrac{1}{2}$

15. arctan 5   **20.** arcsin $(-.4226)$

9.3   Graphs of the inverse relations

The inverse trigonometric relations can be illustrated very well by means of the graphs of the relations. We shall let x be the independent variable, as usual, and construct the graphs of the equations $y = $ arcsin x, $y = $ arccos x, and $y = $ arctan x.

Let x assume all permissible values in the relation $y = $ arcsin x. The restriction on x is $-1 \leqq x \leqq +1$. If general values are plotted for y, we have the graph shown in Figure 9–2. Notice that the curve has the same relation to the y-axis that the curve of $y = \sin x$ has to the x-axis.

Principal values of Arcsin x are shown as a color portion of the curve. Note that Arcsin x is a function; any permissible value of x determines a unique value of y. The range is $-90° \leqq$ Arcsin $x \leqq 90°$ or $-\dfrac{\pi}{2} \leqq$ Arcsin $x \leqq \dfrac{\pi}{2}$.

In a similar way we can graph the inverse of the cosine function. See Figure 9–3. The graph of principal values of Arccos x is shown as a color portion of the curve. Though there are an un-

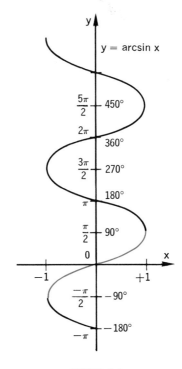

FIGURE 9–2

limited number of values of the arccos x for a given value of x, there is a unique value of Arccos x for a given x. The range is $0° \leq \text{Arccos } x \leq 180°$, or $0 \leq \text{Arccos } x \leq \pi$.

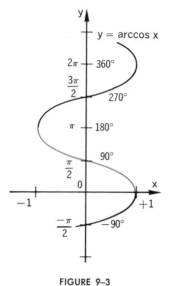

The graph of the arctan x is shown in Figure 9–4. Notice its similarity to the graph of $y = \tan x$ with the axes interchanged. Principal values of Arctan x are shown as a color portion of the curve. For a given value of x, there are an unlimited number of values of arctan x, but there is a unique value of Arctan x for a given value of x. The range of Arctan x is $- 90° < \text{Arctan } x < 90°$ or $-\dfrac{\pi}{2} < \text{Arctan } x < \dfrac{\pi}{2}$.

FIGURE 9–3

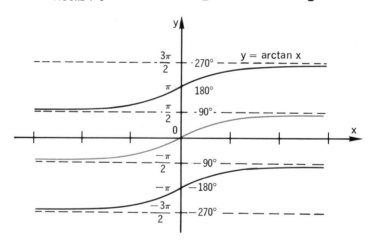

FIGURE 9–4

Exercises

1. Sketch the graph of $y = \text{Arcsin } x$. What is the domain? What is the range?

2. Sketch the graph of $y = \text{Arccos } x$. What is the domain? What is the range?

3. Sketch the graph of $y = \text{Arctan } x$. Is the domain restricted? What is the range?

4. Sketch $y = \arcsin x$, and $y = \arccos x$, on the same coordinate axes. Give four values of y corresponding to points of intersection of the graphs.

9.4   Linear trigonometric equations

You have already solved trigonometric equations of the form $\sin x = k$, $\cos x = k$, and $\tan x = k$ where k is a constant with certain limitations. For a given value of k, there is a unique principal value of x, of the form $x = \text{Arcsin } k$, $x = \text{Arccos } k$, $x = \text{Arctan } k$. A *trigonometric equation* is an equation involving a trigonometric function which is true for some, but not all, values of the variable. If true for all values of the variable, it is an identity.

Let $F(x)$ represent any trigonometric function of x. Then $aF(x) + b = 0$ $(a \neq 0)$ will represent a trigonometric equation linear in $F(x)$. There are certain restrictions upon the values of a and b depending upon the trigonometric function involved. Solving for $F(x)$, we have

$$F(x) = -\frac{b}{a}$$

If $F(x) = \sin x$, then $\left| -\dfrac{b}{a} \right| \leq 1$ since the value of the sine function cannot exceed 1. If, in solving a trigonometric equation, a value is found which is not possible, that value will not give a solution. For example, there is no solution to the equation $\sin x = 2$.

EXAMPLE 1. Solve $2 \sin x - 1 = 0$ for general values of x. Find the principal value of x.

Solution. $2 \sin x - 1 = 0$ $x = \arcsin \dfrac{1}{2}$

$\sin x = \dfrac{1}{2}$ $\therefore x = 30° + n\,360°;\ 150° + n\,360°$

The value of $\text{Arcsin } \dfrac{1}{2}$ is $30°$.

Exercises

Solve the following equations for general values of x in degrees. Indicate the principal value.

1. $2 \cos x - 1 = 0$ 6. $2 \cos x + 1 = 0$
2. $2 \sin x + 1 = 0$ 7. $\sqrt{3} \tan x + 1 = 0$
3. $\tan x - 1 = 0$ 8. $\sin 2x - 1 = 0$ (*Hint:* First find $2x$.)
4. $\sqrt{2} \sin x - 1 = 0$ 9. $\cos 3x - .5 = 0$
5. $2 \cos x - \sqrt{3} = 0$ 10. $\tan 2x - \sqrt{3} = 0$

9.5 Quadratic trigonometric equations

If $F(x)$ represents a trigonometric function, then a trigonometric equation in quadratic form is

$$a[F(x)]^2 + bF(x) + c = 0 \text{ where } a \neq 0$$

As in the case of linear trigonometric equations, there are certain limits on the permissible values of a, b, and c depending upon the function.

The equation is solved by the same methods used for any other quadratic equation. Factoring is applied if possible; completing the square or the quadratic formula can be used if factoring is impossible.

EXAMPLE 1. Solve $2 \sin^2 x - 3 \sin x + 1 = 0$ for principal values of x.

Solution. Factor. $(2 \sin x - 1)(\sin x - 1) = 0$

$$2 \sin x - 1 = 0 \qquad\qquad \sin x - 1 = 0$$

$$\sin x = \frac{1}{2} \qquad\qquad\qquad \sin x = 1$$

$$x = \text{Arcsin } \frac{1}{2} \qquad\qquad x = \text{Arcsin } 1$$

$$x = 30° \qquad\qquad\qquad\quad x = 90°$$

Check:

$$2 \sin^2 30° - 3 \sin 30° + 1 \overset{?}{=} 0 \qquad\qquad 2 \sin^2 90° - 3 \sin 90° + 1 \overset{?}{=} 0$$

$$2 \left(\frac{1}{2}\right)^2 - 3 \left(\frac{1}{2}\right) + 1 \overset{?}{=} 0 \qquad\qquad 2(1)^2 - 3(1) + 1 \overset{?}{=} 0$$

$$\frac{1}{2} - \frac{3}{2} + 1 \overset{?}{=} 0 \qquad\qquad\qquad\qquad 2 - 3 + 1 \overset{?}{=} 0$$

$$0 = 0 \qquad\qquad\qquad\qquad\qquad\qquad 0 = 0$$

EXAMPLE 2. Solve $2 \sin^2 x - \cos x - 1 = 0$ for principal values.

Solution. There are two variables, $\sin x$ and $\cos x$. We can replace $\sin^2 x$ by $1 - \cos^2 x$ and transform the given equation into one with only one variable, $\cos x$. We get

$$2(1 - \cos^2 x) - \cos x - 1 = 0$$
$$2 - 2\cos^2 x - \cos x - 1 = 0$$
$$2\cos^2 x + \cos x - 1 = 0$$

Factoring, $(2 \cos x - 1)(\cos x + 1) = 0$

$$2 \cos x - 1 = 0 \qquad\qquad \cos x + 1 = 0$$

$$\cos x = \frac{1}{2} \qquad\qquad\qquad \cos x = -1$$

$$x = \text{Arccos } \frac{1}{2} \qquad\qquad x = \text{Arccos } (-1)$$

$$x = 60° \qquad\qquad\qquad\quad x = 180°$$

Check:

$$2 \sin^2 60° - \cos 60° - 1 \overset{?}{=} 0 \qquad\qquad 2 \sin^2 180° - \cos 180° - 1 \overset{?}{=} 0$$

$$2 \left(\frac{\sqrt{3}}{2}\right)^2 - \frac{1}{2} - 1 \overset{?}{=} 0 \qquad\qquad 2(0) - (-1) - 1 \overset{?}{=} 0$$

$$\frac{3}{2} - \frac{1}{2} - 1 \overset{?}{=} 0 \qquad\qquad\qquad +1 - 1 \overset{?}{=} 0$$

$$0 = 0 \qquad\qquad\qquad\qquad\qquad 0 = 0$$

Exercises

Solve for principal values of x in Exercises 1–12. Check.

1. $2 \sin^2 x - \sin x - 1 = 0$

2. $\tan^2 x - 1 = 0$

3. $2 \cos^2 x - 5 \cos x + 2 = 0$

4. $4 \sin^2 x - 3 = 0$

5. $2 \cos^2 x - 1 = 0$

6. $\tan^2 x - 2 \tan x = 3$

7. $\sin^2 x - 3 \sin x + 2 = 0$

8. $\cos^2 x - \frac{7}{2} \cos x - 2 = 0$

9. $2 \cos^2 x + 3 \sin x - 3 = 0$

10. $\sin^2 x - \sin x = 0$

11. $\sin^2 x - 2 \sin x - 1 = 0$

12. $\sin x \tan x - \tan x = 0$

9.6 Special types of trigonometric equations

It often happens that trigonometric equations cannot be put into linear or quadratic form. A variety of methods, some of them very ingenious, are available to solve the more difficult types. Graphing or other methods may be used in some special cases to find approximate roots.

Substitution of the fundamental identities or the multiple and fractional angle formulas is often useful in reducing a trigonometric equation to a solvable form. An approach that sometimes succeeds is to factor in such a manner that the product of two or more factors is zero; in the event that this is possible, the equation often reduces to the solution of linear forms. Some examples will illustrate the methods that can be employed. A thorough knowledge of algebraic operations and an understanding of the relations between the trigonometric functions, together with ingenuity, will be needed to solve the more difficult equations.

EXAMPLE 1. Find principal values of x if $\sin x = \cos x$.

Solution. A knowledge of the curves of $y = \sin x$ and $y = \cos x$ indicates a solution in the first quadrant at the point of intersection. At this point $x = 45°$. An algebraic solution is possible, however.

We may divide both members of the equation $\sin x = \cos x$ by $\cos x$ if $\cos x \neq 0$. To test this possibility, we assume that $\cos x = 0$ and find that, if this is true, $x = 90°$. Checking the given equation with $x = 90°$ reveals that $\cos x \neq 0$. Therefore, we can write

$$\frac{\sin x}{\cos x} = \frac{\cos x}{\cos x}$$
$$\tan x = 1$$
$$x = \text{Arctan } 1$$
$$x = 45°$$

Check:
$$\sin 45° \overset{?}{=} \cos 45°$$
$$\frac{\sqrt{2}}{2} = \frac{\sqrt{2}}{2}$$

EXAMPLE 2. Solve for principal values of x : $\sin (x + 30°) = \cos 2x$.

Solution. If $\sin A = \cos B$, then $A + B = 90°$, because the sine and cosine are cofunctions.

Hence,
$$(x + 30°) + 2x = 90°$$
$$3x = 60°$$
$$x = 20°$$

Check:
$$\sin (20° + 30°) \overset{?}{=} \cos (2 \cdot 20°)$$
$$\sin 50° \overset{?}{=} \cos 40°$$
$$.6428 = .6428$$

EXAMPLE 3. Solve for principal values of x : $\sin x + \cos x = 1$.

Solution. Here we can replace $\cos x$ by $\pm\sqrt{1 - \sin^2 x}$. We get

$$\sin x \pm \sqrt{1 - \sin^2 x} = 1$$

or $$\pm\sqrt{1 - \sin^2 x} = 1 - \sin x$$

Squaring, $$1 - \sin^2 x = 1 - 2\sin x + \sin^2 x$$

or $$2\sin^2 x - 2\sin x = 0$$

Factoring, $$2\sin x(\sin x - 1) = 0$$

Hence, $2\sin x = 0$ $\sin x - 1 = 0$

                $x = 0°$ $\sin x = 1$

                                    $x = 90°$

Check: $\sin 0° + \cos 0° \overset{?}{=} 1$ $\sin 90° + \cos 90° \overset{?}{=} 1$

                $0 + 1 \overset{?}{=} 1$ $1 + 0 \overset{?}{=} 1$

                    $1 = 1$ $1 = 1$

It is especially necessary to check roots when both members of the equation have been squared in the solution, because of the possibility of extraneous roots.

EXAMPLE 4. Solve for principal values of x : $2 \tan x \sin x + 2 \sin x = \tan x + 1$.

Solution. Transforming the equation so that the right member is zero, we have

$$2 \tan x \sin x + 2 \sin x - \tan x - 1 = 0$$

Factoring, $$(\tan x + 1)(2 \sin x - 1) = 0$$

Then, $\tan x + 1 = 0$ $2 \sin x - 1 = 0$

             $\tan x = -1$ $\sin x = \dfrac{1}{2}$

         $x = \text{Arctan}\,(-1)$ $x = \text{Arcsin}\,\dfrac{1}{2}$

         $x = -45°$ $x = 30°$

Checks:

(1) $2 \tan\,(-45°) \sin\,(-45°) + 2 \sin\,(-45°) \overset{?}{=} \tan\,(-45°) + 1$

$$2(-1)\left(-\frac{\sqrt{2}}{2}\right) + 2\left(-\frac{\sqrt{2}}{2}\right) \overset{?}{=} (-1) + 1$$

$$\sqrt{2} - \sqrt{2} \overset{?}{=} 0$$

$$0 = 0$$

(2) $2 \tan 30° \sin 30° + 2 \sin 30° \overset{?}{=} \tan 30° + 1$

$$2\left(\frac{\sqrt{3}}{3}\right)\left(\frac{1}{2}\right) + 2\left(\frac{1}{2}\right) \overset{?}{=} \left(\frac{\sqrt{3}}{3}\right) + 1$$

$$\frac{\sqrt{3}}{3} + 1 = \frac{\sqrt{3}}{3} + 1$$

Exercises

Solve for principal values of x.

1. $\sin x + \sin x \cos x = 0$
2. $\cos x - 2 \cos x \sin x = 0$
3. $\sin (x + 10°) = \cos 3x$
4. $\tan 2x = \cot x$
5. $\sin x - \cos x = 0$
6. $\tan x + 1 = \sec x$
7. $\sin x + \cos x = 0$
8. $\tan x + \cot x = 2$
9. $\sin^2 x - \cos^2 x = 0$
10. $\cos x \tan x - \sin^2 x = 0$
11. $\sqrt{3} \cot x \sin x + 2 \cos^2 x = 0$
12. $\sin^2 x = \cos x - 1$
13. $\sin 2x = \cos 3x$
14. $\tan x + \sec x = \sqrt{3}$
15. $\sin x + \frac{1}{2} \sin 2x = 0$
16. $\tan^3 x = 3 \tan x$
17. $\sin 3x = \sin x$
18. $3 \tan^2 x + 4 \sec x + 4 = 0$
19. $2 \sin x \cos x + 4 \sin x = \cos x + 2$
20. Find an approximate solution of $2x = \tan x$ for $0 \leq x \leq \frac{\pi}{2}$ by graphing. (*Hint:* Let $y_1 = 2x$ and $y_2 = \tan x$. Find approximate coordinates where $y_1 = y_2$, that is, at a point of intersection.)

Note: In this equation, x must be expressed in radians.

Chapter Review

Find principal values in Exercises 1–8.

1. $y = \text{Arccos } \dfrac{\sqrt{3}}{2}$
2. $y = \text{Arcsin } \dfrac{\sqrt{2}}{2}$
3. $y = \text{Arctan } 3$
4. $y = \text{Arcsin}\left(-\dfrac{\sqrt{3}}{2}\right)$
5. $y = \text{Arccos } (-1)$
6. $y = \text{Arctan } (-3)$
7. $y = \text{Arcsin } \dfrac{3}{5}$
8. $y = \text{Arccos } \dfrac{5}{7}$

Evaluate.

9. $\cot(\text{Arccot } \sqrt{3})$

11. $\tan\left(\text{Arcsin } \dfrac{1}{\sqrt{2}}\right)$

10. $\sin(\text{Arccos } .8)$

12. $\cos\left[\text{Arcsin}\left(-\dfrac{1}{2}\right)\right]$

Verify without tables.

13. $\text{Arctan } \dfrac{1}{3} + \text{Arctan } 3 = \dfrac{\pi}{2}$

14. $\text{Arctan } \dfrac{1}{5} + \text{Arctan } \dfrac{1}{8} = \dfrac{\pi}{4} - \text{Arctan } \dfrac{1}{2}$

Solve for principal values of x. Find general values of x.

15. $2 \sin x - \sqrt{3} = 0$

16. $\sqrt{3} \cot x + 1 = 0$

17. $4 \cos^2 x - 3 = 0$

18. $2 \cos^2 x - \sin x - 1 = 0$

19. $2 \sin x - \cos x = 0$

20. $\tan 5x - \cot x = 0$

CHAPTER OUTLINE

9.1   Meaning of inverse of a function

9.2   Principal and general values of the inverses of the trigonometric functions

9.3   Graphs of the inverse relations

9.4   Linear trigonometric equations

9.5   Quadratic trigonometric equations

9.6   Special types of trigonometric equations

Sequences and Series $\qquad$ 10

10.1 The meaning of sequence

A *number sequence* is a set of numbers that are arranged in some manner such that one number is identified as first in the sequence, another as second, and so on, and for which there is a rule or pattern relating the numbers. For example, -2, -1, 0, 1, 2, 3 is a sequence; 0, 1, 1, 2, 3, 5, 8 is another sequence. A sequence is sometimes called a *progression*.

The *terms* of a sequence are the numbers in it. The *first term* of a sequence is usually represented by a.

10.2 Arithmetic sequence

An *arithmetic sequence* is a sequence of terms such that each term after the first (a) is equal to the sum of the preceding term and a constant (d) called the *common difference*. The general arithmetic sequence, either finite or infinite, is represented by

$$a, a + d, a + 2d, \cdots$$

EXAMPLE. If the numbers -2, 3, 8, $\cdots$ are terms of an arithmetic sequence, identify a and d and write the next three terms.

Solution. The difference of successive terms gives the value of d. Therefore, $d = 5$ since $3 - (-2) = 5$ and $8 - 3 = 5$. The given numbers are terms of an arithmetic sequence for which $a = -2$, $d = 5$. The next three terms are 13, 18, 23.

Exercises

If the given numbers are terms of an arithmetic sequence, identify a and d and give the next five terms.

1. 1, 2, 3, $\cdots$ **4.** 19, 25, 31, $\cdots$ **7.** 27, 23, 19, $\cdots$

2. 5, 9, 13, $\cdots$ **5.** 0, 7, 14, $\cdots$ **8.** 1.5, 3, 4.5, $\cdots$

3. 17, 29, 41, $\cdots$ **6.** $-9, -2, 5, \cdots$ **9.** 5, $-1, -7, \cdots$

10. $a, a + 3, a + 6, \cdots$ **13.** $\sqrt{3} + 1, \sqrt{3} + 2, \sqrt{3} + 3, \cdots$

11. $-n, 0, n, \cdots$ **14.** $n + 5, n + 11, n + 17, \cdots$

12. $x, 2x, 3x, \cdots$ **15.** $+b, -b, -3b, \cdots$

When we know any term of an arithmetic sequence and the common difference, we can find as many terms of the sequence as we wish, both before and after the given term. Thus, a sequence may be extended to any number of terms. However, we often designate one term as first term a and another term as last term l. The symbols a and l refer to the first and last terms that we wish to consider. Often we are interested in finding the value of a specific term designated by its position with reference to the first term. We usually speak of it as the nth term of the sequence.

EXAMPLE 1. Find the sixth term of a sequence in which the first number is 3 and the common difference is 2.

Solution. Since the number of terms is small we can easily write the sequence.

Number of term:	1	2	3	4	5	6	$\cdots$
Sequence:	3	3 + 2	3 + 2(2)	3 + 3(2)	3 + 4(2)	3 + 5(2)	$\cdots$
Sequence simplified:	3	5	7	9	11	13	$\cdots$

The sixth term is 13.

In the above example, can you see a relation between the number of the term and the multiplier of the common difference?

Consider this sequence.

$$a, \text{ first term}$$
$$a + d, \text{ second term}$$
$$a + 2d, \text{ third term}$$
$$a + (n - 1)d, n\text{th term}$$

If the nth term is the last in the sequence, then

$$l = a + (n - 1)d \qquad \textbf{(I)}$$

Notice that Formula (I) has four variables. If any three of these are known, the fourth is easily found.

EXAMPLE 2. What is the 79th term in the sequence -7, -4, $-1, 2, 5, \cdots$?

Solution. $a = -7$, $d = (-4) - (-7) = 3$, $n = 79$.
$$l = -7 + (79 - 1)3 = 227$$

Exercises

In Exercises 1–6 find the number that is not given for the arithmetic sequence.

	a	d	n	l
1.	11	-2	19	
2.	-13	5		37
3.		-2	7	3
4.	4		11	64
5.	1.5	.5	16	
6.		$\dfrac{2}{3}$	8	15

7. What is the 43rd term in the sequence -19, -15, -11, $\cdots$?

8. The last term in an arithmetic sequence is 143, the common difference is -7, and the number of terms is 63. Find the first term.

9. Find the sixth term in the sequence $-2 + \sqrt{3}$, -1, $-\sqrt{3}$, $\cdots$.

10. Find the seventh term in the sequence $1 + i$, $2 - i$, $3 - 3i$, $\cdots$.

10.3 Arithmetic means

Terms of a sequence that are between the first and last terms are called *means*. Thus, if a sequence has n terms, there are $(n - 2)$ means.

EXAMPLE. Insert 7 arithmetic means between 7 and -2.

Solution. The sequence has 9 terms, $a = 7$, $l = -2$. Hence
$$-2 = 7 + (9 - 1)d$$
$$d = -\frac{9}{8}$$

The sequence is 7, $5\frac{7}{8}$, $4\frac{3}{4}$, $3\frac{5}{8}$, $2\frac{1}{2}$, $1\frac{3}{8}$, $\frac{1}{4}$, $-\frac{7}{8}$, -2.

Exercises

1. Show that the arithmetic mean of two numbers a and b is one half of their sum.

2. Insert one arithmetic mean between 12 and 21.

3. Insert two arithmetic means between -4 and $+5$.

4. Insert three arithmetic means between 1 and 4.

5. Insert two arithmetic means between $\sqrt{2}$ and 10.

6. Insert two arithmetic means between m and t.

7. The first term of an arithmetic sequence of three terms is a. The arithmetic mean of the first and last terms is m. Find the third term.

10.4 Arithmetic series

A *series* is the indicated sum of the terms of a sequence. Usually we use the symbol S_n to represent the sum of n terms. We can write a series in two forms and simplify by adding term by term. The second equation is obtained by reversing the order of the terms in the right member.

$$S_n = a + (a + d) + (a + 2d) + \cdots + (l - 2d) + (l - d) + l$$
$$S_n = l + (l - d) + (l - 2d) + \cdots + (a + 2d) + (a + d) + a$$
$$\overline{2S_n = (a + l) + (a + l) + (a + l) + \cdots + (a + l) + (a + l) +}$$
$$(a + l) \; .$$

or
$$2S_n = n(a + l)$$

Then
$$S_n = \frac{n}{2}(a + l) \tag{II}$$

EXAMPLE. Find the sum of 63 terms of the series $-19 - 13 - 7 - \cdots$.

Solution. $a = -19$, $d = 6$, $n = 63$.

$$S_{63} = \frac{63}{2}(-19 + l)$$

$$= \frac{63}{2}(-19 + [-19 + 62(6)])$$

$$= \frac{63}{2}(-19 - 19 + 372)$$

$$= 10{,}521$$

Exercises

1. Find the sum of the first 11 terms of the series $-3 - 1 + 1 + 3 + \cdots$.

2. Find the sum of 32 terms of the series $.5 + .75 + 1 + 1.25 + \cdots$.

3. The first term of an arithmetic series is -7 and the common difference is 1.5. The sum of n terms is -14. Find n.

4. Cylindrical tiles of uniform size are stacked in the form of a triangle. There are 21 tiles on the bottom row. What is the total number of tiles in the stack?

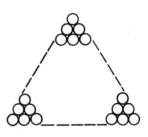

FIGURE 10–1

5. A man has $650 in a bank and is closing out the account by writing one check a week against it. The first check was $20, the second was $25, and so on, each check exceeding the previous one by $5. In how many weeks will the account be closed if there is no service charge?

10.5 Geometric sequence

A *geometric sequence* is a sequence of terms such that each term after the first is the product of the preceding term and a constant (r) called the *common ratio*. For example, the numbers 1, .2, .04, $\cdots$ form a geometric sequence for which $r = .2$. The general form of the sequence is $a, ar, ar^2, \cdots$.

Exercises

1. The first term of a geometric sequence is -3 and the common ratio is $\frac{2}{3}$. Give the next four terms.

2. The first two terms of a geometric sequence are 2, 3. Give the common ratio, and give three more terms in the sequence.

3. Do the numbers $\sqrt{2}$, 2, $\sqrt{8}$, $\cdots$ form a geometric sequence? Why?

4. Do the expressions t^{-2}, t^{-1}, 1, $\cdots$ form a geometric sequence? If so, give three more terms of the sequence.

5. Do the numbers $\sqrt[3]{3^2}$, 3, $3\sqrt[3]{3}$, $\cdots$ form a geometric sequence? If so, give three more terms of the sequence.

We may wish to find the last term of a geometric sequence. We can represent terms in a geometric sequence as follows.

$$a = \text{1st term}$$
$$ar = \text{2nd term}$$
$$ar^2 = \text{3rd term}$$
$$ar^{n-1} = n\text{th term}$$

If we consider the nth term to be the last of the sequence and designate it by l, then

$$l = ar^{n-1} \tag{III}$$

EXAMPLE. Find the 17th term in the sequence $1, \dfrac{1}{2}, \dfrac{1}{4}, \cdots$.

Solution. Since $1 \times \dfrac{1}{2} = \dfrac{1}{2}$, and $\dfrac{1}{2} \times \dfrac{1}{2} = \dfrac{1}{4}$, this is a geometric sequence in which $a = 1, r = \dfrac{1}{2}$. Then

$$l = 1 \left(\frac{1}{2}\right)^{17-1} = \frac{1}{2^{16}} = \frac{1}{65,536}$$

Exercises

1. The first term of a geometric sequence is $\dfrac{1}{2}$, and the common ratio is $\dfrac{2}{3}$. Find the last term in a sequence of 9 terms.

2. If $r = 2$, $n = 5$, and the 5th term is 24, what is the first term of a geometric sequence?

3. Find the eighth term of the geometric sequence 10, .1, .001, $\cdots$.

4. Find the ninth term of the geometric sequence $i, -2, -4i, \cdots$, where $i = \sqrt{-1}$.

5. The fifth term of a geometric sequence is $32\sqrt{2}$ and the common ratio is $-\sqrt{2}$. Write the first four terms.

10.6 Geometric means

In a geometric sequence terms between the first and last are called *geometric means*.

EXAMPLE. Insert two geometric means between 125 and 169.

Solution. We use the formula $l = ar^{n-1}$.

Then
$$169 = 125r^3$$
$$r = \frac{1}{5}\sqrt[3]{169}$$

Hence we have 125, $25\sqrt[3]{169}$, $65\sqrt[3]{13}$, 169.

Exercises

1. Show that the geometric mean of two numbers a and b is the square root of their product.

2. Insert a geometric mean between $\frac{1}{4}$ and 4.

3. Insert two geometric means between 1 and 27.

4. Insert two geometric means between -2 and 54.

5. Insert three geometric means between 2 and $\frac{1}{8}$.

10.7 Geometric series

The sum S_n of n terms of a geometric series can be expressed in the form
$$S_n = a + ar + ar^2 + \cdots + ar^{n-2} + ar^{n-1}$$
Then $S_n - rS_n = S_n(1 - r) = a - ar^n$

Or $\qquad S_n = \dfrac{a - ar^n}{1 - r} = \dfrac{ar^n - a}{r - 1} \qquad$ when $\quad (r \neq 1) \qquad$ **(IV)**

The first form is used when $r < 1$ and the second when $r > 1$.

EXAMPLE. Find the sum of 9 terms of the series $\frac{2}{3} + \frac{1}{3} + \frac{1}{6} + \cdots$.

Solution. The common ratio is the quotient of adjacent terms.
$\frac{1}{3} \div \frac{2}{3} = \frac{1}{2}$ and $\frac{1}{6} \div \frac{1}{3} = \frac{1}{2}$. Hence, this is a geometric series in which
$r = \frac{1}{2}$.

$$S_9 = \frac{\dfrac{2}{3} - \dfrac{2}{3}\left(\dfrac{1}{2}\right)^9}{1 - \dfrac{1}{2}} = \frac{511}{384}$$

Exercises

1. Find the sum of seven terms of the series $\dfrac{1}{2} + \dfrac{1}{4} + \dfrac{1}{8} + \cdots$.

2. Find the sum of nine terms of the series $\dfrac{4}{3} + 2 + 3 + \cdots$.

3. Find the sum of ten terms of the series $\dfrac{5}{3} + 5 + 15 + \cdots$.

4. Find the sum of eight terms of the series $3 - 6i - 12 + \cdots$.

5. Find the sum of twelve terms of the series $2\sqrt{3} + 3 + \dfrac{3\sqrt{3}}{2} + \cdots$.

10.8   Infinite geometric series

In Exercise 1 above you found the sum of seven terms of the series $\dfrac{1}{2} + \dfrac{1}{4} + \dfrac{1}{8} + \cdots$. Let us find the sum of the first 100 terms by means of Formula (IV).

$$S_{100} = \frac{\dfrac{1}{2} - \dfrac{1}{2}\left(\dfrac{1}{2}\right)^{100}}{1 - \dfrac{1}{2}} = \frac{\dfrac{1}{2} - \left(\dfrac{1}{2}\right)^{101}}{\dfrac{1}{2}} = \frac{\dfrac{1}{2}}{\dfrac{1}{2}} - \frac{\left(\dfrac{1}{2}\right)^{101}}{\dfrac{1}{2}} = 1 - \left(\dfrac{1}{2}\right)^{100}$$

Certainly the sum is very nearly equal to 1 since $\left(\dfrac{1}{2}\right)^{100}$ is a very small number. What is the sum of the first 1000 terms? By a method similar to that above we find that $S_{1000} = 1 - \left(\dfrac{1}{2}\right)^{1000}$ which is even nearer to 1 than the sum of the first 100 terms. Will the sum of the series ever equal 1 or exceed it?

If the terms of a series continue indefinitely without limit it is called an *infinite series*. In this section we shall confine our attention to infinite geometric series. We may need to know the sum of such a series. Let us transform formula (IV) so that we can investigate the sum when $n \to \infty$, that is, when the number of terms increases without limit.

$$S_n = \frac{a - ar^n}{1 - r} = \frac{a}{1 - r} - \frac{ar^n}{1 - r}$$

Now let $n \to \infty$. If $|r| > 1$, the numerator of the second term,

$\dfrac{ar^n}{1-r}$, increases without limit as n → ∞, and the sum is not defined. However, when $|r| < 1$, then $r^n \to 0$ as $n \to \infty$ and the limit of the second term is zero. Thus, we can write the limit of the sum of an infinite geometric series as follows.

$$\lim_{n \to \infty} S_n = \frac{a}{1-r} \quad \text{when} \quad |r| < 1$$

More simply the left member can be called S, the sum of an infinite geometric series and the formula is

$$S = \frac{a}{1-r} \quad \text{when} \quad |r| < 1 \tag{V}$$

EXAMPLE 1. Find the limiting value of the infinite geometric series

$$\frac{1}{2} + \frac{1}{4} + \frac{1}{8} + \cdots$$

Solution. The first term $a = \dfrac{1}{2}$; the ratio $r = \dfrac{1}{2}$; and $n \to \infty$. By formula (V) we have

$$S = \frac{\dfrac{1}{2}}{1 - \dfrac{1}{2}} = 1$$

EXAMPLE 2. Express the repeating decimal .454545 ⋯ as a ratio of two integers, that is, as a rational number.

Solution. .454545 ⋯ = .45 + .0045 + .000045 + ⋯

$$= \frac{45}{100} + \frac{45}{10{,}000} + \frac{45}{1{,}000{,}000} + \cdots$$

This is an infinite geometric series with a common ratio of $\dfrac{1}{100}$. We can find the sum by formula (V) as follows.

$$S = \frac{\dfrac{45}{100}}{1 - \dfrac{1}{100}} = \frac{\dfrac{45}{100}}{\dfrac{99}{100}} = \frac{45}{99} = \frac{5}{11}$$

Thus, .454545 ⋯ $= \dfrac{5}{11}$.

Exercises

1. Find the limiting value of the infinite series $\frac{2}{3} + \frac{1}{3} + \frac{1}{6} + \frac{1}{12} + \cdots$.

2. Find $S: 1 + \frac{2}{5} + \frac{4}{25} + \cdots$.

3. Find $S: \sqrt{3} + 1 + \frac{\sqrt{3}}{3} + \cdots$.

4. Find $S: .2 + .02 + .002 + \cdots$.

5. Find $S: .272727 \cdots$. (Suggestion. $.272727 \cdots = .27 + .0027 + .000027 + \cdots$.)

6. Find $S: .123123123 \cdots$.

7. Find $S: 2.205205205 \cdots$. (Suggestion. $2.205205205 \cdots = 2 + .205 + .000205 + .000000205 + \cdots$.)

8. Find $S: .3181818 \cdots$.

10.9 Compound interest

Often money is loaned with the understanding that when earnings accumulate they are to be added to the original investment at specified times and thus become part of a new principal. Interest computed on this basis is called *compound interest.*

If P dollars are loaned at r percent for one interest period, the amount $A_1 = P + Pr = P(1 + r)$. This amount bears interest for the second period at r percent and the second amount $A_2 = P(1 + r) + rP(1 + r) = P(1 + r)^2$.

We can show the accumulated amount of an investment at the end of a number of periods by means of a table.

End of period	1	2	3	4	...	n
Accumulated amount A	$P(1 + r)$	$P(1 + r)^2$	$P(1 + r)^3$	$P(1 + r)^4$	...	$P(1 + r)^n$

The compound interest formula is

$$A = P(1 + r)^n \tag{VI}$$

If the interest period is $\frac{1}{k}$ th of a year, then there are k periods per year and the interest rate is $\frac{1}{k}$ th of the annual rate. The formula becomes

$$A = P\left(1 + \frac{r}{k}\right)^{kn} \tag{VI'}$$

EXAMPLE. Find the amount when $800 is invested for $2\frac{1}{4}$ years at 4% per year, interest being compounded quarterly.

Solution. In $2\frac{1}{4}$ years there are 9 quarters. The quarterly rate is 1%.

$$A = 800(1 + .01)^9 = 800(1.0937) = 874.96 \text{ approx.}$$

The amount is $874.96.

Note: The compound interest formula involves extensive computation. Tables are usually prepared by using the electronic computer. If the deposits are irregular, the computer calculates the interest for each depositor in the bank separately.

Exercises

1. Find the compound amount of $1000 invested for 5 years at 4%, interest being compounded annually.

2. Find the compound amount of $2000 invested for 3 years at 4% per year, interest being compounded semiannually.

3. Find the compound amount of $1200 invested for $3\frac{1}{2}$ years at 5% per year, interest being compounded semiannually.

10.10 Sum of an infinite series

An *infinite series* is the sum of an unlimited number of terms. Consider the series $\frac{1}{2} + \frac{1}{4} + \frac{1}{8} + \frac{1}{16} + \cdots$. (This is a geometric series, but all infinite series are not geometric.) It is clear that we could not write all of the fractions in this series and add them to find the sum. Hence, when we speak of finding such a sum we use the word "sum" in a new way. If S_n is the sum of n terms of a series, and S is a number such that $S > S_n$ for all n, and $S - S_n$ approaches zero as n increases without limit, then the sum of the infinite series is defined to be S.

$$\lim_{n \to \infty} S_n = S$$

This is read "the limit of S_n as n increases without limit equals S."

Not only may a series such as that used as an illustration above have a limit, but the sequence of terms may also have a limit. For example, the sequence $\frac{1}{2}, \frac{1}{4}, \frac{1}{8}, \frac{1}{16}, \cdots$ has the limit 0 as the number of terms increases indefinitely. That is, the value of each successive term becomes smaller and smaller. We could express it thus

$$\lim_{n \to \infty} t_n = 0$$

where t_n is the nth term in the sequence. This is read "the limit of the nth term as n increases without limit equals zero."

It is necessary that the nth term of a series approaches zero as $n \to \infty$ but it is not sufficient. For example, $1 + \dfrac{1}{2} + \dfrac{1}{3} + \dfrac{1}{4} + \cdots + \dfrac{1}{n}$

is a series that has no limit as $n \to \infty$ even though $\lim\limits_{n \to \infty} \dfrac{1}{n} = 0$.

10.11   Convergence and divergence

If the limit of an infinite series is a real number, the series is said to *converge*.

If an infinite series does not converge, it *diverges*.

EXAMPLE 1. Determine whether the infinite series $\dfrac{1}{2} + \dfrac{1}{4} + \dfrac{1}{8} +$ $\cdots$ is convergent.

Solution. This is a geometric series in which $a = \dfrac{1}{2}$, $r = \dfrac{1}{2}$,

$n \to \infty$. Hence, $\lim\limits_{n \to \infty} S_n = \dfrac{\dfrac{1}{2}}{1 - \dfrac{1}{2}} = 1$. Since the sum has a limit,

the series is convergent.

In dealing with an infinite series it is very important to know whether it is convergent. There are a number of ways to determine this. The most direct way, of course, is to compute the limit if this can be done. This method was illustrated in the example above.

If an infinite series is geometric, we can compute the sum by Formula (V), Section 10.8, if $|r| < 1$. Will an infinite geometric series converge when $|r| > 1$? An examination of the formula for the sum reveals that it will *diverge*.

If an infinite series is not geometric, we can sometimes intuitively arrive at a formula for the sum in terms of n, prove its correctness by mathematical induction (Section 10.19), and by examination of the formula determine whether a limit exists.

EXAMPLE 2. Determine whether the infinite series $\dfrac{2}{3} + \dfrac{1}{3} + \dfrac{1}{6} +$ $\cdots$ is convergent.

Solution. This is a geometric series in which $a = \dfrac{2}{3}$, $r = \dfrac{1}{2}$.

Hence $\displaystyle\lim_{n \to \infty} S_n = \dfrac{\dfrac{2}{3}}{1 - \dfrac{1}{2}} = \dfrac{4}{3}$, and the series is convergent.

EXAMPLE 3. Determine whether a limit exists for the following infinite series: $-5 - 3 - 1 + 1 + 3 + \cdots$.

Solution. This is an arithmetic series in which $a = -5$, $d = 2$, $n \to \infty$. $S = \dfrac{n}{2}[a + a + (n - 1)d] = \dfrac{n}{2}[2a + (n - 1)d] =$ $\dfrac{n}{2}[2(-5) + nd - d] = \dfrac{n}{2}(-10 + 2n - 2) = n(n - 6)$. Now, as $n \to \infty$, $n(n - 6) \to \infty$, and hence the series has no limit. This conclusion can be reached by direct examination of the series without setting up the formula for the sum in terms of n. Can you prove that every infinite arithmetic series is divergent?

Exercises

Determine whether each given series is convergent. If so, give the limit.

1. $\dfrac{1}{9} + \dfrac{1}{27} + \dfrac{1}{81} + \cdots + \dfrac{1}{3^{n+1}} + \cdots$

2. $1 + \dfrac{1}{5} + \dfrac{1}{25} + \cdots + \dfrac{1}{5^{n-1}} + \cdots$

3. $\dfrac{8}{3} + \dfrac{32}{9} + \dfrac{128}{27} + \cdots + \dfrac{2^{2n+1}}{3^n} + \cdots$

4. $\dfrac{1}{2} + \dfrac{1}{8} + \dfrac{1}{32} \cdots + \dfrac{1}{2^{2n-1}} + \cdots$

5. $\dfrac{1}{4} + \dfrac{5}{16} + \dfrac{3}{8} + \dfrac{7}{16} + \cdots$

10.12   Certain special series

We shall later make use of certain special series which are considered below.

(1) You know for the series $a + ar + ar^2 + \cdots + ar^{n-1}$, that

$S_n = \dfrac{a - ar^n}{1 - r}$. (See (IV), Section 10.7.) If $|r| > 1$, there is no limit to the sum of n terms as $n \to \infty$. If $|r| < 1$, $\lim\limits_{n \to \infty} S_n = \dfrac{a}{1-r}$.

Since a and r are both real numbers, $\dfrac{a}{1-r}$ is a real number. Hence, the series is convergent if $|r| < 1$.

(2) In the example of Section 10.11 we proved that the series $\dfrac{1}{2} + \dfrac{1}{2^2} + \dfrac{1}{2^3} + \cdots + \dfrac{1}{2^n} + \cdots$ is convergent since it is a geometric series where $|r| < 1$.

(3) Consider the infinite series

$$1 + \frac{1}{2} + \frac{1}{3} + \frac{1}{4} + \frac{1}{5} + \frac{1}{6} + \frac{1}{7} + \frac{1}{8} + \frac{1}{9} + \frac{1}{10} + \cdots + \frac{1}{n} \cdots$$

Grouping terms in a special manner, we have

$$(1) + \left(\frac{1}{2}\right) + \left(\frac{1}{3} + \frac{1}{4}\right) + \left(\frac{1}{5} + \frac{1}{6} + \frac{1}{7} + \frac{1}{8}\right)$$
$$+ \left(\frac{1}{9} + \frac{1}{10} + \frac{1}{11} + \cdots + \frac{1}{16}\right) + \cdots + \frac{1}{n} + \cdots$$

Notice that (the first enclosed expression) $> \dfrac{1}{2}$; (the second enclosed expression) $= \dfrac{1}{2}$; (the third expression) $> \dfrac{1}{2}$, and so on. Then beginning after the second term of the series if we enclose $2, 4$, $8, 16, \cdots$ terms, each sum is greater than $\dfrac{1}{2}$. There are an unlimited number of such expressions, so the series is unlimited. In other words, there is no limit to S_n as $n \to \infty$, and hence the series is divergent.

(4) Consider the infinite series

$$1 + \frac{1}{2^p} + \frac{1}{3^p} + \frac{1}{4^p} + \frac{1}{5^p} + \frac{1}{6^p} + \frac{1}{7^p} + \frac{1}{8^p} + \cdots + \frac{1}{n^p} \cdots$$

$$\text{where } (p > 1)$$

$$1 + \left(\frac{1}{2^p} + \frac{1}{3^p}\right) + \left(\frac{1}{4^p} + \frac{1}{5^p} + \frac{1}{6^p} + \frac{1}{7^p}\right)$$
$$+ \left(\frac{1}{8^p} + \cdots + \frac{1}{15^p}\right) + \cdots$$

Notice that

$$\left(\frac{1}{2^p} + \frac{1}{3^p}\right) < \left(\frac{1}{2^p} + \frac{1}{2^p}\right) = \frac{2}{2^p} = \frac{1}{2^{p-1}}, \text{ since } \frac{1}{3^p} < \frac{1}{2^p}$$

and

$$\left(\frac{1}{4^p} + \frac{1}{5^p} + \frac{1}{6^p} + \frac{1}{7^p}\right) < \frac{1}{4^{p-1}} = \left(\frac{1}{2^{p-1}}\right)^2, \text{ and so on}$$

Hence

$$S_n = \left[1 + \frac{1}{2^p} + \frac{1}{3^p} + \cdots + \frac{1}{n^p}\right] < \left[1 + \frac{1}{2^{p-1}} + \frac{1}{(2^{p-1})^2}\right.$$
$$\left. + \frac{1}{(2^{p-1})^3} + \cdots + \frac{1}{(2^{p-1})^n}\right]$$

This last sum is a geometric series in which $a = 1$, and $r = \frac{1}{2^{p-1}}$. Since $p > 1$, $r < 1$, then $S_n = \frac{1}{1 - \frac{1}{2^{p-1}}} = \frac{1}{1 - \frac{2}{2^p}}$. Since

$p > 1$, $2^p > 2$, and $\frac{2}{2^p} < 1$, we know that $1 - \frac{2}{2^p}$ is a positive number. If we know that S_n remains less than some positive number as $n \rightarrow \infty$, we conclude that the series is convergent.

SUMMARY OF SERIES FOR REFERENCE

1. Convergent: $a + ar + ar^2 + \cdots + ar^{n-1} + \cdots, |r| < 1$

2. Convergent: $\frac{1}{2} + \frac{1}{2^2} + \frac{1}{2^3} + \cdots + \frac{1}{2^n} + \cdots$

3. Divergent: $1 + \frac{1}{2} + \frac{1}{3} + \frac{1}{4} + \frac{1}{5} + \cdots + \frac{1}{n} + \cdots$

4. Convergent: $1 + \frac{1}{2^p} + \frac{1}{3^p} + \frac{1}{4^p} + \frac{1}{5^p} + \cdots + \frac{1}{n^p} + \cdots, p > 1$

10.13 Comparison test for convergence

Suppose we know that the series

(1) $\qquad a_1 + a_2 + a_3 + a_4 + \cdots + a_n + \cdots$

is convergent, each term a_i being positive, and suppose that we wish to determine whether the series

(2) $\qquad b_1 + b_2 + b_3 + b_4 + \cdots + b_n + \cdots$

is convergent, each b_i being positive. If we compare corresponding terms, a_1 and b_1, a_2 and b_2, $\cdots$, a_n and b_n, and find in each case $a_i \geq b_i$, and $a_n \geq b_n$ as $n \to \infty$, then we conclude that series (2) is convergent. For, since each term in (2) is no larger than the corresponding term in (1), the sum of any number of terms of (2) is no larger than the sum of the same number of terms of (1). Hence, if (1) has a limit S, (2) must have a limit less than or equal to S.

If we know that the series

$$(3) \qquad c_1 + c_2 + c_3 + c_4 + \cdots + c_n + \cdots$$

is divergent, each c_i being positive, and wish to determine whether the series

$$(4) \qquad d_1 + d_2 + d_3 + d_4 + \cdots + d_n + \cdots$$

is divergent, we can sometimes compare the two series term by term and reach a conclusion. If each $d_i \geq c_i$, and $d_n \geq c_n$ as $n \to \infty$, then we conclude that (4) is divergent.

In this section we listed four series which are convenient in testing some series for convergence or divergence by comparison.

EXAMPLE. Test for convergence the series

$$\frac{1}{3} + \frac{1}{9} + \frac{1}{27} + \cdots + \frac{1}{3^n} + \cdots$$

Solution. The second series of the summary is

$$\frac{1}{2} + \frac{1}{2^2} + \frac{1}{2^3} + \cdots + \frac{1}{2^n} + \cdots$$

Comparison of the two series term by term shows

$$\frac{1}{3} < \frac{1}{2} ; \quad \frac{1}{9} < \frac{1}{2^2} ; \quad \frac{1}{27} < \frac{1}{2^3} ; \quad \frac{1}{3^n} < \frac{1}{2^n}$$

Since each term in the series to be tested is less than the corresponding term in the comparison series, and since the comparison series converges, the given series is convergent. The series to be tested is also known to be convergent because it is an infinite geometric series with a positive common ratio less than 1.

Exercises

Determine whether each given series is convergent or divergent.

1. $1 + 3 + 5 + \cdots$ **2.** $\dfrac{1}{2 + 1^2} + \dfrac{1}{2 + 2^2} + \dfrac{1}{2 + 3^2} + \cdots$

3. $\dfrac{1}{2} + \dfrac{2}{3} + \dfrac{3}{4} + \cdots$ **6.** $\dfrac{1}{1 \cdot 2} + \dfrac{1}{2 \cdot 2^2} + \dfrac{1}{3 \cdot 2^3} + \cdots$

4. $\dfrac{2}{1} + \dfrac{3}{2} + \dfrac{4}{3} + \cdots$ **7.** $\dfrac{1}{2 \cdot 1} + \dfrac{1}{2 \cdot 2} + \dfrac{1}{2 \cdot 3} + \cdots$

5. $\dfrac{1}{1^2} + \dfrac{1}{3^2} + \dfrac{1}{5^2} + \cdots$ **8.** $1 + \dfrac{1}{1 \cdot 2} + \dfrac{1}{1 \cdot 2 \cdot 3} + \dfrac{1}{1 \cdot 2 \cdot 3 \cdot 4} + \cdots$

10.14   Ratio test for convergence

Another test for convergence of certain series is the ratio test. The test is applicable whenever all terms of a series are positive. The test depends upon the ratio of consecutive terms of the series which must be expressed in general form.

Let $t_1 + t_2 + t_3 + \cdots + t_n + t_{n+1} + \cdots$ be a series each of whose terms is positive. Suppose that

$$\lim_{n \to \infty} \frac{t_{n+1}}{t_n} = r$$

It can be shown that the series is convergent whenever $|r| < 1$ and divergent if $|r| > 1$. If $r = 1$, the test fails because a series may be either convergent or divergent. This assumption is proved as a theorem in higher courses in mathematics.

In applying the ratio test, it is necessary to write general expressions for the $(n + 1)^{\text{th}}$ and the nth terms, express their ratio r, and examine it to determine whether $|r| < 1$ or $|r| > 1$ as $n \to \infty$.

EXAMPLE. Test for convergence the series

$$10 + \frac{10^2}{1 \cdot 2} + \frac{10^3}{1 \cdot 2 \cdot 3} + \cdots + \frac{10^n}{1 \cdot 2 \cdot 3 \cdots n} + \cdots$$

Solution. $t_n = \dfrac{10^n}{1 \cdot 2 \cdot 3 \cdots n}, \quad t_{n+1} = \dfrac{10^{n+1}}{1 \cdot 2 \cdot 3 \cdots (n + 1)}$

$$\lim_{n \to \infty} \frac{\dfrac{10^{n+1}}{1 \cdot 2 \cdot 3 \cdots (n + 1)}}{\dfrac{10^n}{1 \cdot 2 \cdot 3 \cdots n}} = \lim_{n \to \infty} \frac{10}{n + 1} = 0$$

Hence, the series is convergent.

Exercises

Use the ratio test to determine the convergence or divergence of each series.

1. $\dfrac{1}{2^1} + \dfrac{2}{2^2} + \dfrac{3}{2^3} + \cdots$

2. $1 + \dfrac{1}{1 \cdot 2 \cdot 3} + \dfrac{1}{1 \cdot 2 \cdot 3 \cdot 4 \cdot 5} + \dfrac{1}{1 \cdot 2 \cdot 3 \cdot 4 \cdot 5 \cdot 6 \cdot 7} + \cdots$

3. $1 + \dfrac{2}{1 \cdot 2 \cdot 3} + \dfrac{3}{1 \cdot 2 \cdot 3 \cdot 4 \cdot 5} + \dfrac{4}{1 \cdot 2 \cdot 3 \cdot 4 \cdot 5 \cdot 6 \cdot 7} + \cdots$

4. $\dfrac{1}{1 \cdot 2} + \dfrac{1}{1 \cdot 2 \cdot 3 \cdot 4} + \dfrac{1}{1 \cdot 2 \cdot 3 \cdot 4 \cdot 5 \cdot 6} + \cdots$

5. $\dfrac{1}{3} + \dfrac{1}{3^2} + \dfrac{1}{3^3} + \cdots$

6. $\dfrac{1}{1 \cdot 2} + \dfrac{1}{3 \cdot 4} + \dfrac{1}{5 \cdot 6} + \cdots$

10.15   The binomial formula

In previous mathematics courses you have found it necessary to find the square or cube of a binomial expression. Perhaps you have found even higher powers of a binomial when simplifying certain expressions. An important series is generated when $(x + y)^n$ is expanded; let us first consider the special cases where n is a small positive integer.

By direct multiplication where necessary you can readily verify the following.

$$(x + y)^0 = 1$$
$$(x + y)^1 = x + y$$
$$(x + y)^2 = x^2 + 2xy + y^2$$
$$(x + y)^3 = x^3 + 3x^2y + 3xy^2 + y^3$$
$$(x + y)^4 = x^4 + 4x^3y + 6x^2y^2 + 4xy^3 + y^4$$

The following general statements can easily be verified for the above expansions.

1. The expansion of $(x + y)^n$ has $(n + 1)$ terms, n being a positive integer.

2. y is not a factor of the first term and x is not a factor of the last term.

3. In the first and last terms the exponent of the variable is n in each case.

4. From term to term the exponent of x decreases by 1 and the exponent of y increases by 1. The sum of the exponents is n in each term of the expansion.

5. In any term if the exponent of x is multiplied by the numerical coefficient and the product is divided by the number of that term, the result is the numerical coefficient of the following term.

Can you state a rule for the expansion of any positive integral power of a binomial?

How would you expand $(x + y)^6$ without direct multiplication? The exponents of x will decrease, term by term, from 6 to 0 while the exponents of y will increase from 0 to 6. Omitting coefficients at this time we have

$$x^6y^0 + x^5y^1 + x^4y^2 + x^3y^3 + x^2y^4 + x^1y^5 + x^0y^6$$

Statement (5) above enables us to find the coefficients which can be verified by direct multiplication. To find the numerical coefficient of the second term we multiply the exponent of x in the first term, 6, by the coefficient, 1, and divide the result by the number of the term, 1. Thus, the coefficient of the second term is 6. The coefficient of the third term is found similarly; that is, $\dfrac{5 \times 6}{2} = 15$. The coefficient of the fourth term is $\dfrac{4 \times 15}{3} =$ 20. The coefficient of the fifth term is $\dfrac{3 \times 20}{4} = 15$. The coefficient of the sixth term is $\dfrac{2 \times 15}{5} = 6$, and the coefficient of the last term is 1.

Thus, $(x + y)^6 = x^6 + 6x^5y + 15x^4y^2 + 20x^3y^3 + 15x^2y^4 + 6xy^5 + y^6$

In general we can write the binomial expansion as follows.

$$(x+y)^n = x^n + nx^{n-1}y + \frac{n(n-1)}{2}x^{n-2}y^2$$

$$+ \frac{n(n-1)(n-2)}{2 \cdot 3}x^{n-3}y^3 + \cdots + y^n \qquad \text{(VII)}$$

EXAMPLE. $(3a^2 - 2b)^4 = (3a^2)^4 + 4(3a^2)^3(-2b)$

$$+ \frac{4 \cdot 3(3a^2)^2(-2b)^2}{2} + \frac{4 \cdot 3 \cdot 2(3a^2)(-2b)^3}{2 \cdot 3} + \frac{4 \cdot 3 \cdot 2(-2b)^4}{2 \cdot 3 \cdot 4}$$

$$= 81a^8 - 216a^6b + 216a^4b^2 - 96a^2b^3 + 16b^4$$

Exercises

Use the binomial formula to write the expansion of each binomial.

1. $(2x - 3y)^3$

2. $(x - 2y)^4$

3. $(2x + y)^6$

4. $(n + 2)^7$

5. $\left(\dfrac{x}{y} + v\right)^5$

6. $\left(3v - \dfrac{1}{2}w\right)^5$

7. $(2 + i)^4$

8. $(2x + \sqrt{3})^4$

9. $\left(\dfrac{1}{2}a + \dfrac{2}{3}b\right)^5$

10.16 Factorial integer

In the last two sections we have had occasion to find the product of consecutive integers in connection with certain series. For example, the product $1 \cdot 2 \cdot 3 \cdot 4 \cdot 5$ appears in the denominator of the coefficient of the sixth term in the expansion of $(x + y)^n$. Such an expression is called *factorial 5* and the symbol used to express this idea is 5!. If n is any positive integer then factorial n ($n!$ or $\underline{n}$) is the product of n and all positive integers less than n.

$$n! = n(n - 1)(n - 2)(n - 3) \cdots 3 \cdot 2 \cdot 1 \quad \text{(VIII)}$$

Now you will notice that in the expansion of $n!$ we could, if we wished, stop writing the individual factors with any number, d, and write as the final factor $(d - 1)!$.

EXAMPLE. $6! = 6 \cdot 5 \cdot 4 \cdot 3 \cdot 2 \cdot 1$ or, $6 \cdot 5(5 - 1)!$ or $6(6 - 1)!$

There is an advantage in writing the final factor as $(d - 1)!$. It helps us in giving meaning to the rather unfamiliar expression $0!$ which, for the sake of consistency, is frequently needed. From the preceding discussion, it is clear that $n! = n(n - 1)!$. Suppose now that $n = 1$. Then $1! = 1(1 - 1)!$ from which it is evident that we must define $0!$ to have the value of 1. There are other arguments which may be presented to support the fact that $0! = 1$.

Exercises

In Exercises 1–12 give the numerical value.

1. $5!$

2. $7!$

3. $9!$

4. $\dfrac{1}{2}(4!)$

5. $3(6!)$ **7.** $3!\,4!$ **9.** $\dfrac{6!}{3!}$ **11.** $\dfrac{10!}{8!}$

6. $\dfrac{1}{6}(5!)$ **8.** $5!\,3!$ **10.** $\dfrac{9!}{5!}$ **12.** $\dfrac{12!}{11!}$

In Exercises 13–16 write each product in factorial notation.

13. $1 \cdot 2 \cdot 3 \cdot 4 \cdot 5 \cdot 6$ **15.** $1 \cdot 2 \cdot 3 \cdot 4 \cdot 8 \cdot 7 \cdot 6 \cdot 5$

14. $8 \cdot 7 \cdot 6 \cdot 5 \cdot 4 \cdot 3 \cdot 2 \cdot 1$ **16.** $2 \cdot 3 \cdot 4 \cdot 5 \cdot 6 \cdot 7 \cdot 8 \cdot 9$

Simplify each of the following as far as possible, x and y being positive integers, $x > y$, $x > 2$.

17. $\dfrac{x!}{(x-2)!}$ **19.** $\dfrac{(x+1)!}{(x-1)!}$ **21.** $\dfrac{(x-y)!}{(x-y-1)!}$

18. $\dfrac{x!}{(x-y)!}$ **20.** $\dfrac{x!}{(x-y)!\,y!}$ **22.** $\dfrac{x!(x-3)!}{(x-2)!(x-1)!}$

10.17   General term of $(x + y)^n$

Can you find the rth term of the expansion of $(x + y)^n$? The coefficient will be $\dfrac{n(n-1)(n-2)(n-3) \cdots [n-(r-2)]}{2 \cdot 3 \cdot 4 \cdots (r-1)}$.

Why? In the rth term, what is the exponent of x? What is the exponent of y? Will the sum of the exponents equal n?

The rth term of $(x + y)^n$ is

$$\frac{n(n-1)(n-2)(n-3) \cdots (n-r+2)}{2 \cdot 3 \cdot 4 \cdots (r-1)} \; x^{n-r+1}y^{r-1} \quad \textbf{(IX)}$$

EXAMPLE. Find the 5th term in the expansion of $(3a - 2b)^8$.

Solution. $x = 3a$, $y = -2b$, $n = 8$, $r = 5$.

$$\frac{8(7)(6)(5)}{4!}(3a)^4(-2b)^4 = 90{,}720\ a^4b^4$$

Exercises

Write the designated term of the expansion of each binomial.

1. 4th term of $(a + b)^7$ **4.** 7th term of $\left(x - \dfrac{1}{2}y\right)^{10}$

2. 5th term of $(2x - y)^9$ **5.** 4th term of $(a - \sqrt{2})^8$

3. 3rd term of $(x - 3y)^5$ **6.** 6th term of $(3x - 2y)^{11}$

10.18   Proof by mathematical induction

We shall need a method of proof called *mathematical induction* in order to prove that the expansion formula for the binomial $(x + y)^n$ is valid for all positive integral values of n.

Mathematical induction is a proof which depends on a process that is much like climbing a ladder. First we must get on the first step; then we must show that we can always advance from one step to the next. Thus, if we can get onto the first step we can certainly climb to the second; if we are on the second step we can climb to the third; if we are on the third step we can climb to the fourth; and so on, indefinitely, for all steps.

Let us illustrate proof by mathematical induction by finding the sum of consecutive odd integers in a series. Consider the series $1 + 3 + 5 + 7 + \cdots$. What is the sum of the first two terms? The first three terms? The first four terms? What is the sum of n terms? You have no doubt discovered by now that the sum seems to be the square of the number of terms being added. Mathematical induction enables us to *prove* that this is true for the sum of *any* number of terms in the series. There are two essential steps.

   (1) Verify that $S_n = n^2$ is the correct formula for the sum of n terms when $n = 1$, the first possible case. Certainly the sum is 1 and $n^2 = 1$, so the formula $S_n = n^2$ holds for the first case. We are on the first step.

   (2) We must now show that if the formula is true for any special case (say $n = k$) then it is necessarily true for the next case ($n = k + 1$). To do this let us represent the kth term of the series $1 + 3 + 5 + \cdots$. By experimentation we see that the kth term is $2k - 1$. We are to prove that if $1 + 3 + 5 + \cdots + (2k - 1) = k^2$, then

$$1 + 3 + 5 + \cdots + (2k - 1) + (2k + 1) = (k + 1)^2$$

This means that the sum S_k is given by $1 + 3 + 5 + \cdots + (2k - 1) = k^2$, and we must prove that $S_{k+1} = (k + 1)^2$. How can we arrive at a formula for S_{k+1} from our assumption that $S_k = k^2$? By adding the next term $(2k + 1)$ to both members we have

$$S_{k+1} = 1 + 3 + 5 + \cdots + (2k - 1) + (2k + 1) = k^2 + (2k + 1)$$

If we use the formula $S_n = n^2$, how does the value of S_{k+1} found by the formula compare with the above result? The formula $S_n = n^2$ gives us $S_{k+1} = (k+1)^2$. Is the result obtained by direct addition, $k^2 + (2k+1)$, equal to $(k+1)^2$? We can verify this in a manner similar to that used in verifying trigonometric identities as follows.

$$k^2 + (2k+1) = (k+1)^2$$
$$k^2 + 2k + 1 = \quad |$$
$$(k+1)^2 = (k+1)^2$$

Since the formula for the sum for $n = k+1$ gives the same result as the direct computation of the sum of the series, the formula has been proved.

$$S_n = 1 + 3 + 5 + \cdots + (2n-1) = n^2$$

Let us review the thinking involved in a proof by mathematical induction. We must first have a formula or conjecture to prove. Generally we satisfy ourselves that the formula is valid for a number of special cases whether the formula has been given to us or we have found a tentative formula by experimentation. The steps of the proof are outlined as follows.

(a) We must first verify that the formula is true for the first possible case, usually $n = 1$. As an element of the proof it is not required (or desirable) that additional values of n be verified.

(b) We then *assume* that the formula is true for $n = k$ and prove that it is also true for $n = k + 1$. Usually the result obtained by some direct method of arriving at the $(k + 1)$ case from the k case is compared with the result obtained by the formula to be verified.

(c) Since the formula is valid for $n = 1$ (or other first case), it is valid for $n = 2$. Since it is valid for $n = 2$, it is valid for $n = 3$, and so on, indefinitely.

The power of a proof by mathematical induction is great, particularly for formulas about number relations. Its most serious disadvantage is that the formula to be proved must be known or discovered before the method can be applied.

EXAMPLE. Prove that the sum of the first n positive integers is given by the formula $\dfrac{n(n+1)}{2}$.

Solution. We are to prove that $1 + 2 + 3 + 4 + \cdots + n = \dfrac{n(n+1)}{2}$ where n is the number of terms in the series as well as the value of the last term.

(1) Verify that the formula holds for $n = 1$.

$$1 = \frac{1(1+1)}{2} = 1$$

(2) Assume that the formula is true for $n = k$, that is, $S_k = \dfrac{k(k+1)}{2}$. The sum of the series for $(k+1)$ terms can be found directly by adding the term $(k+1)$ to both numbers. We get

$$S_{k+1} = \frac{k(k+1)}{2} + (k+1)$$

Applying the formula to be proved for $n = (k+1)$ we have

$$S_{k+1} = \frac{(k+1)[(k+1)+1]}{2}$$

Does the formula give the same result as adding the $(k+1)$ term directly? Verifying this as an identity we have

$$\frac{k(k+1)}{2} + (k+1) = \frac{(k+1)[(k+1)+1]}{2}$$

$$\frac{k^2+k}{2} + \frac{2k+2}{2} = \frac{(k+1)(k+2)}{2}$$

$$\frac{k^2+3k+2}{2} =$$

$$\frac{(k+1)(k+2)}{2} = \frac{(k+1)(k+2)}{2}$$

Therefore, the formula $S_n = (1 + 2 + 3 + \cdots + n) = \dfrac{n(n+1)}{2}$ is true for all positive integral values of n.

Exercises

In each exercise prove the stated relation by means of mathematical induction. The symbol "n" represents a positive integer.

1. $2 + 4 + 6 + \cdots + (2n) = n(n + 1)$

2. $1 + 4 + 7 + \cdots + (3n - 2) = \dfrac{n(3n - 1)}{2}$

3. $1 + 3 + 6 + \cdots + \dfrac{n(n + 1)}{2} = \dfrac{n}{6}(n + 1)(n + 2)$

4. $1^2 + 2^2 + 3^2 + \cdots + n^2 = \dfrac{n}{6}(n + 1)(2n + 1)$

5. $1^3 + 2^3 + 3^3 + \cdots + n^3 = \dfrac{n^2}{4}(n + 1)^2$

6. Find the sum of the integers between 20 and 40 inclusive.

7. Find the sum of the odd integers between 20 and 40.

8. Find the sum of the even integers between 20 and 40 inclusive.

10.19 The Binomial Theorem

In stating the rule for the expansion of a binomial $(x + y)^n$, Section 10.15, and in giving the formula for the general term of the expansion, Section 10.17, we assumed that the formula was true for n equal to any positive integer even though it was tested for only a few special cases. By the use of mathematical induction we can prove this assumption as a theorem. It is a very important theorem in mathematics and is useful in many fields of mathematics including probability and statistics.

• THE BINOMIAL THEOREM

The binomial formula is true for every positive integral value of n.

$$(x + y)^n = x^n + nx^{n-1}y + \frac{n(n - 1)}{2!}x^{n-2}y^2 + \frac{n(n - 1)(n - 2)}{3!}x^{n-3}y^3 +$$

$$\cdots + \frac{n(n - 1) \cdots (n - r + 2)}{(r - 1)!}x^{n-r+1}y^{r-1} +$$

$$\cdots + nxy^{n-1} + y^n \quad \textbf{(X)}$$

Proof: Step 1. We know that the formula is true for $n = 1$ since we can verify this by inspection.

Step 2. We assume that the formula is true for $n = k$ where k is a positive integer. Then we must prove that the formula is true for $n = k + 1$. If $n = k$, we can write

$$(x + y)^k = x^k + kx^{k-1}y + \frac{k(k - 1)}{2!} x^{k-2}y^2 + \cdots +$$
$$\frac{n(n - 1) \cdots (n - k + 2)}{(k - 1)!} x^{n-k+1}y^{k-1} + \cdots + y^k$$

In order to find the value for $n = k + 1$ directly we can multiply each member of the above equation by $(x + y)$. This gives us

$$(x + y)^k(x + y) = (x + y) \left(x^k + kx^{k-1}y + \frac{k(k - 1)}{2!} x^{k-2}y^2 \right.$$
$$\left. + \cdots + y^k \right)$$

or

$$(x + y)^{k+1} = x \left(x^k + kx^{k-1}y + \frac{k(k - 1)}{2!} x^{k-2}y^2 + \cdots + y^k \right)$$
$$+ y \left(x^k + kx^{k-1}y + \frac{k(k - 1)}{2!} x^{k-2}y^2 + \cdots + y^k \right)$$
$$= x^{k+1} + kx^ky + \frac{k(k - 1)}{2!} x^{k-1}y^2 + \cdots + xy^k$$
$$+ x^ky + kx^{k-1}y^2 + \frac{k(k - 1)}{2!} x^{k-2}y^3 + \cdots + y^{k+1}$$

Combining like terms in the right member we have

$$(x + y)^{k+1} = x^{k+1} + (k + 1)x^ky + \frac{k(k + 1)}{2!} x^{k-1}y^2 + \cdots + y^{k+1}$$

In the binomial formula if $(k + 1)$ is substituted for n, we get the above equation, term by term, as you can easily verify. The formula for $(x + y)^{k+1}$ gives the same result as we get by assuming the formula to be true for $(x + y)^k$ and multiplying both members by $(x + y)$ to find the series for $n = k + 1$. We have verified that if the formula is true for $n = k$, it is true for $n = k + 1$.

In Step 1 we verified the formula for $n = 1$; hence it is true for $n = 2$. If it is true for $n = 2$, it is true for $n = 3$, and so on. The formula is true for any positive integral value of n and the theorem is proved.

Exercises

1. Prove that $(a^n - b^n)$ is divisible by $(a - b)$ for all positive integral values of n. *Hint:* Write $a^{n+1} - b^{n+1}$ in the form $a^{n+1} - ab^n + ab^n - b^{n+1}$ and factor $(a - b)$ from the first two terms and also from the last two terms.

2. Prove that $(a^n + b^n)$ is divisible by $(a + b)$ for all positive odd values of n.

10.20   Pascal's triangle

The coefficients of the terms in the expansion of $(x + y)^n$ can be arranged in the form of a number pyramid called Pascal's triangle.

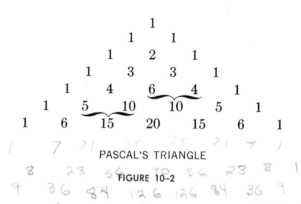

PASCAL'S TRIANGLE

FIGURE 10–2

If two consecutive numbers in any row are added, the sum is a number in the following row, the three numbers forming an isosceles triangle. For example, $1 + 3 = 4$; $6 + 4 = 10$; $5 + 10 = 15$; and so on. This relation makes it possible to extend the triangle as far as may be desired. In any row the second number indicates the power to which the binomial is raised.

Exercises

Use Pascal's triangle down to $n = 7$ to find the numerical coefficients of the expansion and write the expansion of each binomial.

1. $(x + y)^5$ 2. $(a + b)^7$ 3. $(r - s)^6$ 4. $(x - 2)^7$

Chapter Review

1. Extend the sequence 3, 4.5, 6, $\cdots$ to 8 terms.

2. Extend the sequence $\dfrac{1}{4}, \dfrac{1}{10}, \dfrac{1}{25}, \dfrac{2}{125}, \cdots$ to 8 terms.

3. Insert 3 arithmetic means between -4 and $+8$.

4. Insert 3 geometric means between 16 and 1.

5. Find the 24th term of the sequence $-6, -1, 4, \cdots$.

6. Find the 8th term of the sequence $\dfrac{1}{2}, \dfrac{3}{4}, \dfrac{9}{8}, \dfrac{27}{16}, \cdots$.

7. The first term of an arithmetic series is $+12$. Find n if the sum of n terms is 360 and the common difference is $\dfrac{1}{5}$.

8. Find the sum of 10 terms of the geometric series $\dfrac{5}{2} + 5 + 10 + \cdots$.

9. Find the sum of the infinite geometric series $3 + 1 + \dfrac{1}{3} + \dfrac{1}{9} + \cdots$.

10. Express the repeating decimal $.363636 \cdots$ as a simple fraction.

11. Determine whether the series $1 + \dfrac{1}{2} + 2 + \dfrac{3}{2} + \cdots$ is convergent.

12. Determine whether the series $\dfrac{1}{4} + \dfrac{1}{8} + \dfrac{1}{16} + \cdots$ is convergent.

13. Determine whether the series $1 + \dfrac{2}{3} + \dfrac{3}{3^2} + \dfrac{4}{3^3} + \cdots$ is convergent.

14. Write the sixth term of the expansion of $(a + 2)^{10}$.

15. Which has the greater coefficient, the fifth term of $(x - 1)^{15}$ or the tenth term of $(x + 1)^{15}$?

16. Evaluate $\dfrac{9!}{4!\,5!}$.

17. Which is greater $\dfrac{(n + 2)!}{(n - 1)!}$ or $\dfrac{n(n + 1)!}{(n - 2)!}$?

18. Prove by mathematical induction that $2 \cdot 3 + 4 \cdot 5 + 6 \cdot 7 + \cdots + 2n(2n + 1) = \dfrac{n(n + 1)(4n + 5)}{3}$.

19. The formula for the sum of the series $1 \cdot 3 + 2 \cdot 4 + 3 \cdot 5 + \cdots + n(n + 2)$ is $\dfrac{n(n + 1)(2n + 7)}{6}$. Prove it is true for all positive integral values of n.

20. Assume the binomial theorem is true for all rational values of n. Find an approximate value of $\sqrt{6}$ by expressing this number in the form $\sqrt{4+2} = 2\sqrt{1 + \frac{2}{4}} = 2\left(1 + \frac{1}{2}\right)^{\frac{1}{2}}$ and applying the formula.

≈2.45

CHAPTER OUTLINE

Special
Theorems and Functions

11

11.1 Trigonometric form of complex numbers

Every complex number can be written in the form $x + yi$ where x is the real part and yi is the imaginary part. This form is called the *rectangular form* of a complex number. Sometimes the rectangular form is written as the ordered pair (x, y). (See Section 1.10.) Many applications of complex numbers rely on properties which are associated with the angle involved when a complex number is represented by a vector. We shall develop a form to express complex numbers using trigonometric functions.

A complex number can be represented graphically as a point in the complex plane. Let P be the point in the complex plane corresponding to the complex number $x + yi$. Then $OM = x$ and $MP = y$. The distance OP

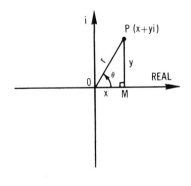

FIGURE 11–1

271

we shall call the *modulus* r and angle MOP we shall call the *amplitude* θ. The modulus is considered positive regardless of the quadrant in which P lies.

Since $\dfrac{y}{r} = \sin\theta$ and $\dfrac{x}{r} = \cos\theta$, we can write the relations

$$y = r\sin\theta ; \qquad x = r\cos\theta$$

Substituting these values for x and y in the rectangular form $x + yi$ we have

$$x + yi = r\cos\theta + i(r\sin\theta)$$

or

$$x + yi = r(\cos\theta + i\sin\theta) \tag{I}$$

The right member of (I) is called the *trigonometric form* of a complex number. Other relationships that are readily seen from the figure are

$$r = \sqrt{x^2 + y^2} \tag{II}$$

$$\theta = \arctan\frac{y}{x} \tag{III}$$

Thus, if x and y are known, r and θ can be found and a complex number in rectangular form $(x + yi)$ can be written in trigonometric form $r(\cos\theta + i\sin\theta)$, and conversely. The amplitude θ is usually expressed in radian measure and, as in trigonometric applications, the angle is placed in standard position. For evaluative purposes, the related angle is found.

EXAMPLE 1. Express $-1 + i$ in trigonometric form.

Solution. It is helpful to plot the complex number on the complex plane. $x = -1$; $y = 1$. Hence, $r = \sqrt{2}$. $\theta = \arctan\dfrac{+1}{-1} = \arctan(-1)$.

We then select a value of θ so that the terminal side lies in the second quadrant. Thus, in radian measure, $\theta = \dfrac{3\pi}{4}$. (See Section 9.2.)

Hence

$$-1 + i = \sqrt{2}\left(\cos\frac{3\pi}{4} + i\sin\frac{3\pi}{4}\right)$$

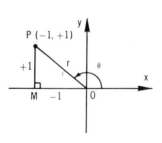

FIGURE 11-2

EXAMPLE 2. Transform $4\left(\cos\dfrac{7\pi}{6} + i\sin\dfrac{7\pi}{6}\right)$ to rectangular form.

Solution. Make a sketch of the complex number on the complex plane.

The related angle to $\dfrac{7\pi}{6}$ is $\dfrac{\pi}{6}$.

Since $x = r\cos\theta$ we have

$$x = 4\cos\frac{7\pi}{6} = -4\cos\frac{\pi}{6}$$

$$= -4\left(\frac{\sqrt{3}}{2}\right) = -2\sqrt{3}$$

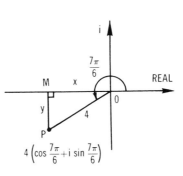

Also, $y = r\sin\theta$, so we have

$$y = 4\sin\frac{7\pi}{6} = -4\sin\frac{\pi}{6}$$

$$= -4\left(\frac{1}{2}\right) = -2$$

FIGURE 11–3

Thus, $4\left(\cos\dfrac{7\pi}{6} + i\sin\dfrac{7\pi}{6}\right) = -2\sqrt{3} - 2i.$

Exercises

Express the following complex numbers in trigonometric form.

1. $1 + i$ **3.** $3i$ **5.** $-3 - 3i$

2. -5 **4.** $2 - 2\sqrt{3}i$ **6.** $3 + 4i$

Express the following complex numbers in rectangular form.

7. $2(\cos 0 + i\sin 0)$ **10.** $\sqrt{2}\left(\cos\dfrac{5\pi}{4} + i\sin\dfrac{5\pi}{4}\right)$

8. $6\left(\cos\dfrac{3\pi}{2} + i\sin\dfrac{3\pi}{2}\right)$ **11.** $12\left(\cos\dfrac{5\pi}{3} + i\sin\dfrac{5\pi}{3}\right)$

9. $1(\cos\pi + i\sin\pi)$ **12.** $3(\cos 2 + i\sin 2)$

13. Express the roots of $x^2 + 1 = 0$ in trigonometric form.

14. Express the roots of $x^2 + x + 1 = 0$ in trigonometric form.

11.2   Operations with complex numbers in trigonometric form

The sum or difference of two complex numbers in rectangular form is easily found; the product or quotient is more difficult.

On the other hand, we shall see that products and quotients are easily found in trigonometric form but sums and differences are difficult.

Given two complex numbers in trigonometric form $r_1(\cos \theta_1 + i \sin \theta_1)$ and $r_2(\cos \theta_2 + i \sin \theta_2)$, let us find the product. By direct multiplication we have

$$r_1(\cos \theta_1 + i \sin \theta_1) \cdot r_2(\cos \theta_2 + i \sin \theta_2) =$$
$$r_1 r_2(\cos \theta_1 \cos \theta_2 + \cos \theta_1 \, i \sin \theta_2 + i \sin \theta_1 \cos \theta_2 + i^2 \sin \theta_1 \sin \theta_2)$$

Applying the commutative and associative principles and replacing i^2 by -1 we get

$$r_1(\cos \theta_1 + i \sin \theta_1) \cdot r_2(\cos \theta_2 + i \sin \theta_2) =$$
$$r_1 r_2[(\cos \theta_1 \cos \theta_2 - \sin \theta_1 \sin \theta_2) + i(\sin \theta_1 \cos \theta_2 + \cos \theta_1 \sin \theta_2)]$$
$$= r_1 r_2[\cos (\theta_1 + \theta_2) + i \sin (\theta_1 + \theta_2)] \qquad \textbf{(IV)}$$

The quotient is found by multiplying numerator and denominator by $(\cos \theta_2 - i \sin \theta_2)$ as follows.

$$\frac{r_1(\cos \theta_1 + i \sin \theta_1)}{r_2(\cos \theta_2 + i \sin \theta_2)} = \frac{r_1(\cos \theta_1 + i \sin \theta_1) \cdot (\cos \theta_2 - i \sin \theta_2)}{r_2(\cos \theta_2 + i \sin \theta_2) \cdot (\cos \theta_2 - i \sin \theta_2)} =$$

$$\frac{r_1}{r_2} \cdot \frac{(\cos \theta_1 \cos \theta_2 + \sin \theta_1 \sin \theta_2) + i(\sin \theta_1 \cos \theta_2 - \cos \theta_1 \sin \theta_2)}{\cos^2 \theta_2 + \sin^2 \theta_2}$$

Since $\cos^2 \theta_2 + \sin^2 \theta_2 = 1$, we have

$$\frac{r_1(\cos \theta_1 + i \sin \theta_1)}{r_2(\cos \theta_2 + i \sin \theta_2)} = \frac{r_1}{r_2} [\cos (\theta_1 - \theta_2) + i \sin (\theta_1 - \theta_2)] \qquad \textbf{(V)}$$

Formulas (IV) and (V) can be stated in the following form.

1. The modulus of the product of two complex numbers is the product of their moduli; the amplitude of the product is the sum of their amplitudes.

2. The modulus of the quotient of two complex numbers is the quotient of their moduli; the amplitude of the quotient is the difference of their amplitudes.

EXAMPLE. Find the product and quotient of $6 \left(\cos \dfrac{\pi}{6} + i \sin \dfrac{\pi}{6} \right)$ and $2 \left(\cos \dfrac{2\pi}{3} + i \sin \dfrac{2\pi}{3} \right)$.

Solution. The modulus of the product is $6 \cdot 2 = 12$. The amplitude of the product is $\dfrac{\pi}{6} + \dfrac{2\pi}{3} = \dfrac{5\pi}{6}$. The product of the complex numbers is

$$6\left(\cos\frac{\pi}{6} + i\sin\frac{\pi}{6}\right) \cdot 2\left(\cos\frac{2\pi}{3} + i\sin\frac{2\pi}{3}\right)$$
$$= 12\left(\cos\frac{5\pi}{6} + i\sin\frac{5\pi}{6}\right)$$

The modulus of the quotient is $6 \div 2 = 3$. The amplitude of the quotient is $\dfrac{\pi}{6} - \dfrac{2\pi}{3} = -\dfrac{\pi}{2} = \dfrac{3\pi}{2}$. The quotient is

$$\frac{6\left(\cos\dfrac{\pi}{6} + i\sin\dfrac{\pi}{6}\right)}{2\left(\cos\dfrac{2\pi}{3} + i\sin\dfrac{2\pi}{3}\right)} = 3\left(\cos\frac{3\pi}{2} + i\sin\frac{3\pi}{2}\right)$$

Exercises

Find the product or quotient as indicated.

1. $2(\cos\pi + i\sin\pi) \cdot 5(\cos 2\pi + i\sin 2\pi)$

2. $3\left(\cos\dfrac{\pi}{2} + i\sin\dfrac{\pi}{2}\right) \cdot 7\left(\cos\dfrac{3\pi}{4} + i\sin\dfrac{3\pi}{4}\right)$

3. $3\sqrt{2}\left(\cos\dfrac{\pi}{4} + i\sin\dfrac{\pi}{4}\right) \div \sqrt{2}\left(\cos\dfrac{\pi}{6} + i\sin\dfrac{\pi}{6}\right)$

4. $6\left(\cos\dfrac{5\pi}{8} + i\sin\dfrac{5\pi}{8}\right) \div 12\left(\cos\dfrac{\pi}{2} + i\sin\dfrac{\pi}{2}\right)$

5. $8\left(\cos\dfrac{3\pi}{4} + i\sin\dfrac{3\pi}{4}\right) \cdot 2\left(\cos\dfrac{5\pi}{4} + i\sin\dfrac{5\pi}{4}\right)$

6. $9.24(\cos 1.8 + i\sin 1.8) \div 3.1(\cos 0.7 + i\sin 0.7)$

Transform to trigonometric form and find the product or quotient as indicated. Express the result in rectangular form.

7. $(1 + i)(-1 - i)$

8. $(\sqrt{3} + i)(-2 + 2i)$

9. $(-4 - 4\sqrt{3}\, i) \div (2i)$

10. $(3 - 3i) \div (-2 + 2i)$

11. Express the results of Exercises 1–6 in rectangular form.

11.3   Powers of complex numbers—DeMoivre's Theorem

If a complex number is to be squared, formula (IV) permits us to write

$$[r(\cos \theta + i \sin \theta)]^2 = r^2(\cos 2\theta + i \sin 2\theta)$$

We shall prove by mathematical induction that

$$[r(\cos \theta + i \sin \theta)]^n = r^n(\cos n\theta + i \sin n\theta) \qquad \textbf{(VI)}$$

where n is any positive integer.

Since the formula is true when $n = 1$ and $n = 2$, as shown above, we assume the formula is true for $n = k$. We then have

$$[r(\cos \theta + i \sin \theta)]^k = r^k(\cos k\theta + i \sin k\theta)$$

Multiplying each member by $r(\cos \theta + i \sin \theta)$ we have

$$
\begin{aligned}
[r(\cos \theta + i \sin \theta)]^{k+1} &= [r^k(\cos k\theta + i \sin k\theta)][r(\cos \theta + i \sin \theta)] \\
&= r^{k+1}(\cos k\theta \cos \theta + \cos k\theta i \sin k\theta + \\
&\qquad i \sin k\theta \cos \theta + i^2 \sin k\theta \sin \theta) \\
&= r^{k+1}[(\cos k\theta \cos \theta - \sin k\theta \sin \theta) + \\
&\qquad i(\sin k\theta \cos \theta + \cos k\theta \sin \theta)] \\
&= r^{k+1}[\cos (k + 1)\theta + i \sin (k + 1)\theta]
\end{aligned}
$$

Since the right member in the last equation is precisely what we have when $n = k + 1$ in Formula (VI), the formula is proved for positive integral values of n. It can be proved, and we shall assume, that the formula is true for n equal to any rational number.

The above Formula (VI) is the basis of DeMoivre's Theorem which may be stated as follows.

• *The nth power of a complex number is a complex number whose modulus is the nth power of the modulus of the given complex number and whose amplitude is n times the amplitude of the given complex number, n being a rational number.*

EXAMPLE 1. Find the 5th power of $1 + i$.

Solution. $1 + i = \sqrt{2}\left(\cos \dfrac{\pi}{4} + i \sin \dfrac{\pi}{4}\right)$

Hence, $(1 + i)^5 = \left[\sqrt{2}\left(\cos \dfrac{\pi}{4} + i \sin \dfrac{\pi}{4}\right)\right]^5$

$$= (\sqrt{2})^5\left(\cos \dfrac{5\pi}{4} + i \sin \dfrac{5\pi}{4}\right)$$

$$= 4\sqrt{2}\left(\cos \dfrac{5\pi}{4} + i \sin \dfrac{5\pi}{4}\right)$$

In rectangular form, $4\sqrt{2}\left(\cos\dfrac{5\pi}{4} + i\sin\dfrac{5\pi}{4}\right) = -4 - 4i$

Thus, $(1 + i)^5 = -4 - 4i$

EXAMPLE 2. Express $\sqrt{i}$ as a complex number in rectangular form.

Solution. $\sqrt{i} = i^{\frac{1}{2}}$.

$$i = 0 + i = 1\left(\cos\frac{\pi}{2} + i\sin\frac{\pi}{2}\right)$$

Therefore, $(i)^{\frac{1}{2}} = \left[1\left(\cos\dfrac{\pi}{2} + i\sin\dfrac{\pi}{2}\right)\right]^{\frac{1}{2}}$

$$= 1^{\frac{1}{2}}\left(\cos\frac{\pi}{4} + i\sin\frac{\pi}{4}\right) = 1\left(\cos\frac{\pi}{4} + i\sin\frac{\pi}{4}\right)$$

Thus, $\sqrt{i} = \dfrac{\sqrt{2}}{2} + \dfrac{\sqrt{2}}{2}i$

Exercises

Express the following powers of complex numbers as a complex number in rectangular form.

1. $(1 - i)^5$ 3. $(-3 + 3i)^3$ 5. $(3 + 4i)^4$

2. $(-2 + 2\sqrt{3}\,i)^4$ 4. $(1 + i)^{10}$ 6. $(-5 + 12i)^2$

7. Verify that DeMoivre's Theorem is true for $n = -1$.

8. Verify that DeMoivre's Theorem is true for $n = \dfrac{1}{2}$.

11.4   Roots of complex numbers

DeMoivre's Theorem is true for all rational values of n and this fact enables us to find roots of numbers by letting $n = \dfrac{1}{2}, \dfrac{1}{3}, \dfrac{1}{4},$ $\cdots$. Thus we can find the pth root of a complex number by the formula

$$(x + yi)^{\frac{1}{p}} = [r(\cos\theta + i\sin\theta)]^{\frac{1}{p}}$$

$$= r^{\frac{1}{p}}\left(\cos\frac{\theta}{p} + i\sin\frac{\theta}{p}\right) \quad \textbf{(VII)}$$

It can be proved that any complex number has p distinct p^{th} roots, that is, it has two square roots, three cube roots, four fourth roots, and so on. By recalling that $\cos\theta = \cos(\theta + 2n\pi)$

and $\sin \theta = \sin (\theta + 2n\pi)$, where $n = 1, 2, 3, \cdots$, we can transform (VII) into the more general form

$$(x + yi)^{\frac{1}{p}} = \{r[\cos (\theta + 2n\pi) + i \sin (\theta + 2n\pi)]\}^{\frac{1}{p}}$$

$$= r^{\frac{1}{p}} \left(\cos \frac{\theta + 2n\pi}{p} + i \sin \frac{\theta + 2n\pi}{p} \right) \quad \text{(VIII)}$$

For $n = p, \; p + 1, \; p + 2, \; \cdots, \; 2p - 1$ we have the same results as for $n = 0, \; 1, \; 2, \; \cdots, \; p - 1$. Hence, there are exactly p distinct p^{th} roots.

EXAMPLE 1. Find the three cube roots of 1, often called the *cube roots of unity*.

Solution. In rectangular form, $1 = 1 + 0i$; in trigonometric form, $1 + 0i = 1 [\cos (0 + 2n\pi) + i \sin (0 + 2n\pi)]$.

Thus, $(1 + 0i)^{\frac{1}{3}} = \{1[\cos (0 + 2n\pi) + i \sin (0 + 2n\pi)]\}^{\frac{1}{3}}$

$$= 1^{\frac{1}{3}} \left(\cos \frac{0 + 2n\pi}{3} + i \sin \frac{0 + 2n\pi}{3} \right)$$

The value of the modulus is always a positive real number; therefore the modulus of the root is 1. By letting $n = 0, 1,$ and 2 successively we have the following cube roots of 1.

$$1 (\cos 0 + i \sin 0) = 1$$

$$1 \left(\cos \frac{2\pi}{3} + i \sin \frac{2\pi}{3} \right) = -\frac{1}{2} + \frac{\sqrt{3}}{2} i$$

$$1 \left(\cos \frac{4\pi}{3} + i \sin \frac{4\pi}{3} \right) = -\frac{1}{2} - \frac{\sqrt{3}}{2} i$$

The cube roots of unity are $1, \; -\frac{1}{2} + \frac{\sqrt{3}}{2} i, \; -\frac{1}{2} - \frac{\sqrt{3}}{2} i$.

This means that: $(1)^3 = 1$; $\left(-\frac{1}{2} + \frac{\sqrt{3}}{2} i \right)^3 = 1$; and

$\left(-\frac{1}{2} - \frac{\sqrt{3}}{2} i \right)^3 = 1$ as can be verified by direct multiplication.

EXAMPLE 2. Solve the equation $x^4 + 1 = 0$ for all roots.

Solution. $x^4 = -1 = -1 + 0i$

Thus, $x = (-1 + 0i)^{\frac{1}{4}}$

By transforming the right member into trigonometric form we can find the four fourth roots of -1.

$$(-1 + 0i)^{\frac{1}{4}} = \{1 \, [\cos \, (\pi + 2n\pi) + i \sin \, (\pi + 2n\pi)]\}^{\frac{1}{4}}$$

$$= 1^{\frac{1}{4}}\left(\cos \frac{\pi + 2n\pi}{4} + i \sin \frac{\pi + 2n\pi}{4}\right)$$

The roots x_1, x_2, x_3, and x_4 are

$$x_1 = 1\left(\cos \frac{\pi}{4} + i \sin \frac{\pi}{4}\right) = \frac{\sqrt{2}}{2} + \frac{\sqrt{2}}{2} i$$

$$x_2 = 1\left(\cos \frac{3\pi}{4} + i \sin \frac{3\pi}{4}\right) = -\frac{\sqrt{2}}{2} + \frac{\sqrt{2}}{2} i$$

$$x_3 = 1\left(\cos \frac{5\pi}{4} + i \sin \frac{5\pi}{4}\right) = -\frac{\sqrt{2}}{2} - \frac{\sqrt{2}}{2} i$$

$$x_4 = 1\left(\cos \frac{7\pi}{4} + i \sin \frac{7\pi}{4}\right) = \frac{\sqrt{2}}{2} - \frac{\sqrt{2}}{2} i$$

Compare these results with those of the cube roots and fourth roots of unity as shown in Section 3.15. Which method of finding the roots is easier? Which method is more adaptable to higher roots of unity and other roots?

Exercises

Find one of the indicated roots.

1. $(1 + i)^{\frac{1}{3}}$ 3. $(-2 - 2i)^{\frac{1}{4}}$ 5. $\sqrt[5]{-1}$
2. $(2\sqrt{3} + 2i)^{\frac{1}{5}}$ 4. $(-4i)^{\frac{1}{10}}$ 6. $\sqrt[3]{i}$

Solve the following equations for all roots.

7. $x^3 + 1 = 0$ 9. $x^4 - 1 = 0$
8. $x^3 - 8 = 0$ 10. $x^5 - 1 = 0$

11.5   An important limit—$\lim\limits_{\alpha \to 0} \dfrac{\sin \alpha}{\alpha}$

It is necessary to consider certain limits of functions in the series we shall study later in this chapter. One of these limits is

$$\lim_{\alpha \to 0} \frac{\sin \alpha}{\alpha} = 1 \qquad\qquad \text{(IX)}$$

We emphasize that α is expressed in radians. An investigation of the tabular values of the sine function and the corresponding radian measure of the angle indicates that the ratio of the sine of an angle to the angle in radian measure approaches the indeterminate form $\dfrac{0}{0}$ as the value of the angle approaches 0. However, the table also indicates that as α assumes very small positive values, the sin α appears to approach the same small value. The following geometric proof will verify that the limit of the ratio $\dfrac{\sin \alpha}{\alpha}$ as the angle α approaches zero, is 1. (See Chapter 19 for a more thorough discussion of limits.)

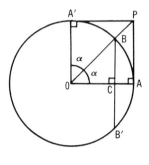

FIGURE 11-4

Let α be a central angle ($\angle AOB$) less than $\dfrac{\pi}{4}$ in a circle whose radius is 1. The sides of the angle are $OA = OB = 1$. Then construct $\angle BOA' \cong \angle AOB$. Construct tangents at A and A' intersecting at P. It is simple to prove that P lies on OB extended. (*Hint:* Assume the perpendicular to OA at A intersects OB extended at P, and assume the perpendicular to OA' at A' intersects OB at P'. Then prove $\triangle OAP \cong \triangle OA'P'$, from which $OP = OP'$ and P' coincides with P.)

Construct $BC \perp OA$ and extend to B' on the circle. The following relationships are known. (See Section 6.4.) $PA = \tan \alpha$; $BC = \sin \alpha$; $OP = \sec \alpha$; arc $AB = $ arc $BA' = $ arc $B'A$; $AP = A'P$; $B'C = CB$.

From the drawing the following inequalities are evident.

(1) $AP + PA' > $ arc ABA'
(2) arc $B'AB > B'B$
(3) $OP > OB$

Since $AP + PA' = 2AP$ and arc $ABA' = 2$arc $AB = 2\alpha$, from (1) we can write: $2AP > 2\alpha$.

Since arc $B'A = $ arc AB making arc $B'AB = 2$arc $AB = 2\alpha$, and $BB' = B'C + CB = 2\ CB$, from (2) we can write: $2\alpha > 2\ CB$. Combining these two inequalities and dividing by 2 we get

$$AP > \alpha > CB$$

or $$\tan \alpha > \alpha > \sin \alpha$$

Dividing by sin α, sin $\alpha \neq 0$, we have

$$\sec \alpha > \frac{\alpha}{\sin \alpha} > 1$$

Taking reciprocals (which reverses the inequality signs) we have

$$\cos \alpha < \frac{\sin \alpha}{\alpha} < 1$$

Now find the limit as $\alpha \to 0$; therefore $\cos \alpha \to 1$ as $\alpha \to 0$. Hence, $\lim\limits_{\alpha \to 0} \dfrac{\sin \alpha}{\alpha} = 1$ because the ratio $\dfrac{\sin \alpha}{\alpha}$ lies between 1 and a quantity which approaches 1 as a limit.

Exercises

Solve the following exercises. ($Hint:$ $\lim\limits_{\alpha \to 0} \dfrac{\sin \alpha}{\alpha} = 1$.)

1. Prove: $\lim\limits_{\alpha \to 0} \dfrac{\tan \alpha}{\alpha} = 1$

2. Find the value of: $\lim\limits_{\alpha \to 0} \dfrac{1 - \cos \alpha}{\alpha \sin \alpha}$ $\left(Hint: \dfrac{1 - \cos \alpha}{\sin \alpha} = \tan \dfrac{\alpha}{2}.\right)$

3. Evaluate: $\lim\limits_{\alpha \to 0} \dfrac{\sin 2\alpha}{\alpha}$

4. Evaluate: $\lim\limits_{\alpha \to 0} \sqrt{\dfrac{1 - \cos \alpha}{2\alpha^2}}$

11.6   Trigonometric series

Values of trigonometric functions for specified values of the angle can be found to any desired degree of accuracy by means of certain series. The numbers in the tables of natural values are calculated in this manner. In this section we shall develop an infinite series for each of the two functions $\sin x$ and $\cos x$. Remember that x must be expressed in radians.

By DeMoivre's Theorem

$$(\cos \alpha + i \sin \alpha)^n = \cos n\alpha + i \sin n\alpha$$

By the Binomial Theorem

$$(\cos \alpha + i \sin \alpha)^n = \cos^n \alpha + n \cos^{n-1} \alpha \, (i \sin \alpha)$$
$$+ \frac{n(n-1)}{2!} \cos^{n-2} \alpha \, (i \sin \alpha)^2$$
$$+ \frac{n(n-1)(n-2)}{3!} \cos^{n-3} \alpha \, (i \sin \alpha)^3 + \cdots$$
$$= \cos^n \alpha + in \cos^{n-1} \alpha \sin \alpha - \frac{n(n-1)}{2!} \cos^{n-2} \alpha \sin^2 \alpha$$
$$- i \frac{n(n-1)(n-2)}{3!} \cos^{n-3} \alpha \sin^3 \alpha + \cdots$$

Grouping the terms not containing i and those containing i we have

$$(\cos \alpha + i \sin \alpha)^n = (\cos^n \alpha - \frac{n(n-1)}{2!} \cos^{n-2} \alpha \sin^2 \alpha + \cdots) +$$

$$i(n \cos^{n-1} \alpha \sin \alpha - \frac{n(n-1)(n-2)}{3!} \cos^{n-3} \alpha \sin^3 \alpha + \cdots)$$

Equating the results of DeMoivre's Theorem and the Binomial Theorem and recalling that when two complex numbers are equal their real parts are equal and their imaginary parts are equal, we can write the two equations

$$\cos n\alpha = \cos^n \alpha - \frac{n(n-1)}{2!} \cos^{n-2} \alpha \sin^2 \alpha +$$

$$\frac{n(n-1)(n-2)(n-3)}{4!} \cos^{n-4} \alpha \sin^4 \alpha + \cdots \quad \textbf{(X)}$$

$$\sin n\alpha = n \cos^{n-1} \alpha \sin \alpha -$$

$$\frac{n(n-1)(n-2)}{3!} \cos^{n-3} \alpha \sin \alpha + \cdots \quad \textbf{(XI)}$$

Let $x = n\alpha$; replacing $n\alpha$ by x and n by $\frac{x}{\alpha}$ everywhere except in the exponents we have

$$\cos x = \cos^n \alpha - \frac{\frac{x}{\alpha}(\frac{x}{\alpha} - 1)}{2!} \cos^{n-2} \alpha \sin^2 \alpha +$$

$$\frac{\frac{x}{\alpha}(\frac{x}{\alpha} - 1)(\frac{x}{\alpha} - 2)(\frac{x}{\alpha} - 3)}{4!} \cos^{n-4} \alpha \sin^4 \alpha + \cdots$$

$$\sin x = \frac{x}{\alpha} \cos^{n-1} \alpha \sin \alpha - \frac{\frac{x}{\alpha}(\frac{x}{\alpha} - 1)(\frac{x}{\alpha} - 2)}{3!} \cos^{n-3} \alpha \sin^3 \alpha + \cdots$$

Writing each equation above so that the ratio $\frac{\sin \alpha}{\alpha}$ appears we have

$$\cos x = \cos^n \alpha - \frac{x(x - \alpha)}{2!} \cos^{n-2} \alpha \frac{\sin^2 \alpha}{\alpha^2} +$$

$$\frac{x(x - \alpha)(x - 2\alpha)(x - 3\alpha)}{4!} \cos^{n-4} \alpha \frac{\sin^4 \alpha}{\alpha^4} + \cdots$$

$$\sin x = x \cos^{n-1} \alpha \frac{\sin \alpha}{\alpha} - \frac{x(x - \alpha)(x - 2\alpha)}{3!} \cos^{n-3} \alpha \frac{\sin^3 \alpha}{\alpha^3} + \cdots$$

Now let $\alpha \to 0$; then $n \to \infty$. Thus, $\cos \alpha \to 1$ and $\dfrac{\sin \alpha}{\alpha} \to 1$. By taking the limit as $\alpha \to 0$, we have

$$\cos x = 1 - \frac{x^2}{2!} + \frac{x^4}{4!} - \frac{x^6}{6!} + \frac{x^8}{8!} - \cdots \qquad \text{(XII)}$$

and

$$\sin x = x - \frac{x^3}{3!} + \frac{x^5}{5!} - \frac{x^7}{7!} + \frac{x^9}{9!} - \cdots \qquad \text{(XIII)}$$

The two series are convergent for all values of x. By replacing x in the above relations with any angle in radians and carrying out the computation as far as desired, approximate natural values of the trigonometric functions can be found to any desired degree of accuracy. Computers can perform these calculations easily.

Exercises

1. Use (XIII) to compute $\sin \dfrac{\pi}{4}$ accurate to two decimal places.

2. Use (XII) to compute $\cos \dfrac{\pi}{4}$ accurate to two decimal places.

3. Compute $\sin 15°$ accurate to three decimal places.

4. Compute $\cos 20°$ accurate to three decimal places.

5. Show that $\cos^2 x - \sin^2 x = \cos 2x$ by means of (XII) and (XIII). (*Hint:* Factor the left member.)

6. Show that $\sin 2x = 2 \sin x \cos x$.

11.7   Exponential series

Perhaps the most well-known and widely used irrational number is π. In 1748 Euler published a work in which he developed another irrational number which was to rank along with π in importance; in his honor the number came to be called e, the Euler number. The number is the limit of the sum of the infinite series

$$e = 1 + \frac{1}{1!} + \frac{1}{2!} + \frac{1}{3!} + \frac{1}{4!} + \cdots + \frac{1}{n!} + \cdots$$

This series does not indicate whether e is transcendental, or, indeed, irrational. An indirect proof that e is irrational can be given. Napier used e as the base of the system of natural logarithms.

Another, and perhaps more useful, way of defining e is the limit of a certain binomial expansion. In this form we have

$$e = \lim_{k \to \infty} \left(1 + \frac{1}{k}\right)^k = 2.7182818 \cdots$$

Much of higher mathematics, especially calculus, involves the number e.

Let v be any variable and by the binomial formula we can write

$$(1 + v)^n = 1 + nv + \frac{n(n-1)}{2!} v^2 + \frac{n(n-1)(n-2)}{3!} v^3 + \cdots$$

Now let k be a variable such that $v = \frac{1}{k}$ and let x be a variable such that $kx = n$. By substituting these values for v and n we get

$$\left(1 + \frac{1}{k}\right)^{kx} = 1 + kx\left(\frac{1}{k}\right) + \frac{kx(kx-1)}{2!}\left(\frac{1}{k}\right)^2 +$$

$$\frac{kx(kx-1)(kx-2)}{3!}\left(\frac{1}{k}\right)^3 + \cdots$$

$$= 1 + x + \frac{x\left(x - \frac{1}{k}\right)}{2!} + \frac{x\left(x - \frac{1}{k}\right)\left(x - \frac{2}{k}\right)}{3!} + \cdots$$

Let $v \to 0$; then $k \to \infty$. We then have

$$\lim_{k \to \infty}\left(1 + \frac{1}{k}\right)^{kx} = 1 + x + \frac{x^2}{2!} + \frac{x^3}{3!} + \frac{x^4}{4!} + \frac{x^5}{5!} + \cdots$$

If $x = 1$, the left member is the definition of e. Thus

$$e = 1 + 1 + \frac{1}{2!} + \frac{1}{3!} + \frac{1}{4!} + \cdots = 2.71828 \cdots \qquad \textbf{(XIV)}$$

If x is a variable, then we have

$$e^x = 1 + x + \frac{x^2}{2!} + \frac{x^3}{3!} + \frac{x^4}{4!} + \cdots \qquad \textbf{(XV)}$$

Exercises

1. Compute e correct to three decimal places using (XIV).

2. Compute e^2 correct to three decimal places using (XV).

11.8 Continuously compounded interest

The exponential function in Section 11.7 has many important and interesting applications. The laws of growth of living organisms involve the form $c \cdot e^x$; another example is that of radioactive decay. We shall illustrate here an application to compound interest.

When money was first loaned, some form of simple interest was charged. Later the concept of compound interest developed when money was invested for periods greater than one year. Then semi-annual and quarterly periods of compounding were introduced. The question naturally arose, "What would be the interest if it is compounded monthly, daily, each second?" This is not at all an improbable situation since many short term loans are negotiated. We shall show how to compute *continuously compounded interest*.

If a principal P is invested at an annual rate r for k years, compounded annually, the amount A is given by the formula

$$A = P(1 + r)^k$$

When interest is compounded n times per year then the rate per period is $\dfrac{r}{n}$ and the number of periods in k years is nk. The formula is then modified to the form

$$A = P\left(1 + \frac{r}{n}\right)^{nk} \qquad \text{(See Section 10.9.)}$$

Let us now consider the special case where $rk = 1$. This could happen if money were invested for 20 years at 5%, for example. Then $r = \dfrac{1}{k}$ and we have

$$A = P\left(1 + \frac{1}{nk}\right)^{nk}$$

If money is compounded continuously, n increases without limit. Thus, $nk \to \infty$, since k cannot equal zero. If the principal $P = 1$, we have the following limiting value of A as $nk \to \infty$.

$$A = \lim_{nk \to \infty} \left(1 + \frac{1}{nk}\right)^{nk} = e$$

That is, if \$1 is continuously compounded at rate r for k years where $rk = 1$, the amount at the end of that time will be \$2.71828 . . . or \$2.72.

Exercises

1. If \$100 is invested at 4% continuously compounded for 25 years, what is the amount at the end of that time?
2. If \$500 is invested at 4% continuously compounded for 50 years, what is the amount at the end of that time.
3. If \$1000 is invested at 5% continuously compounded for 20 years, how much more is the amount than if it were compounded annually?

11.9   Euler's formulas

The great Swiss mathematician Leonard Euler was a very prolific writer on mathematics. His name is associated with a number of important mathematical relations. Among these is the relation between the trigonometric series and the exponential series. See Sections 11.6 and 11.7.

In formula (XV) if we replace x by $i\alpha$, we have

$$e^{i\alpha} = 1 + i\alpha + \frac{(i\alpha)^2}{2!} + \frac{(i\alpha)^3}{3!} + \frac{(i\alpha)^4}{4!} + \cdots$$

$$= 1 + i\alpha - \frac{\alpha^2}{2!} - i\frac{\alpha^3}{3!} + \frac{\alpha^4}{4!} + \cdots$$

By grouping the terms according to whether or not they contain the factor i, we have

$$e^{i\alpha} = \left(1 - \frac{\alpha^2}{2!} + \frac{\alpha^4}{4!} - \frac{\alpha^6}{6!} + \cdots\right) + i\left(\alpha - \frac{\alpha^3}{3!} + \frac{\alpha^5}{5!} - \frac{\alpha^7}{7!} + \cdots\right)$$

Notice that the real part is exactly $\cos \alpha$ by formula (XII) and the coefficient of i in the imaginary part is exactly $\sin \alpha$ by formula (XIII). Thus we have

$$e^{i\alpha} = \cos \alpha + i \sin \alpha \tag{XVI}$$

If $-i\alpha$ had been substituted for x in this development we would have

$$e^{-i\alpha} = \cos \alpha - i \sin \alpha \tag{XVII}$$

By applying formula (XVI) we can write any complex number in *exponential form*, θ in radians.

$$x + yi = r(\cos \theta + i \sin \theta) = re^{i\theta} \qquad \textbf{(XVIII)}$$

If we subtract (XVII) from (XVI) we have

$$e^{i\alpha} - e^{-i\alpha} = 2i \sin \alpha$$

Thus

$$\sin \alpha = \frac{e^{i\alpha} - e^{-i\alpha}}{2i} \qquad \textbf{(XIX)}$$

In a similar manner, if (XVII) and (XVI) are added we have

$$\cos \alpha = \frac{e^{i\alpha} + e^{-i\alpha}}{2} \qquad \textbf{(XX)}$$

Formulas (XIX) and (XX) are called Euler's formulas for $\sin \alpha$ and $\cos \alpha$.

You know from your study of logarithms that there is no real number which is the logarithm of a negative number. By considering a special case of (XVI) we can find a complex number which is the logarithm of a negative number. Let $\alpha = \pi$ and we have

$$e^{i\pi} = \cos \pi + i \sin \pi$$

But $\cos \pi = -1$ and $\sin \pi = 0$. Hence

$$e^{i\pi} = -1 \qquad \textbf{(XXI)}$$

This relation has been described as the most beautiful one in mathematics for it relates three of the most important mathematical numbers: e, π, and i.

If the logarithm to the base e is taken of both members of (XXI) we have

$$\log_e e^{i\pi} = \log_e(-1)$$

or

$$i\pi = \log_e(-1)$$

Note: More generally, $\log_e(-1) = i\pi(2n + 1)$, where $n = 0, 1, 2, \cdots$. This can be shown since $\alpha = (\alpha + 2n\pi)$ if we develop (XXI) by replacing α by $(\pi + 2n\pi)$ or $\pi(2n + 1)$. The logarithm of a negative number $-k$ can be found since $\log_e(-k) = \log_e(-1)k = \log_e(-1) + \log_e k$, a complex number.

Exercises

1. Show that $\log_e(-2) = \log_e 2 + i\pi$.
2. What is $\log_e(-4)$?

Prove formulas in Exercises 3–6 by using Euler's formulas.

3. $\sin 2x = 2\sin x \cos x$
4. $\cos 2x = \cos^2 x - \sin^2 x$
5. $\sin^2 x + \cos^2 x = 1$
6. $\sec^2 x = 1 + \tan^2 x$

Write the following complex numbers in exponential form.

7. $2\left(\cos\dfrac{\pi}{3} + i\sin\dfrac{\pi}{3}\right)$

8. $\dfrac{\sqrt{2}}{2} - \dfrac{\sqrt{2}}{2}i$

9. $-\dfrac{1}{2} + \dfrac{\sqrt{2}}{2}i$

10. $\dfrac{\sqrt{3}}{2} + \dfrac{1}{2}i$

11. Evaluate: i^i.

Chapter Review

1. Express the following complex numbers in trigonometric and in exponential form.
   a. $2 + 2i$ b. $-2 + 2\sqrt{3}i$ c. $6 - 8i$

2. Express the following complex numbers in rectangular and in exponential form.
   a. $4\left(\cos\dfrac{5\pi}{6} + i\sin\dfrac{5\pi}{6}\right)$ c. $3(\cos 1 + i\sin 1)$

   b. $8\left(\cos\dfrac{7\pi}{4} + i\sin\dfrac{7\pi}{4}\right)$

3. Express the following complex numbers in rectangular and trigonometric form.
   a. $2e^{\pi i}$ b. $6e^{\frac{3\pi}{4}i}$ c. $5e^{\frac{3\pi}{2}i}$

4. Find $(2 + 2i)^8$ by DeMoivre's Theorem.

5. Solve for all roots: $x^5 - 32 = 0$.

6. Evaluate: $\displaystyle\lim_{\alpha \to 0} \dfrac{\tan 2\alpha}{\alpha}$.

7. Compute $\cos \dfrac{\pi}{6}$ accurate to 3 decimal places by means of a series.

8. Compute e^3 accurate to one decimal place by means of a series.

9. Find the interest on $1000 invested at 8% compounded continuously for 25 years.

10. Prove by Euler's formulas that $\cos 2x = 2 \cos^2 x - 1$.

CHAPTER OUTLINE

The Straight Line

12

12.1 Review of forms of the equation of a straight line

In Chapter 2 you studied many properties of the graph of a linear function or first degree equation. The *general form* of any first degree equation in two variables is

$$Ax + By + C = 0 \qquad \text{(I)}$$

where A, B, and C are real numbers, but A and B cannot both be zero. An infinite number of ordered pairs of real numbers (x, y) will satisfy any given linear equation and there is a one-to-one correspondence between these ordered pairs and the points of the graph of a straight line in a coordinate plane. For each ordered pair there corresponds a unique point on the graphed line and for each point on the line there corresponds an ordered pair satisfying the equation.

These graphed ordered pairs are sometimes called *Cartesian* coordinates after Descartes, a Frenchman who, at the same time as another Frenchman named Fermat, discovered and developed the use of rectangular coordinate systems as a means of studying algebraic functions. The study of certain functions geometrically, particularly those of first and second degree, by means of their graphs is called *analytic geometry*. Analytic geometry has been called the "Golden Bridge" of mathematics because it permits the study of geometric figures by analytic, or algebraic, methods;

it also permits geometric representation of equations with two variables in a coordinate plane. Many theorems of plane geometry can be more easily proved by analytic methods, that is, by algebraic operations in reference to a coordinate system. There are other theorems, such as many of those involving angle bisectors, which are more difficult to prove analytically than by the usual methods of synthetic geometry. Ideally, one should select the proof which is most direct, either synthetic or analytic.

We shall summarize the pertinent formulas and concepts about the straight line which you have studied in earlier chapters. (See Sections 2.4, 2.5.)

The *slope-intercept* form of the equation of a straight line is

$$y = mx + b \qquad \text{(II)}$$

where m is the slope and b is the y-intercept.

If points $P_1(x_1, y_1)$ and $P_2(x_2, y_2)$ are on a line, the slope is

$$m = \frac{y_2 - y_1}{x_2 - x_1}$$

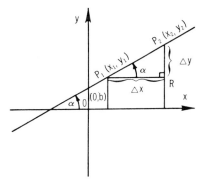

The tangent of the angle of inclination, α (alpha), is equal to the slope ($\tan \alpha = m$). The range of α is $0° \leq \alpha < 180°$. Tan α is positive if $\alpha < 90°$ and negative if $90° < \alpha < 180°$.

FIGURE 12–1

The *point-slope* form of the equation of a line is

$$m = \frac{y - y_1}{x - x_1}$$

or $$y - y_1 = m(x - x_1) \qquad \text{(III)}$$

where m is the slope and $P(x_1, y_1)$ is a point on the line.

If two points $P_1(x_1, y_1)$ and $P_2(x_2, y_2)$ are on a line, the *two-point* form of the equation of a line applies. Since $m = \dfrac{y_2 - y_1}{x_2 - x_1}$, from (III) we can write

$$y - y_1 = \frac{y_2 - y_1}{x_2 - x_1}(x - x_1) \qquad \text{(IV)}$$

In the general form (I), if we let $x = 0$ we find that $y = -\dfrac{C}{B}$ which we have called the y-intercept b. If we let $y = 0$, then $x = -\dfrac{C}{A}$ which we shall call the x-intercept a. The general form can be written

$$\frac{x}{-\dfrac{C}{A}} + \frac{y}{-\dfrac{C}{B}} = 1$$

Hence, the *intercept* form of the equation of a line is

$$\frac{x}{a} + \frac{y}{b} = 1, \; a \neq 0, \; b \neq 0 \qquad \text{(V)}$$

You should learn all of the above forms of the equation of a line and be able to select the form which best suits the problem at hand.

Among other relations that will be frequently needed is the *distance formula*. (See Section 2.2.) If $|\,P_1P_2\,|$ is the distance between two points $P_1(x_1, y_1)$ and $P_2(x_2, y_2)$, then

$$|\,P_1P_2\,| = \sqrt{(x_2 - x_1)^2 + (y_2 - y_1)^2} \qquad \text{(VI)}$$

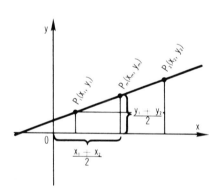

FIGURE 12-2

If $P_m(x_m, y_m)$ are the coordinates of the midpoint of the line segment from P_1 to P_2, see if you can prove that

$$x_m = \frac{x_1 + x_2}{2}$$

and

$$y_m = \frac{y_1 + y_2}{2} \qquad \text{(VII)}$$

If m_1 is the slope of line l_1 and m_2 is the slope of line l_2, then l_1 and l_2 are parallel if and only if $m_1 = m_2$. In other words, *the slopes of parallel lines are equal and two lines are parallel if their slopes are equal.*

What relation do m_1 and m_2 have if l_1 and l_2 are perpendicular? Let α_1 be the angle of inclination of l_1 and α_2 be the angle of inclination of l_2. It can be seen from the drawing that $\alpha_1 +$ $(180° - \alpha_2) = 90°$, or, $\alpha_2 = \alpha_1 + 90°$. Let us take the tangent of both members and we have

$\tan \alpha_2 = \tan (\alpha_1 + 90°)$

$\qquad = -\cot \alpha_1$

or $\tan \alpha_1 \cdot \tan \alpha_2 = -1$
But $m_1 = \tan \alpha_1$ and $m_2 = \tan \alpha_2$; thus, when l_1 is perpendicular to l_2, we have

$$m_1 m_2 = -1 \text{ or } m_1 = -\frac{1}{m_2}$$

If two lines are perpendicular, the slope of one is the negative reciprocal of the slope of the other. The converse of this statement is also true.

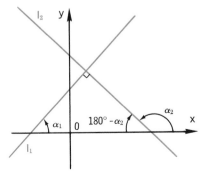

FIGURE 12–3

Exercises

In Exercises 1–10 write the equation in general form of the line which satisfies the given information.

1. The line which passes through the origin and has a slope of 2.
2. The line that passes through $(2, -5)$ and $(-1, 3)$.
3. The line that has an x-intercept of 7 and a y-intercept of -4.
4. The line that has a slope of $-\frac{2}{3}$ and passes through $(5, -1)$.
5. The line that intersects the y-axis at -3 and has a slope of $\frac{3}{4}$.
6. The line with a slope of $\frac{7}{5}$ and x-intercept of -4.
7. The line parallel to $y = 3x - 5$ with a y-intercept of 6.
8. The line parallel to $2x + 3y - 5 = 0$ passing through $(2, 4)$.
9. The line perpendicular to $y = -2x + 5$ with a y-intercept of -3.
10. The line perpendicular to $3x - y = 8$ passing through $(-1, 5)$.
11. Do the points $(1, 5)$, $(-3, 11)$ and $(5, -3)$ lie on a straight line? (*Hint:* The slope of a straight line is constant.)
12. Show that $(-3, 1)$, $(9, -4)$, $(12, 0)$, and $(0, 5)$ are the vertices of a parallelogram.

13. Show that $(-1, 3)$, $(3, 6)$, $(6, 2)$, and $(2, -1)$ are the vertices of a square.

14. Find the midpoint of the line segment between $(-4, 2)$ and $(2, 6)$.

15. Find the perimeter of the triangle with vertices at $(2, -5)$, $(7, 1)$, and $(-2, -1)$.

16. If the point $(5, 3)$ is joined to $(9, 1)$ and to $(2, -3)$, show that the two lines thus determined are perpendicular.

17. If two vertices of an equilateral triangle are at $(-2, 2)$ and $(4, 2)$, find two possible points of the third vertex.

18. Vertices of a triangle are at $(5, 0)$, $(-3, 2)$, and $(-1, -4)$. Find the coordinates of the midpoints of the sides. Find the perimeter of the given triangle. Find the perimeter of the triangle formed by joining the midpoints.

19. The area of a triangle with vertices at (x_1, y_1), (x_2, y_2), and (x_3, y_3) is given by the formula

$$A = \pm \frac{1}{2} \begin{vmatrix} x_1 & y_1 & 1 \\ x_2 & y_2 & 1 \\ x_3 & y_3 & 1 \end{vmatrix}$$

where the sign is chosen so that the area is positive. Find the area of the given triangle in Exercise 18. Find the area of the triangle formed by joining the midpoints of the sides. How do the areas compare?

20. If three of the vertices of a parallelogram are at $(-2, -1)$, $(-1, 4)$, and $(5, 1)$, find the coordinates of the fourth vertex. Find the area of the parallelogram.

12.2 Analytic proofs of theorems from plane geometry

As we stated earlier it is possible to prove theorems from plane geometry either synthetically or analytically. Some analytic proofs are much easier than the proofs you learned in plane geometry, but this is not always true. Some examples will illustrate the analytic method. You may arbitrarily select the position of the figure on the coordinate plane as long as complete generality is preserved. Usually in straight line figures a vertex is located at the origin and one line is made to coincide with the x-axis.

EXAMPLE. Prove that the line segment joining the midpoints of two sides of a triangle is parallel to the third side.

Solution. In complete generality we can let vertex A be at $(0, 0)$, vertex B at $(a, 0)$, and vertex C at (b, c) as shown in the figure. Then M and N are midpoints of sides AC and BC, respectively. To prove MN parallel to AB we need only to show that their slopes are equal.

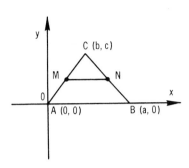

FIGURE 12–4

The slope of $AB = \dfrac{0}{a} = 0$. The coordinates of M by formula (VII) are $\left(\dfrac{b}{2}, \dfrac{c}{2}\right)$ and of N are $\left(\dfrac{a+b}{2}, \dfrac{c+0}{2}\right)$. The slope of MN is

$$\frac{\dfrac{c}{2} - \dfrac{c}{2}}{\dfrac{a+b}{2} - \dfrac{b}{2}} = \frac{0}{\dfrac{a}{2}} = 0$$

Thus, MN is parallel to AB since the slope of each is zero.

Exercises

Prove analytically the following theorems from plane geometry.

1. The diagonals of a rectangle are equal.
2. The diagonals of a square are perpendicular.
3. The line segment joining the midpoints of two sides of a triangle is equal in length to one-half the third side.
4. The medians to the equal sides of an isosceles triangle are equal.
5. The diagonals of a parallelogram bisect each other.
6. The lines joining midpoints of successive sides of a parallelogram form a parallelogram.
7. The lines joining midpoints of successive sides of any quadrilateral form a parallelogram.
8. The square of the hypotenuse of a right triangle is equal to the sum of the squares of the other two sides.

9. The median of a trapezoid is equal in length to one-half the sum of the parallel sides.

10. The sum of the squares of the four sides of a parallelogram is equal to the sum of the squares of the diagonals.

12.3 Families of lines—parallel lines—lines through a common point

We call the set of lines that are parallel to a given line a *family of lines*. It is obvious that the common characteristic of all lines of such a family is that they have the same slope. If m represents the slope of a family of parallel lines, then all members of the family can be written in the form

$$m = \frac{y - y_1}{x - x_1} \quad \text{or} \quad y - y_1 = m(x - x_1)$$

If any point (x_1, y_1) is selected, a line belonging to the family is determined.

EXAMPLE 1. Find the equation of a line passing through $(3, -2)$ which belongs to the family of lines parallel to $3x - y + 7 = 0$.

Solution. Find the slope of the given line by writing the equation in the slope-intercept form. The equation becomes $y = 3x + 7$. The slope of the family of lines parallel to this line is $m = 3$. The required line is

$$3 = \frac{y - (-2)}{x - 3} \quad \text{or} \quad 3x - y - 11 = 0 \text{ in general form}$$

Families of lines are also determined by considering the set of all lines passing through a common point. Each line in such a family has a slope different from other members of the family. If we represent the slope by m we see that for each value of m there is one and only one line through the given point. We can consider m as a variable relating the two variables x and y. A variable such as m which relates two other variables is called a *parameter*. By letting the parameter m vary through all possible values we generate all members of the family of lines through a given point. If $P(x_0, y_0)$ is the given point common to all members of the family of lines, the equation for any member of the family is

$$m = \frac{y - y_0}{x - x_0} \quad \text{or} \quad y - y_0 = m(x - x_0)$$

Example 2. Find the equation of a line belonging to the family of lines passing through $(-4, 1)$ which is parallel to $x + 2y - 5 = 0$.

Solution. The family of lines of which the desired equation is a member is of the form: $m = \dfrac{y - 1}{x + 4}$. The required line is parallel to $x + 2y - 5 = 0$ which has a slope of $-\dfrac{1}{2}$. An easy way to determine the slope is to write the equation in the *slope-intercept* form which is $y = -\dfrac{1}{2}x + \dfrac{5}{2}$. In this form the coefficient of x is the slope. Thus, the equation of the required line is

$$-\frac{1}{2} = \frac{y - 1}{x + 4} \quad \text{or} \quad x + 2y + 2 = 0 \text{ in general form}$$

Exercises

1. Find the equation of the line that is parallel to $3x + 2y + 5 = 0$ and passes through $(1, -2)$.

2. Find the equation of the line that passes through the point of intersection of $x - 3y + 2 = 0$ and $2x + y - 2 = 0$ and has a slope of $\dfrac{3}{2}$. (*Hint:* Solve the equations simultaneously to determine the point of intersection.)

3. Find the equation of the line that is parallel to $2x - 7y = 3$ and passes through $(5, 0)$.

4. Find the equation of the line that passes through the point of intersection of $5x - y + 4 = 0$ and $x - 3y - 1 = 0$ and has a slope of $\dfrac{\sqrt{2}}{2}$.

5. Determine b in the equation $y = 2x + b$ so that the equation is that of a line through $(2, 0)$.

6. Determine m in the equation $y = mx - 4$ so that the equation is that of a line parallel to $2x - 3y = 0$.

7. Find the equation of a line through $(1, 3)$ which forms with the coordinate axes a right triangle whose area is 12. How many solutions are possible?

8. Find the equation of a line passing through $(7, -2)$ which is perpendicular to $3x + 2y - 5 = 0$.

9. If b is a variable (parameter) representing the y-intercept, write the general equation of the family of lines that have equal x- and y-intercepts.

10. Find the equations of the altitudes of the triangle with vertices at $(-5, 3)$, $(2, 9)$, and $(7, -1)$.

12.4   Angle of intersection of lines

Let l_1 and l_2 be two lines that intersect at C, and let their angles of inclination be α_1 and α_2, respectively. Let θ (theta) represent the angle of intersection of the lines. We wish to find θ in terms of α_1 and α_2. Since α_2 is an exterior angle of triangle ABC, it is equal to the sum of the opposite interior angles. Thus, $\alpha_2 = \alpha_1 + \theta$

or $\theta = \alpha_2 - \alpha_1$

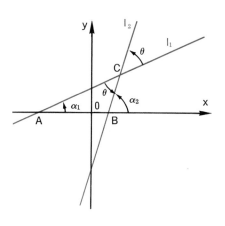

FIGURE 12-5

Then:

$$\tan \theta = \tan (\alpha_2 - \alpha_1)$$

$$\tan \theta = \frac{\tan \alpha_2 - \tan \alpha_1}{1 + \tan \alpha_2 \tan \alpha_1}$$

Since $\tan \alpha_1 = m_1$ and $\tan \alpha_2 = m_2$, we have

$$\tan \theta = \frac{m_2 - m_1}{1 + m_1 m_2} \qquad \text{(VIII)}$$

Note that m_2 is the slope of the left side of θ and m_1 is the slope of the right side of θ. It is evident that the formula fails if either of the lines is parallel to the y-axis but in this event the angle θ can be found directly. By the angle between l_1 and l_2 we mean the acute angle through which l_1 must be rotated to coincide with l_2.

EXAMPLE. Find the angle between $y = 2x - 7$ and $y = -x + 1$.

Solution. $m_1 = 2$; $m_2 = -1$. Thus $\tan \theta = \dfrac{-1 -2}{1 + (2)(-1)} = \dfrac{-3}{-1} = 3$.

Hence $\theta = \text{Arctan } 3 = 71° 34'$ approximately.

If tan θ is a positive number the acute angle from l_1 to l_2 is measured counterclockwise; if tan θ is a negative number the acute angle from l_1 to l_2 is measured clockwise.

Exercises

Graph the following lines and find the indicated angle.

1. Find the angle from $y = 3x + 2$ to $y = x - 4$.
2. Find the angle from $2x - 5y = 4$ to $3x - 2y = 0$.
3. Show that the following lines intersect at a 45° angle.
$$x - 7y - 2 = 0 \text{ and } 4x - 3y - 6 = 0$$
4. Find the equation of a line through the origin making the angle arctan 2 with the line $x + y = 0$. How many solutions are there?
5. Find the equations of the lines through (2, 3) making an angle of 45° with the line $2x - y + 3 = 0$.
6. Show that (3, 5), (7, 5), (9, 8), and (5, 8) are vertices of a parallelogram. Find the equations of its diagonals and find the acute angle between the diagonals.
7. The vertices of a triangle are (0, 0), (5, 0), and (7, 9). Find the angle between the two longest sides.
8. The angle between two lines is 60°. The slope of one line is $\frac{2}{3}$.

    What is the slope of the other?
9. Prove that l_1 and l_2 are perpendicular if $m_1 = -\dfrac{1}{m_2}$.
10. Find the area of a triangle with vertices at $(-3, 1)$, $(5, 3)$, and $(1, 6)$ by the formula, Area $= \dfrac{1}{2} bc \sin A$, where A is determined by formula (VIII). Compare with the area found by the method given in Exercise 19, p. 294, Section 12.1.

12.5   Normal form of the equation of a line

A *normal* is a line perpendicular to another line or a surface. By *normal form* we mean that the equation of a line is given in terms of the length of the normal from the line to the origin.

Let l be a line that does not pass through the origin; let $OC = p$ be the length of its normal to 0; and let ϕ (Greek phi) be the positive angle between the positive x-axis and p. Draw

MC perpendicular to the x-axis. Then $OM = p \cos \phi$, and $MC = p \sin \phi$.

Now, the equation of a line through the origin is of the form $y = mx$. Hence, the equation of line OC is

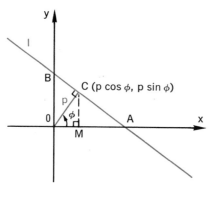

FIGURE 12–6

$$y = \frac{MC}{OM} \cdot x = \frac{p \sin \phi}{p \cos \phi} \cdot x$$

or $x \sin \phi - y \cos \phi = 0$
Since l is perpendicular to OC, its slope is $- \dfrac{\cos \phi}{\sin \phi}$, the negative reciprocal of the slope of OC. Then the equation of l is of the form

$$y = -\frac{\cos \phi}{\sin \phi} x + b$$

or $\qquad\qquad x \cos \phi + y \sin \phi - b \sin \phi = 0$

Since the line passes through C, the equation is satisfied by the coordinates of C. Then

$$p \cos \phi \,(\cos \phi) + p \sin \phi \,(\sin \phi) - b \sin \phi = 0$$
$$p \cos^2 \phi + p \sin^2 \phi - b \sin \phi = 0$$
$$p \,(\cos^2 \phi + \sin^2 \phi) - b \sin \phi = 0$$
$$p = b \sin \phi$$

The equation of l becomes

$$x \cos \phi + y \sin \phi - p = 0 \qquad\qquad \textbf{(IX)}$$

Equation (IX) is called the *normal form* of the equation of a line.

EXAMPLE. Write the equation of a line in general form for which the normal p is 5, the normal making an angle $\phi = 30°$ with the positive x-axis.

Solution. Applying formula (IX) we have

$$x \cos 30° + y \sin 30° - 5 = 0$$
$$\frac{\sqrt{3}}{2} x + \frac{1}{2} y - 5 = 0$$
$$\sqrt{3}x + y - 10 = 0$$

Exercises

1. Find the equation of a line whose normal $p = 3$, the normal making an angle $\phi = 60°$ with the positive direction of the x-axis.

2. What is the equation of a line that makes an angle of $150°$ with the x-axis and is 1 unit from the origin? (Two solutions.)

3. A line makes an angle of $135°$ with the x-axis and is $\sqrt{3}$ units from the origin. Find its equation in general form. (Two solutions.)

4. Write the equation of a line if the point nearest to the origin on the line is $(3, 3)$.

5. A circle with its center at the origin has a radius of 5 units. Write the equation of the family of lines that are tangent to the circle. (*Hint:* Write the equation in normal form and let θ be the parameter angle. By letting θ vary from $0°$ to $360°$ all lines of the family will be determined.)

12.6   Changing a linear equation to normal form

The general form of a linear equation $Ax + By + C = 0$ can be transformed to normal form $x \cos \phi + y \sin \phi - p = 0$ if the relations between the coefficients of the two forms are found. The equations will represent the same line if and only if their corresponding coefficients are proportional.

Hence
$$\frac{A}{\cos \phi} = \frac{B}{\sin \phi} = \frac{C}{-p}$$

Then
$$\sin \phi = -\frac{Bp}{C}, \text{ and } \cos \phi = -\frac{Ap}{C}$$

Dividing the first equation by the second, $(\cos \phi \neq 0)$, we have
$$\frac{\sin \phi}{\cos \phi} = \frac{B}{A} = \tan \phi$$

Let us consider a right triangle with an acute angle ϕ such that $\tan \phi = \dfrac{B}{A}$. The hypotenuse is $\pm \sqrt{A^2 + B^2}$. Thus,

$$\sin \phi = \frac{B}{\pm\sqrt{A^2 + B^2}}, \qquad\qquad \cos \phi = \frac{A}{\pm\sqrt{A^2 + B^2}},$$

and $\quad p = -\dfrac{C}{\pm\sqrt{A^2 + B^2}}$. If these values are substituted in (IX), we have

$$\frac{Ax}{\pm\sqrt{A^2 + B^2}} + \frac{By}{\pm\sqrt{A^2 + B^2}} + \frac{C}{\pm\sqrt{A^2 + B^2}} = 0 \qquad \textbf{(X)}$$

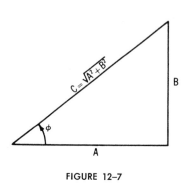

FIGURE 12–7

In order to transform the equation $Ax + By + C = 0$ to normal form we can divide each term by $\pm\sqrt{A^2 + B^2}$. The double sign is used so that a choice can be made to insure that p is positive. The sign that is unlike the sign of C in the given equation is chosen so that the resulting equation is of the form (X), that is, if C is $+$, the $-$ sign is chosen and if C is $-$, the $+$ sign is chosen. If $C = 0$, the sign is chosen so that $\sin \phi$ is positive, that is, the same sign as that of B.

EXAMPLE. Write the equation $2x - 5y + 3 = 0$ in normal form. Find the length of the normal to the origin from the line and the angle that the normal makes with the positive x-axis.

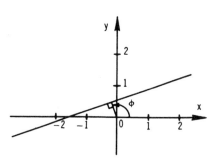

FIGURE 12–8

Solution. $A = 2, B = -5$. Therefore $\pm\sqrt{A^2 + B^2} = \pm\sqrt{2^2 + (-5)^2} = \pm\sqrt{29}$. Since $C = +3$, a positive number, we choose the negative sign and divide each term by $-\sqrt{29}$. This gives us

$$-\frac{2x}{\sqrt{29}} + \frac{5y}{\sqrt{29}} - \frac{3}{\sqrt{29}} = 0$$

The length of the normal is $\dfrac{3}{\sqrt{29}} = .56$, approximately; $\tan \phi = \dfrac{B}{A} = -\dfrac{5}{2}$; $\phi = \arctan(-2.5) = 111°\ 48'$ approximately. The graph of $2x - 5y + 3 = 0$ indicates the above values of p and ϕ are correct.

Exercises

1. Write the equation $6x - 8y - 15 = 0$ in normal form. What is the length of the normal to the origin?

2. Find the distance to the origin from the line $3x + 4y - 1 = 0$ and find the angle that the normal to the origin makes with the x-axis.

3. Find the distance to the origin from $x - 3y - 2 = 0$ and find the angle that the given line makes with the x-axis. (*Hint:* What relation exists between ϕ and α, the angle of inclination?)

4. Find the distance to the origin from $\sqrt{2}x - \sqrt{3}y = 1$ and find the angle between the positive x-axis and the normal from the line.

5. Write the equation of a line parallel to $4x + 3y - 25 = 0$ at a distance of 3 units from the origin.

6. Find the distance between the parallel lines $2x - y + 4 = 0$ and $2x - y - 8 = 0$. (*Hint:* Find the length of the normal of each.)

12.7   Distance to a point from a line

It is often required in analytic geometry that the distance to a point from a line be found. For example, the length of an altitude of a triangle requires that the distance to a vertex from the opposite side be found. In Section 12.6 you learned how to find the distance from a given line to the origin by transforming the equation of the line into normal form. An extension of this method will enable us to develop a formula for the distance d to point $P(x_1, y_1)$ from line $Ax + By + C = 0$. Two cases must be considered; in one case, the point lies on the same side of the line as the origin and in the other the point lies on the opposite side of the line from the origin. If the line segment joining P to the origin does not intersect the line, point P is on the same side of the line as the origin. Let RS be a line in the coordinate plane and let $P(x_1, y_1)$ be a point not on RS. Construct line TV parallel to RS and passing through P. The distance d between the parallel lines is the distance from RS to P.

Let $x \cos \phi + y \sin \phi - p = 0$ be the equation of RS in normal form. Since TV is parallel to RS, the equation of TV is $x \cos \phi + y \sin \phi - (p + d) = 0$. Solving the equation for d we have

$$d = x \cos \phi + y \sin \phi - p$$

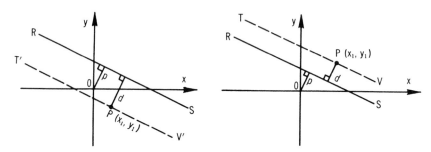

FIGURE 12–9

Since $P(x_1, y_1)$ is on TV its coordinates satisfy the above equation. Thus

$$d = x_1 \cos \phi + y_1 \sin \phi - p \qquad \text{(XI)}$$

If the equation of the given line is in general form, then (XI) becomes

$$d = \frac{A x_1 + B y_1 + C}{\pm \sqrt{A^2 + B^2}} \qquad \text{(XII)}$$

where the sign of the radical is chosen opposite to the sign of C.

The distance given by formulas (XI) and (XII) will be positive if the point and the origin are on opposite sides of the line. The distance will be negative if the point is on the same side of the line as the origin. In an application of the formula the absolute value of d is usually desired.

EXAMPLE. Find the distance to $P(-1, 4)$ from $3x - 7y - 1 = 0$.

Solution. Divide the given equation by $\pm \sqrt{A^2 + B^2} = +\sqrt{58}$, and replace (x_1, y_1) by $(-1, 4)$ in (XII). We have

$$d = \frac{3(-1) - 7(4) - 1}{+\sqrt{58}} = -\frac{32}{\sqrt{58}}$$

$$= -\frac{16\sqrt{58}}{29} = -4.2, \text{ approximately}$$

Exercises

1. Find the distance from $2x + 5y - 2 = 0$ to $(3, -1)$.

2. Find the distance from $x - 7y + 4 = 0$ to $(-4, 2)$.

3. Find the distance from $3x - y + 1 = 0$ to $(0, 0)$.

4. Find and interpret the distance from $2x + 3y + 2 = 0$ to $(2, -2)$.

5. Find the distance between $3x - 5y + 7 = 0$ and $6x - 10y - 2 = 0$.

6. Find the distance between the lines $2x - 3y + 1 = 0$ and $3y - 2x = 5$.

7. Find the lengths of the three altitudes of a triangle with vertices at $(5, 3)$, $(1, -4)$, and $(-4, 1)$.

8. Write the locus of points at a distance of 3 units from $x - 5y + 10 = 0$.

12.8   Bisector of an angle

In the study of geometry you learned that the bisector of an angle is the locus of points equally distant from the sides of the angle. Using this definition, we can find the equations of the bisectors of the angles between two lines.

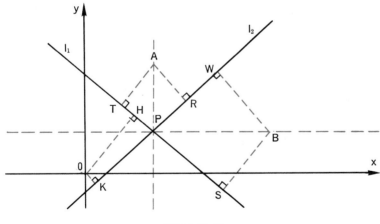

FIGURE 12–10

In the figure, $\overrightarrow{TA}$ and $\overrightarrow{OH}$ agree in direction, and hence $\overrightarrow{TA}$ is positive. However, $\overrightarrow{RA}$ and $\overrightarrow{OK}$ differ in direction, and hence $\overrightarrow{RA}$ is negative. Then, $\overrightarrow{TA} = -\overrightarrow{RA}$. (*Note:* Here we use the symbol $\rightarrow$ to emphasize directed distances from a line.)

Similarly, $\overrightarrow{WB}$ is positive and $\overrightarrow{SB}$ is positive. Then $\overrightarrow{WB} = \overrightarrow{SB}$. Notice that the origin is inside the angle that is bisected by PB but outside the angle bisected by PA.

> • *If the distances from the sides of an angle to a point on its bisector have the same sign, the origin lies within the angle. If the signs differ, the origin is outside the bisected angle.*

If we wish to find the equation of a specific bisector, we first graph the lines and thus determine whether to equate positive distances or to let one distance equal the negative of the other.

EXAMPLE. Find the equation of the line that bisects the acute angles between $l_1 : 2x - 3y + 6 = 0$ and $l_2 : 3x + y - 9 = 0$.

Solution. The graph suggests that angle HJK is the acute angle. The origin lies in this angle and hence $\overrightarrow{HP} = \overrightarrow{KP}$.

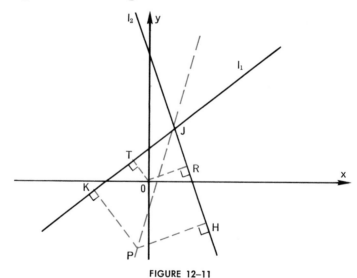

FIGURE 12–11

We write the equations of l_1 and l_2 in normal form.

$$l_1 : \frac{2}{-\sqrt{13}} x + \frac{3}{\sqrt{13}} y - \frac{6}{\sqrt{13}} = 0$$

$$l_2 : \frac{3}{\sqrt{10}} x + \frac{1}{\sqrt{10}} y - \frac{9}{\sqrt{10}} = 0$$

$$\overrightarrow{KP} = \frac{2}{-\sqrt{13}} x_1 + \frac{3}{\sqrt{13}} y_1 - \frac{6}{\sqrt{13}}$$

$$\overrightarrow{HP} = \frac{3}{\sqrt{10}} x_1 + \frac{1}{\sqrt{10}} y_1 - \frac{9}{\sqrt{10}}$$

Since $\overrightarrow{HP} = \overrightarrow{KP}$, we have

$$\frac{2}{-\sqrt{13}} x_1 + \frac{3}{\sqrt{13}} y_1 - \frac{6}{\sqrt{13}} = \frac{3}{\sqrt{10}} x_1 + \frac{1}{\sqrt{10}} y_1 - \frac{9}{\sqrt{10}}$$

Hence

$$\left(\frac{2}{\sqrt{13}} + \frac{3}{\sqrt{10}} \right) x + \left(\frac{1}{\sqrt{10}} - \frac{3}{\sqrt{13}} \right) y + \frac{6}{\sqrt{13}} - \frac{9}{\sqrt{10}} = 0$$

is the equation of the bisector, subscripts being dropped.

Exercises

1. Find the equation of the line that bisects the acute angle between $x - y + 3 = 0$ and $2x + y - 1 = 0$.
2. Find the equation of the line that bisects the obtuse angle between $2x + 5y = 0$ and $3x + y - 7 = 0$.
3. Find the equations of the bisectors of the interior angles of the triangle formed by $x + 2y = 1$, $2x + y = 3$, and $x - y + 5 = 0$. Show that these bisectors are concurrent by showing that their equations have a common solution.

12.9   Polar coordinates

We now introduce a new system of coordinates which identifies a point by means of an ordered pair, a distance and an angle. The distance of the given point from a fixed point in the plane, called the *pole*, is the first member of the ordered pair. The angle between a fixed directed ray called the *polar axis*, which emanates from the pole, and the ray through the point to be identified is the second member. The polar axis is usually a horizontal line directed toward the right from

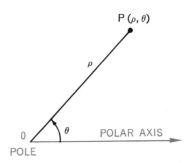

FIGURE 12–12

the pole. The ordered pair of numbers (ρ, θ) identifies point P, ρ (rho) being the distance and θ (theta) being the measure of the angle. The distance ρ is called the *polar distance* or *radius vector*. The positive angle θ is measured *counterclockwise* from the polar axis. Either ρ or θ can be negative as in the example

$$\left(2, \frac{\pi}{2}\right) = \left(-2, \frac{3\pi}{2}\right) = \left(2, -\frac{3\pi}{2}\right)$$

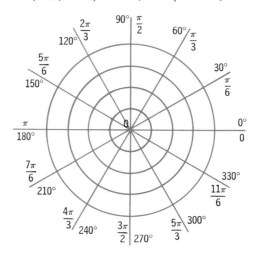

FIGURE 12–13

Graphing in polar coordinates is facilitated by use of polar coordinate paper. Such paper has certain angles and circles whose radii differ by units drawn in for ready use in plotting points.

EXAMPLE. Graph the point $\left(2, \frac{\pi}{3}\right)$.

Solution. First, we designate a point O as the pole and through it draw the polar axis to the right. Second, we measure angle $XOM = \frac{\pi}{3}$. Third, on the terminal side $\overrightarrow{OM}$ we measure 2 units from O in the positive direction of $\overrightarrow{OM}$. This locates the point $P\left(2, \frac{\pi}{3}\right)$.

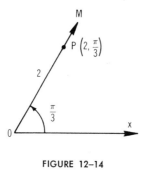

FIGURE 12–14

Exercises

Graph the following points in polar coordinates.

1. $(1, 0)$ **3.** $\left(.25, \dfrac{2\pi}{3}\right)$ **5.** $\left(.5, -\dfrac{3\pi}{2}\right)$

2. $\left(2, \dfrac{\pi}{2}\right)$ **4.** $\left(\dfrac{1}{2}, 1\right)$ **6.** $\left(-1, \dfrac{\pi}{3}\right)$

12.10   Conversion from one system of coordinates to the other

The process of conversion from system to system is explained by superposing one system of reference points and lines on the other so that the two origins coincide and the positive x-axis of the rectangular system coincides with the polar axis of the polar system. On such a figure let P be any point in the plane. In polar coordinates P is identified by the ordered pair (ρ, θ). In rectangular coordinates P is identified by the ordered pair (x, y). Draw MP perpendicular to OX. From the figure we see that

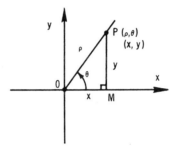

FIGURE 12–15

$$y = \rho \sin \theta , \quad x = \rho \cos \theta , \quad \rho = \sqrt{x^2 + y^2} , \quad \theta = \arctan \frac{y}{x}$$

These relations enable us to convert from one system to another.

EXAMPLE 1. The coordinates of a point in rectangular coordinates are $(-2, 5)$. Express in polar coordinates.

Solution. Given, $x = -2$, $y = 5$. By the above formulas $\rho = \sqrt{(-2)^2 + 5^2} = \sqrt{29}$, and $\theta = \arctan \dfrac{5}{-2}$. Hence, the polar coordinates are $\left(\sqrt{29}, \arctan \dfrac{5}{-2}\right)$, or $\left(\sqrt{29}, 1.95\right)$, or $\left(\sqrt{29}, -4.33\right)$.

EXAMPLE 2. In polar coordinates point A is identified by the ordered pair $\left(-3, \dfrac{2\pi}{3}\right)$. Find its rectangular coordinates.

Solution. From the formulas relating polar and rectangular coordinates,

$$x = -3 \cos \frac{2\pi}{3} = (-3)\left(-\frac{1}{2}\right) = \frac{3}{2}$$

$$y = -3 \sin \frac{2\pi}{3} = (-3)\left(\frac{\sqrt{3}}{2}\right) = -\frac{3\sqrt{3}}{2}$$

The rectangular coordinates of A are $\left(\frac{3}{2}, -\frac{3\sqrt{3}}{2}\right)$.

Exercises

Change from rectangular to polar coordinates.

1. $(3, 4)$ **3.** $(1, 1)$ **5.** $(-1, -3)$

2. $(5, 12)$ **4.** $(-2, 5)$ **6.** $(3, -2)$

Change from polar to rectangular coordinates.

7. $(2, 0)$ **9.** $\left(1.5, \frac{\pi}{2}\right)$ **11.** $(.25, 1)$

8. $\left(1, \frac{\pi}{6}\right)$ **10.** $\left(-2, \frac{\pi}{4}\right)$ **12.** $\left(-3, -\frac{\pi}{2}\right)$

12.11   Equation of a straight line in polar coordinates

Let $Ax + By + C = 0$ be the equation of a line in rectangular coordinates. We can use Section 12.6 to change this equation to normal form. We get

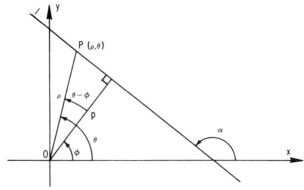

FIGURE 12–16

$$\frac{Ax}{\pm\sqrt{A^2 + B^2}} + \frac{By}{\pm\sqrt{A^2 + B^2}} + \frac{C}{\pm\sqrt{A^2 + B^2}} = 0$$

Then
$$\frac{A}{\pm\sqrt{A^2 + B^2}} = \cos\phi, \quad \frac{B}{\pm\sqrt{A^2 + B^2}} = \sin\phi,$$

$$\frac{C}{\pm\sqrt{A^2 + B^2}} = -p, \quad \frac{\sin\phi}{\cos\phi} = \frac{B}{A} = \tan\phi$$

But we know that $x = \rho \cos\theta$, $y = \rho \sin\theta$.
Substituting these values in the normal form of the equation, we have

$$\rho \cos\theta \cos\phi + \rho \sin\theta \sin\phi - p = 0$$

Hence

$$p = \rho \cos(\theta - \phi) \qquad \text{(XIII)}$$

This is the polar equation of a straight line. The above development shows how to derive this from the rectangular equation. By reversing the steps, we can change from an equation in polar coordinates to an equation in rectangular coordinates.

Notice in (XIII) that θ and ρ are variables, p and ϕ (phi) are constants for any specific line. If we have an equation in rectangular coordinates, α can be found from the relation $\tan\alpha = m = \dfrac{-A}{B}$, or $\alpha = \arctan\left(\dfrac{-A}{B}\right)$. Then we have from the figure $\phi = \alpha - \dfrac{\pi}{2}$, or $\alpha + \dfrac{\pi}{2}$ depending on whether m is negative or positive. If m is negative, $\phi = \alpha - \dfrac{\pi}{2}$, $\sin\phi = -\cos\alpha$, $\cos\phi = \sin\alpha$. If m is positive, $\phi = \alpha + \dfrac{\pi}{2}$, $\sin\phi = \cos\alpha$, $\cos\phi = -\sin\alpha$.

EXAMPLE 1. Graph the equation $2 = \rho \cos(\theta + 20°)$.

Solution. (XIII) can be written in the form $\rho = \dfrac{2}{\cos(\theta + 20°)}$.
We prepare a table of coordinates.

θ	0	10°	25°	40°	100°
ρ	2.1	2.3	2.8	4	−4

Hence, we have the graph of the equation $2 = \rho \cos(\theta + 20°)$ as shown in Figure 12–17.

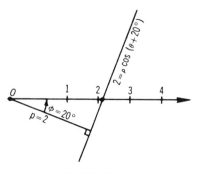

FIGURE 12–17

EXAMPLE 2. Change $3x - 5y + 5 = 0$ to polar form.

Solution. First, we change to normal form.

$$-\frac{3}{\sqrt{34}}x + \frac{5}{\sqrt{34}}y - \frac{5}{\sqrt{34}} = 0$$

Hence $\sin\phi = \dfrac{5}{\sqrt{34}}$,

$\cos\phi = -\dfrac{3}{\sqrt{34}}$, $p = \dfrac{5}{\sqrt{34}}$

Then $\phi = \arctan\left(-\dfrac{5}{3}\right)$

Now, $m = \dfrac{3}{5}$, or $\alpha = \arctan\dfrac{3}{5}$.

Since m is positive, $\phi = \alpha + \dfrac{\pi}{2}$.

Then $\phi = \left(\arctan\dfrac{3}{5}\right) + \dfrac{\pi}{2}$.

In (XIII) substitute for p and ϕ. We have

$$\frac{5}{\sqrt{34}} = \rho \cos\left[\theta - \left(\arctan\frac{3}{5} + \frac{\pi}{2}\right)\right]$$

$$= \rho \cos(\theta - 121°)$$

EXAMPLE 3. Change $2 = \rho \cos\left(\theta - \dfrac{\pi}{4}\right)$ to rectangular coordinates.

Solution. $2 = \rho\left(\cos\theta \cos\dfrac{\pi}{4} + \sin\theta \sin\dfrac{\pi}{4}\right)$

$$= \rho\left(\cos\theta \cdot \frac{\sqrt{2}}{2} + \sin\theta \cdot \frac{\sqrt{2}}{2}\right)$$

or

$$2\sqrt{2} = \rho(\cos\theta + \sin\theta) = \rho\cos\theta + \rho\sin\theta$$

Since $x = \rho\cos\theta$, $y = \rho\sin\theta$, we have

$$x + y - 2\sqrt{2} = 0$$

Exercises

1. Graph $5 = \rho \cos (\theta + 45°)$.
2. Graph $1.5 = \rho \cos (\theta - 10°)$.
3. Change $2x + 3y - 1 = 0$ to polar form.
4. Change $x = 10$ to polar form.
5. Change $4 = \rho \cos \left(\theta - \dfrac{\pi}{3} \right)$ to rectangular coordinates.
6. Change $1 = \rho \cos \theta$ to rectangular coordinates.

Chapter Review

1. Write the equation in general form of a line that has a slope of $-\dfrac{5}{2}$ and passes through the point $(2, -1)$.
2. Write the equation of a line parallel to $3x - y + 4 = 0$ with a y-intercept of 3.
3. Write the equation of a line perpendicular to $4x - 3y + 5 = 0$ passing through the point $(-4, 10)$.
4. Prove analytically that the diagonals of a rhombus are perpendicular bisectors of each other.
5. Let k be a parameter representing the point of intersection with the x-axis of each member of a family of lines. Write the equation of the family of lines which passes through the point $(-4, 3)$.
6. Find the angle from $3x - 2y + 7 = 0$ to $5x + y - 2 = 0$.
7. Prove that the altitudes of a triangle are concurrent by analytic methods.
8. Find the equation in general form of a line whose angle of inclination is $60°$ if the distance to the origin is 2 units.
9. Write the equation of a line parallel to $5x + 12y = 26$ at a distance of 1 unit from the origin.
10. Prove that the bisector of an angle of a triangle divides the opposite side in the same ratio as the sides of the bisected angle.
11. (a) Change the rectangular coordinates of a point $(-4, 2)$ to polar coordinates if the pole coincides with the origin and the polar axis coincides with the right branch of the x-axis.

(b) Change the polar coordinates of a point $\left(6, \dfrac{\pi}{4}\right)$ to rectangular coordinates.

12. Change $3 = \rho \cos\left(\theta + \dfrac{\pi}{3}\right)$ to rectangular coordinates and construct the graph.

CHAPTER OUTLINE

The Circle

13

13.1 Definition of a circle

A *circle* is a locus of points in a plane at a constant distance from a fixed point. The fixed point is the center of the circle and the constant distance is the radius. From an analytic viewpoint this definition can be expressed in terms of the distance formula (Section 12.1) so that the general equation of a circle can be written.

Let $C(h, k)$ be the coordinates of a fixed point and let $P(x, y)$ be any point on a circle with C as center. The constant distance d between C and P is equal to the radius r. Thus, from formula (VI), Section 12.1, we can write

$$d^2 = (x - h)^2 + (y - k)^2$$

or

$$(x - h)^2 + (y - k)^2 = r^2 \quad \textbf{(I)}$$

We shall call (I) the *standard form* of the equation of a circle.

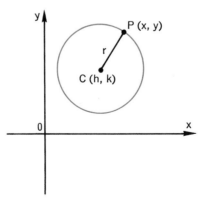

FIGURE 13–1

315

An important special case of the equation of a circle in terms of its center and radius is that where the center is at the origin. In this case (h, k) becomes $(0, 0)$ and equation (I) reduces to

$$x^2 + y^2 = r^2 \qquad \text{(II)}$$

It is frequently desirable to write (I) in expanded form and with terms arranged as a general polynomial in two variables. This is called the *general form* of the equation of a circle and is written as follows:

$$x^2 + y^2 - 2hx - 2ky + h^2 + k^2 - r^2 = 0 \qquad \text{(III)}$$

or

$$x^2 + y^2 + Dx + Ey + F = 0 \qquad \text{(IV)}$$

where $D = -2h$, $E = -2k$, and the constant $F = h^2 + k^2 - r^2$.

If an equation of a circle is given in general form (IV) it can, of course, be graphed by finding a number of ordered pairs (x, y), by substituting permissible values of x and computing corresponding values of y. $|x - h| \leq r$. Why? This is not the most desirable approach to graphing a circle, however. It is better to transform (IV) into (I) in which form the center (h, k) and radius r are obvious. This transformation is accomplished by completing the square of the terms in x and the terms in y. An example will illustrate the method.

EXAMPLE 1. Find the center and radius of $x^2 + y^2 - 4x + 6y - 12 = 0$ and graph the circle.

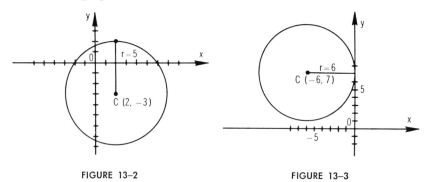

FIGURE 13–2   FIGURE 13–3

Solution. We shall group the terms in x and the terms in y and complete the square for each variable.

Let us transform $x^2 + y^2 - 4x + 6y - 12 = 0$ into $(x^2 - 4x + \quad) + (y^2 + 6y + \quad) = 12$. If each term in the left member is made a perfect square trinomial by adding 4 and 9 respectively, then $+13$ (the sum of $+4$ and $+9$) must be added to the right member of the equation and we have

$$(x - 2)^2 + (y + 3)^2 = 25$$

Thus, the center is $(2, -3)$ and the radius is 5. The graph of the circle is shown in Figure 13–2.

EXAMPLE 2. Write the equation of a circle that is tangent to the y-axis and has its center at $(-6, 7)$. See Figure 13–3.

Solution. A sketch of the circle satisfying the given conditions makes it clear that the radius is 6. Hence, the equation of the circle is

$$(x + 6)^2 + (y - 7)^2 = 36$$

It is important to note the following facts about the equation of a circle.

1. The coefficients of x^2 and y^2 are equal. In the event the coefficients are not 1, the equation may be transformed by division so that they are 1.

2. If $r = 0$, the circle becomes a point; if $r < 0$, a real circle does not exist.

3. There is no term in (IV) containing xy, the product of the variables.

Exercises

In each exercise make a drawing of the figure.

1. In equation (III) what is true if $(h^2 + k^2 - r^2)$ is zero?

2. Show that $2x^2 - 4x + 2y^2 + 12y - 12 = 0$ is the equation of a circle and find its center and radius.

3. Show that $x^2 + y^2 - y = .75$ is the equation of a circle and find its center and radius.

4. Find the center and radius of the circle whose equation is $x^2 + y^2 - 18 = 0$.

5. The center of a circle is at $(-2, 3)$ and its radius is 5. Write the equation of the circle.

6. The center of a circle is at $(4, -3)$ and the circle passes through the origin. Give the equation.

7. The center of a circle is at $(5, 12)$ and the circle is tangent to the line $2x - y + 3 = 0$. Find its equation.

8. Write the equation of the family of circles in which $h = k$ and the radius is 7. Let k be the parameter. (Recall that as parameter k assumes all possible values, the members of the family of circles are determined.) Describe this family of circles.

13.2　Circle determined by three conditions

Notice that each of the equations of a circle, the standard form (I) and the general form (IV), contains three constants for a specific circle. In standard form (I), h, k, and r are required to determine the equation of a specific circle and in general form (IV) D, E, and F are required.

Since coordinates of any point on a circle will satisfy either form it is possible to determine a system of three equations in three variables if three points on the circle are known. If $P_1(x_1, y_1)$, $P_2(x_2, y_2)$ and $P_3(x_3, y_3)$ are three non-collinear points in a plane, there is a unique circle which passes through them. You may recall the compass and straightedge construction of such a circle. In this chapter we are interested in finding the equation of the circle and in constructing its graph in the coordinate plane. Since P_1, P_2, and P_3 lie on the circle, from (IV) we can substitute the coordinates in the general form of the equation of a circle one at a time and write the system of three independent linear equations in D, E, and F. The system is

(1)　$x_1{}^2 + y_1{}^2 + Dx_1 + Ey_1 + F = 0$
(2)　$x_2{}^2 + y_2{}^2 + Dx_2 + Ey_2 + F = 0$
(3)　$x_3{}^2 + y_3{}^2 + Dx_3 + Ey_3 + F = 0$

This system can be solved in any approved manner such as by addition, substitution, determinants, or matrices. Once D, E, and F have been determined the general form of the equation is known. Then by transforming from general to standard form, the values of h, k, and r can be found and the graph of the circle constructed.

If three points are not given, but other information about the circle is known, the circle is uniquely determined, in general, if three conditions are known.

EXAMPLE. Find the equation of the circle which passes through the points $R(2, -1)$, $S(-3, 0)$, and $T(1, 4)$.

Solution. By substitution in the general form $x^2 + y^2 + Dx + Ey + F = 0$ we can write the system of equations

(1) $2^2 + (-1)^2 + 2D - E + F = 0$
(2) $(-3)^2 + 0^2 - 3D + 0 \cdot E + F = 0$
(3) $1^2 + 4^2 + D + 4E + F = 0$

Transforming this system into a system of two equations in two variables by subtracting (2) from (1) and (3) from (1) we have

(4) $5D - E - 4 = 0$
(5) $D - 5E - 12 = 0$

When (4) and (5) are solved we have $D = \dfrac{1}{3}$, $E = -\dfrac{7}{3}$, and from (1) we find $F = -8$.
The general form of the required equation is

$$x^2 + y^2 + \frac{1}{3}x - \frac{7}{3}y - 8 = 0$$

or $$3x^2 + 3y^2 + x - 7y - 24 = 0$$

An alternate solution can be found by substituting the coordinates of the three given points on the circle in Formula (III), Section 13.1. The system is

(6) $2^2 + (-1)^2 - 2h(2) - 2k(-1) + h^2 + k^2 - r^2 = 0$
(7) $(-3)^2 + 0^2 - 2h(-3) - 2k(0) + h^2 + k^2 - r^2 = 0$
(8) $1^2 + 4^2 - 2h(1) - 2k(4) + h^2 + k^2 - r^2 = 0$

In simplified form this system becomes

(9) $h^2 + k^2 - 4h + 2k + 5 - r^2 = 0$
(10) $h^2 + k^2 + 6h - 0k + 9 - r^2 = 0$
(11) $h^2 + k^2 - 2h - 8k + 17 - r^2 = 0$

Transforming to a system of two equations in two variables by subtracting (10) from (9) and (11) from (9) we have

(12) $-10h + 2k - 4 = 0$
(13) $-2h + 10k - 12 = 0$

Solving for h and k we get $h = -\dfrac{1}{6}$ and $k = \dfrac{7}{6}$.

Then from (9) we have $r = \dfrac{13\sqrt{2}}{6}$.

If we replace h, k, and r by these values in Formula (III) and simplify we get

$$3x^2 + 3y^2 + x - 7y - 24 = 0$$

The second method checks the first solution and has the advantage of determining the center (h, k) and the radius r. If the equation of the circle is not to be graphed the first solution is preferred, but if the graph is required, the second is preferred.

Exercises

1. Find the equation of the circle that passes through $(0, 0)$, $(3, 0)$, and $(5, 2)$.
2. Find the equation of the circle that passes through $(-2, 3)$, $(3, 4)$, and $(-5, -1)$.
3. Find the equation of the circle that passes through $(7, -1)$ and whose center is at $(-2, 4)$.
4. The center of a circle is at $(5, -5)$ and it is tangent to the axes. Find its equation.
5. The center of a circle is on the x-axis, its radius is 1, and it passes through $\left(\dfrac{\sqrt{2}}{2}, \dfrac{\sqrt{2}}{2}\right)$. Find the equation.

13.3 Equation of a tangent to a circle

Recall from Section 3.9 that the slope of the tangent line to the graph of the equation $y = f(x)$ is given by the derivative $D_x y$. The equation of a circle is not a simple function for which $D_x y$ can be easily found. We shall accept without proof that, if $x^2 + y^2 = r^2$, then

$$D_x y = -\frac{x}{y} = -\frac{x}{\pm\sqrt{r^2 - x^2}}.$$

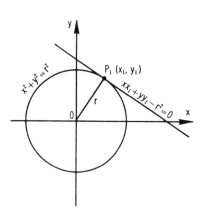

FIGURE 13-4

If point $P_1(x_1, y_1)$ is on the circle then the point-slope form of the equation enables us to write

$$-\frac{x_1}{y_1} = \frac{y - y_1}{x - x_1}$$

Since $x^2 + y^2 = r^2$ is true for every point $P(x, y)$ on the circle, we can write the equation of the tangent line at P_1 in the form

$$x \cdot x_1 + y \cdot y_1 - r^2 = 0 \qquad\qquad (V)$$

You will observe that equation (V) applies only when the center of the circle is at the origin.

EXAMPLE. Find the equation of the tangent line to the circle $x^2 + y^2 = 25$ at the point $(-3, 4)$ on the circle.

Solution. Formula (V) applies with $x_1 = -3$ and $y_1 = 4$. Thus, the equation of the tangent line at $(-3, 4)$ is

$$x(-3) + y(4) - 25 = 0$$

or
$$3x - 4y + 25 = 0$$

Exercises

Draw each figure and write the indicated equation.

1. Find the equation of the tangent to $x^2 + y^2 - 19 = 0$ at $(-2, \sqrt{15})$.

2. Find the equation of the tangent to $3x^2 + 3y^2 - 5 = 0$ at $\left(1, \dfrac{\sqrt{6}}{3}\right)$.

3. Find the equations of the horizontal tangents to the circle $x^2 + y^2 = 25$.

4. Find the equations of the vertical tangents of the circle $x^2 + y^2 - 49 = 0$.

13.4   Length of a tangent to a circle from an exterior point

If $P(x_1, y_1)$ is a point and $x^2 + y^2 = r^2$ is a circle, then P lies outside the circle if $x_1^2 + y_1^2 > r^2$. Why? In this case there are two tangents from P to the circle and it is sometimes necessary to find the length of a tangent, that is, the line segment joining the given point to a point of tangency on the circle.

Let $A(x_2, y_2)$ be the point of tangency of a line through P tangent to the circle. Then triangle OAP is a right triangle in which $OA = r$, $OP =$ the distance d of P from the origin, and $PA = t$, the length of the tangent. Thus,

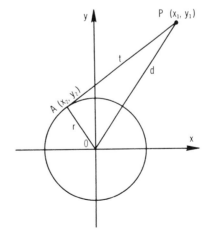

FIGURE 13–5

by the Pythagorean formula $t^2 = d^2 - r^2$, or $t = \sqrt{d^2 - r^2}$. But $d^2 = x_1^2 + y_1^2$, so we have

$$t = \sqrt{x_1^2 + y_1^2 - r^2} \tag{VI}$$

where t is the length of the tangent from $P(x_1, y_1)$ to the circle $x^2 + y^2 = r^2$.

EXAMPLE 1. Find the length of the tangent from $(-4, 7)$ to the circle $x^2 + y^2 = 10$.

Solution. By (VI) the length of the tangent is

$$t = \sqrt{(-4)^2 + 7^2 - 10} = \sqrt{55}$$

If the center of the given circle is not at the origin, the formula for the length of the tangent from an exterior point can be developed as follows. Let $C(h, k)$ be the center of the circle, $P(x_1, y_1)$

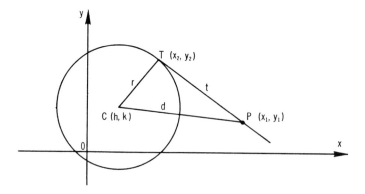

FIGURE 13–6

be the exterior point, and $T(x_2, y_2)$ be a point on the circle where a tangent from P touches the circle. Let $CT = r$, $PC = d$, and $PT = t$. The formula for t in terms of d and r is

$$t = \sqrt{d^2 - r^2}$$

From the equation of the circle, r^2 may be found, and d^2 may be computed by the distance formula. Thus, $d^2 = (x_1 - h)^2 + (y_1 - k)^2$ and the length of the tangent becomes

$$t = \sqrt{(x_1 - h)^2 + (y_1 - k)^2 - r^2} \tag{VII}$$

The length of the tangent from an exterior point is easily found if the given equation of a circle is in standard form since h, k, and r are obvious.

EXAMPLE 2. Find the length of the tangent from $(-1, 3)$ to the circle $(x - 2)^2 + (y + 5)^2 = 16$.

Solution. $h = 2, k = -5, r = 4$. From (VII) we have

$$t = \sqrt{(-1 - 2)^2 + (3 + 5)^2 - 16}$$

$$t = \sqrt{9 + 64 - 16} = \sqrt{57}$$

Exercises

In each exercise draw the figure.

1. Find the length of the tangent from point $(4, 7)$ to the circle $x^2 + y^2 = 7$.

2. Find the length of the tangent from point $(9, 9)$ to the circle $x^2 + y^2 = 2$.

3. Find the length of the tangents from point $(6, 1)$ to the circle $x^2 + y^2 = 37$ and discuss the result.

4. Find the length of the tangent from point $(1, -1)$ to the circle $x^2 + y^2 - 4 = 0$ and discuss the result.

5. Find the length of the tangent from point $(10, 1)$ to the circle $x^2 + y^2 - 6x - 8y = 0$.

6. Find the length of the tangent from point $(2, 3)$ to the circle $3x^2 + 3y^2 - 5x + 7y - \dfrac{17}{18} = 0$.

7. Find the length of the common external tangent to the circles $x^2 + y^2 = 4$ and $(x - 4)^2 + (y - 3)^2 = 1$.

13.5   Systems of two circles through two points—radical axis

Let us consider two circles S and S' which intersect in two real points, that is, points of the coordinate plane.
$S = x^2 + y^2 + Dx + Ey + F = 0$
and
$S' = x^2 + y^2 + D'x + E'y + F' = 0$

A family of circles will pass through the

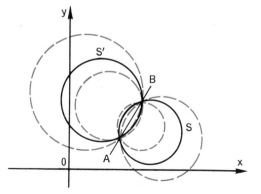

FIGURE 13–7

two points of intersection A and B. If we let k be a parameter we can write the family of circles in the form $S + kS' = 0$ where $k \neq -1$. We find that

$$S + kS' = x^2 + y^2 + Dx + Ey + F + k(x^2 + y^2 + D'x + E'y + F') = 0$$

After rearranging and factoring we have

$$(1 + k)\, x^2 + (1 + k)\, y^2 + (D + kD')\, x + (E + kE')\, y + (F + kF') = 0$$

which may be written in the general form of the equation of a circle as

$$x^2 + y^2 + \frac{D + kD'}{1 + k}\, x + \frac{E + kE'}{1 + k}\, y + \frac{F + kF'}{1 + k} = 0 \quad \textbf{(VIII)}$$

The coordinates of both A and B make $S = 0$ and $S' = 0$, so that these coordinates make $S + kS' = 0$. Thus A and B are the points of intersection of every member of the family of circles. By assigning the parameter k any value except -1 we determine a circle which is a member of the family of circles represented by (VIII).

If $k = -1$, then $S + kS'$ reduces to

$$(D - D')x + (E - E')y + (F - F') = 0 \qquad \textbf{(IX)}$$

unless the circles are concentric. This is the equation of the line through A and B, the points of intersection of S and S'. This line, called the *radical axis* of the family of circles, is the common chord. If the circles do not intersect in real points, the family of circles (VIII) and the radical axis (IX) exist even though points A and B have imaginary coordinates.

EXAMPLE. Write the equation of the family of circles of which $x^2 + y^2 - 2x - 3 = 0$ and $x^2 + y^2 + 2y - 7 = 0$ are members. Write the equation of the radical axis of the family of circles.

Solution. From (VIII) the equation of the family is

$$x^2 + y^2 - \frac{2}{1 + k}\, x + \frac{2k}{1 + k}\, y - \frac{3 + 7k}{1 + k} = 0$$

From (IX) the equation of the radical axis is

$$-2x - 2y + 4 = 0$$

or

$$x + y - 2 = 0$$

Exercises

1. Sketch the non-intersecting family of circles of which $x^2 + y^2 - 10x + 21 = 0$ and $x^2 + y^2 = 4$ are members. Find the equation of the radical axis and construct its graph.

2. Find the equation of the radical axis of the circles $x^2 + y^2 = 9$ and $x^2 + y^2 - 2x - 4y = 0$. Find the points of intersection of the circles. (*Hint:* Find the common solutions of the equations for the radical axis and one of the circles.)

3. Find the equation of the radical axis of the circles $(x - 4)^2 + (y + 5)^2 = 20$ and $x^2 + y^2 + 2x - 6y - 26 = 0$. Draw the figure.

4. Find the equation of the radical axis of the circles $x^2 + y^2 = 1$ and $x^2 + y^2 - 10x + 21 = 0$. Draw the figure.

5. Show that the radical axis is perpendicular to the line of centers of two circles.

13.6   Polar equation of a circle

If the center of a circle is at the pole and the radius is r, then the *polar equation* of a circle is

$$\rho = r \tag{X}$$

(See Section 12.9.)

If any point $P(\rho, \theta)$ lies on the circle, then whatever the value of θ, the polar distance ρ is the radius r of the circle.

A formula for the polar equation of a circle with its center not on the pole can be developed; the general polar form involves the cosine of the difference of two angles. We shall restrict our discussion to the special case above.

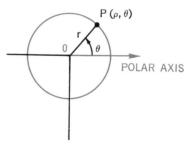

FIGURE 13–8

EXAMPLE 1. Transform the polar equation of a circle $\rho = 3$ to rectangular coordinates if the pole coincides with the origin and the polar axis coincides with the positive x-axis.

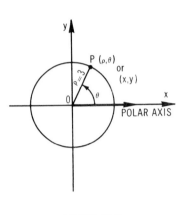

FIGURE 13-9

Solution. Sketch the circle in polar coordinates and superpose a rectangular system of coordinates as stated in the problem. We then have

$$\rho = \sqrt{x^2 + y^2}$$

and the required equation is

$$\sqrt{x^2 + y^2} = 3 \text{ or, } x^2 + y^2 = 9$$

EXAMPLE 2. If the equation of a circle in rectangular coordinates is $x^2 + y^2 = 12$, find the polar equation if the pole and origin coincide and if the polar axis and the positive x-axis coincide.

Solution. $\rho = \sqrt{x^2 + y^2} = \sqrt{12} = 2\sqrt{3}$
Thus, the polar equation is $\rho = 2\sqrt{3}$.

Exercises

In any transformation assume that the pole coincides with the origin and the polar axis with the positive x-axis.

1. The equation of a circle in polar coordinates is $\rho = 5$. Give the equation in rectangular coordinates.
2. The equation of a circle in rectangular coordinates is $x^2 + y^2 = 49$. Give the equation in polar coordinates.
3. The equation of a circle in rectangular coordinates is $x^2 + y^2 = 3$. What is its equation in polar coordinates?

Chapter Review

1. Find the center and radius of the circle with the equation $x^2 + y^2 - 2x + 4y - 11 = 0$.
2. Write the equation of the circle that is tangent to the y-axis and with its center at $(-3, 7)$.

3. Write the equation of the circle that passes through the points $(-2, 1)$, $(5, 6)$, and $(-3, 6)$.

4. Write the equation of a circle with its center at $(-8, 3)$ that passes through the point $(-6, -4)$.

5. Find the length of a tangent line from the point $(5, -1)$ to the circle $x^2 + y^2 + 6x - 10y - 2 = 0$.

6. Find the points of intersection of the circles $(x + 1)^2 + (y + 2)^2 = 20$ and $(x - 2)^2 + (y + 4)^2 = 12$. Write the equation of the radical axis.

CHAPTER OUTLINE

The Parabola

14

14.1 The conic sections

A conic section is a locus of points in a plane such that for any point of the locus the ratio of its distance from a fixed point to its distance from a fixed line is constant. The fixed point is called a *focus* and the fixed line is called a *directrix*. The term *conic sec-*

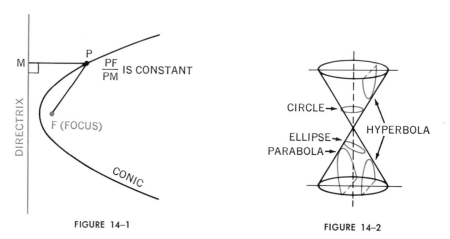

FIGURE 14–1   FIGURE 14–2

tion, or simply *conic,* is due to the fact that the loci can be formed by the intersection of a plane with a conical surface.

There are four distinct conics and four degenerate cases. The circle, parabola, ellipse, and hyperbola are the conics and a point, line, and two intersecting or parallel lines are the degenerate cases. The circle is sometimes considered a special case of the ellipse. How can a plane intersect a conical surface to produce the degenerate cases as sections?

Let l be a fixed line and F a fixed point. Then, if $P(x, y)$ represents all points such that $\dfrac{PF}{PM}$

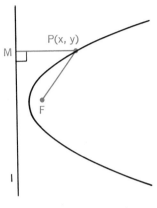

is a constant, the locus of P is a conic section. The ratio $\dfrac{PF}{PM}$ is defined to be e, the *eccentricity* of the conic section.

A conic section for which $e = 1$ is a *parabola*. If $e < 1$, the conic is an *ellipse;* if $e > 1$ the conic is a *hyperbola*.

Stated as a simple locus, *the parabola is the locus of points equidistant from a fixed point*

FIGURE 14–3

and a fixed line. The parabola is the path of an object given a velocity in a gravitational field. A thrown ball, or any projectile, will follow a parabolic path unless acted upon by additional forces or thrown directly upward. Since air friction normally is present, the path is usually only approximately a parabola for a projectile. Parabolic mirrors are used in reflecting telescopes and search lights because they have the property of reflecting parallel rays to a point. If a source of energy (light, sound, heat, radio waves, etc.) is placed at the focus of a parabolic reflector the rays will be reflected into a pencil-like beam.

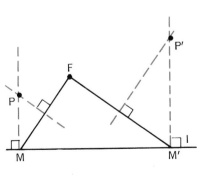

FIGURE 14–4

Given a point and a line we shall show a method of constructing points of a parabola. If M, any point on l the directrix, is joined by a straight line to F, the focus, and the perpendicular bisector of MF is constructed, it will intersect the perpendicular to line l from M at a point P on the parabola. To prove this, draw PF and prove that $PF \cong PM$. By selecting another point M' on l and repeating the construction, additional points on the parabola may be found.

14.2   Equation of a parabola

Let l be the directrix and F be the focus of a parabola. In this book we shall consider only the cases where l is parallel to one of the axes. Draw FT perpendicular to l and the midpoint V will be

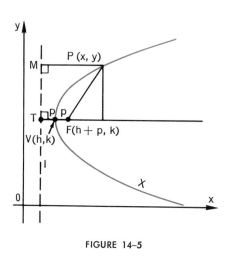

FIGURE 14–5

on the parabola since $\dfrac{FV}{VT} = 1$.

V is called the *vertex* of the parabola. Let V have the coordinates (h, k) and let the distance $VF = p$. Thus $VT = p$. The coordinates of F are $(h + p, k)$ and the equation of l is $x = h - p$.

Now consider any point $P(x, y)$ on the parabola for which l is the directrix and F the focus. From the definition of a parabola $\dfrac{PF}{PM} = 1$.

The coordinates of M are $(h - p, y)$. By the distance formula

$$PF = \sqrt{[x - (h + p)]^2 + (y - k)^2}$$

and

$$PM = x - (h - p)$$

Thus we have

$$\frac{PF}{PM} = 1, \text{ or } PF \cong PM$$

Substituting, $\sqrt{[x - (h + p)]^2 + (y - k)^2} = x - (h - p)$

Squaring, $[x - (h + p)]^2 + (y - k)^2 = [x - (h - p)]^2$

or

$$x^2 - 2x(h + p) + (h + p)^2 + (y - k)^2 = x^2 - 2x(h - p) + (h - p)^2$$

Simplifying, we get

$$(y - k)^2 = 4p(x - h) \tag{I}$$

If the directrix is parallel to the y-axis we get (I) but if the directrix is parallel to the x-axis, we get

$$(x - h)^2 = 4p(y - k) \tag{II}$$

Formulas (I) and (II) are called the *standard forms* of the equation of a parabola.

In the special case where the vertex is at the origin, $V\ (h,\ k) = (0,\ 0)$, we have

$$y^2 = 4px \tag{I'}$$

and

$$x^2 = 4py \tag{II'}$$

In (I) or (I'), if p is positive the curve is open to the right; if p is negative the curve is open to the left. In (II) or (II'), if p is positive the curve is open upward; if p is negative the curve is open downward.

If (I) and (II) are expanded and written as polynomials we have the *general form* of the equation of a parabola. Equation (I) becomes

$$y^2 - 4px - 2ky + k^2 + 4ph = 0 \tag{III}$$

and equation (II) becomes

$$x^2 - 2hx - 4py + h^2 + 4pk = 0 \tag{IV}$$
$$y^2 + Dx + Ey + F = 0 \tag{V}$$

or

where $D = -4p$, $E = -2k$, $F = k^2 + 4ph$, and

$$x^2 + Dx + Ey + F = 0 \quad \textbf{(VI)}$$

where $D = -2h$, $E = -4p$, $F = h^2 + 4pk$.

The line through the focus F perpendicular to the directrix l is the *axis* of the parabola. The axis passes through the vertex V. A parabola is symmetrical with respect to its axis.

A line segment RS perpendicular to the axis through the focus with endpoints on the parabola is called the *latus rectum*.

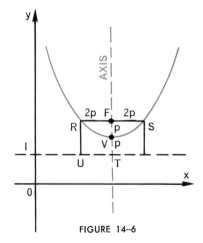

FIGURE 14–6

The length of the latus rectum is $4p$ which can be shown by noting that $\dfrac{RF}{RU} = 1$ and $RU = FT = 2p$. $RF = 2p$ and $RS = 4p$.

EXAMPLE 1. Give the coordinates of the focus and the equation of the directrix of the parabola $y^2 = 12x$.

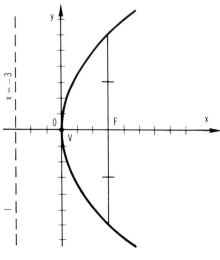

FIGURE 14–7

Solution. The vertex V is at $(0,\ 0)$ since the equation is in the form of (I'). $4p = 12$; therefore $p = 3$. The focus F is 3 units to the right of the vertex V and hence the coordinates of F are $(3,\ 0)$. The equation of the directrix is $x = -3$.

EXAMPLE 2. Give the coordinates of the vertex and the focus, the equation of the directrix, and the equation of the axis of the parabola $x^2 - 4x - 12y - 32 = 0$. Find the length of the latus rectum. Sketch the parabola.

Solution. Writing the equation in standard form, we have

$$x^2 - 4x + 4 = 12y + 36$$

or

$$(x - 2)^2 = 12(y + 3)$$

Thus, the coordinates of the vertex are $(2,\ -3)$. To find p we write $4p = 12$, hence $p = 3$. Since p is positive the parabola opens upward and the focus is 3 units above the vertex. The focus is at $(2,\ 0)$ and the equation of the directrix is $y = -6$. The

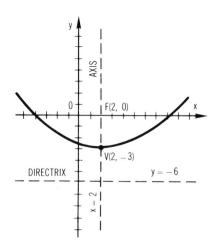

FIGURE 14–8

axis passes through the vertex and focus; its equation is $x = 2$. The length of the latus rectum is $4p = 12$ units. A sketch of the parabola can be made using the above information.

Exercises

In each exercise draw the figure.

1. Give the coordinates of the focus and the equation of the directrix of the parabola $x^2 - 11y = 0$.

2. Give the coordinates of the focus and the equation of the directrix of the parabola $3y^2 - 19x = 0$.

3. Give the coordinates of the vertex and the focus, the equation of the directrix, and the equation of the axis of the parabola $x^2 - 6x - 10y - 1 = 0$. Find the length of the latus rectum.

4. Give the coordinates of the vertex and the focus, the equation of the directrix, and the equation of the axis of the parabola $y^2 + 3x - 6y = 0$. Find the length of the latus rectum.

In Exercises 5–10, write the equation and make a sketch of the parabola given.

5. Vertex $(0, 0)$, focus $(2, 0)$.

6. Focus $(3, 5)$, directrix $y = 3$.

7. Vertex $(-2, 1)$, axis, $y = 1$, length of latus rectum 4, p is positive.

8. Focus $(2, -6)$, $p = -2$, axis $x = 2$.

9. Endpoints of latus rectum $(0, 3)$ and $(0, -3)$, p is negative.

10. Three points on the curve are $(0, 0)$, $(-1, 2)$, and $(3, -2)$. (*Hint:* Plot the points and determine D, E, F in (V) or (VI).)

14.3   Tangent and normal to a parabola

As you know, the slope of the tangent to the graph of $y = f(x)$ is $D_x y$. If the equation of a parabola is in general form (VI), the equation can be solved for y and we have

$$y = -\frac{x^2 + Dx + F}{E} = -\frac{x^2}{E} - \frac{D}{E}x - \frac{F}{E}$$

We can find $D_x y$ as follows.

$$y + \Delta y = -\frac{(x + \Delta x)^2}{E} - \frac{D}{E}(x + \Delta x) - \frac{F}{E}$$

$$y + \Delta y = -\frac{x^2}{E} - \frac{2x\Delta x}{E} - \frac{\overline{\Delta x}^2}{E} - \frac{D}{E}x - \frac{D}{E}\Delta x - \frac{F}{E}$$

$$\underline{y \qquad\quad = -\frac{x^2}{E} \qquad\qquad\qquad - \frac{D}{E}x \qquad\qquad - \frac{F}{E}}$$

$$\Delta y = \qquad -\frac{2x\Delta x}{E} - \frac{\overline{\Delta x}^2}{E} \qquad - \frac{D}{E}\Delta x$$

Divide by Δx.

$$\frac{\Delta y}{\Delta x} = -\frac{2x}{E} - \frac{\Delta x}{E} - \frac{D}{E}$$

$$D_x y = \lim_{\Delta x \to 0} \frac{\Delta y}{\Delta x} = \frac{-2x - D}{E}$$

Since $D = -2h$ and $E = -4p$ we have

$$D_x y = \frac{-2x + 2h}{-4p} = \frac{x - h}{2p}$$

If the equation of the parabola is in the form of (V) it can be shown that $D_x y = \dfrac{-D}{2y + E} = \dfrac{2p}{y - k}$.

Thus, for a parabola with a vertical axis, the slope of a tangent to the curve is

$$D_x y = \frac{x - h}{2p} \tag{VII}$$

and for a parabola with a horizontal axis the slope of a tangent is

$$D_x y = \frac{2p}{y - k} \tag{VIII}$$

The equation of the tangent at any point on a parabola can be written by applying the point-slope form of the equation of a line.

EXAMPLE 1. Find the equation of the tangent to the parabola $2x^2 - 3x + 2y - 4 = 0$ at the point where $x = -2$.

Solution. We have shown that $D_x y = \dfrac{-2x - D}{E}$; in this example $D = -\dfrac{3}{2}$ and $E = 1$. Thus, $D_x y = \dfrac{-4x + 3}{2}$. The slope of the tangent to the curve where $x = -2$ is $\dfrac{-4(-2) + 3}{2} = \dfrac{11}{2}$.

We may also find $D_x y$ by the definition of derivative or by Formula (VII) if h and p are found.

Since $y = -x^2 + \dfrac{3}{2} x + 2$, the value of y at $x = -2$ is -5.

The tangent passes through $(-2, -5)$ and its slope is $\dfrac{11}{2}$. The point-slope form of the equation of a line gives

$$\frac{11}{2} = \frac{y+5}{x+2} \quad \text{or} \quad 11x - 2y + 12 = 0$$

The *normal* to a curve at any point on it is the line perpendicular to the tangent at the point. Thus, the slope of the normal is the negative reciprocal of the slope of the tangent at any point. The slope of the normal is

$$-\frac{1}{D_x y} = \frac{2p}{h-x} \quad \text{(from (VII))} \tag{IX}$$

or

$$-\frac{1}{D_x y} = \frac{k-y}{2p} \quad \text{(from (VIII))} \tag{X}$$

EXAMPLE 2. Find the equation of the normal to the parabola $y^2 - 2x + 6y - 5 = 0$ at $(-5, -1)$.

Solution. Find $D_x y$ by (VIII). The given equation may be written in the form $(y+3)^2 = 2(x+7)$ which shows $h = -7$, $k = -3$, $p = \dfrac{1}{2}$. Hence, $D_x y = \dfrac{2p}{y-k} = \dfrac{1}{-1+3} = \dfrac{1}{2}$. The slope of the tangent at $(-5, -1)$ is $\dfrac{1}{2}$; the slope of the normal is -2. The equation of the normal is

$$-2 = \frac{y+1}{x+5} \quad \text{or} \quad 2x + y + 11 = 0$$

Exercises

Find the equation of the tangent and the normal to the given parabola at the indicated point.

1. $x^2 + 4x - y + 1 = 0$ at $(0, 1)$.
2. $y^2 - x + y - 5 = 0$ at $(1, -3)$.
3. $2x^2 - 7x + 5y - 11 = 0$ at the point whose abscissa is -1.
4. $2y^2 + 4x - 3y - 11 = 0$ at the point whose ordinate is 2.
5. Find the slopes of the tangent lines at the endpoints of the latus rectum of the parabola $y^2 - 4x - 2y + 9 = 0$. What relationship to each other do these tangents have?

6. Find the point on the parabola $x^2 - 6x - 2y + 1 = 0$ for which the tangent line makes a 45° angle with the positive x-axis.

7. At what point on the parabola $x^2 + 4y + 4 = 0$ is the normal perpendicular to the directrix?

8. A well known law of physics states that the angle of incidence of a ray of light equals the angle of reflection. The angles are measured between the rays and the normal to the reflecting surface. If a beam of rays parallel to the axis of a parabolic surface are reflected, it can be shown that the rays converge at the focus. Make a construction of a parabola and a number of rays parallel to the axis and show that the reflected rays seem to pass through the focus if the angle of incidence and the angle of reflection are equal. Prove that this is true analytically.

14.4 Translation of axes

Sometimes it is desirable to change the axes with respect to which a graph is drawn. There are two basic transformations of the plane which preserve metric properties of a figure, *translation* and *rotation*. In a translation of axes the new axes are parallel to the given axes; in a rotation of axes the new axes have the same origin but are not parallel to the given axes. We shall consider only translation of axes in this book.

Consider a point $P(x, y)$ in a coordinate plane with respect to a given x-axis and y-axis. It may be desirable to express P in coordinates with respect to new axes such that the x'-axis is parallel to the x-axis, and the y'-axis is parallel to the y-axis. Let the intersection of the new axes be at the point (h, k). All points given with respect to the x'-axis and y'-axis will be designated by a prime (′) notation. Thus the coordinates of P with respect to the new axes are (x', y'). In order to transform a point (x, y) into (x', y') the relation between the new and old

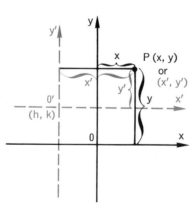

FIGURE 14–9

coordinates is required. Now, it can be seen from the figure that

$$x = x' + h, \text{ and } y = y' + k \qquad \textbf{(XI)}$$

A parabola with its vertex at (h, k) is of the form $(y - k)^2 = 4p(x - h)$ or $(x - h)^2 = 4p(y - k)$. Now let us translate the axes so that the y'-axis is the line $x = h$ and the x'-axis is the line $y = k$. The point of intersection of the axes is (h, k), the vertex of the parabola. Thus, in terms of coordinates of the new axes, every point of the curve is transformed according to Formula (XI), and the equation of the parabola becomes

$$y'^2 = 4px' \qquad \textbf{(XII)}$$

or

$$x'^2 = 4py' \qquad \textbf{(XIII)}$$

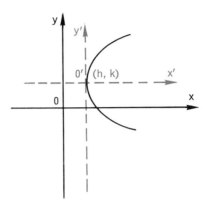

FIGURE 14–10

The new axes may intersect at any point, but a common and most useful transformation is to translate the origin to the vertex of the parabola.

EXAMPLE. (a) Express the equation of the parabola $(y - 1)^2 = 6(x + 4)$ to new axes such that $x = x' - 4$ and $y = y' + 1$. (b) Express the equation in terms of a coordinate system (x'', y'') for which the origin is at $(3, -2)$.

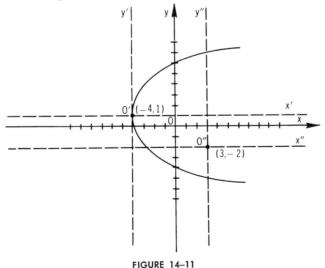

FIGURE 14–11

Solution. (a) Replace x by $x' - 4$ and y by $y' + 1$. We have the equation $y'^2 = 6x'$ as the equation of the parabola with respect to the x'-axis and the y'-axis. The new origin is at the vertex.

(b) Replace x by $x'' + 3$ and y by $y'' - 2$. The equation with respect to axes which intersect at $(3, -2)$ is

$$(y'' - 3)^2 = 6(x'' + 7)$$

Exercises

1. Write the equation of the parabola $(x - 3)^2 = 4(y + 5)$ with respect to axes which intersect at $(3, -5)$.

2. Write the equation of the parabola $y^2 = 4px$ with respect to axes which intersect at $(3, 0)$.

3. Write the equation of the parabola $x^2 = 4py$ with respect to axes translated so that the origin is at $(0, 4)$.

4. Write the equation of the parabola $y^2 = 4px$ with respect to axes translated so that the origin is at $(p, 0)$.

14.5   Polar equation of a parabola

The simplest form of the polar equation of a parabola is obtained if the focus is taken as the pole and a line perpendicular to the directrix is taken as the polar axis. By definition, for any point P on a parabola

$$\frac{PF}{PM} = 1$$

or

$$PF \cong PM$$

But, $PM = ST = SF + FV + VT$

$$= \rho \cos \theta + p + p$$

Therefore $\rho = \rho \cos \theta + 2p$

Solving for ρ we get

$$\rho = \frac{2p}{1 - \cos \theta} \quad \textbf{(XIV)}$$

Equation (XIV) is called the *polar equation of a parabola* with its focus at the pole.

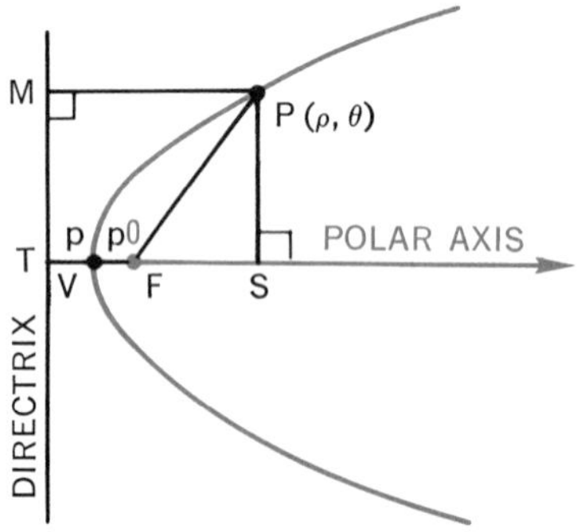

FIGURE 14-12

To transform an equation in rectangular coordinates to polar coordinates we must recognize that in the standard form $y^2 = 4px$ the vertex is at the origin, but in the polar equation, the pole is assumed to be at the focus. Thus, a translation of origin is necessary so that $y^2 = 4px$ becomes $y'^2 = 4p(x' + p)$. We can now replace x' by $\rho \cos \theta$ and y' by $\rho \sin \theta$ and we have

$$(\rho \sin \theta)^2 = 4p(\rho \cos \theta + p)$$
$$\rho^2 \sin^2 \theta = 4p\rho \cos \theta + 4p^2$$
$$\rho^2 \sin^2 \theta - 4p\rho \cos \theta - 4p^2 = 0$$

Solving for ρ by the quadratic formula and choosing the positive value of the double sign so that ρ will be positive we have

$$= \frac{4p \cos \theta + \sqrt{16p^2 \cos^2 \theta + 16p^2 \sin^2 \theta}}{2 \sin^2 \theta}$$

$$= \frac{4p \cos \theta + 4p\sqrt{\cos^2 \theta + \sin^2 \theta}}{2 \sin^2 \theta}$$

$$= \frac{4p \cos \theta + 4p}{2 \sin^2 \theta}$$

$$= \frac{2p(\cos \theta + 1)}{1 - \cos^2 \theta}$$

$$= \frac{2p(\cos \theta + 1)}{(1 + \cos \theta)(1 - \cos \theta)}$$

$$\rho = \frac{2p}{1 - \cos \theta}$$

Thus, the polar equation is independent of the translation of the origin to the focus but it must be remembered when graphing that the pole is at the focus in the polar equation of the parabola but the origin is at the vertex in the basic rectangular form (I') of the equation.

EXAMPLE. Change the equation of the parabola $y^2 = 5x$ to the polar equation where the pole is at the focus and the polar axis coincides with the positive x-axis.

Solution. $4p = 5$; therefore $p = \dfrac{5}{4}$.

The polar equation is $\rho = \dfrac{2.5}{1 - \cos \theta}$.

Exercises

1. The equation of a parabola in rectangular coordinates is $y^2 = -7x$. Find the equation in polar coordinates if the pole is at the focus.

2. The equation of a parabola in polar coordinates is $\rho = \dfrac{7}{1 - \cos \theta}$.

Find the equation in rectangular coordinates if the origin is at the vertex. Find the equation in rectangular coordinates if the focus is at the origin.

Chapter Review

1. Give the coordinates of the vertex and the focus, and write the equation of the directrix of the parabola $(x - 7)^2 = 8(y - 3)$.

2. Give the coordinates of the vertex and the focus, and write the equation of the directrix of the parabola $y^2 - 2x + 10y + 27 = 0$.

3. Write the equation of the latus rectum of the parabola $x^2 - 8x - 12y - 20 = 0$ and find the coordinates of its endpoints.

4. Write the equation of a parabola which has a focus at $(3, -5)$ and whose directrix is $y = -2$. What are the coordinates of the vertex?

5. Write the equation of the tangent to the parabola $x^2 + 4x - 5y + 9 = 0$ at the point where the abscissa is 1. Write the equation of the normal at the same point.

6. Write the equation of the locus of the center of a circle that is tangent to the line $x = 5$ and passes through the point $(2, 7)$.

7. A family of lines is parallel to the line $2x + y - 4 = 0$. Write the equation of the line which is a member of this family that is tangent to the parabola $x^2 - 4y = 0$. Write the equation of the line of this family that is a normal to the parabola.

8. Find the points of intersection of $x^2 - 4x - 4y - 4 = 0$ and $y^2 + 2x = 0$.

CHAPTER OUTLINE

The Ellipse **15**

15.1   Definition of an ellipse

An *ellipse* is the conic section with an eccentricity less than
one. Thus, an ellipse is the locus of points such that for any point
of the locus the ratio of the distance from a fixed point to the
distance from a fixed line is a positive real number less than
one. Thus the locus is an ellipse
if $\dfrac{PF}{PM} < 1$. As in the case of
the parabola, the fixed point is
a *focus* and the fixed line is a
directrix. Recall that the ratio $\dfrac{PF}{PM}$
is the constant e, the eccentricity.
An ellipse has two foci and two
directrices.

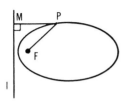

FIGURE 15–1

An *ellipse* is the section of a
conical surface made by a plane
that intersects all elements of the
cone.

341

The definition of an ellipse can be given in another way. *An ellipse is the locus of points in a plane such that the sum of the distances from two fixed points to any point of the locus is a constant.*

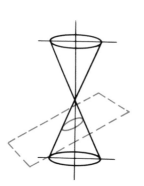

The fixed points are the foci, F and F'. This means that $FP + F'P = FP' + F'P' = FP'' + F'P'' = FP''' + F'P'''$, and so on, for all points of the locus. This property of the ellipse enables us to draw an ellipse by placing a thumb tack on a drawing board at each of two points, F and F', and then using a piece of string greater than $2FF'$ tied in a loop. The loop of string equal in length to $FP + F'P + FF'$ is placed over the tacks and a pencil is inserted at P. As the pencil is moved around the loop keeping the string taut, an ellipse is traced.

FIGURE 15–2

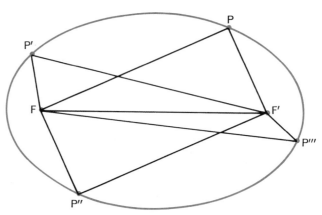

FIGURE 15–3

By modifying the distance FF' and the length of the loop, various sizes and shapes of ellipses can be traced. If F coincides with F', what special case results?

15.2   Equation of an ellipse

The standard equation of an ellipse can be derived from the definition in terms of the eccentricity e.

Let F be a focus and RS a directrix in a coordinate plane with

$RS \perp OX;$ construct FT perpendicular to RS. If e is a positive number less than 1, construct a vertex V on FT such that $\dfrac{FV}{VT} = e$.

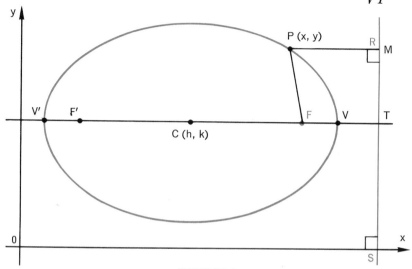

FIGURE 15-4

If FT is divided externally in the same ratio, vertex V' is determined. Bisect VV' and call this point $C(h, k)$ the center of the ellipse. Construct F' such that $F'C = CF$. Let $P(x, y)$ be any point on the ellipse; construct $PM \perp RS$. Let a be the length CV.

The coordinates of important points are $C(h, k)$; $V(a + h, k)$; $V'(-a + h, k)$; $F(ae + h, k)$; $F'(-ae + h, k)$; $T\left(\dfrac{a}{e} + h, k\right)$; $M\left(\dfrac{a}{e} + h, y\right)$; $P(x, y)$.

From the definition of an ellipse, $\dfrac{PF}{PM} = e$, we have $PF = e \cdot PM$ or $(PF)^2 = e^2(PM)^2$. By the distance formula we can replace $(PF)^2$ and $(PM)^2$ and have

$$[x - (ae + h)]^2 + (y - k)^2 = e^2\left[x - \left(\frac{a}{e} + h\right)\right]^2$$

or

$$x^2 - 2aex - 2hx + a^2e^2 + 2aeh + h^2 + (y - k)^2 =$$
$$e^2x^2 - 2eax - 2e^2hx + a^2 + 2aeh + e^2h^2$$

Simplifying, we get $(x - h)^2(1 - e^2) + (y - k)^2 = a^2(1 - e^2)$

Dividing by $a^2(1 - e^2)$ we have

$$\frac{(x - h)^2}{a^2} + \frac{(y - k)^2}{a^2(1 - e^2)} = 1 \quad (e < 1)$$

Let $a^2(1 - e^2) = b^2$ and we have the *standard form* of the equation of an ellipse where a and b are positive numbers.

$$\frac{(x - h)^2}{a^2} + \frac{(y - k)^2}{b^2} = 1 \qquad \textbf{(I)}$$

If the center $C(h, k)$ is at the origin $(0, 0)$, the standard form of the equation of an ellipse reduces to

$$\frac{x^2}{a^2} + \frac{y^2}{b^2} = 1 \qquad \textbf{(II)}$$

Let us define $c = ae$, or $e = \dfrac{c}{a}$ where $a > c$. The distance $VV' = 2a$ which we shall call the *major axis;* then a is the *semi-major axis.* The distance BB' we shall call the *minor axis* and $CB = b$ is the

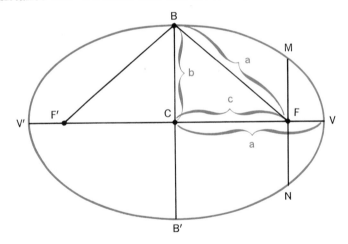

FIGURE 15–5

semi-minor axis. In the derivation of the standard form we let $a^2(1 - e^2) = b^2$. This can be verified by recognizing that $F'V + VF = 2a = F'B + BF$; hence, since $F'B = BF$, we find that $BF = a$. By the Pythagorean Theorem applied to right triangle BCF we have: $a^2 = b^2 + c^2$. Since $c = ae$, and $c^2 = a^2e^2$ it can be shown that $b^2 = a^2(1 - e^2)$. As for the parabola, the line segment MN is called the *latus rectum.* The latus rectum is a chord perpendicular to the axis through a focus. If, in Formula (II),

$x = c$ the value of y is $\pm \dfrac{b}{a} \sqrt{a^2 - c^2}$ or $\pm \dfrac{b^2}{a}$. The coordinates of

M are $\left(c, \dfrac{b^2}{a} \right)$ and, hence, $FM = \dfrac{b^2}{a}$. The length of the latus rectum

MN is $\dfrac{2b^2}{a}$.

If the major axis of the ellipse is parallel to the y-axis, the standard form of the equation becomes

$$\frac{(y - k)^2}{a^2} + \frac{(x - h)^2}{b^2} = 1 \qquad \textbf{(III)}$$

When the center is at the origin (III) reduces to

$$\frac{y^2}{a^2} + \frac{x^2}{b^2} = 1 \qquad \textbf{(IV)}$$

EXAMPLE 1. Write the equation of the ellipse with its center at $(-2, 3)$, the semi-major axis equal to 7, and the eccentricity equal to $\dfrac{1}{2}$. The major axis is parallel to the x-axis.

Solution. $h = -2$; $k = 3$; $a = 7$; $e = \dfrac{1}{2}$. In order to use the standard form (I) we must compute b^2. Since $b^2 = a^2(1 - e^2)$, we have $b^2 = 49 \left(1 - \dfrac{1}{4} \right) = \dfrac{147}{4}$.

The equation of the ellipse is

$$\frac{(x + 2)^2}{49} + \frac{(y - 3)^2}{\dfrac{147}{4}} = 1 \quad \text{or} \quad \frac{(x + 2)^2}{49} + \frac{4(y - 3)^2}{147} = 1$$

EXAMPLE 2. Find the equation of the ellipse with its center at $(0, 3)$, its directrix parallel to the x-axis, the major axis 12, and the eccentricity $\dfrac{1}{2}$. Find the length of the latus rectum.

Solution. The equation will be of form (III). Why? $h = 0$; $k = 3$; $a = 6$; $b^2 = 36 \left(1 - \dfrac{1}{4} \right) = 27$. The equation is

$$\frac{(y - 3)^2}{36} + \frac{x^2}{27} = 1$$

The length of the latus rectum is $\dfrac{2b^2}{a} = \dfrac{2(27)}{6} = 9$.

EXAMPLE 3. Find the equation of the ellipse whose foci are at $F(3, 5)$ and $F'(1, 5)$ and whose eccentricity is $\frac{2}{3}$.

Solution. The center is at $(2, 5)$ the midpoint of FF'. Thus, $c = 1$. Since $e = \frac{c}{a}$ we have $\frac{2}{3} = \frac{1}{a}$ so that $a = \frac{3}{2}$. From $a^2 = b^2 + c^2$ we can find that $b^2 = \frac{5}{4}$. The equation is

$$\frac{(x - 2)^2}{\frac{9}{4}} + \frac{(y - 5)^2}{\frac{5}{4}} = 1, \quad \text{or} \quad \frac{4(x - 2)^2}{9} + \frac{4(y - 5)^2}{5} = 1$$

Exercises

In each exercise draw the figure.

1. Find the equation of the ellipse whose center is at the origin, directrix is parallel to the y-axis, semi-major axis is 10, and eccentricity is $\frac{1}{2}$.

2. Find the equation of the ellipse whose center is at the origin, directrix is parallel to the x-axis, semi-major axis is 2, and eccentricity is $\frac{3}{4}$.

3. Find the eccentricity of the ellipse with equation $\frac{x^2}{9} + \frac{y^2}{4} = 1$. Find the coordinates of the foci, the vertices, and the equations of the directrices. Find the length of the latus rectum.

4. Find the eccentricity of the ellipse whose equation is $5x^2 + 8y^2 = 40$. Find the length of the major and minor axes. Find the coordinates of the endpoints of both latera recta.

5. Write the equation of the ellipse whose center is at $(2, -2)$, semi-major axis is 7, and eccentricity is $\frac{2}{3}$, the directrix being perpendicular to the x-axis.

6. Find the equation of the ellipse whose center is at the origin, one focus at $(4, 0)$, and the corresponding vertex at $(5, 0)$.

7. Find the length of the axes of the ellipse whose foci are at $F(2, 1)$ and $F'(-4, 1)$, and whose eccentricity is .6.

8. Find the foci of an ellipse whose eccentricity is .7, whose center is at $(3, 0)$, and whose major axis is 9, the directrix being parallel to the x-axis.

9. Find the equation of the circle that passes through the end-points of the latera recta of the ellipse $\dfrac{x^2}{16} + \dfrac{y^2}{12} = 1$.

10. The orbit of an earth satellite is an ellipse with the center of the earth at one focus. The eccentricity of the orbit is .16 and the major axis is 10,440 miles. If the mean diameter of the earth is 7920 miles find the greatest and least distances of the satellite from the surface of the earth.

15.3 Second derivation of the equation of an ellipse

The standard form of the equation of an ellipse can be derived from the definition that an ellipse is the locus of points in a plane such that the sum of the distances from two fixed points is a constant.

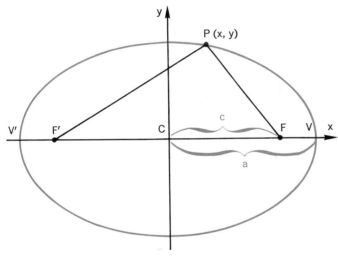

FIGURE 15–6

Let us consider the special case where the center is at the origin. The foci F and F' are located so that $F'C = CF = c$. Also, $V'C = CV = a$. If $P(x, y)$ is any point on the locus, then from the definition we have $F'P + PF$ equals a constant. If P is considered at vertex V, we see from this special case that the constant is $2a$. From the distance formula we have

$$F'P + PF = 2a$$

$$\sqrt{(x + c)^2 + y^2} + \sqrt{(x - c)^2 + y^2} = 2a$$

or $$\sqrt{(x + c)^2 + y^2} = 2a - \sqrt{(x - c)^2 + y^2}$$

Squaring, we have

$$(x + c)^2 + y^2 = 4a^2 + (x - c)^2 + y^2 - 4a\sqrt{(x - c)^2 + y^2}$$

Simplifying, we get

$$a^2 - xc = a\sqrt{(x - c)^2 + y^2}$$

Squaring again

$$a^4 - 2a^2xc + x^2c^2 = a^2[(x - c)^2 + y^2]$$

Simplifying

$$x^2(a^2 - c^2) + a^2y^2 = a^2(a^2 - c^2)$$

Dividing by $a^2(a^2 - c^2)$ we have

$$\frac{x^2}{a^2} + \frac{y^2}{a^2 - c^2} = 1$$

But $a^2 - c^2 = b^2$; therefore

$$\frac{x^2}{a^2} + \frac{y^2}{b^2} = 1 \qquad \textbf{(II)}$$

If we choose the center at (h, k), by applying the same procedures as above we can derive the standard form of the ellipse (I).

SUMMARY OF RELATIONS ASSOCIATED WITH AN ELLIPSE

1. $\dfrac{PF}{PM} = e,\ (e < 1)$ 4. Length of latus rectum $M'N = \dfrac{2b^2}{a}$

2. $e = \dfrac{c}{a},\ (a > c)$ 5. $FT = 2p = \dfrac{a}{e} - ae$

3. $a^2 = b^2 + c^2$

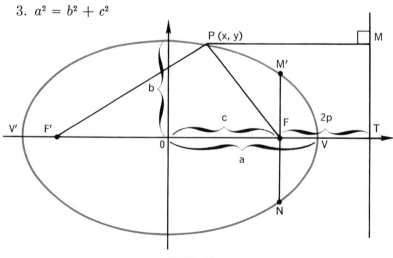

FIGURE 15–7

An ellipse is the path of an object in orbit such as the planets around the sun and satellites around the planets. Elliptic gears have special uses where slow, powerful action is needed. Sometimes bridge arches are elliptic in shape. An ellipse has the property that light rays (or other radiated energy) emitted from one focus will be reflected to the other focus. This property of an ellipse is utilized in the construction of "whispering galleries" where walls and ceilings are roughly elliptical. Any sound emitted from a position at one focus is reflected from walls and ceiling to the other focus where even a whisper can be heard distinctly although other sounds may be in the room.

Exercises

1. The foci of an ellipse are at $F(-2, 0)$ and $F'(2, 0)$. The sum of the distances from a point P on the ellipse to F and F' is 14. Find the equation of the ellipse and give its eccentricity.

2. The foci of an ellipse are at $F(1, -1)$ and $F'(1, 5)$. The point $P(4, 2)$ is on the ellipse; give the equation of the ellipse.

3. Write the equations of the circles which are internally and externally tangent to the ellipse $4x^2 + 9y^2 = 36$ if the three conics are concentric (have the same center).

4. Find the eccentricity of an ellipse with a major axis of 10 units and a minor axis of 6 units.

5. Find the eccentricity of an ellipse if the distance between the foci is 8 units and the distance between the vertices is 12 units. Find the length of the latus rectum.

15.4   Tangent and normal to an ellipse

The slope of the tangent to an ellipse is given by $D_x y$. (See Section 3.9.) The derivative of the standard form $\dfrac{x^2}{a^2} + \dfrac{y^2}{b^2} = 1$ can be shown equal to $-\dfrac{b^2 x}{a^2 y}$, but the proof is beyond the scope of this book. Thus, the slope of the tangent to an ellipse at the point $P(x, y)$ on the ellipse is $-\dfrac{b^2 x}{a^2 y}$. The equation of the tangent line can be found by applying the point-slope form of the equation of a line.

The slope of the normal at a point on an ellipse is the negative reciprocal of the slope of the tangent. Thus, the slope of the normal is $\dfrac{a^2 y}{b^2 x}$.

EXAMPLE. Find the equations of the tangent and the normal to the ellipse $\dfrac{x^2}{25} + \dfrac{y^2}{16} = 1$ at the point $\left(2, \dfrac{4\sqrt{21}}{5}\right)$.

Solution. At $\left(2, \dfrac{4\sqrt{21}}{5}\right)$ the slope of the tangent is

$$-\frac{b^2x}{a^2y} = -\frac{16(2)}{25\left(\dfrac{4\sqrt{21}}{5}\right)} = \frac{-8}{5\sqrt{21}} \cdot$$ The equation of the tangent is

$$-\frac{8}{5\sqrt{21}} = \frac{y - \dfrac{4\sqrt{21}}{5}}{x - 2}$$

or $$8x + 2\sqrt{21}\,y - 100 = 0$$

The slope of the normal is $\dfrac{5\sqrt{21}}{8}$. The equation of the normal is

$$\frac{5\sqrt{21}}{8} = \frac{y - \dfrac{4\sqrt{21}}{5}}{x - 2}$$

or $$525x - 40\sqrt{21}\,y - 378 = 0$$

Exercises

In each exercise draw the figure.

1. Find the equations of the tangent and the normal to the ellipse $\dfrac{x^2}{49} + \dfrac{y^2}{16} = 1$ at $\left(\dfrac{7\sqrt{3}}{2}, 2\right)$.

2. Find the equation of the horizontal tangents of the ellipse $\dfrac{x^2}{25} + \dfrac{y^2}{64} = 1$.

3. Find the equation of the vertical tangents of the ellipse $\dfrac{x^2}{9} + \dfrac{y^2}{4} = 1$.

4. Find the slopes and equations of the tangent lines at the endpoints of the latus rectum through the right-hand focus of the ellipse $\dfrac{x^2}{64} + \dfrac{y^2}{16} = 1$.

5. In the ellipse $\dfrac{x^2}{25} + \dfrac{y^2}{9} = 1$ find the equation of the normal at the point $\left(4, \dfrac{9}{5}\right)$ on the curve. Show that the normal bisects the angle between the lines from the foci to this point.

15.5   The general form of the equation of an ellipse

A second degree equation of the form

$$Ax^2 + Cy^2 + Dx + Ey + F = 0 \qquad \text{(V)}$$

where $A \neq 0$, $C \neq 0$, and A and C have the same sign, $F \neq 0$, is the *general form* of the equation of an ellipse. If $A = C$, the ellipse is a circle. You will note that there is no xy term, that is, in the second term Bxy, $B = 0$. If $B \neq 0$, the ellipse undergoes rotation which is not treated in full in this text.

By grouping and completing the square with equation (V) we can transform it into standard form (I) or (III). In either form the center (h, k), the semi-major axis a, and the semi-minor axis b are obvious. Thus a sketch of the ellipse can be made. If additional accuracy is desired, the endpoints of the latera recta can be computed so that the eight known points provide the basis for a satisfactory sketch.

EXAMPLE. Find the coordinates of the center, the foci, and the vertices of the ellipse $9x^2 + 4y^2 - 18x + 16y - 11 = 0$. Sketch the ellipse.

Solution. By grouping and completing the square we have

$$(9x^2 - 18x + \quad) + (4y^2 + 16y + \quad) = 11$$
$$9(x^2 - 2x + 1) + 4(y^2 + 4y + 4) = 11 + 9 + 16$$
$$9(x - 1)^2 + 4(y + 2)^2 = 36$$

$$\frac{(x - 1)^2}{4} + \frac{(y + 2)^2}{9} = 1 \quad \text{or} \quad \frac{(y + 2)^2}{9} + \frac{(x - 1)^2}{4} = 1$$

(Equation III is used since $a > b$.)

The coordinates of the center are $(1, -2)$; the semi-major axis $a = 3$; the semi-minor axis $b = 2$. Then $a^2 = b^2 + c^2$ so we have $9 = 4 + c^2$, or $c = \pm\sqrt{5}$. The coordinates of the foci are: $F(1, -2 + \sqrt{5})$ and $F'(1, -2 - \sqrt{5})$. The coordinates of the vertices are $V(1, 1)$ and $V'(1, -5)$. The sketch of the ellipse is shown in the figure.

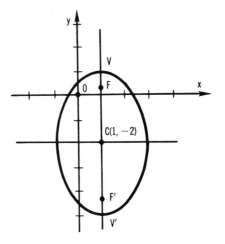

FIGURE 15–8

Exercises

1. Find the center, foci, eccentricity, and equation of the directrices of the ellipse $25x^2 + y^2 - 100x + 6y + 84 = 0$. Sketch the ellipse.

2. Find the center, foci, eccentricity, equation of the directrix, and the length of the latus rectum of the ellipse $18x^2 + 12y^2 - 144x - 48y + 120 = 0$. Sketch the ellipse.

3. Sketch an ellipse which is tangent to the coordinate axes and has a center at $(-3, 7)$. Write the equation in general form.

4. Consider the coefficients of the general form of the equation of an ellipse as variables; how many points on the ellipse must be known before the coefficients can be found? Explain.

5. Find the points of intersection of $y^2 = 12x$ and $16x^2 + 3y^2 = 48$.

15.6 Polar equation of an ellipse

The simplest form of the polar equation of an ellipse is determined if a focus is at the pole and the polar axis is perpendicular to the directrix corresponding to the focus. (See Section 14.5.)

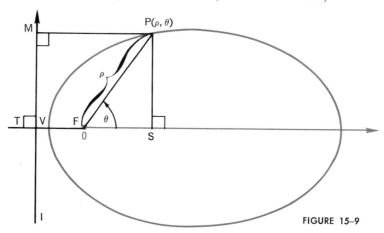

FIGURE 15–9

Let F be a focus, l the corresponding directrix, and $P(\rho, \theta)$ a point on the ellipse. By definition, $\dfrac{PF}{PM} = e$ or $PF = e \cdot PM$ where $e < 1$ for the ellipse. $PM = SF + FT$; $SF = \rho \cos \theta$. Let $FT = 2p$. (See Section 15.3.) Then, since $PF = \rho$, we have: $\rho = e(SF + FT) = e(\rho \cos \theta + 2p)$. Solving for ρ we get

$$\rho = \frac{2ep}{1 - e \cos \theta}, \ (e < 1) \qquad \textbf{(VI)}$$

Note that for the parabola $e = 1$ and the equation reduces to $\rho = \dfrac{2p}{1 - \cos \theta}$ which is equation (XIV), Section 14.5.

Equation (VI) is the *polar equation of an ellipse* when a focus coincides with the pole and the polar axis is perpendicular to the corresponding directrix. In this derivation the polar axis is directed away from the directrix; if the polar axis is directed toward the directrix we have the form

$$\rho = \frac{2ep}{1 + e \cos \theta} \qquad \text{(VII)}$$

EXAMPLE. The equation of an ellipse in rectangular coordinates is $16x^2 + 49y^2 = 784$. Find the equation in polar coordinates if the pole is at a focus and the polar axis is directed toward the right branch of the x-axis.

Solution. As for the parabola, it can be shown that the polar equation of an ellipse is independent of the translation of the origin at the center of the ellipse to the pole at a focus. Putting the equation in standard form we have

$$\frac{x^2}{49} + \frac{y^2}{16} = 1$$

Thus, $a = 7$ and $b = 4$. Since $a^2 = b^2 + c^2$, $c = \sqrt{33}$. $e = \dfrac{c}{a}$; hence $e = \dfrac{\sqrt{33}}{7}$. Also, $2p = \dfrac{a}{e} - ae = \dfrac{b^2}{c} = \dfrac{16}{\sqrt{33}}$. The polar equation of the ellipse is

$$\rho = \frac{\dfrac{\sqrt{33}}{7} \cdot \dfrac{16}{\sqrt{33}}}{1 - \dfrac{\sqrt{33}}{7} \cos \theta}$$

or

$$\rho = \frac{16}{7 - \sqrt{33} \cos \theta}$$

You are reminded that the origin of the rectangular coordinate system is at the center and the pole is at the left-hand focus with the polar axis directed toward the positive x-axis.

Exercises

1. The equation of an ellipse in rectangular coordinates is $9x^2 + 16y^2 = 144$. Find the equation in polar coordinates.

2. The equation of an ellipse in rectangular coordinates is $3x^2 + 5y^2 = 15$. Find the equation in polar coordinates.

3. The equation of an ellipse in polar coordinates is known to be $\rho = \dfrac{4}{3 - \sqrt{5}\cos\theta}$. Find the equation in rectangular coordinates if the center is at the origin.

Chapter Review

1. Find the center, foci, vertices, endpoints of the latera recta, and sketch the curve of the ellipse $\dfrac{(x-4)^2}{12} + \dfrac{(y-6)^2}{3} = 3$.

2. Find the center, foci, vertices, and endpoints of the latera recta and sketch the curve of the ellipse $x^2 + 2y^2 + 2x - 12y + 11 = 0$.

3. Write the equation of an ellipse with its center at the origin if the eccentricity is $\dfrac{1}{2}$ and the distance between the foci is 1, the foci having the same ordinate.

4. Write the equation of the locus of points such that the sum of the distances from the points $(5, -1)$ and $(-1, -1)$ is 10 units.

5. Find the equations of the tangent lines to the ellipse $8x^2 + y^2 - 16x + 2y = 0$ at the points on the curve where the abscissa is 1.

6. Prove that the equation of the tangent to an ellipse $\dfrac{x^2}{a^2} + \dfrac{y^2}{b^2} = 1$ from a point $P(x_1, y_1)$ on the curve is given by the formula $\dfrac{x_1 x}{a^2} + \dfrac{y_1 y}{b^2} = 1$.

CHAPTER OUTLINE

The Hyperbola

16

16.1 Definition of a hyperbola

A hyperbola is the conic section with an eccentricity greater than one. A hyperbola, then, is the locus of points such that for any point of the locus the ratio of the distance from a fixed point to the distance from a fixed line is a constant greater than 1. In Figure 16–1 the locus is a hyperbola if $\dfrac{PF}{PM} > 1$. The fixed point F is a focus and the fixed line d is a directrix. The constant ratio $\dfrac{PF}{PM}$ or $\dfrac{P'F}{P'M}$ is the eccentricity e. The hyperbola has two foci and two directrices but, in contrast with the ellipse, the directrices lie between the foci. There are two branches of a hyperbola.

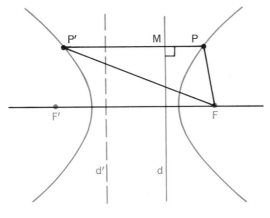

FIGURE 16–1

A hyperbola is the section of a conical surface formed when a plane intersects the conical surface so that both parts of the surface are cut by the plane.

The definition of a hyperbola in terms of the eccentricity is equivalent to the definition that *the hyperbola is the locus of points in a plane such that for any point of the locus the difference of the distances from two fixed points is a constant.* The two fixed points

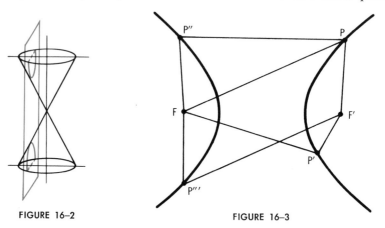

FIGURE 16–2   FIGURE 16–3

are F and F', the foci. Thus, $FP - F'P = FP' - F'P' = F'P'' - FP'' = F'P''' - FP''' =$ and so on, for all points of the locus.

A simple method of drawing a hyperbola makes use of the above definition. Place thumb tacks at the points to be used as foci. Tie a string to a pencil, allowing two free lengths of string. Knot together the ends of the string so that the lengths from the knot to

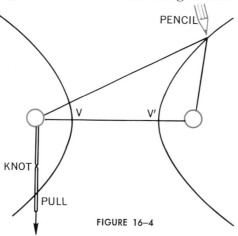

FIGURE 16–4

the pencil differ less than the distance between the foci FF'. Loop both strands over one tack and run the longer strand around the other tack. Hold the strings below the knot and draw taut by means of the pencil. (See Figure 16–4.) Keeping the strings taut, pull on the strings; the pencil will trace part of one branch of a hyperbola. By reversing the position of the knot and pencil another portion of the hyperbola may be drawn.

16.2   Equation of a hyperbola

The hyperbola is a curve of infinite length and does not enclose an area as does the ellipse. The standard form of the equation of a hyperbola is developed in the same way as that of the ellipse. (See Section 15.2.) A difference occurs at the point where b^2 is set equal to $a^2(1 - e^2)$. In the case of the ellipse, e is less than 1 and hence $(1 - e^2)$ is positive. In the hyperbola, where e is greater than 1, $(1 - e^2)$ is negative and, since b^2 must be positive, we must let $b^2 = -a^2(1 - e^2)$ or $a^2(e^2 - 1)$. Thus we have as the standard form of the equation of a hyperbola

$$\frac{(x - h)^2}{a^2} - \frac{(y - k)^2}{b^2} = 1 \tag{I}$$

where a and b are positive numbers.

If the center $C(h, k)$ is at the origin the standard form reduces to

$$\frac{x^2}{a^2} - \frac{y^2}{b^2} = 1 \tag{II}$$

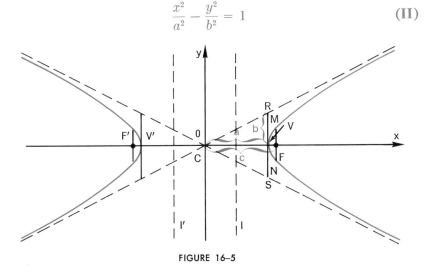

FIGURE 16-5

Let us define $c = ae$; thus $e = \dfrac{c}{a}$, $(a < c)$. The distance $VV' = 2a$ which is called the *transverse axis*. The distance $2b$ is called the *conjugate axis*. If the center is at the origin, the coordinates of important points are: $V(a, 0)$; $V'(-a, 0)$; $F(c, 0)$; $F'(-c, 0)$; $R(a, b)$; $M\left(c, \dfrac{b^2}{a}\right)$. The equation of the directrices l and l' are $x = \dfrac{a}{e}$ and

$x = \dfrac{-a}{e}$, respectively. If $R(a, b)$ and $S(a, -b)$ are each joined
to the center forming two intersecting lines, these lines are called
the *asymptotes* of the hyperbola. $RS = 2b$. The *asymptotes* are
lines which the branches of the curve approach as the curve re-
cedes from the center. The asymptotes can serve as guides to aid
in sketching a hyperbola. The length of the latus rectum MN is
$\dfrac{2b^2}{a}$ and, as in the other conics, is a chord through a focus.
Since $e = \dfrac{c}{a}$ and $b^2 = a^2(e^2 - 1)$ we can show that $c^2 = a^2 + b^2$ and
hence $OR = OF = c$.

Equations (I) and (II) were developed with the assumption that
the transverse axis of the hyperbola was parallel to the x-axis. If
the transverse axis is parallel to the y-axis the standard form of the
equation of a hyperbola becomes

$$\frac{(y - k)^2}{a^2} - \frac{(x - h)^2}{b^2} = 1 \qquad \text{(III)}$$

When the center is at the origin, (III) reduces to

$$\frac{y^2}{a^2} - \frac{x^2}{b^2} = 1 \qquad \text{(IV)}$$

Two hyperbolas such that the transverse axis of one is the conjugate axis of the other, and conversely, are said to be *conjugate*
hyperbolas. Conjugate hyperbolas share the same asymptotes.

EXAMPLE 1. Write the equation of the hyperbola with its center
at $C(-3, 1)$, a focus at $F(2, 1)$, and the eccentricity $e = \dfrac{5}{4}$.

Solution. The transverse axis is parallel to the x-axis since CF is
a line parallel to the x-axis. The equation will be in standard form
(I). Now $e = \dfrac{c}{a}$ where $e = \dfrac{5}{4}$ and $c = 5$. (The focus is 5 units to the
right of the center.) Thus, $\dfrac{5}{4} = \dfrac{5}{a}$ so that $a = 4$. Then $b^2 = c^2 - a^2$
and hence $b = 3$. The equation is

$$\frac{(x + 3)^2}{16} - \frac{(y - 1)^2}{9} = 1$$

EXAMPLE 2. Find the equation of a hyperbola if the foci are at $F(2, 5)$ and $F'(-4, 5)$, and the transverse axis is 4 units long.

Solution. The center is the midpoint of FF'; thus the coordinates of the center are $C(-1, 5)$. $CF = c = 3$. The transverse axis $= 2a = 4$; hence $a = 2$. $c^2 = a^2 + b^2$; $9 = 4 + b^2$; $b^2 = 5$. The equation of the hyperbola is

$$\frac{(x + 1)^2}{4} - \frac{(y - 5)^2}{5} = 1$$

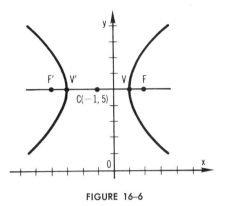

FIGURE 16–6

Exercises

Draw the figure for each exercise.

1. Find the equation of the hyperbola whose center is at $(3, -1)$, the equation of whose directrix is $x = 5$, and whose eccentricity is $\frac{3}{2}$.

2. Find the length of the transverse and conjugate axes of the hyperbola $\frac{x^2}{9} - \frac{y^2}{10} = 1$. Find the length of the latus rectum.

3. Find the coordinates of the foci of the hyperbola $\frac{y^2}{64} - \frac{x^2}{36} = 1$. What is the eccentricity?

4. Find the foci, directrices, eccentricity, and the axes of the hyperbola $\frac{(x - 3)^2}{12} - \frac{(y + 5)^2}{24} = 2$.

5. Find the equation of the hyperbola whose center is at $(-2, -2)$, the equation of whose directrix is $y = 1$, and whose eccentricity is 1.6.

In Exercises 6–9 write the equation of the hyperbola given.

6. Foci at $(-5, 0)$ and $(5, 0)$; eccentricity $\frac{5}{3}$.

7. Vertices at $(1, 2)$ and $(1, -2)$; conjugate axis $= 2$.

8. Center at $(-3, 1)$; transverse axis $= 8$ and is parallel to the x-axis; length of latus rectum $= 8$.

9. Center at $(4, -2)$; focus at $(7, -2)$; vertex at $(6, -2)$.

10. Derive the standard form of the equation of a hyperbola (II) from the definition that the hyperbola is the locus of points such that, for every point of the locus $P(x, y)$, the difference of the distances from P to the foci $F(c, 0)$ and $F'(-c, 0)$ is a constant equal to $2a$.

16.3   Additional relations associated with a hyperbola

If the center of a hyperbola is at the origin, it is easily shown that the curve does not exist for values of x between $-a$ and $+a$. In the situation where $|x| < a$, we have $\dfrac{y^2}{b^2} = \dfrac{x^2}{a^2} - 1$ and, since $\dfrac{|x|}{a} < 1$, y^2 will be equal to a negative number. Thus, there are no real points for $-a < x < a$. Note that we have assumed an equation of form (II). For form (IV), there are no real points if $|y| < a$.

If the equation of a hyperbola $\dfrac{x^2}{a^2} - \dfrac{y^2}{b^2} = 1$ is solved for y we have

$$y = \pm \frac{bx}{a} \sqrt{1 - \frac{a^2}{x^2}}$$

Now consider the limit of the right member as x increases without limit. Since $\dfrac{a^2}{x^2} \to 0$ under this condition, y approaches $\pm \dfrac{bx}{a}$. Then the hyperbola approaches the lines $\dfrac{x}{a} \pm \dfrac{y}{b} = 0$ as x increases (or decreases) without limit. These lines, $\dfrac{x}{a} + \dfrac{y}{b} = 0$ and $\dfrac{x}{a} - \dfrac{y}{b} = 0$ are the equations of the asymptotes of the hyperbola. It is very helpful to draw the asymptotes first when making a sketch of a hyperbola.

As pointed out earlier two conjugate hyperbolas share the same asymptotes. Let H be any hyperbola with its center at the origin and a transverse axis parallel to the x-axis. Then H' will represent the hyperbola conjugate to H. The equation of H is

$$\frac{x^2}{a^2} - \frac{y^2}{b^2} = 1 \text{ and the equation of } H' \text{ is } \frac{y^2}{b^2} - \frac{x^2}{a^2} = 1$$

The focus F of H is $(ae, 0)$ and the focus G of H' is $(0, ae)$. The foci of H and H' lie on a circle with a radius $ae = c = \sqrt{a^2 + b^2} = VV'$.

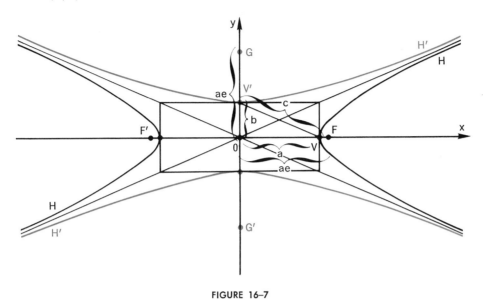

FIGURE 16-7

If $a = b$ in the standard form of a hyperbola, it is an *equilateral hyperbola* and the asymptotes are perpendicular. A special case of the equilateral hyperbola is when the coordinate axes are the asymptotes. The equation of such a hyperbola is $xy = k$, where k is a positive or negative constant. The branches of the equilateral hyperbola lie in the first and third quadrants if k is positive and in the second and fourth quadrants if k is negative.

The hyperbola is basic to LORAN, a system of radio location and guidance of planes and ships. The operation is based upon the time delay of radio signals received from two points.

Certain mirrors in telescopes are hyperbolic in form.

In military applications, the hyperbola is useful in locating the source of sound (such as an enemy gun position). Two observers at points which are the foci of a family of hyperbolas record differences in time of arrival of the same sound and thus determine a certain hyperbola in the family. If two other foci are chosen and another hyperbola is determined, the intersection of these hyperbolas when sketched on a map locate the source of the sound.

SUMMARY OF RELATIONS ASSOCIATED WITH A HYPERBOLA WITH CENTER AT THE ORIGIN

1. $\dfrac{PF}{PM} = e \; (e > 1)$

2. $e = \dfrac{c}{a} \; (a < c)$

3. $c^2 = a^2 + b^2$

4. Length of latus rectum

$$MN = \frac{2b^2}{a}$$

5. $FT = 2p = ae - \dfrac{a}{e} = \dfrac{b^2}{c}$

6. Equations of asymptotes

$$\frac{x}{a} \pm \frac{y}{b} = 0$$

7. Equations of directrices

$$x = \pm \frac{a}{e}$$

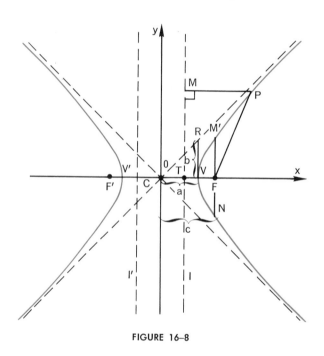

FIGURE 16–8

Exercises

In each exercise draw the figure.

1. Find the equations of the asymptotes of the hyperbola $\dfrac{x^2}{36} - \dfrac{y^2}{81} = 1$.

2. Find the foci, vertices, length of the latus rectum, and the equation of the asymptotes of the hyperbola $\dfrac{x^2}{25} - \dfrac{y^2}{16} = 1$.

3. The equations of the asymptotes of a hyperbola are $x - 2y = 0$ and $x + 2y = 0$. The hyperbola passes through the point $(2, 0)$. Find the equation of the hyperbola.

4. The foci of a hyperbola are at $F(0, 3)$ and $F'(0, -3)$ and the hyperbola passes through $P(0, 2)$. Find its eccentricity.

5. Prove that the eccentricity of an equilateral hyperbola is $\sqrt{2}$.

6. Prove that the product of the distances of any point on a hyperbola from the asymptotes is a constant.

16.4 Tangent and normal to a hyperbola

The slope of the tangent to a hyperbola is given by $D_x y$ which can be shown to be $\dfrac{b^2 x}{a^2 y}$. (Compare with the slope of the tangent to an ellipse, Section 15.4.)

The slope of the normal is $-\dfrac{a^2 y}{b^2 x}$. Knowing a point on the curve enables us to write the equation of a tangent or normal to the curve at a given point by the point-slope form of the equation of a line.

Example. Find the equations of the tangent and the normal to the hyperbola $\dfrac{x^2}{9} - \dfrac{y^2}{4} = 1$ at the point $(6, 2\sqrt{3})$.

Solution. The slope of the tangent is $\dfrac{b^2 x}{a^2 y} = \dfrac{4(6)}{9(2\sqrt{3})} = \dfrac{4\sqrt{3}}{9}$.
The equation of the tangent is

$$\frac{4\sqrt{3}}{9} = \frac{y - 2\sqrt{3}}{x - 6} \qquad \text{or} \qquad 4x - 3\sqrt{3}y - 6 = 0$$

The slope of the normal is $-\dfrac{a^2 y}{b^2 x} = -\dfrac{3\sqrt{3}}{4}$. The equation of the normal is

$$-\frac{3\sqrt{3}}{4} = \frac{y - 2\sqrt{3}}{x - 6} \qquad \text{or} \qquad 9x + 4\sqrt{3}y - 72 = 0$$

Exercises

1. Find the equations of the tangent and normal to the hyperbola $\dfrac{x^2}{16} - \dfrac{y^2}{4} = 1$ at $\left(5, \dfrac{3}{2}\right)$.

2. Find the equations of the vertical tangents of the hyperbola $\dfrac{x^2}{25} - \dfrac{y^2}{9} = 1$.

3. Find the equations of the tangents and normals at the ends of the latera recta of the hyperbola $\dfrac{x^2}{36} - \dfrac{y^2}{64} = 1$.

4. A certain equilateral hyperbola lies in the first and third quadrants with the coordinate axes as asymptotes. Find the equation of the hyperbola if the line $x + y = 4$ is tangent to the curve. (*Hint:* The equation is of the form $xy = k$.)

16.5   General form of the equation of a hyperbola

A second degree equation of the form

$$Ax^2 + Cy^2 + Dx + Ey + F = 0 \qquad\qquad (V)$$

where $A \neq 0$, $C \neq 0$, and A and C have different signs, $F \neq 0$, is the *general form* of the equation of a hyperbola. As for the ellipse, in this course we will assume that $B = 0$ so that the xy term vanishes and the axes are parallel to the coordinate axes.

By grouping and completing the square we can put (V) in the form of (I) or (III). Thus we can determine h, k, a, and b so that a sketch can be easily made. The vertices and asymptotes provide a basis for a rough sketch and if additional accuracy is desired, the endpoints of the latera recta can be computed.

EXAMPLE. Find the coordinates of the center, the foci, and the vertices of the hyperbola $25x^2 - 9y^2 - 100x - 72y - 269 = 0$. Find the equations of the asymptotes and sketch the curve.

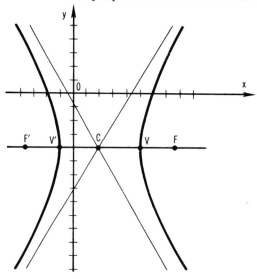

FIGURE 16–9

Solution. Grouping and completing the square we have

$$(25x^2 - 100x + \quad) - (9y^2 + 72y + \quad) = 269$$
$$25(x^2 - 4x + 4) - 9(x^2 + 8y + 16) = 269 + 100 - 144$$
$$25(x - 2)^2 - 9(y + 4)^2 = 225$$
$$\frac{(x - 2)^2}{9} - \frac{(y + 4)^2}{25} = 1$$

Thus the center is $C(2, -4)$; $a = 3$; $b = 5$; $c = \sqrt{a^2 + b^2} = \sqrt{34}$. Coordinates of the foci are $F(2 + \sqrt{34}, -4)$ and $F'(2 - \sqrt{34}, -4)$. The coordinates of the vertices are $V(5, -4)$ and $V'(-1, -4)$. The equations of the asymptotes are: $\dfrac{(x - 2)}{3} \pm \dfrac{(y + 4)}{5} = 0$. The sketch of the hyperbola is shown in Figure 16–9.

Exercises

1. Find the coordinates of the center, the axes, and the eccentricity of the hyperbola $9x^2 - 4y^2 - 90x - 24y + 153 = 0$. Sketch the curve.
2. Find the coordinates of the center, the foci, the vertices, and the equations of the asymptotes of the hyperbola $49x^2 - 25y^2 + 294x + 200y - 1184 = 0$. Sketch the curve.
3. Sketch the curve $9x^2 - 4y^2 - 54x - 40y - 55 = 0$.
4. Find the coordinates of the center, the foci, the vertices, and the equations of the asymptotes of the hyperbola $y^2 - 25x^2 + 50x = 50$. Find the length of the latus rectum. Sketch the curve.

16.6   Polar equation of a hyperbola

The polar equation of the hyperbola can be developed in the same manner as that of the parabola and ellipse. The polar equation is

$$\rho = \frac{2ep}{1 - e \cos \theta}, \ (e > 1) \qquad \textbf{(VI)}$$

where e is the eccentricity and $2p$ is the distance from the focus to the directrix.

It is clear that (VI) is the polar equation of any conic section where the pole is at a focus and the polar axis is perpendicular to the directrix and directed away from it. (See Section 14.5 and Section 15.6.) If the polar axis is directed toward the directrix the polar equation of a conic section is

$$\rho = \frac{2ep}{1 + e \cos \theta} \qquad \textbf{(VII)}$$

If the polar axis is parallel to the directrix it can be shown that the polar equation of a conic section is of the form

$$\rho = \frac{2ep}{1 \pm e \sin \theta} \qquad \text{(VIII)}$$

Thus, if $e = 1$, the equation is a parabola; if $e < 1$, the equation is an ellipse; if $e > 1$, the equation is a hyperbola.

Exercises

1. The equation of a hyperbola in rectangular coordinates is $\dfrac{x^2}{16} - \dfrac{y^2}{9} = 1$. Find the equation in polar coordinates if the pole is at a focus and the polar axis is perpendicular to the directrix and directed toward it.

2. The equation of a hyperbola in polar coordinates is $\rho = \dfrac{8}{3 - 4 \cos \theta}$. What is the equation in rectangular coordinates if the center is at the origin? (*Hint.* Divide numerator and denominator by 3; determine e and p. Then $e = \dfrac{c}{a}$ and $2p = ae - \dfrac{a}{e}$.)

3. Graph $\rho = \dfrac{2ep}{1 + e \cos \theta}$ if $e = 1$, $p = \dfrac{1}{2}$.

4. Show that the equation $\rho = \dfrac{2ep}{1 - e \cos \theta}$ can be written in the form $\rho = p \csc^2 \dfrac{\theta}{2}$ when $e = 1$.

Chapter Review

1. Find the center, foci, vertices, ends of the latera recta, and sketch the hyperbola $\dfrac{(x - 4)^2}{36} - \dfrac{(y - 5)^2}{4} = 1$.

2. Find the center, foci, vertices, ends of the latera recta, and sketch the hyperbola $9x^2 - 16y^2 - 36x + 96y + 36 = 0$.

3. Show that if $A = -C$ in the general form of the equation of a hyperbola (V) the equation represents an equilateral hyperbola.

4. Write the equation of the tangent to the hyperbola $x^2 - 4y^2 + 2x + 8y - 7 = 0$ at $(1,1)$.

5. Write the equation of the hyperbola which has vertices at $(-5, -2)$ and $(-5, 4)$ if the eccentricity is $\frac{3}{2}$. Write the equations of the asymptotes.

6. Write the equations of the conjugate hyperbolas which share the asymptotes $4x + 3y - 11 = 0$ and $4x - 3y - 5 = 0$.

7. Write the equation of the hyperbola with center at the origin, one end of the conjugate axis at $(10, 0)$, and the length of the latus rectum equal to 40.

8. If $2x - y = 0$ and $2x + y - 4 = 0$ are the equations of the asymptotes of a hyperbola, and the hyperbola passes through $(5, 9)$, write its equation.

9. Write the equation of the hyperbola whose foci are $(0, 0)$ and $(4, 4)$ and whose transverse axis is 2 units.

10. Graph $\rho = \dfrac{4}{2 - 3 \sin \theta}$.

CHAPTER OUTLINE

16.1   Definition of a hyperbola

16.2   Equation of a hyperbola

16.3   Additional relations associated with a hyperbola

16.4   Tangent and normal to a hyperbola

16.5   General form of the equation of a hyperbola

16.6   Polar equation of a hyperbola

Permutations, Combinations, and Probability   **17**

17.1   Choice of ways

Suppose there are two tunnels under a river by which one can enter a city from the west and three highways by which one can leave the city going east. After entering by the first tunnel, one has the choice of three exits, and so there are three routes by way of the first tunnel. Likewise, there are three routes by way of the second tunnel. Altogether there are $2 \times 3 = 6$ possible routes through the city from west to east.

The above illustration of choice of ways is an example of the important principle:

> ● FUNDAMENTAL PRINCIPLE OF CHOICE
>
> If one thing can be done in any one of h ways, and if, after it has been done in one of these ways, a second thing can be done in k ways, then the two things can be done in the stated order in $h \cdot k$ ways.
>
> This principle can be extended to cover three or more successive choices.

EXAMPLE. On a trip a man took 3 suits, 2 ties, and 2 hats. How many different choices of these items of clothing can he wear?

Solution. There are $3 \times 2 \times 2 = 12$ different choices possible. This can be shown by the following "tree." After choosing one of the three suits, s_1, s_2, s_3, he can choose one of the two ties, t_1, t_2. He may then choose one of the two hats, h_1, h_2. Thus there are 12 choices each of which differs from the other in some way.

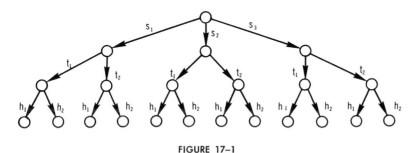

FIGURE 17–1

Exercises

1. A man has 3 hats, 3 suits, and 4 pairs of shoes. How many choices of outfits with these items can he wear?

2. Any one of three trains will take Mr. Exley from his home to his office building in time for work, and any one of four elevators will carry him to his floor. How many possible choices of transportation by train and elevator can he select?

3. A girl has 5 dresses, 3 pairs of shoes, and 3 coats suitable for wear at her work. How many choices of outfits with these items are possible?

4. A penny, a nickel, and a dime are tossed simultaneously. Each can land heads or tails up. In how many different ways can the coins land?

5. A manufacturer of television sets makes two basic chassis, one for general use and one of extra high quality for distant reception. Either chassis may be fitted in any of the manufacturer's cabinets. There are two table models and three console models made by this manufacturer with a choice of blond, walnut, or mahogany finish. How many different television set types are produced by this manufacturer?

17.2   Permutations

Suppose that seniors Allan, Bob, and Chuck have been selected to act as advisors to the members of the freshman class in regard to school activities. Each boy has been asked to give a five-minute talk to the assembled freshmen. How many different ways may the program be arranged? If Allan speaks first then either Bob or Chuck can speak second, and so on. Let us list the possible arrangements of the boys on the program.

1. Allan	1. Allan	1. Bob	1. Bob	1. Chuck	1. Chuck
2. Bob	2. Chuck	2. Allan	2. Chuck	2. Allan	2. Bob
3. Chuck	3. Bob	3. Chuck	3. Allan	3. Bob	3. Allan

There are six distinct arrangements of the boys on the program.

Applying the Principle of Choice from Section 17.1 we can confirm this because there are 3 possible ways of selecting the first speaker, then two possible ways of selecting the second speaker, and finally, one possible way of selecting the third speaker. Thus there are $3 \times 2 \times 1 = 6$ possible arrangements.

• A distinct arrangement of a set of elements is a *permutation*.

In the above example we permuted 3 elements with all of them taken at a time.

Now suppose that there is time for only two speakers on the program. How many ways can a program be arranged if two of the three boys are to be selected? Let us list the possible program arrangements.

1. Allan	1. Allan	1. Bob	1. Bob	1. Chuck	1. Chuck
2. Bob	2. Chuck	2. Allan	2. Chuck	2. Allan	2. Bob

There are six ways to permute three elements taken two at a time as can be verified by the Principle of Choice.

In how many distinct ways can the five letters A, B, C, D, and E be arranged? By the Principle of Choice there are 5 ways of selecting the first letter; there are 4 ways of making the second selection; there are 3 ways of making the third selection; there are 2 ways of making the fourth selection; and there is only one way of making the final selection. Thus the number of distinct arrangements of 5 elements is: $5 \times 4 \times 3 \times 2 \times 1 = 120$. You may systematically list the arrangements if you wish to verify that there are 120 possible distinct arrangements.

How many distinct ways can the five letters A, B, C, D, and E be arranged three at a time? By the Principle of Choice there are $5 \times 4 \times 3 = 60$ ways, which can be verified by counting them.

If there are n elements in a set, then the symbol $_nP_n$ will denote the number of permutations of n elements all (n) taken at a time. As we have seen $_5P_5 = 120$. If there are n elements in a set which are to be taken r at a time, then $_nP_r$ will denote the number of permutations of n elements r at a time. In the example where 3 letters out of 5 are to be arranged in order we have seen that $_5P_3 = 60$.

> **Principle:** The number of permutations of n elements n at a time is given by the formula
>
> $$_nP_n = n(n - 1)(n - 2) \cdots 2 \cdot 1 = n! \qquad \textbf{(I)}$$

> **Principle:** The number of permutations of n elements r at a time is given by the formula
>
> $$_nP_r = n(n - 1)(n - 2) \cdots (n - r + 1) \qquad \textbf{(II)}$$

In factorial notation we may write formula (II) in the form

$$_nP_r = \frac{n!}{(n - r)!} \qquad \textbf{(III)}$$

EXAMPLE 1. In how many ways can five books be selected from a group of eleven books?

Solution. We must find the number of permutations of 11 elements taken 5 at a time.

$$_{11}P_5 = \frac{11!}{(11 - 5)!} = \frac{11!}{6!} = 11 \cdot 10 \cdot 9 \cdot 8 \cdot 7 = 55,440$$

There are 55,440 ways of selecting 5 books from 11.

Exercises

Evaluate each expression in Exercises 1–8.

1. $_4P_3$	**3.** $_7P_1$	**5.** $_{11}P_{10}$	**7.** $_7P_4$
2. $_5P_2$	**4.** $_6P_3$	**6.** $_{11}P_1$	**8.** $_5P_5$

9. There are 5 persons who are applicants for 3 different positions in a store, each person being qualified for each position. In how many ways is it possible to fill the positions?

10. How many different three-digit whole numbers can be written by using the digits 1, 2, 3, 4, 5, 6 without repeating digits?

11. There are 21 students in a class that meets in a room that has 24 chairs. In how many ways is it possible for the students to be seated?

12. Assume that 8 cans of vegetables, all different, are to be placed in a row on a shelf. In how many different arrangements is it possible to place them?

13. Four flags are used to make signals. If the flags are all different and each distinct order makes a different signal, how many signals can be given if 3 flags are used at a time?

14. Prove $_nP_r = n(n - 1)(n - 2) \cdots (n - r + 1)$.

15. Prove $n(n - 1)(n - 2) \cdots (n - r + 1) = \dfrac{n!}{(n - r)!}$.

16. If $n = r$, prove that $0! = 1$ if the formula for $_nP_r$ is to hold.

17. Find the value of $_nP_0$.

18. How many different arrangements of three letters can be formed from the letters of the word *SKATE*? If each selection must contain at least one vowel, how many such arrangements of three letters can be made?

19. A state of the United States uses six-digit license plate numbers. How many distinct numbers can have 6 different digits?

20. How many license plate numbers are possible for a state using 2 letters followed by 4 numbers if the 2 letters in one plate cannot be alike and only numbers which have all digits different are counted?

17.3 Permutations of *n* elements with some elements alike

Consider the problem of making distinct arrangements of the five letters of the word *TEETH*. One of these arrangements is *ETETH*, but there are several arrangements with the same appearance since the *E*'s or *T*'s may be reversed. These arrangements are exactly the same unless we "tag" the *E*'s and *T*'s; hence we shall count the arrangement *ETETH* only once.

In a simpler case, how many permutations of the letters of the word *TEE* are there? By tagging the *E*'s as E_1 and E_2 we have

TE_1E_2	E_1TE_2	E_1E_2T
TE_2E_1	E_2TE_1	E_2E_1T

There are six arrangements when subscripts are taken into account but only three *distinct* arrangements with subscripts removed.

Principle: The number of permutations of n elements of which t are alike is given by the formula

$$\frac{{}_nP_n}{t!} = \frac{n!}{t!} \tag{IV}$$

This formula may be extended if more than one of the elements appears more than once. For example, given n elements, if t are alike and s are also alike, then the number of permutations is $\dfrac{n!}{t!\,s!}$.

EXAMPLE 1. What is the number of permutations of the letters of the word $TEETH$?

Solution. The number of permutations is

$$\frac{5!}{2!\cdot 2!} = \frac{5\cdot 4\cdot 3\cdot 2\cdot 1}{2\cdot 1\cdot 2\cdot 1} = 30$$

EXAMPLE 2. What is the number of permutations of the letters of the word $MISSISSIPPI$?

Solution. $\dfrac{11!}{4!\,4!\,2!} = \dfrac{11\cdot 10\cdot 9\cdot 8\cdot 7\cdot 6\cdot 5\cdot 4\cdot 3\cdot 2\cdot 1}{(4\cdot 3\cdot 2\cdot 1)(4\cdot 3\cdot 2\cdot 1)(2\cdot 1)} = 34{,}650$

Exercises

1. How many different arrangements can be made of 10 pieces of silverware laid in a row if three are spoons, four are forks, and three are knives?

2. What is the number of distinct permutations of the letters of the word $MONOPOLY$?

3. How many different auto license plates of the same state can have the digits 3, 5, 5, 6, 2, 6?

4. A man has 3 copies of one book, 2 copies of another, and 4 single copies of other books. How many ways may these books be arranged on a shelf if the like copies are unmarked?

5. Find the prime factors of 540. How many arrangements of the six factors are possible?

17.4   Combinations

You have used the word "combination" with several meanings, all related to making selections or groupings. There is the lock combination to your school locker; there is the combination of heredity and environment; a jazz "combo" is composed of a few selected instruments; a Miss America contestant should have a combination of beauty, brains, and talent, and so on. We shall make a careful mathematical definition of the word combination as follows.

• A set of elements considered without regard to the order in which they occur is a *combination*.

Suppose that we are to select 3 boys from a group of 5 to work on a certain project. By the Principle of Choice we can select the first boy in 5 ways, the second boy in 4 ways, and the third boy in 3 ways, or a total of $5 \times 4 \times 3 = 60$ ways. But consider these 60 possible selections; will each group of 3 be different from every other group? Not at all! There is no difference between A, B, and C as one selection, A, C, and B, as another, and B, C, and A as a third, and so on. For each group of 3 there are 3! ways they can be arranged in order. Thus, if *order of selection is disregarded*, there are $60 \div 3!$ or 10 different groups of 3 that can be selected from the 5 boys.

$$\frac{60}{3 \cdot 2 \cdot 1} = 10$$

If we identify the boys as A, B, C, D, and E, we can list the 10 distinct groups of 3 boys as follows.

ABC	ABD	ABE	ACD	ACE
ADE	BCD	BCE	BDE	CDE

Recall that the *number of permutations* of 5 boys taken 3 at a time is $\dfrac{5!}{2!}$, or 60. In the case of permutations *order is important*. But we must divide the number of permutations by 3! to find the *number of combinations* in which *order is not considered*.

In general, the number of combinations of n elements taken r at a time is equal to the number of permutations divided by $r!$. Letting $_nC_r$ represent the number of combinations of n elements r at a time, we can write the formula as follows.

$$_nC_r = \frac{_nP_r}{r!} = \frac{n!}{(n - r)! \, r!} \tag{V}$$

An alternate notation for $_nC_r$ is $\dbinom{n}{r}$.

EXAMPLE. Three winners are to be determined in a race having 8 runners. How many different sets of winners can there be if order is not considered? How many ways may there be first, second, and third place winners?

Solution. If we are not interested in the order of the winners, we can find the number of such sets by the formula $_8C_3 = \dfrac{8!}{5!\,3!} = \dfrac{8 \cdot 7 \cdot 6}{3 \cdot 2} = 56$. If order of winning first, second, and third places is considered, we can find the number of possible winner groups by the formula $_8P_3 = \dfrac{8!}{5!} = 8 \cdot 7 \cdot 6 = 336$.

Exercises

In Exercises 1–8 evaluate the given expression.

1. $_4C_2$ **3.** $_4C_1$ **5.** $_7C_3$ **7.** $_{12}C_7$

2. $_4C_3$ **4.** $_4C_4$ **6.** $_7C_7$ **8.** $_{20}C_{15}$

9. How many different sums of three coins can be formed from the contents of a box that contains half-dollars, quarters, dimes, nickels, and pennies if each sum is composed of coins of different value?

10. The cast of a school play is to be selected from 7 eligible girls and 9 eligible boys. The play requires 4 girls and 3 boys. In how many ways can the set of players be selected, assuming that each boy can play any male part and each girl can play any female part?

11. A menu offers 3 kinds of meat, 7 kinds of vegetables, 3 beverages, and 4 desserts. If a customer selects 1 kind of meat, 2 vegetables, 1 dessert, and 1 beverage, how many possible combinations are there for a meal?

12. How many diagonals has a convex polygon that has twenty-four vertices?

13. Prove that $_nP_r = r!\,_nC_r$.

14. Prove that $_nC_r = _nC_{n-r}$.

15. Show that the numerical coefficient of the rth term $(r \geq 1)$ in the binomial expansion of $(x + y)^n$ is $_nC_{r-1}$. Show that the binomial formula becomes
$$(x + y)^n = _nC_0 x^n + _nC_1 x^{n-1}y + _nC_2 x^{n-2}y^2 + \cdots$$
$$+ _nC_{r-1} x^{n-r+1}y^{r-1} + \cdots$$

Write the expansion of $(a + b)^6$ by the formula above with combinatorial notation for the coefficients.

16. Write the coefficient of the 13th term of $(r + s)^{22}$.

17. Write the sum of the fourth, fifth, and sixth term of $(1 + .1)^{10}$.

18. Show that $_6C_2 + {_6C_3}$ is equal to $_7C_3$.

19. Show that $_nC_r + {_nC_{r+1}}$ is equal to $_{n+1}C_{r+1}$.

17.5 Probability

If someone says that it is probable that it will rain he means that it is likely that it will rain. Something that is probable is likely to occur and something that is improbable (has a low probability) usually does not happen. In this section we shall define the probability of an event in careful mathematical terms.

When the referee of a football game flips a coin to determine the team which has the choice of kicking off, an assumption is made that each team has an equal chance. There are only two possible results, heads or tails, and only one face can come up on each throw. We neglect the very small possibility that the coin is lost or comes to rest on edge. The probability of a coin coming up heads, then, is $\frac{1}{2}$.

An event that is certain to happen has a probability of $+1$ and an event that cannot happen has a probability of 0. Thus, the probability p of an event is a number between 0 and 1 inclusive, $0 \leqq p \leqq 1$, that is the ratio of the number of successful outcomes of the event to the total number of possible outcomes. In the case of flipping a coin there are two possible outcomes (heads or tails) and only one can come up on each flip. The probability of success for heads is $\frac{1}{2}$. It is interesting to observe that the probability is $\frac{1}{2}$ regardless of the outcome of earlier trials.

A trial of an event is a circumstance which permits the event to occur or fail to occur. If the event occurs, we say that there has been a success; if the event fails to occur, we say there has been a failure. If there are t trials with s successes and f failures, then we have the relation $t = s + f$.

At any trial of an event if there are s ways in which it can succeed and f ways in which it can fail, then the probability of success p is defined to be

$$p = \frac{s}{s + f} \tag{VI}$$

The probability of failure q is defined to be

$$q = \frac{f}{s+f} \qquad \text{(VII)}$$

It is easily shown that the relation between p and q is

$$p + q = 1 \qquad \text{(VIII)}$$

Probability also applies to events that cannot be accurately determined or predicted as can the flip of a coin. What is the probability that you will have an automobile accident tonight? What is the probability that your high school team will win its game this week? What is the probability that a man of age 50 will live until he is 70 ? What is the probability that a manufactured article will pass inspection? What is the probability that a satellite will go into orbit? These are examples where the variables are many and varied and not always subject to control or determination. Such probabilities certainly exist but they can be determined only by statistical methods. Life insurance companies study millions of cases and in the light of this experience can report with considerable reliability the probability that a man of 50 will live to be 70 years old. In this chapter we shall consider primarily mathematical probability in which the events, successes, and failures are well defined and probability of success can be computed by means of formula (VI).

EXAMPLE 1. A cubical block has the numbers from 1 to 6 painted on the faces, one number on each face. What is the probability that the number 4 will come up if the block is randomly thrown? What is the probability that 4 will not come up on one throw?

Solution. On each throw there are six possible ways the block may come up of which only one is 4. Thus, the ratio of the number of ways the desired event can succeed to the total number of possible outcomes gives the probability of success of $\frac{1}{6}$. The probability of failure is $\frac{5}{6}$ since there are 5 ways the event can fail out of 6 possible ways. The sum of the probabilities of success and failure is $\frac{1}{6} + \frac{5}{6} = 1$.

EXAMPLE 2. A box in the athletic office of a high school contains 3 baseballs, 7 softballs and 11 tennis balls. If a ball is drawn at random from the box, what is the probability that it will be a baseball? What is the probability that it will not be a tennis ball?

Solution. There are 3 ways a baseball can be drawn and 18 ways that another type of ball can be drawn. When $s = 3$ and $f = 18$, the probability of success in drawing a baseball is $p = \dfrac{3}{3 + 18} = \dfrac{1}{7}$.

There are 11 ways of drawing a tennis ball and 10 ways of failing to draw a tennis ball. The probability of failure to draw a tennis ball is $q = \dfrac{10}{11 + 10} = \dfrac{10}{21}$. An alternate solution involves finding the probability that the ball will be a tennis ball, $\dfrac{11}{21}$, and subtracting the result from 1, since the sum of the probabilities of failure and success is 1.

Exercises

1. In a box are 4 black socks, 5 white socks, and 2 red socks. If one sock is drawn at random, what is the probability that it will not be red? What is the probability that it will be white or red?

2. If one playing card is drawn at random from a deck of 52, what is the probability that it will be the ace of spades? What is the probability that it will be any spade?

3. If 4 pennies are tossed simultaneously, what is the probability that 4 heads will come up?

4. If 5 coins are tossed, what is the probability that 2 heads and 3 tails will come up?

5. How many ways can a hand of 5 cards be dealt from a deck of 52 playing cards? (*Hint:* What is the number of combinations of 52 things taken 5 at a time?) How many ways can 5 hearts be dealt from a deck of 52 playing cards? (*Hint:* What is the number of combinations of 13 things taken 5 at a time?) What is the probability of dealing 5 hearts from a deck of 52 well shuffled playing cards?

17.6 Compound probability

Two events may be classified as mutually exclusive or independent. Mutually exclusive events are those in which a success of one necessitates failure of the other. If a coin comes up heads on one toss it cannot come up tails on the same toss; if a die (singular of dice) comes up 6 it cannot come up any other number on the same throw; if you are 68 inches tall at the present time you are not any other height, and so on. However, two events such as "it is raining" and "I am going to the ballgame" are independent in the sense we use the term here. We may go to the ballgame whether it rains or not. If Joe and Lynn work on Exercise 5 in a list of problems the success or failure of one does not affect that of the other so the two events of Joe solving the problem and Lynn solving the problem are independent.

If we throw the block described in the preceding section with the numbers from 1 to 6 on the faces, success of two different numbers coming up on one throw are mutually exclusive events. What is the probability that either 2 or 5 will come up on a single throw? We know that the probability of 2 coming up is $\frac{1}{6}$ and the probability of 5 coming up is also $\frac{1}{6}$. There are two ways that we may have success on one throw, that is, if 2 comes up or if 5 comes up. Thus, there are 2 possibilities of success out of 6 ways; the probability of either 2 or 5 coming up on one throw is $\frac{2}{6}$ or $\frac{1}{3}$. This probability is the sum of the probabilities of 2 coming up and of 5 coming up.

> **Principle:** If p_1 is the probability of success of one event and p_2 is the probability of success in a mutually exclusive event, then the probability p of success of either one or the other of the events is the sum of the probabilities.

$$p_1 + p_2 = p$$

Two consecutive throws of the block described above produce independent events, that is, success of any number coming up on the first throw does not affect the second throw. What is the probability of 5 coming up on two consecutive throws? We know that the probability of success on each throw is $\frac{1}{6}$. How many ways can success occur on two throws? How many possible ways can the faces come up on two trials? Listed below are all possible events that can occur if the block is thrown twice.

First	Second	First	Second	First	Second	First	Second	First	Second	First	Second
1	1	2	1	3	1	4	1	5	1	6	1
1	2	2	2	3	2	4	2	5	2	6	2
1	3	2	3	3	3	4	3	5	3	6	3
1	4	2	4	3	4	4	4	5	4	6	4
1	5	2	5	3	5	4	5	5	5	6	5
1	6	2	6	3	6	4	6	5	6	6	6

We see that there is only one successful event out of 36 possible events if 5 must come up twice in succession. Thus the probability of success for this event is $\frac{1}{36}$. What is the probability of throwing either a 3 or 4 on the first throw and either a 2, 5 or 6 on the second throw? There are 6 successful outcomes out of a possible 36 giving a probability of $\frac{1}{6}$ which is the product of the separate probabilities.

> **Principle:** If p_1 is the probability of success of one event and p_2 is the probability of success of an independent event, then the probability p of success of both events is the product of the probabilities.

$$p_1 \cdot p_2 = p$$

EXAMPLE 1. What is the probability that heads will come up three consecutive times when a coin is flipped three times? What is the probability that all three coins will land heads up if three coins are flipped simultaneously?

Solution. In each case the events are independent. The probability of heads for either situation is $\frac{1}{2} \cdot \frac{1}{2} \cdot \frac{1}{2} = \frac{1}{8}$.

EXAMPLE 2. There are eight girls who belong to a certain school club. The sponsor of the club is to select two of the girls to represent the club on a PTA program. If Barbara and Pat are members of the club what is the probability that they will both be chosen?

Solution. There is a probability of $\frac{1}{8}$ that Barbara will be selected as first choice. Then, since 7 girls remain, there is a probability of $\frac{1}{7}$ that Pat will be selected. The probability that Barbara and Pat will be selected in that order is $\frac{1}{8} \cdot \frac{1}{7} = \frac{1}{56}$. The probability that Pat and Barbara will be chosen in that order is also $\frac{1}{56}$. Thus, the probability that Barbara and Pat will be selected is $\frac{2}{56}$ or $\frac{1}{28}$.

Alternate solution. We see that the total number of ways of selecting 2 girls from among 8 is $_8C_2 = \frac{8!}{6!\,2!} = 28$. Only one of these selections is composed of Barbara and Pat (recall that combinations disregard order). The probability that the two girls will be selected is $\frac{1}{28}$.

EXAMPLE 3. Assume that three dice are thrown simultaneously.
(a) What is the probability that 4's will come up on all three?
(b) What is the probability that exactly one 4 will come up?
(c) What is the probability that at least one 4 will come up?

Solution. (a) Since the event of 4 coming up on each die is independent of what happens on the other dice, the probability that 4 will come up on all three is $\frac{1}{6} \cdot \frac{1}{6} \cdot \frac{1}{6} = \frac{1}{216}$.

(b) In order to find the probability that exactly one 4 will come up note that the probability of 4 on one die is $\frac{1}{6}$ and the probability that 4 will not come up on one die is $\frac{5}{6}$. Thus the probability that 4 will come up on the first die only is $\frac{1}{6} \cdot \frac{5}{6} \cdot \frac{5}{6}$. Since there are three dice the probability of 4 coming up exactly once is

$$3\left(\frac{1}{6} \cdot \frac{5}{6} \cdot \frac{5}{6}\right) = \frac{75}{216} = \frac{25}{72}$$

(c) The probability that at least one 4 comes up is the sum of the probability that exactly one 4 comes up, the probability that exactly two 4's come up, and the probability that 4 comes up on all three dice. Thus the probability of at least one 4 is

$$\underset{\text{one 4}}{\frac{75}{216}} + \underset{\text{two 4's}}{3 \cdot \frac{1}{6} \cdot \frac{1}{6} \cdot \frac{5}{6}} + \underset{\text{three 4's}}{\frac{1}{216}} = \underset{\text{at least one 4}}{\frac{91}{216}}$$

The above probabilities can be verified by writing in table form all of the 216 possible combinations and counting the number of successful combinations for each condition.

Exercises

1. Suppose that two dice are thrown. What is the probability that 3 will come up on both?

2. Two faces of a cube are colored red, two are blue, and two are white. If the cube is tossed what is the probability that it will show either red or blue?

3. A die is thrown twice. What is the probability that 5 will come up on the first throw and 4 will come up on the second?

4. A die is thrown three times. What is the probability that 6 will come up all three times?

5. Three faces of a cube are black, two are white, and one is green. If the cube is tossed randomly what is the probability that a face will show that is not white?

6. Six nails are fixed in an inclined board as illustrated. A bead represented by M whose diameter is slightly less than the distance between A and B is allowed to roll downward against A such that the probability that it will be deflected to either side is $\frac{1}{2}$. It is then deflected from either B or C where the probability is also $\frac{1}{2}$ that it will go to either side. What is the probability that the bead will strike E? What is the probability that it will strike F?

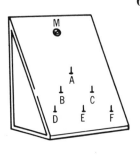

FIGURE 17–2

7. Suppose that there is a box in the shape of a cube that has been evacuated of all air except one molecule. Further suppose that one half of the box is painted white and the other black. As you know, the air molecule will be in rapid motion colliding with and rebounding from the internal walls of the box. What is the probability that the molecule will be in the black half of the box at any instant? If two molecules are in the box, what is the probability that both will be in the black half at any instant? If there are 10^{10} molecules of air in the box, what is the probability that all of them will be in the black half of the box at any instant? Is there any possibility that a mouse in the white half of the box could suffocate? Explain.

8. In one dresser drawer a man has 9 pairs of socks, 3 of which are black and 6 of which are gray. In another drawer he has 17 handkerchiefs, 11 of which are white and the remaining ones colored. In the dark the man selects two socks and a handkerchief at random. What is the probability that he has a pair of black socks and a white handkerchief?

9. There are 31 components of a telemetering device installed in a satellite. The probability that each component will function properly is .99 or higher. What is the minimum probability that the device will operate satisfactorily if a single defective part causes it to malfunction?

10. A mathematics class has 12 girls and 15 boys. A committee of 3 pupils is to be selected from the class by drawing lots. What is the probability that all members of the committee will be boys? What is the probability that there will be exactly one girl on the committee? What is the probability that there will be at least one girl on the committee?

11. There are 100 clocks in a certain overseas shipment. Assume that there are 4 clocks damaged in shipment but the packaging gives no indication of such damage. If a dealer buys 6 clocks without examining the contents, what is the probability that he does not have a damaged clock?

12. A deck of 52 cards contains 4 suits of 13 cards each. What is the probability of a bridge hand of 13 cards being all of one suit? If a woman plays bridge an average of 100 hands per week, what is the probability that she will hold a hand of one suit during a 5-year period?

17.7   The Binomial Theorem and probability

Many questions about probability can be answered by means of the binomial expansion. Exercise 15, page 375, established the relationship between the coefficients and combinatorial notation. Two forms of the expansion are given below.

A. $(x + y)^n = x^n + nx^{n-1}y + \dfrac{n(n - 1)}{2!} x^{n-2}y^2$

$+ \dfrac{n(n - 1)(n - 2)}{3!} x^{n-3}y^3 + \cdots$

$+ \dfrac{n(n - 1)(n - 2) \cdots (n - r + 2)}{(r - 1)!} x^{n-r+1}y^{r-1} + \cdots$

$+ nxy^{n-1} + y^n$

B. $(x + y)^n = {}_nC_0x^n + {}_nC_1x^{n-1}y + {}_nC_2x^{n-2}y^2 + {}_nC_3x^{n-3}y^3 + \cdots$

$+ {}_nC_{r-1}x^{n-r+1}y^{r-1} + \cdots + {}_nC_{n-1}xy^{n-1} + {}_nC_ny^n$

It is thus possible to find the coefficient of any term of the expansion to any power quickly and easily by the combination formula.

Suppose that 5 coins are flipped simultaneously and the probability that 2 coins will come up heads and 3 will come up tails is to be found. Let p_h represent the probability that heads will come up on one coin on one toss and let p_t represent the probability that tails will come up on one toss. $p_h = p_t = \dfrac{1}{2}$. If 5 coins are tossed we can replace x in the binomial expansion by p_h, and y by p_t. Since there are 5 coins let $n = 5$ and the binomial formula becomes

$$(p_h + p_t)^5 = 1p_h^5 + 5p_h^4p_t + 10p_h^3p_t^2 + 10p_h^2p_t^3 + 5p_hp_t^4 + 1p_t^5$$

The terms of the expansion can be interpreted as follows.

$1p_h^5 = 1\left(\dfrac{1}{2}\right)^5 = \dfrac{1}{32}$, which is the probability that 5 heads will come up.

$5p_h^4p_t = 5\left(\dfrac{1}{2}\right)^4\left(\dfrac{1}{2}\right) = \dfrac{5}{32}$, which is the probability that 4 heads and 1 tail will come up.

$10p_h^3p_t^2 = 10\left(\dfrac{1}{2}\right)^3\left(\dfrac{1}{2}\right)^2 = \dfrac{10}{32}$ or $\dfrac{5}{16}$, which is the probability that 3 heads and 2 tails will come up.

$10p_h^2p_t^3 = 10\left(\dfrac{1}{2}\right)^2\left(\dfrac{1}{2}\right)^3 = \dfrac{10}{32}$ or $\dfrac{5}{16}$, which is the probability that 2 heads and 3 tails will come up.

$5p_hp_t^4 = 5\left(\dfrac{1}{2}\right)\left(\dfrac{1}{2}\right)^4 = \dfrac{5}{32}$, which is the probability that 1 head and 4 tails will come up.

$1p_t^5 = 1\left(\dfrac{1}{2}\right)^5 = \dfrac{1}{32}$, which is the probability that 5 tails will come up.

We can determine other probabilities from the above expansion. For example, what is the probability of at least 2 heads coming up if 5 coins are tossed simultaneously? The first, second, third, and fourth terms represent the condition that two or more heads come up; thus the probability of this happening is

$$\frac{1 + 5 + 10 + 10}{32} = \frac{26}{32} \text{ or } \frac{13}{16}$$

Let us consider more difficult questions about probability and see if the binomial expansion gives a solution. Recall Example 3, page 381, in which three dice were thrown simultaneously and we were to determine the probability that (a) three 4's come up; (b) exactly one 4 will come up; (c) at least one 4 will come up. Let p_4 represent the probability that 4 comes up on one throw of one die and let q_4 represent the probability of failure of 4 to come up under the same circumstances. Since three dice are thrown we can write the binomial expansion as follows.

$$(p_4 + q_4)^3 = p_4{}^3 + 3p_4{}^2q_4 + 3p_4q_4{}^2 + q_4{}^3$$

(a) The value of p_4 is $\dfrac{1}{6}$ and of q_4 is $\dfrac{5}{6}$. Thus the probability that all three dice will come up 4 is $\left(\dfrac{1}{6}\right)^3 = \dfrac{1}{216}$.

(b) The probability that exactly one 4 will come up is found by evaluating the third term $3p_4q_4{}^2$. We have: $3\left(\dfrac{1}{6}\right)\left(\dfrac{5}{6}\right)^2 = \dfrac{75}{216}$ or $\dfrac{25}{72}$.

(c) The probability of at least one 4 is found by evaluating the sum of the first three terms since these are the cases in which this condition is satisfied. We have

$$\left(\frac{1}{6}\right)^3 + 3\left(\frac{1}{6}\right)^2\left(\frac{5}{6}\right) + 3\left(\frac{1}{6}\right)\left(\frac{5}{6}\right)^2 = \frac{1}{216} + \frac{15}{216} + \frac{75}{216} = \frac{91}{216}$$

An alternate method for solving part (c) is to find the probability that no 4 will come up and subtract this probability of failure of 4 to come up from 1, since you recall that the sum of the probability of success and the probability of failure of an event is 1. The probability of failure of at least one 4 to come up is $\left(\dfrac{5}{6}\right)^3 = \dfrac{125}{216}$. Thus the probability of success of at least one 4 to come up is $1 - \dfrac{125}{216} = \dfrac{91}{216}$, the desired probability.

The preceding examples illustrate what is known as a *binomial experiment*. In such an experiment the number of trials n is fixed and the trials are independent. This means in an experiment with coins that the number of coins n is known (since each coin on each toss is considered an event or trial whether tossed consecutively or simultaneously) and the outcome on one trial does not affect the outcome on another. In a binomial experiment the probability of success of an event is constant and every event must end in either success or failure. The number of successes is important rather than the order of successes. If coins are tossed in a binomial experiment the probability of heads is always $\frac{1}{2}$ on each toss of each coin and we are interested only in the total number of coins coming up heads rather than which coins come up heads.

Let p be the probability of success of an event and q be the probability of failure of the event on one trial. Suppose there are n trials of the event in a binomial experiment; we can write

$$(p + q)^n = {}_nC_0p^n + {}_nC_1p^{n-1}q + {}_nC_2p^{n-2}q^2 + {}_nC_3p^{n-3}q^3 + \cdots$$

(1) The probability of exactly n successes is ${}_nC_0p^n$.

(2) The probability of exactly $n-1$ successes is ${}_nC_1p^{n-1}q$.

(3) The probability of exactly $n-2$ successes is ${}_nC_2p^{n-2}q^2$.

(4) The probability of exactly $n-3$ successes is ${}_nC_3p^{n-3}q^3$.

(5) The probability of exactly r successes is ${}_nC_{n-r}p^rq^{n-r}$ or ${}_nC_rp^rq^{n-r}$.

We may be interested in the sum of a number of probabilities, such as the probability of at least r successes (r successes or more). The following interpretations of the binomial expansion can be made.

(1) The probability of at least n successes is ${}_nC_0p^n$.

(2) The probability of at least $n-1$ successes is ${}_nC_0p^n + {}_nC_1p^{n-1}q$.

(3) The probability of at least $n-2$ successes is ${}_nC_0p^n + {}_nC_1p^{n-1}q + {}_nC_2p^{n-2}q^2$.

(4) The probability of at least $n-3$ successes is ${}_nC_0p^n + {}_nC_1p^{n-1}q + {}_nC_2p^{n-2}q^2 + {}_nC_3p^{n-3}q^3$.

(5) The probability of at least r successes is ${}_nC_0p^n + {}_nC_1p^{n-1}q + \cdots + {}_nC_{n-r}p^rq^{n-r}$.

EXAMPLE. If 5 coins are tossed simultaneously prepare a probability table for all possible cases which gives the probability of exactly r heads and the probability of at least r heads.

Solution. $p = \frac{1}{2}$; $q = \frac{1}{2}$.

$$(p + q)^5 = {}_5C_0p^5 + {}_5C_1p^4q + {}_5C_2p^3q^2 + {}_5C_3p^2q^3 + {}_5C_4pq^4 + {}_5C_5q^5$$

$$= 1\left(\frac{1}{2}\right)^5 + 5\left(\frac{1}{2}\right)^4\left(\frac{1}{2}\right) + 10\left(\frac{1}{2}\right)^3\left(\frac{1}{2}\right)^2 + 10\left(\frac{1}{2}\right)^2\left(\frac{1}{2}\right)^3$$

$$+ 5\left(\frac{1}{2}\right)\left(\frac{1}{2}\right)^4 + 1\left(\frac{1}{2}\right)^5$$

$$= \frac{1}{32} + \frac{5}{32} + \frac{10}{32} + \frac{10}{32} + \frac{5}{32} + \frac{1}{32}$$

Probability Table: $n = 5$, $p = .50$; $r = 0, 1, 2, 3, 4, 5$.

r	Exactly r successes	At least r successes
0	1/32 or .031	1
1	5/32 or .157	.969
2	10/32 or .312	.812
3	10/32 or .312	.500
4	5/32 or .157	.188
5	1/32 or .031	.031

How can the table for *Exactly r successes* be found from the table of *At least r successes*? Which is a cumulative table? *Hint:* To find the probability of exactly 2 successes, subtract the probability of at least 3 successes from that of at least 2 successes. .812 − .500 = .312.

Exercises

1. Prepare binomial probability tables for $n = 5$ and $p_1 = .10$, $p_2 = .20$, $p_3 = .30$, $p_4 = .40$, and $p_5 = .50$. Prepare one column for each probability for *At least r successes* where $r = 0, 1, 2, 3, 4, 5$. Can this table be extended to $p_6 = .60$, $p_7 = .70$, $p_8 = .80$, and $p_9 = .90$ without additional computation? Explain and complete the table.

2. Prepare a binomial probability table for $n = 10$, $p = .50$ giving probabilities for at least r successes where $r = 0, 1, 2, 3, \cdots, 10$.

3. By reading values from the tables prepared in Exercise 1 what is the probability that an event with a probability of success of .30 will occur at least twice in five consecutive trials if the trials are independent? What is the probability of the event occurring at least 3 times? at least 4 times?

4. The probability of success of an event is .40. In 5 independent trials what is the probability of success of at least 4 events? What is the probability of success on exactly 4 events in the 5 trials?

5. Ten coins are tossed simultaneously. From the table calculated in Exercise 2, what is the probability that at least 5 heads will come up? What is the probability that exactly 2 heads will come up?

6. Two boys play each other frequently in the game of table tennis. Over a long period of time it has happened that Jim can usually beat Tom 3 times out of 5. In a series of 10 games what is the probability that they will each win 5 games?

7. It has been determined experimentally that the probability of success of an event is .70. In 5 trials what is the probability that there will be at least 4 successful results?

8. A "wheel of fortune" at a county fair has the numbers from 1 to 10 each of which has an equal probability of success. What is the probability for the number 7 coming up in 5 consecutive spins of the wheel? What is the probability of 7 coming up exactly once in 5 spins? What is the probability of 7 coming up at least once?

9. If 10 coins are thrown onto a table, what is the probability that at least 4 will be heads, but no more than 6 will be heads?

10. On one street there are three families with 5 children each. If the probability that a child is male is .50, what is the probability that any one family has exactly 3 boys? What is the probability that all three families have two or more boys each?

Chapter Review

1. If a high school girl has 5 skirts and 8 blouses, how many ways can she combine these articles of clothing?

2. How many ways can the letters of the word FERMAT be arranged? (A Frenchman named Fermat did much to develop the theory of probability. Another French mathematician named Pascal is credited as being the father of probability.)

3. How many ways can the letters of the word ABSCISSA be arranged?

4. A regular dodecahedron has 12 faces, each of which is a regular pentagon. There are 30 edges and 20 vertices in the solid. How many internal diagonals are there in a regular dodecahedron?

5. Write the 10th term of the expansion of $(x - 2)^{14}$ using the formula for combinations to determine the value of the coefficient.

6. If 9 coins are tossed simultaneously what is the probability that exactly 7 coins will come up heads? What is the probability that at least 7 coins will come up heads?

7. There are 20 books on a shelf, 5 of which have black covers, 3 have red covers, 4 have blue covers, and the remainder have various other colored covers. If a book is taken from the shelf in the dark, what is the probability that the color of the cover is neither red or blue?

8. If a committee of 4 pupils is to be selected randomly from a class of 32, 19 of which are girls, what is the probability that there will be 2 boys and 2 girls on the committee?

9. The batting average of a baseball player is .300. What is the probability that he will hit twice in a row?

10. In a class of 30 pupils what is the probability that no two will have the same birthday date?

CHAPTER OUTLINE

Empirical Relations—Statistics

18

18.1 The meaning of statistics

A common characteristic of modern business, science, education, and indeed most aspects of life, is the tremendous amount of detailed information that has been compiled about every conceivable subject. Whenever things are counted or measured there results a set of numbers called *data*. Each number of the set is a *datum*. Businesses compile data on costs, sales, wages, production, profits, and so on. Scientists gather data on the behavior of sub-atomic particles and of the stars—and almost everything in between. Biological and psychological studies are sources of mountains of data. Television programs stand or fall on the ratings of public opinion polls based on statistical sampling. The polio innoculation of millions provided a basis for a gigantic statistical study. In fact, everywhere we turn today we are faced with sets of numbers which have a bearing on our life. The systematic handling of these data we call *statistics*.

The techniques of collection, organization, analysis, and presentation of data are called *descriptive statistics*. If the interpretation of the data is carried through to conclusions and predictions we call this aspect *inferential statistics*. Only an expert statistician is able to draw valid inferences after a careful study of the analysis of the data. We shall concern ourselves in this chapter principally with descriptive statistics.

There is always an element of approximation in dealing with statistics. The measurements in collections of data are approximate numbers. The samples selected for study may not perfectly represent the entire body of data. Probability is a feature of the interpretation of statistics and anyone aspiring to become a statistician should study this subject thoroughly.

18.2   Measures of central tendency—the arithmetic mean

All averages are measures of central tendency. An average is a number which represents a set of numbers. The ordinary average is found by adding the numbers in the set together and dividing by the number of elements in the set. This kind of average is the *arithmetic mean*. For example, the arithmetic mean of 89, 73, and 92 is $\dfrac{89 + 73 + 92}{3} = 84\frac{2}{3}$. Frequently we say simply *mean* when the arithmetic mean is intended.

If X is a variable used to represent any element of a set of data, then the arithmetic mean $\bar{X}$ (read "X bar") of n numbers is given by the formula

$$\bar{X} = \frac{X_1 + X_2 + X_3 + \cdots + X_n}{n} \tag{I}$$

There is a convenient symbolism to indicate the sum of a set of numbers which makes use of the capital Greek letter *sigma* (Σ) called the *summation symbol*. The sum of specified terms can be abbreviated as follows.

$$\sum_{i=1}^{n} X_i = X_1 + X_{\bar{2}} + X_3 + \cdots + X_n$$

The left member is read "the summation of X-sub-i from $i = 1$ to n." The symbol X_i represents successive elements of the set of data as i assumes successive integral values from 1 to n.

The formula for the arithmetic mean then becomes

$$\bar{X} = \frac{1}{n} \sum_{i=1}^{n} X_i \tag{II}$$

EXAMPLE. Find the arithmetic mean of: 17, 19, 19, 20, 21.

Solution. $n = 5$.

$$\bar{X} = \frac{1}{n} \sum_{i=1}^{n} X_i = \frac{1}{5} (17 + 19 + 19 + 20 + 21) = 19\tfrac{1}{5}$$

The arithmetic mean can be considered as the center of balance of the data if the elements are thought of as weights.

Exercises

1. Find the mean of 87.2, 68.5, 74.8, 94.0, 82.2, 96.1.
2. A farmer sold hogs that weighed 241 lb., 305 lb., 289 lb., 262 lb., 300 lb., 267 lb. What was the mean of the weights?
3. On a vacation trip a family traveled 329 miles on Saturday, 401 miles on Sunday, 105 miles on Monday, 443 miles on Tuesday, 306 miles on Wednesday, 211 miles on Thursday, 511 miles on Friday. Find the mean distance travelled per day.
4. John's percent grades on five tests were 84, 72, 91, 64, 83. Find the mean.
5. The mean height of 5 boys is 67 inches. If one boy is 5 feet tall and another is 6 feet tall, give possible heights for the other 3 boys.

18.3 Measures of central tendency—the median

For some purposes the median is a more useful measure of a group of data than the arithmetic mean. The *median* M_d is the mid-value of a set of data.

Before the median can be found the *raw data* should be put into an *array*. Numbers which are in no special order are raw data and to form an array we arrange them into an ordered sequence, usually in order of increasing size. The *range* is the difference of the largest and smallest numbers in the array.

EXAMPLE 1. Make an array of the following scores made by pupils on a test. What is the range? (82, 79, 91, 57, 71, 87, 64, 95, 73, 75, 62)

Solution. The array is: 57, 62, 64, 71, 73, 75, 79, 82, 87, 91, 95. The range is $95 - 57 = 38$.

The median of an odd number of numbers is the middle number of their array. The median of an even number of numbers is the arithmetic mean of the two middle numbers of their array.

EXAMPLE 2. What is the median of the numbers 17, 31, 15, 28, 35, 30, 29, 19, 19? What is the range?

Solution. First make an array: 15, 17, 19, 19, 28, 29, 30, 31, 35. There are nine numbers; hence the middle or fifth number from either end is 28. The median is 28. The range is $35 - 15 = 20$.

EXAMPLE 3. What is the median of the numbers .014, .019, .010, .023, .045, .009? What is the range?

Solution. The array is: .009, .010, .014, .019, .023, .045. Since there are six numbers, an even number, the median is the mean of the two middle numbers. Thus, $M_d = \dfrac{.014 + .019}{2} = .0165$. The range is $.045 - .009 = .036$.

Exercises

1. Find the median of $64, $82, $51, $90, $67, $71, $58, $94, $63. What is the range?

2. What is the median of 5'7", 4'8", 6'1", 5'5", 8'0", 9'1", 6'7", 5'4"? What is the range?

3. Find the difference between the arithmetic mean and the median of the following numbers. 144, 175, 192, 138, 166, 159, 171, 180, 162. If the number 127 is added to the data, how does this affect the mean and the median?

4. Will the median be affected if the numbers at the extremes of an array are changed? Will the mean be affected by such changes? Can the mean and median ever coincide?

5. Consider the following experiment. There is a light metal rod one meter long suspended at the middle so that it balances. Suppose that one-gram weights are hung on the rod at the following distances from one end: 5 cm., 20 cm., 37 cm., 44 cm., 52 cm., 68 cm., 71 cm., 85 cm. It is observed that the rod does not balance at the 50 cm. mark. Where must one more one-gram weight be hung so that the rod will be balanced? (*Hint:* Since the weights are equal, 50 must be the mean of the nine distances.) What is the median of the distances?

18.4   Measures of central tendency—the mode

The *mode* of a set of numbers is that number which appears more frequently than any other in the set. It is most easily found after making an array. The mode of the numbers 1.29, 1.37, 1.29, 1.25, 1.37, and 1.29 is 1.29. This number appears three times in the set and no other number appears more than twice. It may happen that the mode is not always determined, particularly in a small set of numbers. There may be more than one mode in a group of numbers; data with two modes are said to be *bimodal*. The mode is of importance in such data as sizes of shoes or clothing. Why?

Exercises

1. Find the mode: 36.1, 42.4, 63.5, 51.7, 60.8, 63.5, 42.4, 56.0, 63.5, 55.1.

2. Find the mode: .412, .408, .410, .408, .401, .401, .410, .420, .408.

3. On a very easy arithmetic test given to a large number of students, would the mode of the scores likely be higher or lower than the mean? On a very difficult test would the mode of the scores likely be higher or lower than the mean?

18.5 Other means—geometric, harmonic, quadratic

In addition to the arithmetic mean there are other means of a set of numbers which may be better suited to describe the set. The *geometric mean G* is given by the formula

$$G = \sqrt[n]{X_1 \cdot X_2 \cdot X_3 \cdots X_n} \tag{III}$$

It is used when the sequence X_1, X_2, $\cdots$ X_n has the characteristics of a geometric sequence. (See Section 10.5.)

For certain purposes the *harmonic mean H* is useful. The formula is

$$H = \cfrac{n}{\cfrac{1}{X_1} + \cfrac{1}{X_2} + \cdots \cfrac{1}{X_n}} = \cfrac{n}{\sum\limits_{i=1}^{n} \cfrac{1}{X_i}} \tag{IV}$$

To compare the use of the harmonic mean with the arithmetic mean the following example is given.

EXAMPLE. One man on a trip travels two hours at a rate of 50 miles per hour and then on a superhighway travels the next two hours at a rate of 60 miles per hour. What is his average speed?

Another man travels 100 miles at the rate of 50 miles per hour and then on a superhighway travels the next 100 miles at the rate of 60 miles per hour. What is his average speed?

Solution. The average speed of the first man is given by the arithmetic mean of 50 mph and 60 mph. $\bar{X} = \dfrac{50 + 60}{2} = 55$ miles per hour. The average speed of the second man is given by the harmonic mean of 50 mph and 60 mph. $H = \dfrac{2}{\dfrac{1}{50} + \dfrac{1}{60}} = 54.5$ miles per hour, approximately. We can show the truth of these averages as follows. The first man travels a total distance of 220 miles in 4 hours or at an average speed of 55 miles per hour. The second man travels a total distance of 200 miles in $3\frac{2}{3}$ hours or at an average speed of 54.5 miles per hour.

- When equal times are involved the arithmetic mean of the speeds is used; when equal distances are involved the harmonic mean is needed.

Another mean that has important special uses is the *quadratic mean,* or *root-mean-square.* The quadratic mean is the square root of the mean of the squares of the numbers in a set of data. If $X_1, X_2, \cdots X_n$ are the numbers in the set, then the quadratic mean Q is given by the formula

$$Q = \sqrt{\frac{X_1^2 + X_2^2 + X_3^2 + \cdots + X_n^2}{n}} \quad \text{or} \quad \sqrt{\frac{\sum\limits_{i=1}^{n} X_i^2}{n}} \quad \text{(V)}$$

EXAMPLE. Find the quadratic mean of 1.3, 1.5, 1.7, 1.0, 1.1.

Solution. $Q = \sqrt{\dfrac{1.3^2 + 1.5^2 + 1.7^2 + 1.0^2 + 1.1^2}{5}}$

$= \sqrt{\dfrac{8.44}{5}} = 1.3$, approximately

Exercises

1. Find the quadratic mean of 6, 6, 7, 8, 8, 8, 11, 11, 12.
2. Find the geometric mean of 243, 81, 27, 9, 3.
3. Find the harmonic mean of 3, 4, 5, 6.
4. Compute the quadratic mean of 2.5, 2.5, 2.5, 3.5, 3.5, 3.8, 4.0, 4.2.
5. For the following set of numbers compute $\bar{X}, M_d, G, H, Q$. (3, 2, 6, 8, 5)

18.6   Measures of variability—mean deviation, semi-interquartile range

The arithmetic mean and median are measures of central tendency and hence are statistics which describe a certain important characteristic of a set of data. They do not indicate, however, anything about the variability of the data. For example, the mean of 35, 40, and 45 is 40; the mean of 10, 40, and 70 is also 40. It is clear that the variability is much greater in the second case than in the first but this is not at all indicated by the mean.

Two measures of variability are the mean deviation and the semi-interquartile range. If the deviations from the mean, $X_i - \bar{X}$, are found, it is evident from the nature of the arithmetic mean that the sum of the deviations from the mean is zero, that is, $\sum_{i=1}^{n}(X_i - \bar{X}) = 0$. Some of the deviations from the mean are positive and some are negative; the algebraic sum is zero as you can easily verify. However, if the signs are ignored, that is, if the absolute values of the deviations are considered, it is possible to find the average of the deviations. The arithmetic mean of the absolute values of the deviations from the mean of a set of data is called the *mean deviation*. In the example 35, 40, 45, the deviations from the mean are -5, 0, $+5$ respectively. The arithmetic mean of the absolute values of these deviations is $\frac{5 + 0 + 5}{3} = 3\frac{1}{3}$. Thus the mean deviation is 3.3 approximately. In the example 10, 40, 70, the deviations from the mean are -30, 0, $+30$ respectively. The mean deviation is $\frac{30 + 0 + 30}{3} = 20$. The formula for mean deviation is

$$M.D. = \frac{1}{n} \sum_{i=1}^{n} | X_i - \bar{X} | \qquad \text{(VI)}$$

Another measure of the variability of a set of data is the semi-interquartile range. As the word *quartile* implies this is the average of the quartile deviations. If the array of a set of data is divided into four equal parts, each part is called a quartile. The median divides the data into two equal parts and thus is the second quartile point. By a method similar to that used for the median, each half can be divided into two equal parts giving the first and third quartile points. We shall call Q_1 the point below which $\frac{1}{4}$ of the data lie; Q_2 is the midpoint or median below which $\frac{1}{2}$ the data

lie; Q_3 is the point below which $\frac{3}{4}$ of the data lie. The formula

for Q (*the semi-interquartile range*) is

$$Q = \frac{Q_3 - Q_1}{2} \qquad \text{(VII)}$$

EXAMPLE. Find the semi-interquartile range of the following numbers: 38, 47, 18, 26, 32, 41, 30, 27, 21, 35, 31, 29, 32, 25, 22.

Solution. Make an array. 18, 21, 22, 25, 26, 27, 29, 30, 31, 32, 32, 35, 38, 41, 47. The midpoint or median is 30. Q_1 is 25 and Q_3 is 35. The semi-interquartile range is: $Q = \dfrac{35 - 25}{2} = 5$.

Exercises

1. Find the value of the semi-interquartile range Q for the numbers in Example 1, Section 18.3.

2. Find the mean deviation for the data in Exercise 1 at the end of Section 18.2.

3. In the example in Section 18.6 above, which is the greater, *M.D.* or Q?

18.7 Measures of variability—standard deviation

At the beginning of this chapter on statistics it was said that we are interested in finding a number that will represent a group of data. We then defined several measures of central tendency any one of which might be taken to represent a group of numbers. Then we defined two measures of variability which tell something about the dispersion or spread of the numbers in a set. We now define another measure of variability that is often associated with the arithmetic mean to give a meaningful description of a set of data. This measure is called the *standard deviation*. It, like the mean deviation, is a measure of the average amounts by which individual items of data vary or deviate from the arithmetic mean of all the numbers that compose the data.

The *standard deviation* of a set of numbers is the quadratic mean of the individual deviations from the arithmetic mean. An individual deviation is the result of subtracting the arithmetic mean from the individual number, that is, $X_i - \bar{X}$. As we have seen some of these differences will be negative, but since they are to be squared in computing their quadratic mean the results will be positive. If $\bar{X}$ represents the mean and X_i $(i = 1, 2, \cdots, n)$ represents the numbers of a set of data, then the standard deviation σ (sigma, lower case) for the data is

$$\sigma = \sqrt{\frac{1}{n} \sum_{i=1}^{n} (X_i - \bar{X})^2} \qquad \text{(VIII)}$$

In the example 35, 40, 45, the deviations are -5, 0, $+5$ and their squares are 25, 0, 25 respectively. The standard deviation $\sigma =$ $\sqrt{\dfrac{25 + 0 + 25}{3}} = \dfrac{\sqrt{150}}{3} = 4.1$, approximately.

The standard deviation of 10, 40, 70 is

$$\sigma = \sqrt{\frac{(-30)^2 + 0^2 + (+30)^2}{3}} = 24.5, \text{ approximately}$$

The standard deviation is the most important measure of variability.

EXAMPLE. Compute the arithmetic mean and the standard deviation for the following numbers: 54, 57, 59, 59, 60, 60, 61, 61, 62, 62, 62, 63, 63, 63, 64, 65, 65, 66, 66, 67, 68, 68, 68, 68, 68, 69, 69, 69, 70, 71, 71, 72, 72, 73, 75, 76, 77, 79, 81, 83, 90.

Solution. $\bar{X} = \dfrac{1}{41} (54 + 57 + \cdots + 90) = 68$. The deviations are: $54 - 68$, $57 - 68$, $59 - 68$, $\cdots$, $90 - 68$, or: -14, -11, -9, $\cdots$, $+22$. The squares of the deviations are 196, 121, 81, $\cdots$, 484. The mean of these squares is 54.39. Thus, the standard deviation $\sigma = \sqrt{54.39} = 7.3$.

Exercises

1. Compute the standard deviation of .6, .6, .7, .8, 1.0, 1.2, 1.4.

2. An astronomer made ten measurements of the angular distance between two stars. In degrees his measurements are given below. Compute the standard deviation. $11.21°$, $11.17°$, $10.93°$, $11.06°$, $11.20°$, $10.97°$, $11.10°$, $11.05°$, $11.23°$, $11.01°$.

3. Compute the standard deviation and the mean deviation of the numbers: 56, 83, 74, 49, 58, 65, 72, 41, 75, 63, 66, 57, 68, 53, 61. Which measure of variability is greater?

18.8 The frequency distribution

When the number of elements in a set of data becomes large (perhaps 50 or more) it is desirable to group the data into a system called a *frequency distribution*. By grouping we mean that a number of classes are determined and all elements that are found in a class are tallied and grouped together. An example will illustrate how data are grouped into a frequency distribution.

EXAMPLE 1. Suppose there are 200 boys in a certain school and the weights of these boys are to be studied. School health records will provide the data directly. How would the frequency distribution be prepared?

Solution. First, the raw data would be copied from the records onto a data sheet. Next an array would be made from the raw data and the range found. Let us assume the smallest weight is 99 pounds and the highest weight is 203 pounds. The range is $203 - 99 = 104$ pounds.

The data must now be grouped into classes; eleven classes, covering 10 pounds each, seems to be suitable. Let the lowest class be from 95 pounds to 105 pounds, the next class from 105 to 115 pounds, and so on where 95, 105, 115 $\cdots$ are called *class limits.* If a given weight falls on one of these class limits, such as 115 pounds, we shall agree that the weight will be tallied in the higher class, $115-125$ rather than $105-115$. Very conveniently the midpoints of the classes, called the *class marks* and represented by X, follow the sequence 100, 110, 120, $\cdots$, 200. The form of the frequency distribution is as follows.

Class limits	Class mark (X)	Tally	Frequency $F(X)$
95–105	100	///	3
105–115	110	7HL //	7
115–125	120	7HL 7HL 7HL	15
125–135	130	7HL 7HL 7HL 7HL 7HL 7HL ////	34
135–145	140	7HL 7HL 7HL 7HL 7HL 7HL 7HL 7HL //	42
145–155	150	7HL 7HL 7HL 7HL 7HL 7HL 7HL ///	38
155–165	160	7HL 7HL 7HL 7HL ////	24
165–175	170	7HL 7HL 7HL	15
175–185	180	7HL 7HL /	11
185–195	190	7HL //	7
195–205	200	////	4

Total 200

The *class interval* is the width of each class; the class interval is 10 in the above example. It is desirable for most purposes that all class intervals in a distribution be equal.

The class mark is the average of the class limits. The number of classes in a distribution can vary from 5 to 20 depending upon various factors such as range, the number of elements in the data, the purpose of grouping, and so on. Some frequency distributions may have fewer than 5 classes or more than 20, but this is usually not desirable. If fewer than 5 classes are recorded, the grouping is too coarse and if there are more than 20 classes the distribution is unwieldy. The frequency $F(X)$ is the sum of the tallies of a class.

It should be emphasized that an element of data loses its identity in a frequency distribution. That is, after tallying in a certain class, for example a weight of 138 pounds tallied above in the class 135–145, the weight is grouped with all others in the class. An important assumption is made in working with such a distribution; it is that *the data in any class are uniformly distributed over the class.* The result of this assumption is that each class mark is the mean of the data tabulated in its class. Usually, only a very slight error is introduced by this assumption.

EXAMPLE 2. Make a frequency distribution of the following scores made by a class of 7th grade pupils on an arithmetic test of 20 problems. 13, 19, 17, 15, 20, 9, 16, 15, 17, 14, 10, 16, 19, 20, 13, 17, 15, 18, 12, 16, 14, 18, 16, 7, 17, 19, 15.

Solution. First make an array. We have: 7, 9, 10, 12, 13, 13, 14, 14, 15, 15, 15, 15, 16, 16, 16, 16, 17, 17, 17, 17, 18, 18, 19, 19, 19, 20, 20. The range is $20 - 7 = 13$. Let us form 7 classes, each with a class interval of 2. In order to include the smallest number we shall let the lowest class limit be 6.5.

Class limits	Class mark (X)	Tally	Frequency F(X)
6.5– 8.5	7.5	/	1
8.5–10.5	9.5	//	2
10.5–12.5	11.5	/	1
12.5–14.5	13.5	////	4
14.5–16.5	15.5	7/// ///	8
16.5–18.5	17.5	7/// /	6
18.5–20.5	19.5	7///	5

Total   27

The choice of class limits can vary considerably and the student is cautioned to interpret their meaning properly in any distribution studied.

Exercises

1. Make a frequency distribution of the following weights of children in a certain fourth grade class. 64, 71, 57, 67, 74, 65, 59, 62, 67, 75, 72, 84, 60, 68, 72, 91, 55, 69, 71, 93, 69, 71, 69, 75, 59, 60, 70, 76, 62, 66, 77, 62, 68, 81, 68, 63, 79, 88, 57, 78.

2. Twenty-six pairs of students in a civil engineering class made independent measurements of the length of the college campus. They reported the following results in feet. Make a frequency distribution of the data. 2013.3, 2012.8, 2013.4, 2012.2, 2012.0, 2013.0, 2012.2, 2011.8, 2011.7, 2012.6, 2013.5, 2012.4, 2012.1, 2012.6, 2013.9, 2013.7, 2012.8, 2012.3, 2012.6, 2011.4, 2012.3, 2011.6, 2012.2, 2012.7, 2012.4, 2012.7. How would you handle the data if the last measure was reported as 2112.7 ft. rather than 2012.7 ft.?

18.9   Graphical representation of data

Once a frequency distribution has been made, it is a relatively simple matter to make a graph to represent the data. The class marks X are measured on the horizontal axis and the frequency $F(X)$ is measured on the vertical axis. A vertical bar graph called a *histogram* can then be made. Below is the histogram of the frequency distribution from Example 2, Section 18.8 of the arithmetic test scores of 27 pupils in a 7th grade class.

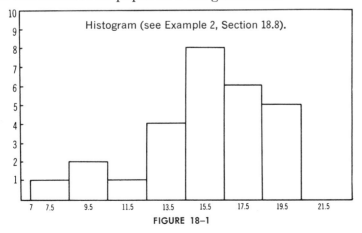

FIGURE 18–1

Another frequently used graphical form for statistical data is the *frequency polygon*. It is sometimes called a broken line graph. The base of the polygon is the horizontal axis. Below is the frequency polygon for the example in Section 18.8 concerning the arithmetic test scores.

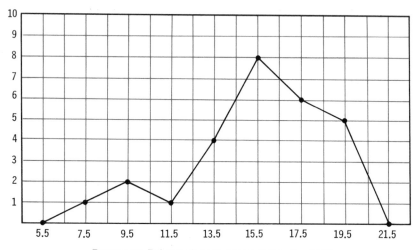

Frequency Polygon (see Example 2, Section 18.8).

FIGURE 18–2

Other means of graphical representation of statistical data include circle graphs, divided bar graphs, pictograms, and multiple line graphs.

Exercises

1. Make a histogram for the frequency distribution in Exercise 1, p. 401. (Section 18.8.)

2. Make a frequency polygon for the data in Exercise 2, p. 401. (Section 18.8.)

3. Make a histogram for the weights of 200 boys in the example page 399.

4. Compile the results of heads and tails for tossing 5 coins 160 times. Make a frequency distribution and frequency polygon for the number of heads. Compare experimental results with the expected probabilities.

18.10 Computation of the arithmetic mean, median, and standard deviation from a frequency distribution

In order to find the arithmetic mean of a set of numbers, one must find the sum of the numbers and divide by the number in the set. In a frequency distribution the individual numbers lose their identity and an assumption must be made. (See Section 18.8.) The assumption is that the individual numbers in each class are uniformly distributed over the class. Thus, the weight of each class is balanced at the midpoint or class mark of that class. For example, if the numbers 23, 24, 25, 26, 27 fall in a class with limits 22.5–27.5, they have the same sum as if each of the five numbers were 25, the class mark. The sum of the numbers in a class may be found by multiplying the class mark by the frequency $F(X)$ of its class. The sum of all the numbers in a given set may be found by adding the results of this computation for all the classes of the frequency distribution. The sum of the numbers in a class is $X \cdot F(X)$ and the sum of all the numbers in the set is $\Sigma X F(X)$.

EXAMPLE 1. Given the following frequency distribution for the scores of 100 students on a mathematics test, compute the arithmetic mean. (Column 5 in this table is for later use; it can be omitted from present consideration.)

(1)	(2)	(3)	(4)	(5)
				Cumulative
Class limits	Class mark	Frequency		frequency
	X	$F(X)$	$XF(X)$	cum $F(X)$
97.5–102.5	100	4	400	100
92.5– 97.5	95	9	855	96
87.5– 92.5	90	17	1530	87
82.5– 87.5	85	27	2295	70
77.5– 82.5	80	22	1760	43
72.5– 77.5	75	11	825	21
67.5– 72.5	70	7	490	10
62.5– 67.5	65	3	195	3
	$\Sigma F(X) = 100$		$8350 = \Sigma X F(X)$	

Solution. It is seen from column (3) that $\Sigma F(X)$ equals the number N of individuals in the distribution. The assumption that the individuals in each class are uniformly distributed over the class means, for example, that some of the 9 students in the second class have scores above 95 and some have scores below 95 but the average or mean of these 9 scores is 95. Thus the sum of their scores is $9 \times 95 = 855$. The mean of the distribution is found by finding the sum of the column headed $XF(X)$ and dividing by N. The formula for the arithmetic mean of data in a frequency distribution is

$$\bar{X} = \frac{\Sigma XF(X)}{N} \qquad \qquad \text{(IX)}$$

For this distribution

$$\bar{X} = \frac{8350}{100} = 83.50$$

The median M_d is found by locating the midpoint of the distribution, that is, the number or point below which 50% of the numbers fall. The method of linear interpolation is used. (See Appendix A.7.) This is done by preparing a *cumulative frequency distribution* in which the sum of the frequencies up to and including the class being considered is found and recorded. See column (5) in the table above. $(3 + 7 = 10, 3 + 7 + 11 = 21, 3 + 7 + 11 + 22 = 43$, and so on.) We see that 50% of 100, the number in the distribution, is 50, so that we must locate the point below which are found 50 scores. From the cumulative frequency column we see that 43 scores fall below the point 82.5, the upper limit of the class which has 43 as its cumulative frequency value. Likewise, 70 scores fall below the point 87.5. Apparently the median point is within the class 82.5–87.5, called the *median class*. If we subtract 43 from 50 we find that 7 scores above the point 82.5 are required to reach the midpoint of the distribution. Since there are 27 scores in the median class, it is clear that $\frac{7}{27}$ of 5, the class interval, must be added to the lower limit of that class in order to reach the midpoint.

$$M_d = 82.5 + \frac{7}{27} \times 5 = 82.5 + 1.3 = 83.8$$

It is known that the median divides the numbers in a distribution into two equal parts. In like manner, the *quartiles* divide a distribution into four equal parts, and *percentiles* divide it into 100 equal parts. *Deciles* divide it into ten equal parts.

As we have said the method given above for finding the median is a form of linear interpolation. A similar interpolative method may be used to find any *percentile* value. If the 80th percentile is to be found, for example, 80% of N may be taken and the point in the distribution below which 80% of the distribution falls may be found in the same manner as the 50%-point, the median.

The standard deviation is the quadratic mean of the deviations from the arithmetic mean. (See Section 18.7.) In a frequency distribution deviations from the mean can be found for a given class by subtracting the mean from the class mark and multiplying this result by the frequency of the class. Thus, $(X_i - \bar{X})\, F(X_i)$ represents the deviations from the arithmetic mean of all the scores in a given class, where X_i represents the class mark of the ith class and $F(X_i)$ is its frequency. Then $(X_i - \bar{X})^2\, F(X_i)$ represents the squares of the deviations from the arithmetic mean of the distribution for the ith class. The standard deviation can be found by computing the quadratic mean of these deviations in the manner described in Section 18.7.

$$\sigma = \sqrt{\frac{\sum_{i=1}^{n} (X_i - \bar{X})^2 F(X_i)}{N}} \qquad \text{where } n \text{ is the number of classes and } N \text{ is } \Sigma F(X) \qquad \textbf{(X)}$$

EXAMPLE 2. Find the standard deviation of the 100 scores on the mathematics test whose results are given in the table, p. 403.

Solution. We repeat the X and $F(X)$ columns of the given frequency distribution. Then we find $(X - \bar{X})$, $(X - \bar{X})F(X)$, and $(X - \bar{X})^2\, F(X)$. The results are shown in the following table.

X	$F(X)$	$X - \bar{X}$	$(X - \bar{X})F(X)$	$(X - \bar{X})^2F(X)$
100	4	16.5	66.0	1089.00
95	9	11.5	103.5	1190.25
90	17	6.5	110.5	718.25
85	27	1.5	40.5	60.75
80	22	−3.5	−77.0	269.50
75	11	−8.5	−93.5	794.75
70	7	−13.5	−94.5	1275.75
65	3	−18.5	−55.5	1026.75
$\Sigma F(X) = 100$				$\Sigma(X - \bar{X})^2F(X) = 6425.00$

We see that $\Sigma(X - \bar{X})^2 \, F(X) = 6425.00$.

Thus, $\sigma = \sqrt{\dfrac{6425.00}{100}} = \sqrt{64.2500} = 8.0$

The standard deviation is approximately 8.0. The square of the standard deviation, called the *variance*, is often used as a measure of variability.

The arithmetic mean is the most important measure of central tendency, and the standard deviation is the most important measure of variability. Both have extensive applications in more complex statistics than those covered in this book.

Exercises

Given the following distribution of I.Q.'s in a senior class in a high school, find the mean, median, and standard deviation.

Class limits	X	F(X)
132.5–137.5	135	1
127.5–132.5	130	2
122.5–127.5	125	5
117.5–122.5	120	8
112.5–117.5	115	13
107.5–112.5	110	21
102.5–107.5	105	30
97.5–102.5	100	27
92.5– 97.5	95	16
87.5– 92.5	90	12
82.5– 87.5	85	4
77.5– 82.5	80	1

18.11   Normal distribution curve

When data regarding a large number of measurements are examined it is usually observed that (*a*) there are few large deviations from the mean; (*b*) negative deviations and positive deviations usually occur with about the same frequency; (*c*) small deviations are much more frequent than large ones. The question arises whether it is possible to give an equation in two variables, say x and y, which will exhibit the three characteristics listed above. More than one hundred fifty years ago one such equation was given. It is

$$y = ke^{-h^2x^2} \qquad \text{(XI)}$$

In this equation h and k are constants chosen or determined by the particular situation being considered and e is the base of the system of natural logarithms, $e = 2.71828 \cdots$. (See Section 11.7.) The equation is simplified if we let $h = k = 1$. The equation then becomes

$$y = e^{-x^2} \qquad \text{(XII)}$$

Since e is approximately equal to $\dfrac{11}{4}$ we can write

$$y = \left(\frac{4}{11}\right)^{x^2}$$

as a simplified approximation to the first equation stated above. Now, by assigning values to x and computing corresponding values of y we get a set of ordered pairs of numbers which can be plotted and connected to produce the graph of the equation. This graph is the *normal probability curve*, or curve of *normal distribution of errors*, or *normal frequency curve*. There are methods for modifying the equation of the curve and hence the curve itself for particular sets of data, but we shall not discuss the process here.

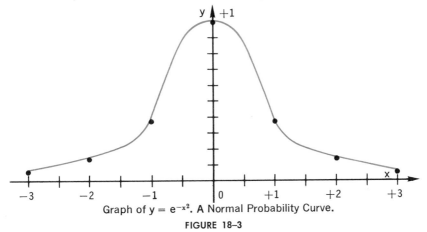

Graph of $y = e^{-x^2}$. A Normal Probability Curve.

FIGURE 18–3

The abscissas of points on the curve represent deviations and the ordinates are proportional to the probabilities of occurrence, or expected occurrence.

Exercises

1. In the function $y = ke^{-h\,x^2}$ let $h = \dfrac{1}{2}$, $k = .4$ and construct the graph.

2. Toss 10 coins 100 times and record the number of tails on each toss. Compare the normal curve with the graph of frequency of a result y and number of tails per toss x.

18.12   Binomial expansion coefficients and normal distribution

This figure shows a mechanical device often used to illustrate visually a normal probability distribution. There is a board in which nails are fixed at A, B, C, . . . extending outward some

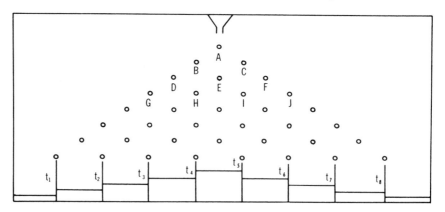

FIGURE 18–4

distance from the board. At the top is a reservoir or funnel for holding beads or shot. At the bottom are baffles t_1, t_2, t_3, . . . which make pockets or slots for holding the beads after they have fallen from the top. The board is placed on end or inclined on a level table and the beads are allowed to drop from the reservoir bouncing on the nails and into the pockets. They will usually be distributed so that they approximate the curve of normal distribution.

Let M be a bead released from the reservoir and allowed to fall on nail A. The bead will then fall to the right of A or to the left. If it falls to the left, it will strike B and again fall to the right or to the left. Thus each nail brings into operation a chance bounce, right or left, until the bead falls into a pocket at the bottom.

There is one path by which the bead can reach B and one path by which it can reach C from A. Hence, it is equally probable that it will fall on B or on C. That is, the probability that it will fall on B is $\frac{1}{2}$. If it falls on B it will then fall on D or on E. The probability that it will fall on D is $\frac{1}{2} \times \frac{1}{2} = \frac{1}{4}$. (See Section 17.5.) Likewise, if M falls on C it must then fall on E or F. The probability that it will fall on E after falling on C is $\frac{1}{4}$. Thus, there is 1 chance in 4 that M will fall on D, 1 in 4 that it will fall on F, and 2 in 4 that it will fall on E. If 4 beads were dropped we would expect that 1 would fall on D, 2 on E, and 1 on F.

We can reason in a slightly different way. There is only one path from A to D, one from A to F, and there are two from A to E (A to B to E and A to C to E). Since we assume that it is equally likely that the bead will follow one path as any other, the probability of reaching E is twice as great as that of reaching D.

It can be further shown that the number of paths from A to G is 1, A to J is 1, A to H is 3, and A to I is 3. Hence, the probability of a bead falling on H is three times as great as that of falling on G. Notice that H, for example, can be reached by way of D or by way of E, and hence the number of paths to H is the sum of the number of paths to D and the number to E. And likewise the number of paths to any point can be found by adding the numbers of paths to points diagonally above it. This is precisely the method by which the numbers in Pascal's triangle are obtained. (See Section 10.20.) But these numbers are the coefficients in the expansion of $(x + y)^n$ where n is any positive integer. Therefore, the probability of a bead falling on any given nail is proportional to the coefficient of a term in the binomial expansion of the power corresponding to the row in which the nail appears.

Now let us mark off equal lengths on a horizontal line and at consecutive points let us draw vertical segments whose lengths are proportional to the numbers in a row of Pascal's triangle (Figure 18-5, page 410). Next let a smooth curve be drawn connecting the tops of these segments. This curve suggests the probable distribution of beads in the pockets. The figure is based upon $n = 8$ in the expression $(x + y)^n$. If larger values of n are taken the curve is modified but its general shape remains the same. Notice the similarity of this curve to the normal distribution curve shown in Section 18.11.

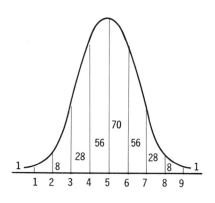

FIGURE 18–5

Exercises

1. Draw a smooth curve connecting the tops of the ordinates whose lengths are proportional to the coefficients in the expansion of $(x + y)^{12}$.

2. A teacher graded 64 test papers and ranked them from poorest to best. He decided to give marks A, B, C, D, E, F (A highest) in proportion to the coefficients in the expansion of $(x + y)^5$. How many papers received each mark?

18.13   **Interpretation of standard deviation**

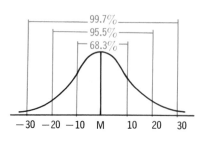

FIGURE 18–6

If data are normally distributed, that is, if the graph of the distribution closely follows the normal curve, the standard deviation σ enables us to understand important characteristics of the distribution.

Statisticians have proved that if data are normally distributed, then 99.7% of all items are in the range of three standard deviations from the arithmetic mean. This can be represented by $\bar{X} \pm 3\sigma$ (read "X-bar plus or minus 3 sigma") which is understood to mean the range from $\bar{X} - 3\sigma$ to $\bar{X} + 3\sigma$. In other words, there are only three chances in 1000 that an item of data will be more than three standard deviations from the mean of the data. Figure 18–6 illustrates this statement. Other ranges are also indicated.

The following table shows in more detail the fractional parts of a normally distributed set of data for specified ranges about the mean.

t	P	t	P
0.0	0.000	1.7	0.9111
0.1	0.080	1.8	0.928
0.2	0.159	1.9	0.943
0.3	0.236	1.96	0.950
0.4	0.311	2.0	0.955
0.5	0.383	2.1	0.964
0.6	0.451	2.2	0.972
0.7	0.516	2.3	0.979
0.8	0.576	2.4	0.984
0.9	0.632	2.5	0.988
1.0	0.683	2.58	0.990
1.1	0.729	2.6	0.991
1.2	0.770	2.7	0.993
1.3	0.807	2.8	0.995
1.4	0.838	2.9	0.996
1.5	0.866	3.0	0.997
1.6	0.891	3.5	0.9995
1.65	0.900	4.0	0.9999

In this table P is the fractional part of items and t is the limit of deviation of items from $\bar{X}$ in terms of σ as the unit, without regard to whether the deviation is positive or negative. That is, a deviation of $.5\sigma$, for example, may be $+.5\sigma$ or $-.5\sigma$. This means that the area which corresponds to the indicated fractional part of items lies between the ordinates $-.5\sigma$, $+.5\sigma$, the x-axis, and the curve. Thus, the base of the figure is $.5\sigma - (-.5\sigma) = 1\sigma$. All of this is taken into account in the table, so that the entry

$.5\sigma$ for t corresponds to 0.383 for P which can be interpreted as meaning that 0.192 of the items are less than $\bar{X}$ and deviate from it by no more than $.5\sigma$, and 0.192 of the items are greater than $\bar{X}$ and deviate from it by no more than $.5\sigma$.

The expressions $\bar{X} + t\sigma$ and $\bar{X} - t\sigma$, then, indicate the upper and lower limits of the range of numbers in the data for any selected value of t, and the table tells us what fractional part of the items lie within these limits if the data are normally distributed.

An example will clarify the discussion. Suppose the mean and standard deviation for a certain set of data are computed and it is found that $\bar{X} = 50$ and $\sigma = 10$. Then the expression $\bar{X} \pm t\sigma$ becomes $50 \pm 10t$. Now if we wish to find what fractional part of the numbers in the data differ from the mean by no more than 10, we let $t = 1$ and have the range 40 to 60 $(50 - 10$ to $50 + 10)$. The table shows that for $t = 1$, that is, within one standard deviation of the mean, 0.683 of the items are within the indicated range.

As another example, suppose we wish to find the upper and lower limits within which 90% of the items of a set of normally distributed data are to be found. Suppose the mean and standard deviation are computed and it is found that $\bar{X} = 65$ and $\sigma = 6$. Then $65 - 6t$ and $65 + 6t$ are the lower and upper limits of the desired range. We look in the table and find that for $P = 0.900$ or 90% the value of t is 1.65. That is, 90% of the items are within 1.65σ of $\bar{X}$. Now, $\sigma = 6$, and hence $1.65\sigma = 9.9$. Thus, 90% of the items lie between $65 - 9.9$ or 55.1 and $65 + 9.9$ or 74.9.

Another question that can be answered with the aid of the table is this. Suppose that an item is taken by chance from a set of data; what is the probability that it varies from the mean by no more than $t\sigma$? The answer is given by the value of P corresponding to the selected value of t in the table. Thus if $\bar{X} = 65$, $\sigma = 6$, as in the preceeding example, and we take $t = 2$, then the table tells us that the probability that the item varies no more than $t\sigma$, in this case 12, from 65 is 0.955. In other words, the probability is .955 that an item selected randomly from the data will lie within 2 standard deviations from the mean, that is, between 53 and 77.

Exercises

1. A teacher decides to give marks on a certain test by marking "on the curve." It is determined that the C group will be comprised of all pupils whose test scores fall in the range $\bar{X} \pm$

.5σ, the B group from $\bar{X} + .5\sigma$ to $\bar{X} + 1.5\sigma$, the A group all those above $\bar{X} + 1.5\sigma$, the D group from $\bar{X} - .5\sigma$ to $\bar{X} - 1.5\sigma$, and the F group all those below $\bar{X} - 1.5\sigma$. What percent of the class will receive each letter mark?

2. The mean of a set of normally distributed numbers is 140 and the standard deviation is 20. What percent of the numbers fall in the range 120 to 160 ? What percent fall in the range 130 to 150 ? What is the probability that a number selected at random from the data will be in the range 110 to 200 ?

3. In the set of numbers described in Exercise 2 what is the probability that a number selected at random from the data will be greater than 160 ? Less than 100 ?

4. In the set of numbers from Exercise 2 find the range about the mean which includes 90% of the numbers. Find the point below which 90% of all the numbers lie.

18.14   Sampling techniques—standard error

One of the founders of statistics, Karl Pearson, has said that the fundamental problem of statistics is that of sampling. The present era might be called the age of the public opinion poll, which is a sampling of opinions. Television program ratings, election predictions, and a host of other statistical survey results appear daily in the newspapers and magazines. Perhaps the public is more aware of statistics in this connection than in the more important areas of biological and medical research and industrial quality control. All of these studies and many more depend upon sampling techniques.

It rarely happens that 100% of a *population* or *universe* (all of the items or individuals concerned) is accessible as a source of data. Hence a *sample* of the population must be selected in some way. Then, based upon this sample, certain inferences can be made about the population from which the sample was drawn. The sample should be *representative* of the population, that is, the various characteristics of the population pertinent to the study should be sampled in about the same ratio as they exist in the population. Such a sample is usually selected from the universe in some random manner and is called a *random sample*. The technique of insuring randomness in the sample is a difficult one and we shall say here only that chance plays a dominant role.

Suppose, for example, that the mean height of 1031 high school senior boys in a certain large city is desired, but it is impractical to arrange to measure all of them. However, it is learned that 100 senior boys of this group are organized into an all-city boys chorus in which all high schools are represented in proportion to their enrollments of boys. It is *assumed* that musical talent in singing has no relationship to height. Hence, this sample of 100 boys is assumed to be random with respect to height. At a practice session of the chorus with all members present, an actual measurement of the height of the 100 boys is made correct to the nearest tenth of an inch. The data are tabulated and the arithmetic mean and standard deviation are computed and found to be, $\bar{X} = 67.6$ inches and $\sigma = 2.7$ inches. The problem now is to estimate the mean and standard deviation of the heights of the entire population, that is, of all 1031 senior boys in the city.

It is apparent that we could give a large range with the mean of the sample 67.6 as the midpoint (for example, 47.6 to 87.6). We could say with nearly complete certainty that the true mean of all 1031 boys, which we can represent by $\tilde{X}$ (read "X tilde"), lies somewhere within this range. However, this range is so broad as to be of little value. On the other hand, if we take a narrow range around 67.6, say 67.5 to 67.7, we cannot predict with any great degree of certainty that $\tilde{X}$ is in this range.

Generally, some level of confidence is desired, such as 5% or 1%. A 1% level of confidence means that there is less than a 1% chance that the sample mean differs from the true mean by a certain amount; a 5% level of confidence means there is less than a 5% chance that the sample mean differs from the true mean by a certain amount.

There is a statistic called the *standard error of the mean* which permits us to give a level of confidence about the sample mean. The formula is

$$\sigma_{\bar{x}} = \frac{\sigma}{\sqrt{N}} \qquad \text{(XIII)}$$

where N is the number in the sample and σ is the standard deviation. The symbol $\sigma_{\bar{x}}$ is read "sigma sub-x bar" or "the standard error of the mean." The standard error of any statistic behaves like the standard deviation, that is, probabilities of occurrence may be determined by referring to the table on p. 411. Recall that the range $\bar{X} \pm 1\sigma$ contains 68.3% of the individual items in the data if it is normally distributed and $\bar{X} \pm 1.65\sigma$ contains approximately 90% of the items. Sample means are also distributed about the true mean but with the standard error as a measure of their variability. There is a 68.3% chance that the sample mean $\bar{X}$ of a population lies in the range $\tilde{X} \pm \sigma_{\bar{x}}$. Likewise, there is a .90 probability that the sample mean lies in the range $\tilde{X} \pm 1.65\sigma_{\bar{x}}$.

Now, returning to our example, let us compute the range of heights for which we can say that there is a probability of .90 that the mean height of the 1031 boys lies within it. First we compute $\sigma_{\bar{x}} = \dfrac{2.7}{\sqrt{100}} = .27$. Therefore, there is a probability of .90 that the true mean $\tilde{X}$ is within the range $67.6 \pm (1.65)(.27) = 67.6 \pm .4$, that is, (67.2 to 68.0). From the formula for $\sigma_{\bar{x}}$ we see that the larger the sample, the smaller the range for a given level of confidence, since the divisor $\sqrt{N}$ (Formula (XIII), above) increases with the number of items. Furthermore, we must sacrifice accuracy by giving a wider range if we desire a higher level of confidence. In this example, if a 5% level of confidence is desired, we would give the range $\bar{X} \pm 1.96\sigma_{\bar{x}}$. A 1% level of confidence is given by the range $\bar{X} \pm 2.58\sigma_{\bar{x}}$. This means that $2.58\sigma_{\bar{x}}$ will determine a range about $\bar{X}$ such that there is not more than one chance in a hundred that the true mean of the population will lie outside the range $\bar{X} \pm 2.58\sigma_{\bar{x}}$. Thus, the probability is .99 that the true mean lies in the range $67.6 \pm (2.58)(.27) = 67.6 \pm .6$, (67.0 to 68.2).

Great care must be taken in using standard error statistics. It may happen that unconsidered factors influence the sample and thus cause the mean of the sample to differ greatly from the true mean of the population. For example, it could happen that boys who participate in a boys chorus are shorter on the average than their classmates because they do not fare as well in athletics and so have more time for singing, although this is not likely to be true. Tables of random numbers have been prepared by statisticians and can be used to select a sample with good assurance that it is random.

Exercises

1. A random sample of 50 acorns from an oak tree reveals a mean diameter of 16.2 mm. and a standard deviation of 1.4 mm. Find the standard error of the mean. What is the range about the mean of the sample which will give a .90 probability that

the true mean diameter of all acorns of the tree will fall within it? What range will give a 95% chance that the true mean will fall within it?

2. What is the probability that the sample mean of a set of data will fall within two standard errors from the true mean?

3. In the following frequency distribution compute the mean, standard deviation, and standard error of the mean. Then answer the following questions. (a) If this distribution represents a random sample of 2361 items, what will be the range about the mean of the sample that will give a probability of .95 that the true mean of the total group will fall within it? (b) What is the probability that the mean of the population will be less than one point from the mean of the sample? (c) What range about the mean will give a 1% level of confidence that the true mean of the group will fall within it? (d) What range about the mean of the data will contain 50% of the sample?

FREQUENCY DISTRIBUTION

Class mark	Frequency
4	1
6	3
8	5
10	12
12	17
14	13
16	7
18	4
20	2

4. In a certain town a random sample of 100 families showed that the mean number of hours the television set was turned on per day was 3.6 hours. The standard deviation was 1.4 hours. Make a 5% level of confidence statement about the mean number of hours that families of this town have their television set turned on.

Chapter Review

Experiment for Exercises 1–10. A small metal object was weighed on a laboratory balance by each of 15 pupils in a class. Each performed the weighing according to directions and with an effort to be as accurate as possible. The weight in grams of the object was reported as follows:

2.341 ; 2.347 ; 2.338 ; 2.350 ; 2.344 ; 2.342 ; 2.345 ; 2.348 ; 2.340 ; 2.345 ; 2.343 ; 2.344 ; 2.347 ; 2.341 ; 2.344.

1. Make an array of the data and find the range.
2. What is the median weight?
3. What is the arithmetic mean of the weighings?
4. What is the modal weight?
5. What is the mean deviation of the data?
6. What is the standard deviation of the weighings?
7. What is the probability that another pupil will find the weight to be greater than 2.340 in an independent weighing?
8. What is the standard error of the mean?
9. What is the range about the mean within which there is a probability of .95 that the sample mean lies?
10. Do the measures seem to be normally distributed? Discuss.

Experiment for Exercises 11–16. In a certain university the achievement of students is reported as a number from 6 to 0, where 6 is the highest rating. The point average for all courses taken by each student in a semester is then computed. The point averages for the freshman class are summarized in the following frequency distribution.

Point Average	Class Mark	Frequency
5.5–6.5	6	37
4.5–5.5	5	104
3.5–4.5	4	231
2.5–3.5	3	163
1.5–2.5	2	110
.5–1.5	1	69
below .5	0	24 (principally students who withdrew)

11. Find the arithmetic mean of the point averages.
12. Find the median of the data.
13. Find the standard deviation of the data.
14. What point average must a student achieve in order to be at the 90th percentile mark?

15. If all students who rank in the lowest 15% of the freshman class are dismissed from the university, what is the lowest point average a student can make and still remain in school?

16. What is the probability that a student selected at random will have a point average of 5.0 or higher?

CHAPTER OUTLINE

Limits

19

19.1   Concept of limit

The concept of limit has been considered informally at several points in this text. At the time we defined the derivative of a function, we used the idea of finding the limit of a certain ratio, $\frac{\Delta y}{\Delta x}$, as Δx approaches zero. Later we studied the convergence and divergence of sequences and series. Of particular interest in this regard is the limit of the sum of an infinite geometric series considered in Section 10.10. In these presentations we appealed to your intuitive understanding of the meaning of limit. In this chapter we shall formalize the definition of limit so that a firm foundation for the calculus may be laid.

The limit concept pervades much of higher mathematics and is, indeed, the principal distinguishing characteristic of analysis from algebra. Analysis is that branch of advanced mathematics which is composed primarily of calculus and its applications. Anyone who expects to enter a technical field such as science, engineering, biology, economics, sociology, and so on, must be conversant with the calculus. And to study calculus successfully, one must be well-versed in the study of limits.

We shall present in this introductory section a review of many of the ideas about limits which should already be a part of your background. What do we mean when we say that the limit of the nth term of a convergent infinite series (or sequence) is zero *as n increases without limit*? By the expression "as n increases without limit," we mean "as n approaches infinity" and write $n \to \infty$. If the nth term of $\frac{1}{2} + \frac{1}{4} + \frac{1}{8} + \frac{1}{16} + \cdots$ is represented by $\frac{1}{2^n}$, does the limit of $\frac{1}{2^n}$ equal zero as n increases without limit? This can be symbolized by $\lim\limits_{n \to \infty} \frac{1}{2^n} = 0$. (See Section 10.10.) Intuitively, it is clear that as n increases, the denominator of $\frac{1}{2^n}$ increases, and the value of the fraction approaches zero.

Now let us consider the sum $\frac{1}{2} + \frac{1}{4} + \frac{1}{8} + \cdots + \frac{1}{2^n}$ as n increases without limit. This sum and, in fact, any series, approaches a limit under these conditions if it never exceeds some constant, regardless of the value of n. The limit of the sum itself is the real number being approached as n increases indefinitely. In this example the limit is 1, which can be illustrated by a drawing.

FIGURE 19–1

Note that the sum of n terms is represented by the length of the line segment from zero to the nth point to the right of zero. As n increases without limit, the points representing the sum cluster closer and closer to 1, but always remain less than 1. Thus, the limit of the sum $\frac{1}{2} + \frac{1}{4} + \frac{1}{8} + \cdots + \frac{1}{2^n}$ as n approaches infinity is 1.

An infinite series which approaches a limit as n increases indefinitely is *convergent;* otherwise, the series is *divergent.* The harmonic series $1 + \frac{1}{2} + \frac{1}{3} + \frac{1}{4} + \cdots + \frac{1}{n}$ is divergent because the sum increases without limit as n approaches infinity, even though the nth term approaches zero. (See Section 10.12.) Do you recall that a geometric series is convergent if and only if $|r| < 1$? Perhaps you should review the proof that this is true.

Now let us turn our attention to the limit of certain simple functions. What is the limit of $(2x + 3)$ as x approaches zero? What is the limit as x approaches 4? As x approaches -2? If you answered 3, 11, -1, respectively, you were correct. What is the limit of $(x^2 - 4)$ as x approaches 2? What is the limit of $\frac{x^2 - 4}{x - 2}$ as x approaches 2? The questions of this paragraph have all been easy to answer except, possibly, the last one. Can you find an expression which has the same value for all real replacements of x as $\dfrac{x^2 - 4}{x - 2}$?

A little experimentation will reveal that $(x + 2)$ is equivalent to $\dfrac{x^2 - 4}{x - 2}$ except for one real replacement of x. Which one? We shall agree that $\lim\limits_{x \to 2} \dfrac{x^2 - 4}{x - 2}$ is equal to $\lim\limits_{x \to 2} (x + 2)$. Since the second limit is clearly 4, we know that $\lim\limits_{x \to 2} \dfrac{x^2 - 4}{x - 2} = 4$. The fact that x cannot be replaced by 2 in this equation does not affect the value of the limit. As the value of x gets closer and closer to 2, the value of $\dfrac{x^2 - 4}{x - 2}$ comes closer and closer to 4.

Suppose we restrict ourselves at this time to polynomial functions with real coefficients of the form

$$P(x) = a_0 x^n + a_1 x^{n-1} + a_2 x^{n-2} + \cdots + a_{n-1} x + a_n$$

and let the domain of P be the set of all real numbers. Then, for any real number r, $P(r)$ exists and is a real number. We shall define the limit of such a polynomial function as x approaches r as $P(r)$. In symbols this is represented by $\lim\limits_{x \to r} P(x) = P(r)$.

To illustrate this important concept, we provide the following examples.

EXAMPLE 1. Show by giving a number of ordered pairs that the limit of $(2x + 3)$ as x approaches 0 is 3.

Solution. Let x take on the successive values .1, .01, .001, and .0001. The corresponding values of $(2x + 3)$ are shown in the table.

x	.1	.01	.001	.0001
$2x + 3$	3.2	3.02	3.002	3.0002

Observe that the closer the value of x is to zero, the closer the value of $(2x + 3)$ is to 3. By the equation $\lim\limits_{x \to r} P(x) = P(r)$ for polynomial functions, we can write $\lim\limits_{x \to 0} (2x + 3) = 2(0) + 3 = 3$.

EXAMPLE 2. Show that $\lim\limits_{x \to 4} (x^2 - 4) = 12$ by selecting replacements of x near 4.

Solution. We are free to choose values less than 4 or greater than 4 as shown in the following tables.

x	3.8	3.9	3.99	3.999
$x^2 - 4$	10.44	11.21	11.9201	11.992001

x	4.1	4.01	4.001	4.0001
$x^2 - 4$	12.81	12.0801	12.008001	12.00080001

Now consider the rational function $f(x) = \dfrac{x^3}{x}$. What is the graph of $y = \dfrac{x^3}{x}$? Is it a parabola? Make a sketch. What value of x is *not* in the domain? Do you see that the graph is a parabola with one point removed, the vertex? Suppose we wish to find the limit of $\dfrac{x^3}{x}$ as x approaches 2. By taking values of x sufficiently close to 2, we see that $\dfrac{x^3}{x}$ approaches 4 as x approaches 2. Note that $\dfrac{x^3}{x}$ equals 4 if x is replaced by 2. What is $\lim\limits_{x \to 0} \dfrac{x^3}{x}$? What difficulty do we have in this case that was not present when x approached 2? Replacing x by values close to zero, but not equal to zero, we obtain the table of values shown below.

x	1	.1	.01	.001	.0001
$\dfrac{x^3}{x}$	1	.01	.0001	.000001	.00000001

It appears that $\lim\limits_{x \to 0} \dfrac{x^3}{x} = 0$. Observe that 0 is not in the domain of the function. Nevertheless, the limit of the function exists as x *approaches* zero; the limit is zero itself. An alternate way of showing that $\lim\limits_{x \to 0} \dfrac{x^3}{x} = 0$ is to transform $\dfrac{x^3}{x}$ into x^2 since the two functions are equal for all values of x except $x = 0$. Note that we are investigating $\dfrac{x^3}{x}$ as x *approaches* zero and the situation at $x = 0$ is immaterial. Then, because x^2 is a polynomial, $\lim\limits_{x \to 0} x^2 = 0$.

As a technique for finding the limit of certain functions, we can sometimes transform the given function into polynomial form and then evaluate the polynomial. This is based upon the relationship $\lim\limits_{x \to r} P(x) = P(r)$. The method succeeds whenever the modification is possible *even if the given function is not defined at that point.*

EXAMPLE 3. Find $\lim\limits_{x \to 2} \dfrac{x^2 - 4}{x - 2}$.

Solution. $\lim\limits_{x \to 2} \dfrac{x^2 - 4}{x - 2} = \lim\limits_{x \to 2} \dfrac{(x + 2)(x - 2)}{(x - 2)} = \lim\limits_{x \to 2} (x + 2) = 4.$

We must be careful to observe that $\dfrac{x^2 - 4}{x - 2} = x + 2$ for all real replacements of x *except* 2. This does not affect the value of the limit as x *approaches* 2.

Exercises

Find the limit in each exercise, if it exists.

1. $\lim\limits_{x \to 2} x^2$

2. $\lim\limits_{n \to \infty} \left(1 - \dfrac{1}{2} + \dfrac{1}{4} - \dfrac{1}{8} + \cdots + \dfrac{1}{2^{n-1}} \right)$

3. $\lim\limits_{n \to 0} \left(5^n + \dfrac{1}{5^n} \right)$

4. $\lim\limits_{n \to \infty} \left(2 + \dfrac{1}{2} + \dfrac{1}{8} + \cdots + \dfrac{2}{4^{n-1}} \right)$

5. $\lim\limits_{x \to 5} (3x - 8)$

6. $\lim\limits_{x \to 3} \dfrac{x^2 - 9}{x - 3}$

7. $\lim\limits_{x \to 3} \dfrac{x^2 - 9}{x + 3}$

8. $\lim\limits_{x \to 3} \dfrac{x + 3}{x^2 - 9}$

9. $\lim\limits_{x \to -2} (x^4 - x^2 + x - 2)$

10. $\lim\limits_{x \to -1} \dfrac{x^3 + 1}{x + 1}$

11. Write a table of values to show that $\lim\limits_{x \to 1} \dfrac{4x + 5}{x + 2}$ is 3.

12. Write a table of values which will give an indication of the value of $\lim\limits_{x \to 10} \dfrac{2^x}{x^2}$.

13. Find $\lim\limits_{n \to \infty} \dfrac{n + 1}{n}$. (*Hint:* First transform $\dfrac{n + 1}{n}$ into $1 + \dfrac{1}{n}$ and then find the limit.)

14. Find $\lim\limits_{n \to \infty} \dfrac{3n - 5}{n}$.

15. Find $\lim\limits_{n \to \infty} \dfrac{n^2 + n - 3}{n^2}$.

16. Find $\lim\limits_{n \to \infty} \dfrac{(n+2)(2n-1)}{n^2}$.

19.2   A more careful approach to the limit of a linear function

As a means of finding the limit of a function as the variable approaches some real number, consider the graph of the linear function $y = mx + b$. Suppose we wish to find the limit L of

$(mx + b)$ as x approaches some real number a. By choosing values of x sufficiently close to a, we can make the value of $(mx + b)$ as close to L as we please. For example, given $2x + 3$, we shall show that $\lim_{x \to 2} (2x + 3) =$

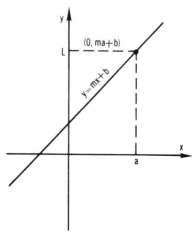

7 by the method outlined in the preceding sentence. Suppose we require that the value of $(2x + 3)$ be within .1 of 7. That is, we specify that $6.9 < (2x + 3) < 7.1$. Can you find a range of values of x around 2 so that the desired condition is met? Will $1.9 < x < 2.1$ satisfy the requirement that $6.9 < (2x + 3) < 7.1$? Let us replace x in $y = 2x + 3$ by 1.9 and

FIGURE 19–2

2.1, successively, and find out. This gives us $6.8 < (2x + 3) < 7.2$ and so we have *not* chosen a range of values of x around 2 sufficiently close for $(2x + 3)$ to be within .1 of 7. Let us try $1.95 < x < 2.05$, so that x is within .05 of 2. This gives us $6.9 < (2x + 3) < 7.1$, and we have succeeded in finding a range of values of x around 2 sufficiently narrow to guarantee that the value of $(2x + 3)$ is within .1 of 7. Will any range less than .05 around 2 also be acceptable?

Now suppose that the restriction on the range of values of $(2x + 3)$ is narrowed to within .01 of 7. Can you find a range of values of x around 2 which will guarantee this? Do you think that if we stay within .005 of 2 for values of x, the restriction on $(2x + 3)$ will be met? In symbols, is $1.995 < x < 2.005$ sufficient to insure that $6.99 < (2x + 3) < 7.01$?

Let us generalize the preceding problem and say that we must find a range of values of x around 2 which will satisfy the requirement that $(2x + 3)$ is within ϵ units of 7. Do you think that the requirement is met when x is within $\frac{\epsilon}{2}$ units of 2? Test this conjecture. Will any positive number less than $\frac{\epsilon}{2}$ also be sufficiently small?

Graphically, we can illustrate the concept of making the value of $(mx + b)$ as close to L as desired, where $L = ma + b$, by finding a range of values of x sufficiently close to a. Then $\lim_{x \to a} (mx + b) = L$.

Consider the neighborhood of L, evaluated as $(ma + b)$, between $L - \epsilon$ and $L + \epsilon$, where ϵ is some positive real number. Suppose we wish to guarantee that the value of $(mx + b)$ falls within this range by restricting the range of values of x in the neighborhood of a. How close to a must the value of x be selected in order to insure that $L - \epsilon < (mx + b) < L + \epsilon?$ Let the values of x be limited by the range $a - \delta < x < a + \delta$, where δ is some positive real number. We do not insist that x may be replaced by a itself, even though this can always be done in a linear function.

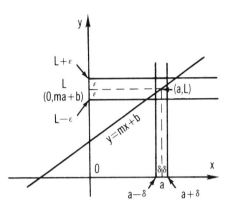

FIGURE 19-3

The critical question is: Can we find a value of δ that will insure that the value of $(mx + b)$ falls within the range of values from $L - \epsilon$ to $L + \epsilon$ *no matter how small ϵ is chosen?*

If we can find such a value of δ, regardless of the choice of ϵ, then we say that the limit of $(mx + b)$ as x approaches a is L. Graphically, this means that we are faced with the problem of restricting replacements of x in the neighborhood of a, no matter how narrow the limitation of values of $(mx + b)$ in the neighborhood of L, so that the graph of $y = mx + b$ passes through the *sides* and not the top and bottom of the rectangle formed by the lines $y = L - \epsilon, y = L + \epsilon,$ $x = a - \delta, x = a + \delta$. See Figure 19-3. In other words, the limit of $(mx + b)$ as x approaches a is L if one can construct a rectangle centered on the point (a, L) so that the graph of $y = mx + b$ does not intersect the line segments in the rectangle formed by $y = L + \epsilon$ and $y = L - \epsilon$. The challenge is: "You may select any positive number ϵ, and I can find a positive number δ so that $L - \epsilon < (mx + b) < L + \epsilon$ whenever $a - \delta < x < a + \delta$." If the challenge can be answered, then $\lim_{x \to a} (mx + b) = L$.

EXAMPLE 1. How close to 2 must x be chosen so that $5x - 1$ is within .01 of 9?

Solution. We must satisfy the condition that
$$9 - .01 < (5x - 1) < 9 + .01 \text{ or } - .01 < (5x - 1) - 9 < .01,$$

found by subtracting 9 from each member of the double inequality. Transforming this, we get the equivalent form

$$-.01 < 5x - 10 < .01$$

Dividing all members by 5 we have

$$-.002 < x - 2 < .002$$

Adding 2 to all members we get

$$2 - .002 < x < 2 + .002 \text{ or } 1.998 < x < 2.002$$

Thus, if we restrict the domain as shown so that values of x are within .002 of 2, we can insure that $5x - 1$ is within .01 of 9. Try several special cases.

EXAMPLE 2. Find a positive number δ to prove that $\lim_{x \to a} (mx + b) = ma + b$ if $(mx + b)$ is within ϵ units of $(ma + b)$.

Solution. We must satisfy the double inequality

$$(ma + b) - \epsilon < mx + b < (ma + b) + \epsilon$$

This can be transformed into

$$-\epsilon < (mx + b) - (ma + b) < \epsilon$$
or
$$-\epsilon < m(x - a) < \epsilon$$

Dividing by m we have

$$\frac{-\epsilon}{m} < x - a < \frac{\epsilon}{m}$$
or
$$a - \frac{\epsilon}{m} < x < a + \frac{\epsilon}{m}$$

If m is positive, then $\delta = \dfrac{\epsilon}{m}$, but if m is negative, $\delta = -\dfrac{\epsilon}{m}$. We see that no matter how small ϵ is selected to "pinch down" on the range of values of $(mx + b)$ around $(ma + b)$, we can always find a value of δ which will insure that $(mx + b)$ is in the desired range whenever x is within δ units of a. The choice of δ is $\dfrac{\epsilon}{|m|}$, or any smaller positive number.

Exercises

1. What is the restriction on x in the neighborhood of 5 so that $3x - 8$ is within .1 of 7?
2. What interval of the domain satisfies $-.01 < 4 - 2x < .01$?
3. What interval of the domain satisfies $7.8 < 5x + 3 < 8.2$?
4. Show that the limit of $2x - 6$ is 2 as x approaches 4 by finding a value $\delta > 0$ for any $\epsilon > 0$ so that $2 - \epsilon < (2x - 6) < 2 + \epsilon$ whenever $4 - \delta < x < 4 + \delta$.

5. Find the domain in each case so that the range of the functions are as given.

   a. $2.9 < x - 2 < 3.1$ **c.** $15.99 < 15x + 1 < 16.01$

   b. $-.01 < \dfrac{x + 1}{2} < .01$ **d.** $3.7 < \dfrac{3x - 2}{4} < 4.3$

19.3   Definition of the limit of a function

In the previous sections we have prepared the way for a careful and rigorous definition of the limit of a function. The definition given in this section was first formulated by Cauchy, an eminent French mathematician, early in the Nineteenth Century. This elegant statement of the limit concept is widely used even today, although more modern formulations are possible.

Before the definition is presented, we shall need to look at an abbreviated way of writing a double inequality of the form $a - \delta < x < a + \delta$. In the last section we found that an equivalent statement is $-\delta < x - a < \delta$. This is a condensed form of the two inequalities $x - a > -\delta$ and $x - a < \delta$. It is possible to use absolute value notation to represent this relationship. Recall that $|x| = x$ if $x \geq 0$; $|x| = -x$ if $x < 0$. Can you express $|x| < 5$ as a double inequality? Why is $-5 < x < 5$ equivalent to $|x| < 5$? Do you see that $|x| < 5$ means that $x < 5$ if $x \geq 0$ and $-x < 5$ if $x < 0$? But $-x < 5$ is equivalent to $x > -5$, so we have shown that $|x| < 5$ expresses the same relationship as $-5 < x < 5$.

EXAMPLE 1. Express $-\delta < x - a < \delta$ as a single inequality involving absolute value symbols.

Solution. $-\delta < x - a < \delta$ is equivalent to $|x - a| < \delta$. This is true because $|x - a| < \delta$ means that $x - a < \delta$ if $x \geq a$, but $x - a > -\delta$ if $x < a$.

Now we are able to present Cauchy's definition of the limit L of a function $f(x)$ as x approaches a.

> **Definition:** The limit of a function $f(x)$ as x approaches a is L, written $\lim\limits_{x \to a} f(x) = L$, if, for every real number $\epsilon > 0$, there exists a real number $\delta > 0$ such that $|f(x) - L| < \epsilon$ whenever $0 < |x - a| < \delta$.

The preceding statement, while rather involved, merely expresses in careful mathematical language the concepts presented in Section 19.2. It is interpreted as follows. When values of x are selected in the neighborhood of a, values of $f(x)$ are in the neighborhood of L. If it is required that $f(x)$ be *arbitrarily close* to L, say within ϵ units of L, then it is possible to meet this requirement by selecting values of x *sufficiently close* to a, that is, within δ units of a. Whenever the preceding statements are satisfied, we say that $f(x)$ approaches the limit L as x approaches a.

The inequality $0 < |x - a|$ in the last line of the definition means that $x \neq a$. Explain why this is true. Thus, it is not required that a be in the domain of $f(x)$.

An important mathematical concept which can be carefully defined using limits is that of continuity. It is intuitively clear that a function is continuous if there are no "breaks" in the graph of the function. A rigorous mathematical definition of continuity can be made based on the limit concept as follows.

> **Definition:** A function f is continuous at $x = a$ if $f(a)$ exists and if $\lim_{x \to a} f(x) = f(a)$.

It is seen that all polynomial functions are continuous at all points since $P(r)$ exists and $\lim_{x \to r} P(x) = P(r)$.

Can you restate the definition of continuity of a function using the same format as found in the definition of the limit of a function?

EXAMPLE 2. Show that $f(x) = x^2 + 2x$ is continuous at $x = 2$.

Solution. If $f(x) = x^2 + 2x$, then $f(2) = 2^2 + 2 \cdot 2 = 8$. Thus, $f(2)$ exists. Now we must establish that $\lim_{x \to 2} (x^2 + 2x) = 8$. Since $x^2 + 2x$ is a polynomial, the limit is $f(2)$ and the function is continuous at $x = 2$.

EXAMPLE 3. Show that $\lim_{x \to 2} \dfrac{x^2 - 4}{x - 2} = 4$ using the definition of limit given in this section. Is the function continuous?

Solution. We must satisfy the inequality $\left| \dfrac{x^2 - 4}{x - 2} - 4 \right| < \epsilon$ by finding a value of δ where $0 < |x - 2| < \delta$. A step-by-step transformation of the first inequality into the second is shown below.

$$\left| \frac{x^2 - 4}{x - 2} - 4 \right| < \epsilon$$

$$-\epsilon < \frac{x^2 - 4}{x - 2} - 4 < \epsilon$$

$$4 - \epsilon < \frac{x^2 - 4}{x - 2} < 4 + \epsilon$$

$$4 - \epsilon < \frac{(x-2)(x+2)}{(x-2)} < 4 + \epsilon, \, x \neq 2$$
$$4 - \epsilon < x + 2 < 4 + \epsilon$$
$$-\epsilon < x - 2 < \epsilon$$
$$\text{or } |x - 2| < \epsilon$$

Finally, since $x \neq 2$, we have $0 < |x - 2| < \epsilon$. Thus, by selecting $\delta \leq \epsilon$ we can satisfy the required inequality. The function $f(x) = \frac{x^2 - 4}{x - 2}$ is not continuous at $x = 2$ because $f(2)$ is undefined.

Exercises

1. From the definition of limit prove that $\lim_{x \to 0} x = 0$.

2. Prove $\lim_{x \to \frac{1}{2}} (2x - 1) = 0$ by the definition.

3. Prove that $f(x) = x + 2$ is continuous at $x = -2$.

4. Given that $\epsilon = .01$, find δ such that the following limits are verified using the definition.

   a. $\lim_{x \to -1} (5x + 3) = -2$ **c.** $\lim_{x \to 3} \frac{2x - 5}{2} = \frac{1}{2}$

   b. $\lim_{x \to 1} \frac{x - 1}{3} = 0$ **d.** $\lim_{x \to 0} (4x + 5) = 5$

5. Show that the following functions are either continuous or not continuous at the given point.

   a. $f(x) = x + 5$ at $(1, 6)$ **c.** $f(x) = \frac{x^2 - 16}{x + 4}$ at $(4, 0)$

   b. $f(x) = x^2 + 2x - 1$ at $(0, -1)$ **d.** $f(x) = \frac{x^2 - 16}{x - 4}$ at $(4, 8)$

19.4   Theorems about limits

In order for limits of functions to become useful as a tool in analysis, it is necessary to develop formulas for the operations with limits. These include addition, subtraction, multiplication, and division as well as other operations such as involution and evolution. We shall state the principles as theorems without proof since the proofs tend to become involved and beyond the scope of the text. Each theorem may be proved by using the definition of limit given in the previous section.

First we shall state a theorem for finding the limit of a special function, the constant function.

● THEOREM 1

If $f(x) = c$, where c is any real number, then $\lim_{x \to a} f(x) = c$ for any real number a.

The theorems for addition, subtraction, multiplication, division, involution, and evolution all follow a pattern; fortunately the pattern is the simplest possible one as is seen by the statement of these theorems below. Assume that $\lim_{x \to a} f(x) = F$ and $\lim_{x \to a} g(x) = G$, for any real number a.

● THEOREM 2

The limit of the sum of two functions, $f(x)$ and $g(x)$, is the sum of the limits of the functions, as x approaches a.

$$\lim_{x \to a} [f(x) + g(x)] = \lim_{x \to a} f(x) + \lim_{x \to a} g(x) = F + G$$

● THEOREM 3

The limit of the difference of two functions is the difference of the limits of the functions, as x approaches a.

$$\lim_{x \to a} [f(x) - g(x)] = \lim_{x \to a} f(x) - \lim_{x \to a} g(x) = F - G$$

● THEOREM 4

The limit of the product of two functions is the product of the limits of the functions, as x approaches a.

$$\lim_{x \to a} [f(x) \cdot g(x)] = \left[\lim_{x \to a} f(x) \right] \left[\lim_{x \to a} g(x) \right] = F \cdot G$$

● THEOREM 5

The limit of the quotient of two functions is the quotient of the limits of the functions, as x approaches a.

$$\lim_{x \to a} \frac{f(x)}{g(x)} = \frac{\lim_{x \to a} f(x)}{\lim_{x \to a} g(x)} = \frac{F}{G}, \; G \neq 0$$

As a special case combining Theorem 1 and Theorem 4, we have the following theorem where one of the functions is a constant. If $f(x) = c$, the theorem below follows.

● THEOREM 6

The limit of the product of a constant and a function is the product of the constant and the limit of the function, as

x approaches a.

$$\lim_{x \to a} [c \cdot g(x)] = c \lim_{x \to a} g(x) = cG$$

In addition to the above theorems we may extend the list to include powers and roots of functions as follows.

- THEOREM 7

  The limit of the nth power of a function is the nth power of the limit of the function, if n is a positive integer, as x approaches a.

  $$\lim_{x \to a} [f(x)]^n = \left[\lim_{x \to a} f(x)\right]^n = F^n$$

- THEOREM 8

  The limit of the nth root of a function is the nth root of the limit of the function, if n is a positive integer, as x approaches a.

  $$\lim_{x \to a} \sqrt[n]{f(x)} = \sqrt[n]{\lim_{x \to a} f(x)} = \sqrt[n]{F}$$

As a final theorem in this rather lengthy list, we present without proof a theorem about the composite of two functions. If $f(x)$ and $g(x)$ are two functions of x, the *composite* of f and g is defined to be $f[g(x)]$. Usually the composite of two functions is *not* commutative.

- THEOREM 9

  The limit of the composite of two functions is the first named function of the limit of the second, as x approaches a.

  $$\lim_{x \to a} f[g(x)] = f\left[\lim_{x \to a} g(x)\right] = f(G)$$

As we stated earlier, the proofs of the limit theorems given here are beyond the scope of the text, but you are encouraged to try your hand at proving them using the definition of limit given in Section 19.3. Ordinarily, these theorems are proved in a rigorous course in calculus.

Exercises

1. Prove $\lim_{x \to 0} x^2 = 0$ by using the fact that $x \cdot x = x^2$.

2. Find $\lim_{x \to 1} \left(\dfrac{x - 3}{2x + 4}\right)$.

3. Find $\lim_{x \to 2} [(3x - 7) + (5x + 3)]$.

4. Find $\lim_{x \to 3} (x - 1)^3$ in two ways.

5. Find $\lim_{x \to -1} \sqrt{x^2 - 1}$.

6. Show that $\lim_{x \to 2} (x^2 - 5x + 6) = \lim_{x \to 2} (x - 2) \cdot \lim_{x \to 2} (x - 3) = 0$.

7. Find $\lim_{x \to 5} (x^2 - 2x - 15)$ in two ways.

8. Show that $\lim_{x \to 1} \dfrac{x^n - 1}{x - 1} = n$.

9. Find $\lim_{x \to 1} [3(x + 2)^2 - 5(x + 2) - 3]$ using Theorem 9.

10. Express $\lim_{x \to a} (px^2 + qx + r)$ as the product of the limits of two linear functions.

Chapter Review

1. Find $\lim_{n \to \infty} \left(\dfrac{1}{2} - \dfrac{1}{4} + \dfrac{1}{8} - \dfrac{1}{16} + \cdots + (-1)^{n+1} \dfrac{1}{2^n} \right)$ if it exists.

2. Replace n with 2, 4, 6, and 8 and make an estimate of the following limit to the nearest hundredth.

$$\lim_{n \to \infty} \left(1 + \dfrac{1}{2^0} + \dfrac{1}{2^1} + \dfrac{1}{2^2} + \dfrac{1}{2^3} + \cdots + \dfrac{1}{2^{n-2}} \right)$$

3. Estimate $\lim_{n \to \infty} \left(\dfrac{1}{1!} + \dfrac{1}{2!} + \dfrac{1}{3!} + \dfrac{1}{4!} + \cdots + \dfrac{1}{n!} \right)$.

Find each of the following limits, if it exists.

4. $\lim_{x \to 3} x^2$

5. $\lim_{x \to -5} \left(\dfrac{1}{x} \right)$

6. $\lim_{x \to 1} |x - 1|$

7. $\lim_{x \to -3} \dfrac{x^2 + 2x - 3}{x - 1}$

8. $\lim_{x \to 5} \sqrt{x - 1}$

9. $\lim_{n \to \infty} \dfrac{2n^2 - 3n + 5}{n^2}$

Find the domain for the given range of each function.

10. $4.9 < x - 5 < 5.1$

11. $2.2 < \dfrac{3x - 1}{2} < 2.8$

12. From the definition of limit of a function, prove that $\lim_{x \to \frac{1}{2}} (2x + 4) = 5$.

13. If $\epsilon = .01$, find δ such that the following limits are as given. (*Hint:* See Section 19.2.)

    a. $\lim\limits_{x \to 2} (2x - 1) = 4$ **b.** $\lim\limits_{x \to 4} (4 - x) = 0$

Show whether each function is or is not continuous at the given point.

14. $f(x) = x^2 - 4$ at $(2, 0)$ 15. $f(x) = \dfrac{x^2 - 5x + 6}{x - 3}$ at $(3, 1)$

Use the theorems of this chapter to find the following limits.

16. $\lim\limits_{x \to 4} (x - 2)^3$

17. $\lim\limits_{x \to 2} x(3 + 2x)(x - 4)$

18. $\lim\limits_{x \to \pi} (x + \sin x)$

CHAPTER OUTLINE

    19.1   Concept of limit

    19.2   A more careful approach to the limit of a linear function

    19.3   Definition of the limit of a function

    19.4   Theorems about limits

APPENDIX

COMPUTATION

Computation

A.1 Approximate numbers

Some numbers are *exact* and other numbers are *approximate*. A number which is the result of an estimate or measurement is approximate; other real numbers are exact. The triangles and other figures of geometry and trigonometry are *idealized;* that is, they are considered exact and perfect. When we say that the sides of a triangle have the exact ratio $1:2:\sqrt{3}$, we refer to an idealized $30°-60°-90°$ triangle because if we undertake to construct such a triangle we realize that, because of imperfections of instruments and human limitations, it is impossible to know when we have constructed a line whose length is exactly 1, or 2, or $\sqrt{3}$ units. In all geometric theorems and in many trigonometric situations, the lengths of lines and the sizes of angles are hypotheses. They exist only in the mind of the thinker. You should learn to distinguish between imperfect physical objects with their imperfect representation in drawings and the perfect mathematical world of idealized figures and generalized concepts.

When a mechanic or an engineer makes measurements and records them as numbers, he is not dealing with a hypothesis or an idealized figure. He is dealing with the reality of an actual figure whose measurements which he obtains are subject to the imperfections of his instruments and his own senses and muscular control as well as atmospheric temperature and other variable factors. Unlike our *idealized figures*, the numbers by which he records his measurements are always *approximate numbers*.

If the length of a line segment is measured by means of a scale on which hundredths of an inch are marked, one can be reasonably sure that he knows the length correct to the nearest hundredth. He records this by means of a number that has a sequence of digits. For example, the number may be 40.21 inches. In this number, the 4 records 40 inches, the 0 records 0 inches, the 2 records 2 tenths of an inch, and the 1 records 1 hundredth of an inch. If the actual length is slightly less or slightly more than 40.21 inches, we still write the 1 in hundredths place, expecting that anyone who sees the number will understand that the digit 1 is somewhat in doubt but that the measurement is accurate within .5 of .01 inch. That is, the length is 40.21 $\pm$ .005 inches which is read "40.21 plus or minus .005 inches." The notation $\pm$ indicates that the length is greater than 40.205 inches but less than 40.215 inches. In this number, .005 is called the *absolute error*. The *precision* of measurement is indicated by the absolute error. The greater the absolute error, the less is the precision. The absolute error is sometimes called the *tolerance* and the range from the least possible value to the greatest possible value is the *tolerance interval*.

We call the digits 4, 0, 2, 1 in the number 40.21 *significant digits* because each records the result of measurement. In the number 630 the 6 and 3 are significant but 0 is not, unless the measurement is given to the nearest unit. We assume 630 is a measurement to the nearest 10 units with an absolute error of 5. We can write 630 $\pm$ 5 to represent this more carefully. If we write 630 $\pm$ .5, zero is significant as measurement to the nearest unit is indicated.

Now suppose that we measure the first line segment with a scale on which thousandths of an inch are marked, and suppose that we record 40.210 inches. The final zero is significant because it records that there are no thousandths to be added to 40.21. The zero is in doubt by .5 of .001, and the length is 40.210 $\pm$ .0005 inches where .0005 is the absolute error. The precision of this measure is greater than that of the first measurement of the line segment.

If we measure a distance on the ground by means of a pole whose length is one rod (16.5 ft.) accurate to one part in a thousand, and record the distance as 27,513 rods, we have no confidence in the last two digits on the right (13) because the pole had to be applied 27,513 times and the error of one in a thousand is multiplied by 27,513. The measurement should be recorded as 27,500 rods with the understanding that the digit 5 is in doubt. Thus the zeros are not significant. The last significant digit in an approximate number, whether zero or not, is always in doubt. A final zero in a whole number will be significant if it indicates the result of precision in measurement to the nearest unit. If it is significant, this fact should be indicated by placing a line under it as in 72$\underline{0}$ or by writing the tolerance interval as in 720 ± .5.

In scientific notation only significant digits are recorded in the first factor. The maximum distance from the earth to the sun is 94,450,000 miles to the nearest thousand miles. In this example the zero following the 5 is significant but the remaining three zeros are not. In scientific notation this number is written 9.4450×10^7. Thus, it is obvious that scientific notation gives a real advantage in indicating significant zeros.

SUMMARY OF FACTS ABOUT SIGNIFICANT DIGITS

(a) In a number that records measurement, any non-zero digit is significant.

(b) Zero is significant if it lies between significant digits.

(c) Zero is significant if it follows a significant digit at the end of a decimal fraction.

(d) Zero may be significant if it is at the end of a whole number; if it is significant it should be underlined as in 275,2$\underline{0}$0. In this example, the zero in tens place is significant because it is between significant digits.

(e) All zeros in scientific notation are significant.

EXAMPLES

Approximate numbers	Number of significant digits
4.20	3
25,000	2
25,00$\underline{0}$	5
3070	3
30.70	4
.0040	2
1.0040	5

Exercises

Give the number of significant digits in each of the following approximate numbers.

1. 203   4. 85,000   7. .02020

2. 5.70   5. 1.0020   8. 7.30×10^3

3. .00574   6. 3400   9. 200.0

A.2   Accuracy and precision

Since each significant digit in an approximate number is a part of the record of a measurement, the number of significant digits is an indication of the degree of accuracy of measurement. The *accuracy* of a measurement depends upon the *relative error* which is defined as *the ratio of the absolute error to the measured value.* For example, the absolute error of the approximate number 3.6 is .05 and the relative error is $\frac{.05}{3.6} = 0.014$. You can see that the accuracy of measurement is directly related to the number of significant digits in the measured quantity. The greater the number of significant digits, the greater the degree of accuracy, if the same units of measurement are used in making two measurements of the same quantity. For example, 2105.0 centimeters indicates a more accurate measurement than 2105 centimeters because the relative error is smaller.

The *precision* of a measurement is inversely related to the absolute error. (See Section A.1.) Thus, the smaller the absolute error the greater the precision, if the same units of measurement are used in making two measurements of the same quantity. In other words, precision is indicated by the position of the decimal point in the absolute error. For example, 11.4 inches indicates a more precise measurement than 114 inches. The absolute error in the first case is .05, and in the second case it is .5.

One measurement may have greater precision but less accuracy than another. A measurement of .025 inches has an absolute error of .0005 indicating a high degree of precision. A measurement of 243.1 inches has an absolute error of .05 which is not as precise as the first measurement. The relative error of .025 is $\frac{.0005}{.025} = .02$.

The relative error of 243.1 is $\frac{.05}{243.1}$ or approximately .0002. Thus, 243.1 is much more accurate than .025 though it is less precise.

Summary: Precision of measurement is inversely related to the absolute error; accuracy depends upon the relative error, which is related to the number of significant digits in the measurement.

Exercises

Find the absolute error and the relative error in each of the following measurements. Compare the precision and the accuracy.

1. 74
2. 5.80
3. 27.15
4. .0050
5. 93,000,000
6. 2.4×10^{-4}

A.3   Rounding off a number

When a number is to be rounded off to some designated number of significant digits, the digit following the last significant digit is inspected and if it is greater than 5 the preceding digit is increased by 1; if it is less than 5 the inspected digit is dropped. In each case all digits following the one inspected are dropped. If the digit inspected is 5 followed by no other digits or only by zero, the preceding digit is left unchanged if it is even and increased by 1 if it is odd. If the digit inspected is 5 but other non-zero digits follow, the preceding digit is increased by 1.

EXAMPLE. Round off to tenths. 24.47, 6.25, 18.75, 10.81, 5.2513, 3.049, 135.968.

Solution. 24.5, 6.2, 18.8, 10.8, 5.3, 3.0, 136.0.

Notice that when an approximate number is rounded off, the absolute error is increased and hence the precision is decreased. Also, accuracy is decreased because the number of significant digits is decreased. We should remark, however, that the accuracy and precision that are thus lost may not be real; the rounded number may be a better representation of known facts than the unrounded number.

Exercises

Round off each approximate number to three significant digits.

1. 47.85
2. 4.599
3. 12040
4. 16750
5. .02316
6. 7045.2
7. 41397.358
8. 2.00×10^5
9. 3.862×10^{-3}

A.4 Computation with approximate numbers

The fundamental principle relating to computation with approximate numbers is as follows.

> **Principle:** I. Addition and Subtraction: The sum or difference of numbers is no more precise than the least precise number in the computation.
> II. Multiplication, Division, Roots and Powers: The result is no more accurate than the least accurate number in the computation.

If exact numbers are involved in a computation, the accuracy of the result depends only upon the approximate numbers involved and not upon the exact numbers. In the formula $C = 2\pi r$, the number of significant digits in r determines the accuracy of C. In this case, π is expressed to at least the same number of digits as r. For example, if the radius of a circle is measured and found to be 1.60 inches, the circumference is 10.1 inches, not 10.05312 inches, which is the result of $2 \times 3.1416 \times 1.60$. The radius has three significant digits and the circumference cannot be computed with greater accuracy. Generally the result has the *same* degree of accuracy, but the last significant digit in the result will be doubtful. In other words, the circumference is 10.1 inches, but we do not guarantee that the third digit is significant.

Addition and Subtraction

In the addition or subtraction of approximate numbers, the precision of the sum or difference depends upon the *precision* of the given numbers. The rule is this: A sum or difference of approximate numbers has the same absolute error as the largest absolute error of any of the given numbers. When adding 2.58, 31.774 and 179.7, we have absolute errors of .005, .0005 and .05 respectively. The sum is rounded off to the nearest tenth, that is, it has an absolute error of .05, the largest of the absolute errors of the addends.

Multiplication, Division, and Roots

In the multiplication, division, and extraction of square roots of approximate numbers, the accuracy of the product, quotient, or root depends upon the *accuracy* of the given numbers. The rule is: The product, quotient, or root of approximate numbers will be assumed to have the same number of significant digits as the least number of significant digits in any of the given numbers. When multiplying or dividing the approximate numbers 1.573 and 2.4, for example, the product or quotient can have at most two significant digits since the least accurate approximate number, 2.4, has two. The product is $1.573 \times 2.4 = 3.7752$ or 3.8 .

Caution: *You are not to assume that a given number is approximate merely because it contains a decimal fraction. Such a number might be exact as in the case where it represents an interest rate.*

EXAMPLE 1. The given numbers are lengths of line segments in centimeters. Find the sum.

Solution. See the sum computed at the right. The sum is 45.9 cm. Why is the sum rounded off to one decimal place in this example? (Remember, in a sum or difference, the size of the largest absolute error determines the absolute error of the result.)

```
  21.42
  13.03
   9.1
   2.304
 ──────
  45.854

Sum 45.9
```

EXAMPLE 2. The sides of a rectangle are measured and found to be 11.5 inches and 4.3 inches. Find the area.

Solution. See the solution at the right. The area is 49 square inches. Why? (Remember, in a product or quotient, the number of significant digits in the least accurate factor determines the number of significant digits in the result.)

```
   11.5
    4.3
  ─────
   3 45
  46 0
  ─────
  49.45

Area 49
```

Exercises

1. The following numbers represent lengths of line segments in inches. Find their sum. 16.4, 17.31, 11.051, 7.10, 3.650.

2. These numbers represent areas of geometric figures in square centimeters. Find the sum. 52.314, 61.404, 59.003, 70.155, 82.20.

3. The radius of a circle is 4.0 cm. Find its area.

4. The radius of a sphere is 1.00 in. Find its volume.

All numbers in exercises 5–8 are approximate.

5. Multiply: 2.5×73.4.

6. Compute: $\dfrac{3.78 \times 5.1}{.072}$.

7. Multiply: $41.3 \pm .05 \times 7.4 \pm .05$. First multiply the maximum values together; then multiply the minimum values together. How many digits agree with the product of 41.3 and 7.4 in each case? How many significant digits are in the result?

8. Compute: $(94.7 + 13.544) \times 2.500$. How many significant digits are in the result? Check by applying the distributive principle.

A.5   Accuracy in angle measurement

Measurements of angles as well as line lengths are approximate numbers. It is not common to report angle measurements in tenths or hundredths of a degree, although this is done in certain applications. Generally an angle is measured in degrees, minutes, and seconds. How many significant digits are in the approximate number 32° 41′? In 87° 128′ 13″? It is clear that counting the number of digits reported will not guarantee accuracy equivalent to a corresponding number of digits in a linear measurement. The following table indicates the approximate corresponding degree of accuracy of linear and angular measurement in degrees, minutes, and seconds.

Number of significant digits in linear measurement	corresponds to:	Angular measure to nearest
1		5°
2		1°
3		10′
4		1′
5		6″
6		1″

In applying this table to determine the number of significant digits in the result of a computation, the accuracy of the angle measure is counted equivalent to the corresponding number of significant digits of linear measure.

EXAMPLE. In a computation involving a triangle, two sides are given as 23.4 inches and 17.9 inches, and the included angle is 53° measured to the nearest degree. (a) How many significant digits should be used in the result? (b) If the angle is given as 53° 20′ measured to the nearest ten minutes, how many significant digits will be in the result?

Solution. (a) The linear measures contain 3 significant digits each; the angular measure to the nearest degree is equivalent to two significant digits. The result will have two significant digits.

(b) If the angle is given to the nearest 10 minutes, which is equivalent to 3 significant digits, the result will have, at most, 3 significant digits.

Exercises

In each exercise give the number of significant digit in the result of computations with the given approximate numbers.

1. 12.04, 31.6, 64°
2. 450, 375, 19° 38′ 11″
3. 7.8, 3.9, 18° 24′
4. 48° 10′, 15.87, 19.51
5. 1200, 1700, 41° 16′ 22″
6. 170° 4′, 56.810, 130.27
7. 89, 124, 1° 42′
8. 6.743, 8.209, 32° 18′ 30″

A.6   Tables of approximate numbers

You have had many occasions to use tables in your study of mathematics. You have probably had need of tables of powers and roots, tables of values of the trigonometric functions, and tables of logarithms. There are numerous other business, scientific, and special purpose tables to which you will refer from time to time. You may wonder what degree of significance is provided by such tables when the values found in them are used in computation.

As a general rule, the values found in tables have the degree of significance indicated by the number of significant digits in the tabular values. In the table of roots (Table 1), the values are given to four significant digits. In the table of natural values of the trigonometric functions (Table 2), the numbers are likewise given to four significant digits. This is consistent with angles given to the nearest minute. (See Section A.5.)

The case of logarithms is somewhat more complicated. The table of logarithms (Table 3) is called a four-place table because the mantissas are given to four significant digits. The characteristic of the logarithm together with the mantissa will provide a five digit logarithm, in general. It has been found, however, that four-place tables of logarithms are equivalent to four significant digits in the given number, and that five-place tables are equivalent to five significant digits. Thus, the interpolation procedure used with the four-place mantissas in Table 3 should give four significant digits in the result if other approximate numbers have at least this degree of accuracy. (The few exceptions to this generality may be ignored.)

If you are required to solve computational problems which involve tabular values, you should secure tables whose number of significant digits is not less than that found in the least accurate approximate number in the computation. If you find it necessary to use four-place tables when the other approximate numbers in the problem are accurate to five significant digits or more, the result of the computation must be rounded off to four significant digits.

A.7 Linear interpolation

Interpolation is a procedure whereby an estimate of the value of a function is made *between* two or more known values of the function. For example, if $y = f(x)$ is a tabulated function with x given for each integral value between 0 and 1000 (as in certain tables of square roots, logarithms, etc.), then interpolation enables us to find an approximate value of y for a value of x expressed in tenths. We can find the square root of 28.4 by interpolation if a table gives $\sqrt{28}$ and $\sqrt{29}$. There are also procedures for estimating the value of a function for values of the independent variable *beyond* the tabulated or known values called *extrapolation*. The age of the earth is estimated by extrapolation since the geological and astronomical evidence of historical times permits scientists to extrapolate time backward.

The simplest method of interpolation is *linear interpolation* in which the assumption is made that the function being interpolated is a straight line between known values. We shall present a geometric explanation and also an algebraic explanation of linear interpolation.

Consider a tabulated function $y = f(x)$ and let a and b be two consecutive values of x in the table. Then $f(a)$ and $f(b)$ will be two consecutive values of $f(x)$ which can be read directly from the table. The problem of interpolation is to find a value of $f(a + \Delta x)$ where $\Delta x < |b - a|$. In Figure A–1, D' is a point on the curve between A and B with the ordinate $f(a + \Delta x)$. Point D has an abscissa

$(a + \Delta x)$ but is on the line segment AB. Linear interpolation assumes that D coincides with D'; this is approximately true if

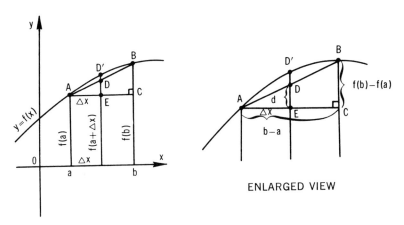

FIGURE A–1

$|b - a|$ is small and if the graph of $f(x)$ does not have great curvature between $x = a$ and $x = b$. Triangle ABC is similar to triangle AED so we can write the proportion as follows.

$$\frac{d}{f(b) - f(a)} = \frac{\Delta x}{b - a}$$

In this proportion, a, b, $f(a)$, $f(b)$, and Δx are known or can be found; thus, d can be computed. The value of $f(a + \Delta x)$ is approximately $f(a) + d$.

EXAMPLE. If $\sqrt{27} = 5.196$ and $\sqrt{28} = 5.292$, as found in a table of square roots, find an approximate value of $\sqrt{27.3}$.

Solution. $y = f(x) = \sqrt{x}$. $a = 27$; $b = 28$; $f(a) = 5.196$; $f(b) = 5.292$; $\Delta x = 27.3 - 27 = .3$. Thus, we can write

$$\frac{d}{5.292 - 5.196} = \frac{.3}{28 - 27} \quad \text{or} \quad d = .029$$

Thus, $\sqrt{27.3} = 5.196 + .029 = 5.225$ approximately.

Algebraically we can assume that a straight line of the form $y = mx + p$ passes through points represented by consecutive values of a tabulated $y = f(x)$. The coordinates of the points are $(a, f(a))$ and $(b, f(b))$. These ordered pairs satisfy both the tabulated function and the straight line. Hence, the values of m and p can be determined by substituting these coordinates in the equation $y = mx + p$ and solving for m and p. We have

$$f(a) = ma + p \quad \text{and} \quad f(b) = mb + p$$

Solving for m we have

$$m = \frac{f(b) - f(a)}{b - a}$$

Also,
$$p = f(a) - \frac{a[f(b) - f(a)]}{b - a}$$

The equation of the line becomes

$$y = \left(\frac{f(b) - f(a)}{b - a}\right) x + f(a) - \frac{a[f(b) - f(a)]}{b - a}.$$

or
$$y = \left(\frac{f(b) - f(a)}{b - a}\right) (x - a) + f(a)$$

We may now replace x by any value between a and b and find the corresponding value of y. We see that $(x - a)$ is the value of Δx determined in the geometrical approach; also, the expression $\left(\dfrac{f(b) - f(a)}{b - a}\right) (x - a)$ is the value of d.

The steps in linear interpolation to find an approximate value of $f(x_1)$ between tabulated values of $f(x)$ are as follows.

1. Find consecutive tabular values of x, (a and b), such that $a < x_1 < b$.
2. Compute $f(b) - f(a)$ and $b - a$.
3. Compute $x_1 - a$.
4. Find $d = \left(\dfrac{f(b) - f(a)}{b - a}\right) (x_1 - a)$.
5. Then $f(x_1) = f(a) + d$ approximately.

Quadratic and *cubic interpolation* may be done by assuming that a quadratic or cubic curve fits the tabulated function in the neighborhood where the interpolation is to be made. Three points are required for quadratic interpolation, and four points are required for cubic interpolation. These points are used to evaluate the coefficients of the quadratic or cubic interpolation function and the desired value can be found by substituting a value of the independent variable in this function.

Interpolation procedures will be used in this book to find logarithms to four significant digits and to find natural values of the trigonometric functions to the nearest minute.

A.8   Computation with logarithms

It is assumed that you are familiar with the use of logarithms as an aid to computation; this section will summarize the principles which you can use in order to perform certain computations in chapters throughout the book.

The two systems of logarithms in use are *common logarithms* (base 10) and *natural logarithms* (base e). (See Section 11.7.) In this chapter we are concerned only with common logarithms. Table 3 gives mantissas of logarithms of numbers to four places. Table 2 gives mantissas of trigonometric functions to four places. Both tables are of common logarithms.

Common logarithms are exponents of the base 10. The equation $10^x = N$ can be written to show the relation between a number N and its logarithm x. The equation $\log_{10} N = x$ expresses the same relationship between N and x. The base 10 is usually omitted when we work with common logarithms. Since logarithms are exponents, the laws governing exponents also apply to logarithms.

In words, the laws of logarithms can be stated as follows.

(1) If two numbers, X and Y, are to be multiplied, find the logarithm of each number and add. The sum is the logarithm of the product XY.

(2) If two numbers, X and Y, are to be divided, find the logarithm of each number and subtract the logarithm of the divisor from the logarithm of the dividend. The difference is the logarithm of the quotient $\frac{X}{Y}$, $Y \neq 0$.

(3) If a number, X, is to be raised to the nth power, find the logarithm of X and multiply by n. The result is the logarithm of the nth power of X, X^n.

In mathematical symbolism these laws are written as follows.

(1) $\log_a XY = \log_a X + \log_a Y$

(2) $\log_a \dfrac{X}{Y} = \log_a X - \log_a Y$, $Y \neq 0$

(3) $\log_a X^n = n \log_a X$, where n is a rational number.

The common logarithm of a number is composed of two parts, the *characteristic* and the *mantissa*. The characteristic precedes the decimal point in the logarithm and is determined by the position of the decimal point in the number. The simplest way to find the characteristic of the logarithm of a number is to convert the number to scientific notation. The exponent of 10 in this form is always the characteristic of the logarithm of the number.

EXAMPLE 1. Find the logarithms of the following numbers.

a. 12.3   b. 5,280   c. 2.74   d. .0351

Solution. Mantissas can be found by referring to Table 3. To determine the characteristic convert each number to scientific notation as follows.

a. 1.23×10^1 b. 5.28×10^3 c. 2.74×10^0 d. 3.51×10^{-2}
The logarithms are as follows.

a. log 12.3 = 1.0899
b. log 5,280 = 3.7226
c. log 2.74 = 0.4378
d. log .0351 = -2 + .5453 or 8.5453 $-$ 10 (because -2 is equal to 8. $-$ 10). For some uses we can write log .0351 = -1.4547.

If the logarithm of a number is known, then the number which corresponds to it is known as the *antilogarithm*.

EXAMPLE 2. Find the antilogarithm of each of the following common logarithms.

a. 4.8825   b. 7.3911 $-$ 10   c. 1.9424

Solution. In each antilogarithm we shall find three significant digits.

a. antilog 4.8825 = 76,300
b. antilog 7.3911 $-$ 10 = .00246
c. antilog 1.9424 = 87.6

In each case, the decimal point of the result may be checked by converting the antilogarithm to scientific notation and comparing the exponent of 10 in this form with the given characteristic.

The logarithms of trigonometric functions may be found directly from Table 2. This avoids finding the natural value in Table 2 and then getting the logarithm of this value from Table 3.

EXAMPLE 3. Find the following logarithms.

a. log sin 24°   b. log tan 58° 30′

Solution. Referring to Table 2, we get
a. log sin 24° = 9.6093 − 10   b. log tan 58° 30′ = 10.2127 − 10

Note: It is called to your attention that each logarithm given in Table 2 has −10 added to it.

As a review of methods of computation with logarithms, two examples will be given.

EXAMPLE 4. Perform the following computation with logarithms.

$$\frac{37.9\sqrt{488}}{(1.28)^3}$$

Solution. From Table 3, logarithms of the numbers are
log 37.9 = 1.5786 ;   log 488 = 2.6884 ;   log 1.28 = 0.1072

The computation may be performed as follows.

$$+\quad\begin{array}{l} \log 37.9 = 1.5786 \\ \tfrac{1}{2}\log 488 = 1.3442 \\ \hline 2.9228 \end{array}$$

$$-\quad\begin{array}{l} \log \text{ of numerator} = 2.9228 \\ 3\log 1.28 = 0.3216 \\ \hline \log \text{ of result} = 2.6012 \\ \text{result} = 399 \end{array}$$

EXAMPLE 5. Perform the following computation using logarithms.

$$D = \frac{67.3\sin 55°}{35.5}$$

Solution.

$$+\quad\begin{array}{l} \log 67.3 = 1.8280 \\ \log \sin 55° = 9.9134 - 10 \\ \hline 11.7414 - 10 \end{array}$$

$$-\quad\begin{array}{l} \log \text{ of numerator} = 11.7414 - 10 \\ \log 35.5 = 1.5502 \\ \hline \log D = 10.1912 - 10 \text{ or } 0.1912 \\ D = 1.55 \end{array}$$

Exercises

Perform the following computations using logarithms.

1. 38.6 × 891 × .0158

2. $\dfrac{6.15 \times 7.94}{3.28}$

3. $\dfrac{23,500}{7,520 \times 56.6}$

5. $(1.07)^3 \times 428$

7. $52.8 \tan 16°$

4. $\sqrt{45.2 \times 9.63}$

6. $\dfrac{78.2 \times 4.22}{88.3}$

8. $\sqrt[3]{\dfrac{31.7 \cos 67°}{5.43}}$

A.9   Slide rule computation

Although the availability of calculators and computers has increased in recent years, there are many times when quick approximate computations are desirable and the calculator is too far away or is in use. There is an extensive need for technical workers such as engineers, scientists, and technical aids to be able to perform such computations speedily. The *slide rule* is the constant companion of many of these people.

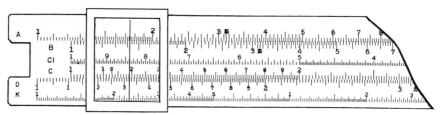

FIGURE A–2

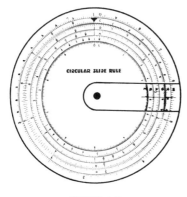

FIGURE A–3

We shall not be able to teach you to become an expert in slide rule operations in one brief section. Competence in use of the slide rule, like competence in the use of any other manipulative device, can be achieved only through extensive practice. In this section we shall make some comments about the principles of operation of the slide rule and its advantages and disadvantages. You are encouraged to form a slide rule club at your school or by other means to familiarize yourself with its operation.

The basic scales on a slide rule (scale **C** and scale **D**) are calibrated so that the distance from the index (end point) to any numerical reading on the scale is proportional to the logarithm of the number. Thus, adding lengths of two scales is equivalent to adding the logarithms of the numbers involved. Hence, the product of two numbers is found by arranging the scales so that the line segments proportional to the logarithms of the numbers are physically added. Similarly, subtracting line lengths is equivalent to subtracting logarithms of two numbers so that the quotient of the numbers is found.

A comparison of the **A** scale with the **D** scale permits finding the squares and square roots of numbers. The proper use of other scales on the rule varies with the type and maker of the rule.

Some advantages of the slide rule are obvious; it provides an extremely quick and easy way to perform certain computations. There are three principal disadvantages to the use of the slide rule: (1) Addition and subtraction of numbers cannot be performed on the rule, so one must resort to longhand or machine computation when sums and differences are involved in a computation. (2) There is no easy way to determine the position of the decimal point in the result. The experienced slide rule operator generally estimates the result mentally and, except in unusual cases, can determine the position of the decimal point without undue effort. (3) The slide rule is generally limited in accuracy to three significant digits. There are slide rules in existence which can give four or even five significant digits but these are not commonly used. Considering the basic **C** and **D** scales it is possible to make a reasonable estimate of the fourth digit when using the left-hand portion of the scales, while even the third digit must be estimated on the right-hand portion of these same scales.

The limitation on the accuracy of a computation to three significant digits is not always a serious handicap. It frequently happens that the significance of the approximate numbers in the computation is not greater than three digits and hence the results given by the slide rule are very satisfactory. Also, the operator may use a slide rule for quick rough approximations and perform the more accurate detailed computations later, on a desk calculator or by longhand.

Exercises

1. Give the number of significant digits in each of the following approximate numbers.

   a. 3800   **c.** .300   **e.** 58,20$\underline{0}$

   b. 42.0   **d.** .003   **f.** 7.20×10^5

2. Give the absolute error for each of the approximate numbers in Exercise 1.

3. Multiply $3.2 \pm .05$ by $7.34 \pm .005$ in three ways. **a.** Multiply maximum values together; **b.** multiply minimum values together; **c.** multiply 3.2 by 7.34. What conclusion can be reached about the number of significant digits in the product?

4. Compare the precision and accuracy of the following approximate numbers.
   a. .027 and 3.81   **b.** 7200 and 17,500

5. In a table of square roots of integers find $\sqrt{73.6}$ to the nearest hundredth, by interpolation. Compare the result with direct computation.

6. Perform the following computations using logarithms. Interpolate when necessary. Round off the result to the proper number of significant digits.

   a. $\dfrac{14.9 \times 7.86}{2.84}$

   b. $\dfrac{16.6 \sin 47° 20'}{3.95}$

   c. $\sqrt{(45.22) \times (1.765)^3}$

   d. $\sqrt{\dfrac{32.8 \tan 75°}{6.74}}$

7. (Optional) Perform the computations in Exercise 6 by the use of a slide rule.

8. Determine which number is larger.
   a. $25^{\frac{7}{8}}$ or $28^{\frac{10}{9}}$ **b.** 3^{21} or 95^5

9. Given the function f defined by $f(x) = \sqrt{x}$. If $f(16) = 4$ and $f(25) = 5$, use linear interpolation to find $\sqrt{18}$.

TABLES

TABLE 1
Approximate Square Roots

N	$\sqrt{N}$	N	$\sqrt{N}$	N	$\sqrt{N}$
1	1.000	51	7.141	101	10.05
2	1.414	52	7.211	102	10.10
3	1.732	53	7.280	103	10.15
4	2.000	54	7.348	104	10.20
5	2.236	55	7.416	105	10.25
6	2.449	56	7.483	106	10.30
7	2.646	57	7.550	107	10.34
8	2.828	58	7.616	108	10.39
9	3.000	59	7.681	109	10.44
10	3.162	60	7.746	110	10.49
11	3.317	61	7.810	111	10.54
12	3.464	62	7.874	112	10.58
13	3.606	63	7.937	113	10.63
14	3.742	64	8.000	114	10.68
15	3.873	65	8.062	115	10.72
16	4.000	66	8.124	116	10.77
17	4.123	67	8.185	117	10.82
18	4.243	68	8.246	118	10.86
19	4.359	69	8.307	119	10.91
20	4.472	70	8.367	120	10.95
21	4.583	71	8.426	121	11.00
22	4.690	72	8.485	122	11.05
23	4.796	73	8.544	123	11.09
24	4.899	74	8.602	124	11.14
25	5.000	75	8.660	125	11.18
26	5.099	76	8.718	126	11.22
27	5.196	77	8.775	127	11.27
28	5.292	78	8.832	128	11.31
29	5.385	79	8.888	129	11.36
30	5.477	80	8.944	130	11.40
31	5.568	81	9.000	131	11.45
32	5.657	82	9.055	132	11.49
33	5.745	83	9.110	133	11.53
34	5.831	84	9.165	134	11.58
35	5.916	85	9.220	135	11.62
36	6.000	86	9.274	136	11.66
37	6.083	87	9.327	137	11.70
38	6.164	88	9.381	138	11.75
39	6.245	89	9.434	139	11.79
40	6.325	90	9.487	140	11.83
41	6.403	91	9.539	141	11.87
42	6.481	92	9.592	142	11.92
43	6.557	93	9.644	143	11.96
44	6.633	94	9.695	144	12.00
45	6.708	95	9.747	145	12.04
46	6.782	96	9.798	146	12.08
47	6.856	97	9.849	147	12.12
48	6.928	98	9.899	148	12.17
49	7.000	99	9.950	149	12.21
50	7.071	100	10.00	150	12.25

TABLE 1 (continued)
Approximate Square Roots

N	$\sqrt{N}$	N	$\sqrt{N}$	N	$\sqrt{N}$
151	12.29	201	14.18	251	15.84
152	12.33	202	14.21	252	15.87
153	12.37	203	14.25	253	15.91
154	12.41	204	14.28	254	15.94
155	12.45	205	14.32	255	15.97
156	12.49	206	14.35	256	16.00
157	12.53	207	14.39	257	16.03
158	12.57	208	14.42	258	16.06
159	12.61	209	14.46	259	16.09
160	12.65	210	14.49	260	16.12
161	12.69	211	14.53	261	16.16
162	12.73	212	14.56	262	16.19
163	12.77	213	14.59	263	16.22
164	12.81	214	14.63	264	16.25
165	12.85	215	14.66	265	16.28
166	12.88	216	14.70	266	16.31
167	12.92	217	14.73	267	16.34
168	12.96	218	14.76	268	16.37
169	13.00	219	14.80	269	16.40
170	13.04	220	14.83	270	16.43
171	13.08	221	14.87	271	16.46
172	13.11	222	14.90	272	16.49
173	13.15	223	14.93	273	16.52
174	13.19	224	14.97	274	16.55
175	13.23	225	15.00	275	16.58
176	13.27	226	15.03	276	16.61
177	13.30	227	15.07	277	16.64
178	13.34	228	15.10	278	16.67
179	13.38	229	15.13	279	16.70
180	13.42	230	15.17	280	16.73
181	13.45	231	15.20	281	16.76
182	13.49	232	15.23	282	16.79
183	13.53	233	15.26	283	16.82
184	13.56	234	15.30	284	16.85
185	13.60	235	15.33	285	16.88
186	13.64	236	15.36	286	16.91
187	13.67	237	15.39	287	16.94
188	13.71	238	15.43	288	16.97
189	13.75	239	15.46	289	17.00
190	13.78	240	15.49	290	17.03
191	13.82	241	15.52	291	17.06
192	13.86	242	15.56	292	17.09
193	13.89	243	15.59	293	17.12
194	13.93	244	15.62	294	17.15
195	13.96	245	15.65	295	17.18
196	14.00	246	15.68	296	17.20
197	14.04	247	15.72	297	17.23
198	14.07	248	15.75	298	17.26
199	14.11	249	15.78	299	17.29
200	14.14	250	15.81	300	17.32

TABLE 2
Circular and Trigonometric Functions

MEASURE Degree	Radian	SINE Value	Log	TANGENT Value	Log	COTANGENT Value	Log	COSINE Value	Log		
0° 00′	0.0000	.0000	——	.0000	——	——	——	1.0000	.0000	1.5708	90° 00′
10	0.0029	.0029	7.4637	.0029	7.4637	343.77	2.5363	1.0000	.0000	1.5679	50
20	0.0058	.0058	7.7648	.0058	7.7648	171.89	2.2352	1.0000	.0000	1.5650	40
30	0.0087	.0087	7.9408	.0087	7.9409	114.59	2.0591	1.0000	.0000	1.5621	30
40	0.0116	.0116	8.0658	.0116	8.0658	85.940	1.9342	.9999	.0000	1.5592	20
50	0.0145	.0145	8.1627	.0145	8.1627	68.750	1.8373	.9999	.0000	1.5563	10
1° 00′	0.0175	.0175	8.2419	.0175	8.2419	57.290	1.7581	.9998	9.9999	1.5533	89° 00′
10	0.0204	.0204	8.3088	.0204	8.3089	49.104	1.6911	.9998	9.9999	1.5504	50
20	0.0233	.0233	8.3668	.0233	8.3669	42.964	1.6331	.9997	9.9999	1.5475	40
30	0.0262	.0262	8.4179	.0262	8.4181	38.188	1.5819	.9997	9.9999	1.5446	30
40	0.0291	.0291	8.4637	.0291	8.4638	34.368	1.5362	.9996	9.9998	1.5417	20
50	0.0320	.0320	8.5050	.0320	8.5053	31.242	1.4947	.9995	9.9998	1.5388	10
2° 00′	0.0349	.0349	8.5428	.0349	8.5431	28.636	1.4569	.9994	9.9997	1.5359	88° 00′
10	0.0378	.0378	8.5776	.0378	8.5779	26.432	1.4221	.9993	9.9997	1.5330	50
20	0.0407	.0407	8.6097	.0407	8.6101	24.542	1.3899	.9992	9.9996	1.5301	40
30	0.0436	.0436	8.6397	.0437	8.6401	22.904	1.3599	.9990	9.9996	1.5272	30
40	0.0465	.0465	8.6677	.0466	8.6682	21.470	1.3318	.9989	9.9995	1.5242	20
50	0.0495	.0494	8.6940	.0495	8.6945	20.206	1.3055	.9988	9.9995	1.5213	10
3° 00′	0.0524	.0523	8.7188	.0524	8.7194	19.081	1.2806	.9986	9.9994	1.5184	87° 00′
10	0.0553	.0552	8.7423	.0553	8.7429	18.075	1.2571	.9985	9.9993	1.5155	50
20	0.0582	.0581	8.7645	.0582	8.7652	17.169	1.2348	.9983	9.9993	1.5126	40
30	0.0611	.0610	8.7857	.0612	8.7865	16.350	1.2135	.9981	9.9992	1.5097	30
40	0.0640	.0640	8.8059	.0641	8.8067	15.605	1.1933	.9980	9.9991	1.5068	20
50	0.0669	.0669	8.8251	.0670	8.8261	14.924	1.1739	.9978	9.9990	1.5039	10
4° 00′	0.0698	.0698	8.8436	.0699	8.8446	14.301	1.1554	.9976	9.9989	1.5010	86° 00′
10	0.0727	.0727	8.8613	.0729	8.8624	13.727	1.1376	.9974	9.9989	1.4981	50
20	0.0756	.0756	8.8783	.0758	8.8795	13.197	1.1205	.9971	9.9988	1.4952	40
30	0.0785	.0785	8.8946	.0787	8.8960	12.706	1.1040	.9969	9.9987	1.4923	30
40	0.0814	.0814	8.9104	.0816	8.9118	12.251	1.0882	.9967	9.9986	1.4893	20
50	0.0844	.0843	8.9256	.0846	8.9272	11.826	1.0728	.9964	9.9985	1.4864	10
5° 00′	0.0873	.0872	8.9403	.0875	8.9420	11.430	1.0580	.9962	9.9983	1.4835	85° 00′
		Value COSINE	Log	Value COTANGENT	Log	Value TANGENT	Log	Value SINE	Log	Radian Degree	ANGLE

TABLE 2 (Continued)
Circular and Trigonometric Functions

Measure Degree	Radian	Sine Value	Log	Tangent Value	Log	Cotangent Value	Log	Cosine Value	Log		
5° 00′	0.0873	.0872	8.9403	.0875	8.9420	11.430	1.0580	.9962	9.9983	1.4835	85° 00′
10	0.0902	.0901	8.9545	.0904	8.9563	11.059	1.0437	.9959	9.9982	1.4806	50
20	0.0931	.0929	8.9682	.0934	8.9701	10.712	1.0299	.9957	9.9981	1.4777	40
30	0.0960	.0958	8.9816	.0963	8.9836	10.385	1.0164	.9954	9.9980	1.4748	30
40	0.0989	.0987	8.9945	.0992	8.9966	10.078	1.0034	.9951	9.9979	1.4719	20
50	0.1018	.1016	9.0070	.1022	9.0093	9.7882	.9907	.9948	9.9977	1.4690	10
6° 00′	0.1047	.1045	9.0192	.1051	9.0216	9.5144	.9784	.9945	9.9976	1.4661	84° 00′
10	0.1076	.1074	9.0311	.1080	9.0336	9.2553	.9664	.9942	9.9975	1.4632	50
20	0.1105	.1103	9.0426	.1110	9.0453	9.0098	.9547	.9939	9.9973	1.4603	40
30	0.1134	.1132	9.0539	.1139	9.0567	8.7769	.9433	.9936	9.9972	1.4573	30
40	0.1164	.1161	9.0648	.1169	9.0678	8.5555	.9322	.9932	9.9971	1.4544	20
50	0.1193	.1190	9.0755	.1198	9.0786	8.3450	.9214	.9929	9.9969	1.4515	10
7° 00′	0.1222	.1219	9.0859	.1228	9.0891	8.1443	.9109	.9925	9.9968	1.4486	83° 00′
10	0.1251	.1248	9.0961	.1257	9.0995	7.9530	.9005	.9922	9.9966	1.4457	50
20	0.1280	.1276	9.1060	.1287	9.1096	7.7704	.8904	.9918	9.9964	1.4428	40
30	0.1309	.1305	9.1157	.1317	9.1194	7.5958	.8806	.9914	9.9963	1.4399	30
40	0.1338	.1334	9.1252	.1346	9.1291	7.4287	.8709	.9911	9.9961	1.4370	20
50	0.1367	.1363	9.1345	.1376	9.1385	7.2687	.8615	.9907	9.9959	1.4341	10
8° 00′	0.1396	.1392	9.1436	.1405	9.1478	7.1154	.8522	.9903	9.9958	1.4312	82° 00′
10	0.1425	.1421	9.1525	.1435	9.1569	6.9682	.8431	.9899	9.9956	1.4283	50
20	0.1454	.1449	9.1612	.1465	9.1658	6.8269	.8342	.9894	9.9954	1.4254	40
30	0.1484	.1478	9.1697	.1495	9.1745	6.6912	.8255	.9890	9.9952	1.4224	30
40	0.1513	.1507	9.1781	.1524	9.1831	6.5606	.8169	.9886	9.9950	1.4195	20
50	0.1542	.1536	9.1863	.1554	9.1915	6.4348	.8085	.9881	9.9948	1.4166	10
9° 00′	0.1571	.1564	9.1943	.1584	9.1997	6.3138	.8003	.9877	9.9946	1.4137	81° 00′
10	0.1600	.1593	9.2022	.1614	9.2078	6.1970	.7922	.9872	9.9944	1.4108	50
20	0.1629	.1622	9.2100	.1644	9.2158	6.0844	.7842	.9868	9.9942	1.4079	40
30	0.1658	.1650	9.2176	.1673	9.2236	5.9758	.7764	.9863	9.9940	1.4050	30
40	0.1687	.1679	9.2251	.1703	9.2313	5.8708	.7687	.9858	9.9938	1.4021	20
50	0.1716	.1708	9.2324	.1733	9.2389	5.7694	.7611	.9853	9.9936	1.3992	10
10° 00′	0.1745	.1736	9.2397	.1763	9.2463	5.6713	.7537	.9848	9.9934	1.3963	80° 00′
		Value Cosine	Log	Value Cotangent	Log	Value Tangent	Log	Value Sine	Log	Radian Angle	Degree

TABLE 2 (Continued)
Circular and Trigonometric Functions

Measure Degree	Radian	Sine Value	Log	Tangent Value	Log	Cotangent Value	Log	Cosine Value	Log		
10° 00′	**0.1745**	.1736	9.2397	.1763	9.2463	5.6713	.7537	.9848	9.9934	**1.3963**	**80° 00′**
10	0.1774	.1765	9.2468	.1793	9.2536	5.5764	.7464	.9843	9.9931	1.3934	50
20	0.1804	.1794	9.2538	.1823	9.2609	5.4845	.7391	.9838	9.9929	1.3904	40
30	**0.1833**	.1822	9.2606	.1853	9.2680	5.3955	.7320	.9833	9.9927	**1.3875**	**30**
40	0.1862	.1851	9.2674	.1883	9.2750	5.3093	.7250	.9827	9.9924	1.3846	20
50	0.1891	.1880	9.2740	.1914	9.2819	5.2257	.7181	.9822	9.9922	1.3817	10
11° 00′	**0.1920**	.1908	9.2806	.1944	9.2887	5.1446	.7113	.9816	9.9919	**1.3788**	**79° 00′**
10	0.1949	.1937	9.2870	.1974	9.2953	5.0658	.7047	.9811	9.9917	1.3759	50
20	0.1978	.1965	9.2934	.2004	9.3020	4.9894	.6980	.9805	9.9914	1.3730	40
30	**0.2007**	.1994	9.2997	.2035	9.3085	4.9152	.6915	.9799	9.9912	**1.3701**	**30**
40	0.2036	.2022	9.3058	.2065	9.3149	4.8430	.6851	.9793	9.9909	1.3672	20
50	0.2065	.2051	9.3119	.2095	9.3212	4.7729	.6788	.9787	9.9907	1.3643	10
12° 00′	**0.2094**	.2079	9.3179	.2126	9.3275	4.7046	.6725	.9781	9.9904	**1.3614**	**78° 00′**
10	0.2124	.2108	9.3238	.2156	9.3336	4.6382	.6664	.9775	9.9901	1.3584	50
20	0.2153	.2136	9.3296	.2186	9.3397	4.5736	.6603	.9769	9.9899	1.3555	40
30	**0.2182**	.2164	9.3353	.2217	9.3458	4.5107	.6542	.9763	9.9896	**1.3526**	**30**
40	0.2211	.2193	9.3410	.2247	9.3517	4.4494	.6483	.9757	9.9893	1.3497	20
50	0.2240	.2221	9.3466	.2278	9.3576	4.3897	.6424	.9750	9.9890	1.3468	10
13° 00′	**0.2269**	.2250	9.3521	.2309	9.3634	4.3315	.6366	.9744	9.9887	**1.3439**	**77° 00′**
10	0.2298	.2278	9.3575	.2339	9.3691	4.2747	.6309	.9737	9.9884	1.3410	50
20	0.2327	.2306	9.3629	.2370	9.3748	4.2193	.6252	.9730	9.9881	1.3381	40
30	**0.2356**	.2334	9.3682	.2401	9.3804	4.1653	.6196	.9724	9.9878	**1.3352**	**30**
40	0.2385	.2363	9.3734	.2432	9.3859	4.1126	.6141	.9717	9.9875	1.3323	20
50	0.2414	.2391	9.3786	.2462	9.3914	4.0611	.6086	.9710	9.9872	1.3294	10
14° 00′	**0.2444**	.2419	9.3837	.2493	9.3968	4.0108	.6032	.9703	9.9869	**1.3264**	**76° 00′**
10	0.2472	.2447	9.3887	.2524	9.4021	3.9617	.5979	.9696	9.9866	1.3235	50
20	0.2502	.2476	9.3937	.2555	9.4074	3.9136	.5926	.9689	9.9863	1.3206	40
30	**0.2531**	.2504	9.3986	.2586	9.4127	3.8667	.5873	.9681	9.9859	**1.3177**	**30**
40	0.2560	.2532	9.4035	.2617	9.4178	3.8208	.5822	.9674	9.9856	1.3148	20
50	0.2589	.2560	9.4083	.2648	9.4230	3.7760	.5770	.9667	9.9853	1.3119	10
15° 00′	**0.2618**	.2588	9.4130	.2679	9.4281	3.7321	.5719	.9659	9.9849	**1.3090**	**75° 00′**
		Value Cosine	Log	Value Cotangent	Log	Value Tangent	Log	Value Sine	Log	Radian Angle	Degree

461

TABLE 2 (Continued)
Circular and Trigonometric Functions

Measure Degree	Radian	Sine Value	Log	Tangent Value	Log	Cotangent Value	Log	Cosine Value	Log		
15° 00'	**0.2618**	.2588	9.4130	.2679	9.4281	3.7321	.5719	.9659	9.9849	**1.3090**	**75° 00'**
10	0.2647	.2616	9.4177	.2711	9.4331	3.6891	.5669	.9652	9.9846	1.3061	50
20	0.2676	.2644	9.4223	.2742	9.4381	3.6470	.5619	.9644	9.9843	1.3032	40
30	**0.2705**	.2672	9.4269	.2773	9.4430	3.6059	5570	.9636	9.9839	**1.3003**	**30**
40	0.2734	.2700	9.4314	.2805	9.4479	3.5656	.5521	.9628	9.9836	1.2974	20
50	0.2763	.2728	9.4359	.2836	9.4527	3.5261	.5473	.9621	9.9832	1.2944	10
16° 00'	**0.2792**	.2756	9.4403	.2867	9.4575	3.4874	.5425	.9613	9.9828	**1.2915**	**74° 00'**
10	0.2822	.2784	9.4447	.2899	9.4622	3.4495	.5378	.9605	9.9825	1.2886	50
20	0.2851	.2812	9.4491	.2931	9.4669	3.4124	.5331	.9596	9.9821	1.2857	40
30	**0.2880**	.2840	9.4533	.2962	9.4716	3.3759	.5284	.9588	9.9817	**1.2828**	**30**
40	0.2909	.2868	9.4576	.2994	9.4762	3.3402	.5238	.9580	9.9814	1.2799	20
50	0.2938	.2896	9.4618	.3026	9.4808	3.3052	.5192	.9572	9.9810	1.2770	10
17° 00'	**0.2967**	.2924	9.4659	.3057	9.4853	3.2709	.5147	.9563	9.9806	**1.2741**	**73° 00'**
10	0.2996	.2952	9.4700	.3089	9.4898	3.2371	.5102	.9555	9.9802	1.2712	50
20	0.3025	.2979	9.4741	.3121	9.4943	3.2041	.5057	.9546	9.9798	1.2683	40
30	**0.3054**	.3007	9.4781	.3153	9.4987	3.1716	.5013	.9537	9.9794	**1.2654**	**30**
40	0.3083	.3035	9.4821	.3185	9.5031	3.1397	.4969	.9528	9.9790	1.2624	20
50	0.3112	.3062	9.4861	.3217	9.5075	3.1084	.4925	.9520	9.9786	1.2596	10
18° 00'	**0.3142**	.3090	9.4900	.3249	9.5118	3.0777	.4882	.9511	9.9782	**1.2566**	**72° 00'**
10	0.3171	.3118	9.4939	.3281	9.5161	3.0475	.4839	.9502	9.9778	1.2537	50
20	0.3200	.3145	9.4977	.3314	9.5203	3.0178	.4797	.9492	9.9774	1.2508	40
30	**0.3229**	.3173	9.5015	.3346	9.5245	2.9887	.4755	.9483	9.9770	**1.2479**	**30**
40	0.3258	.3201	9.5052	.3378	9.5287	2.9600	.4713	.9474	9.9765	1.2450	20
50	0.3287	.3228	9.5090	.3411	9.5329	2.9319	.4671	.9465	9.9761	1.2421	10
19° 00'	**0.3316**	.3256	9.5126	.3443	9.5370	2.9042	.4630	.9455	9.9757	**1.2392**	**71° 00'**
10	0.3345	.3283	9.5163	.3476	9.5411	2.8770	.4589	.9446	9.9752	1.2363	50
20	0.3374	.3311	9.5199	.3508	9.5451	2.8502	.4549	.9436	9.9748	1.2334	40
30	**0.3403**	.3338	9.5235	.3541	9.5491	2.8239	.4509	.9426	9.9743	**1.2305**	**30**
40	0.3432	.3365	9.5270	.3574	9.5531	2.7980	.4469	.9417	9.9739	1.2276	20
50	0.3462	.3393	9.5306	.3607	9.5571	2.7725	.4429	.9407	9.9734	1.2246	10
20° 00'	**0.3491**	.3420	9.5341	.3640	9.5611	2.7475	.4389	.9397	9.9730	**1.2217**	**70° 00'**
		Value Log Cosine		Value Log Cotangent		Value Log Tangent		Value Log Sine		Radian Degree Angle	

TABLE 2 (Continued)
Circular and Trigonometric Functions

MEASURE		SINE		TANGENT		COTANGENT		COSINE			
Degree	Radian	Value	Log	Value	Log	Value	Log	Value	Log		
20° 00′	**0.3491**	.3420	9.5341	.3640	9.5611	2.7475	.4389	.9397	9.9730	**1.2217**	**70° 00′**
10	0.3520	.3448	9.5375	.3673	9.5650	2.7228	.4350	.9387	9.9725	1.2188	50
20	0.3549	.3475	9.5409	.3706	9.5689	2.6985	.4311	.9377	9.9721	1.2159	40
30	**0.3578**	.3502	9.5443	.3739	9.5727	2.6746	.4273	.9367	9.9716	**1.2130**	**30**
40	0.3607	.3529	9.5477	.3772	9.5766	2.6511	.4234	.9356	9.9711	1.2101	20
50	0.3636	.3557	9.5510	.3805	9.5804	2.6279	.4196	.9346	9.9706	1.2072	10
21° 00′	**0.3665**	.3584	9.5543	.3839	9.5842	2.6051	.4158	.9336	9.9702	**1.2043**	**69° 00′**
10	0.3694	.3611	9.5576	.3872	9.5879	2.5826	.4121	.9325	9.9697	1.2014	50
20	0.3723	.3638	9.5609	.3906	9.5917	2.5605	.4083	.9315	9.9692	1.1985	40
30	**0.3752**	.3665	9.5641	.3939	9.5954	2.5386	.4046	.9304	9.9687	**1.1956**	**30**
40	0.3782	.3692	9.5673	.3973	9.5991	2.5172	.4009	.9293	9.9682	1.1926	20
50	0.3811	.3719	9.5704	.4006	9.6028	2.4960	.3972	.9283	9.9677	1.1897	10
22° 00′	**0.3840**	.3746	9.5736	.4040	9.6064	2.4751	.3936	.9272	9.9672	**1.1868**	**68° 00′**
10	0.3869	.3773	9.5767	.4074	9.6100	2.4545	.3900	.9261	9.9667	1.1839	50
20	0.3898	.3800	9.5798	.4108	9.6136	2.4342	.3864	.9250	9.9661	1.1810	40
30	**0.3927**	.3827	9.5828	.4142	9.6172	2.4142	.3828	.9239	9.9656	**1.1781**	**30**
40	0.3956	.3854	9.5859	.4176	9.6208	2.3945	.3792	.9228	9.9651	1.1752	20
50	0.3985	.3881	9.5889	.4210	9.6243	2.3750	.3757	.9216	9.9646	1.1723	10
23° 00′	**0.4014**	.3907	9.5919	.4245	9.6279	2.3559	.3721	.9205	9.9640	**1.1694**	**67° 00′**
10	0.4043	.3934	9.5948	.4279	9.6314	2.3369	.3686	.9194	9.9635	1.1665	50
20	0.4072	.3961	9.5978	.4314	9.6348	2.3183	.3652	.9182	9.9629	1.1636	40
30	**0.4102**	.3987	9.6007	.4348	9.6383	2.2998	.3617	.9171	9.9624	**1.1606**	**30**
40	0.4131	.4014	9.6036	.4383	9.6417	2.2817	.3583	.9159	9.9618	1.1577	20
50	0.4160	.4041	9.6065	.4417	9.6452	2.2637	.3548	.9147	9.9613	1.1548	10
24° 00′	**0.4189**	.4067	9.6093	.4452	9.6486	2.2460	.3514	.9135	9.9607	**1.1519**	**66° 00′**
10	0.4218	.4094	9.6121	.4487	9.6520	2.2286	.3480	.9124	9.9602	1.1490	50
20	0.4247	.4120	9.6149	.4522	9.6553	2.2113	.3447	.9112	9.9596	1.1461	40
30	**0.4276**	.4147	9.6177	.4557	9.6587	2.1943	.3413	.9100	9.9590	**1.1432**	**30**
40	0.4305	.4173	9.6205	.4592	9.6620	2.1775	.3380	.9088	9.9584	1.1403	20
50	0.4334	.4200	9.6232	.4628	9.6654	2.1609	.3346	.9075	9.9579	1.1374	10
25° 00′	**0.4363**	.4226	9.6259	.4663	9.6687	2.1445	.3313	.9063	9.9573	**1.1345**	**65° 00′**
		Value	Log	Value	Log	Value	Log	Value	Log	Radian	Degree
		COSINE		COTANGENT		TANGENT		SINE		ANGLE	

TABLE 2 (Continued)
Circular and Trigonometric Functions

Measure Degree	Radian	Sine Value	Log	Tangent Value	Log	Cotangent Value	Log	Cosine Value	Log		
25° 00′	0.4363	.4226	9.6259	.4663	9.6687	2.1445	.3313	.9063	9.9573	1.1345	65° 00′
10	0.4392	.4253	9.6286	.4699	9.6720	2.1283	.3280	.9051	9.9567	1.1316	50
20	0.4422	.4279	9.6313	.4734	9.6752	2.1123	.3248	.9038	9.9561	1.1286	40
30	0.4451	.4305	9.6340	.4770	9.6785	2.0965	.3215	.9026	9.9555	1.1257	30
40	0.4480	.4331	9.6366	.4806	9.6817	2.0809	.3183	.9013	9.9549	1.1228	20
50	0.4509	.4358	9.6392	.4841	9.6850	2.0655	.3150	.9001	9.9543	1.1199	10
26° 00′	0.4538	.4384	9.6418	.4877	9.6882	2.0503	.3118	.8988	9.9537	1.1170	64° 00′
10	0.4567	.4410	9.6444	.4913	9.6914	2.0353	.3086	.8975	9.9530	1.1141	50
20	0.4596	.4436	9.6470	.4950	9.6946	2.0204	.3054	.8962	9.9524	1.1112	40
30	0.4625	.4462	9.6495	.4986	9.6977	2.0057	.3023	.8949	9.9518	1.1083	30
40	0.4654	.4488	9.6521	.5022	9.7009	1.9912	.2991	.8936	9.9512	1.1054	20
50	0.4683	.4514	9.6546	.5059	9.7040	1.9768	.2960	.8923	9.9505	1.1025	10
27° 00′	0.4712	.4540	9.6570	.5095	9.7072	1.9626	.2928	.8910	9.9499	1.0996	63° 00′
10	0.4742	.4566	9.6595	.5132	9.7103	1.9486	.2897	.8897	9.9492	1.0966	50
20	0.4771	.4592	9.6620	.5169	9.7134	1.9347	.2866	.8884	9.9486	1.0937	40
30	0.4800	.4617	9.6644	.5206	9.7165	1.9210	.2835	.8870	9.9479	1.0908	30
40	0.4829	.4643	9.6668	.5243	9.7196	1.9074	.2804	.8857	9.9473	1.0879	20
50	0.4858	.4669	9.6692	.5280	9.7226	1.8940	.2774	.8843	9.9466	1.0850	10
28° 00′	0.4886	.4695	9.6716	.5317	9.7257	1.8807	.2743	.8829	9.9459	1.0821	62° 00′
10	0.4916	.4720	9.6740	.5354	9.7287	1.8676	.2713	.8816	9.9453	1.0792	50
20	0.4945	.4746	9.6763	.5392	9.7317	1.8546	.2683	.8802	9.9446	1.0763	40
30	0.4974	.4772	9.6787	.5430	9.7348	1.8418	.2652	.8788	9.9439	1.0734	30
40	0.5003	.4797	9.6810	.5467	9.7378	1.8291	.2622	.8774	9.9432	1.0705	20
50	0.5032	.4823	9.6833	.5505	9.7408	1.8165	.2592	.8760	9.9425	1.0676	10
29° 00′	0.5062	.4848	9.6856	.5543	9.7438	1.8040	.2562	.8746	9.9418	1.0646	61° 00′
10	0.5090	.4874	9.6878	.5581	9.7467	1.7917	.2533	.8732	9.9411	1.0617	50
20	0.5120	.4899	9.6901	.5619	9.7497	1.7796	.2503	.8718	9.9404	1.0588	40
30	0.5149	.4924	9.6923	.5658	9.7526	1.7675	.2474	.8704	9.9397	1.0559	30
40	0.5178	.4950	9.6946	.5696	9.7556	1.7556	.2444	.8689	9.9390	1.0530	20
50	0.5207	.4975	9.6968	.5735	9.7585	1.7437	.2415	.8675	9.9383	1.0501	10
30° 00′	0.5236	.5000	9.6990	.5774	9.7614	1.7321	.2386	.8660	9.9375	1.0472	60° 00′
		Value Cosine	Log	Value Cotangent	Log	Value Tangent	Log	Value Sine	Log	Radian Angle	Degree

TABLE 2 (Continued)

Circular and Trigonometric Functions

MEASURE Degree	Radian	SINE Value	Log	TANGENT Value	Log	COTANGENT Value	Log	COSINE Value	Log		
30° 00′	0.5236	.5000	9.6990	.5774	9.7614	1.7321	.2386	.8660	9.9375	1.0472	60° 00′
10	0.5265	.5025	9.7012	.5812	9.7644	1.7205	.2356	.8646	9.9368	1.0443	50
20	0.5294	.5050	9.7033	.5851	9.7673	1.7090	.2327	.8631	9.9361	1.0414	40
30	0.5323	.5075	9.7055	.5890	9.7701	1.6977	.2299	.8616	9.9353	1.0385	30
40	0.5352	.5100	9.7076	.5930	9.7730	1.6864	.2270	.8601	9.9346	1.0356	20
50	0.5381	.5125	9.7097	.5969	9.7759	1.6753	.2241	.8587	9.9338	1.0326	10
31° 00′	0.5410	.5150	9.7118	.6009	9.7788	1.6643	.2212	.8572	9.9331	1.0297	59° 00′
10	0.5440	.5175	9.7139	.6048	9.7816	1.6534	.2184	.8557	9.9323	1.0268	50
20	0.5469	.5200	9.7160	.6088	9.7845	1.6426	.2155	.8542	9.9315	1.0239	40
30	0.5498	.5225	9.7181	.6128	9.7873	1.6319	.2127	.8526	9.9308	1.0210	30
40	0.5527	.5250	9.7201	.6168	9.7902	1.6212	.2098	.8511	9.9300	1.0181	20
50	0.5556	.5275	9.7222	.6208	9.7930	1.6107	.2070	.8496	9.9292	1.0152	10
32° 00′	0.5585	.5299	9.7242	.6249	9.7958	1.6003	.2042	.8480	9.9284	1.0123	58° 00′
10	0.5614	.5324	9.7262	.6289	9.7986	1.5900	.2014	.8465	9.9276	1.0094	50
20	0.5643	.5348	9.7282	.6330	9.8014	1.5798	.1986	.8450	9.9268	1.0065	40
30	0.5672	.5373	9.7302	.6371	9.8042	1.5697	.1958	.8434	9.9260	1.0036	30
40	0.5701	.5398	9.7322	.6412	9.8070	1.5597	.1930	.8418	9.9252	1.0007	20
50	0.5730	.5422	9.7342	.6453	9.8097	1.5497	.1903	.8403	9.9244	0.9978	10
33° 00′	0.5760	.5446	9.7361	.6494	9.8125	1.5399	.1875	.8387	9.9236	0.9948	57° 00′
10	0.5789	.5471	9.7380	.6536	9.8153	1.5301	.1847	.8371	9.9228	0.9919	50
20	0.5818	.5495	9.7400	.6577	9.8180	1.5204	.1820	.8355	9.9219	0.9890	40
30	0.5847	.5519	9.7419	.6619	9.8208	1.5108	.1792	.8339	9.9211	0.9861	30
40	0.5876	.5544	9.7438	.6661	9.8235	1.5013	.1765	.8323	9.9203	0.9832	20
50	0.5905	.5568	9.7457	.6703	9.8263	1.4919	.1737	.8307	9.9194	0.9803	10
34° 00′	0.5934	.5592	9.7476	.6745	9.8290	1.4826	.1710	.8290	9.9186	0.9774	56° 00′
10	0.5963	.5616	9.7494	.6787	9.8317	1.4733	.1683	.8274	9.9177	0.9745	50
20	0.5992	.5640	9.7513	.6830	9.8344	1.4641	.1656	.8258	9.9169	0.9716	40
30	0.6021	.5664	9.7531	.6873	9.8371	1.4550	.1629	.8241	9.9160	0.9687	30
40	0.6050	.5688	9.7550	.6916	9.8398	1.4460	.1602	.8225	9.9151	0.9658	20
50	0.6080	.5712	9.7568	.6959	9.8425	1.4370	.1575	.8208	9.9142	0.9628	10
35° 00′	0.6109	.5736	9.7586	.7002	9.8452	1.4281	.1548	.8192	9.9134	0.9599	55° 00′
		Value COSINE	Log	Value COTANGENT	Log	Value TANGENT	Log	Value SINE	Log	Radian ANGLE	Degree

TABLE 2 (Continued)
Circular and Trigonometric Functions

MEASURE		SINE		TANGENT		COTANGENT		COSINE			
Degree	Radian	Value	Log	Value	Log	Value	Log	Value	Log		
35° 00′	0.6109	.5736	9.7586	.7002	9.8452	1.4281	.1548	.8192	9.9134	**0.9599**	**55° 00′**
10	0.6134	.5760	9.7604	.7046	9.8479	1.4193	.1521	.8175	9.9125	0.9570	50
20	0.6167	.5783	9.7622	.7089	9.8506	1.4106	.1494	.8158	9.9116	0.9541	40
30	0.6196	.5807	9.7640	.7133	9.8533	1.4019	.1467	.8141	9.9107	**0.9512**	**30**
40	0.6225	.5831	9.7657	.7177	9.8559	1.3934	.1441	.8124	9.9098	0.9483	20
50	0.6254	.5854	9.7675	.7221	9.8586	1.3848	.1414	.8107	9.9089	0.9454	10
36° 00′	0.6283	.5878	9.7692	.7265	9.8613	1.3764	.1387	.8090	9.9080	**0.9425**	**54° 00′**
10	0.6312	.5901	9.7710	.7310	9.8639	1.3680	.1361	.8073	9.9070	0.9396	50
20	0.6341	.5925	9.7727	.7355	9.8666	1.3597	.1334	.8056	9.9061	0.9367	40
30	0.6370	.5948	9.7744	.7400	9.8692	1.3514	.1308	.8039	9.9052	**0.9338**	**30**
40	0.6400	.5972	9.7761	.7445	9.8718	1.3432	.1282	.8021	9.9042	0.9308	20
50	0.6429	.5995	9.7778	.7490	9.8745	1.3351	.1255	.8004	9.9033	0.9279	10
37° 00′	0.6458	.6018	9.7795	.7536	9.8771	1.3270	.1229	.7986	9.9023	**0.9250**	**53° 00′**
10	0.6487	.6041	9.7811	.7581	9.8797	1.3190	.1203	.7969	9.9014	0.9221	50
20	0.6516	.6065	9.7828	.7627	9.8824	1.3111	.1176	.7951	9.9004	0.9192	40
30	0.6545	.6088	9.7844	.7673	9.8850	1.3032	.1150	.7934	9.8995	**0.9163**	**30**
40	0.6574	.6111	9.7861	.7720	9.8876	1.2954	.1124	.7916	9.8985	0.9134	20
50	0.6603	.6134	9.7877	.7766	9.8902	1.2876	.1098	.7898	9.8975	0.9105	10
38° 00′	0.6632	.6157	9.7893	.7813	9.8928	1.2799	.1072	.7880	9.8965	**0.9076**	**52° 00′**
10	0.6661	.6180	9.7910	.7860	9.8954	1.2723	.1046	.7862	9.8955	0.9047	50
20	0.6690	.6202	9.7926	.7907	9.8980	1.2647	.1020	.7844	9.8945	0.9018	40
30	0.6720	.6225	9.7941	.7954	9.9006	1.2572	.0994	.7826	9.8935	**0.8988**	**30**
40	0.6749	.6248	9.7957	.8002	9.9032	1.2497	.0968	.7808	9.8925	0.8959	20
50	0.6778	.6271	9.7973	.8050	9.9058	1.2423	.0942	.7790	9.8915	0.8930	10
39° 00′	0.6807	.6293	9.7989	.8098	9.9084	1.2349	.0916	.7771	9.8905	**0.8901**	**51° 00′**
10	0.6836	.6316	9.8004	.8146	9.9110	1.2276	.0890	.7753	9.8895	0.8872	50
20	0.6865	.6338	9.8020	.8195	9.9135	1.2203	.0865	.7735	9.8884	0.8843	40
30	0.6894	.6361	9.8035	.8243	9.9161	1.2131	.0839	.7716	9.8874	**0.8814**	**30**
40	0.6923	.6383	9.8050	.8292	9.9187	1.2059	.0813	.7698	9.8864	0.8785	20
50	0.6952	.6406	9.8066	.8342	9.9212	1.1988	.0788	.7679	9.8853	0.8756	10
40° 00′	0.6981	.6428	9.8081	.8391	9.9238	1.1918	.0762	.7660	9.8843	**0.8727**	**50° 00′**
		Value	Log	Value	Log	Value	Log	Value	Log	Radian	Degree
		COSINE		COTANGENT		TANGENT		SINE		ANGLE	

TABLE 2 (Continued)
Circular and Trigonometric Functions

Measure Degree	Radian	Sine Value	Log	Tangent Value	Log	Cotangent Value	Log	Cosine Value	Log		
40° 00′	0.6981	.6428	9.8081	.8391	9.9238	1.1918	.0762	.7660	9.8843	0.8727	50° 00′
10	0.7010	.6450	9.8096	.8441	9.9264	1.1847	.0736	.7642	9.8832	0.8698	50
20	0.7040	.6472	9.8111	.8491	9.9289	1.1778	.0711	.7623	9.8821	0.8668	40
30	0.7069	.6494	9.8125	.8541	9.9315	1.1708	.0685	.7604	9.8810	0.8639	30
40	0.7098	.6517	9.8140	.8591	9.9341	1.1640	.0659	.7585	9.8800	0.8610	20
50	0.7127	.6539	9.8155	.8642	9.9366	1.1571	.0634	.7566	9.8789	0.8581	10
41° 00′	0.7156	.6561	9.8169	.8693	9.9392	1.1504	.0608	.7547	9.8778	0.8552	49° 00′
10	0.7185	.6583	9.8184	.8744	9.9417	1.1436	.0583	.7528	9.8767	0.8523	50
20	0.7214	.6604	9.8198	.8796	9.9443	1.1369	.0557	.7509	9.8756	0.8494	40
30	0.7243	.6626	9.8213	.8847	9.9468	1.1303	.0532	.7490	9.8745	0.8465	30
40	0.7272	.6648	9.8227	.8899	9.9494	1.1237	.0506	.7470	9.8733	0.8436	20
50	0.7301	.6670	9.8241	.8952	9.9519	1.1171	.0481	.7451	9.8722	0.8407	10
42° 00′	0.7330	.6691	9.8255	.9004	9.9544	1.1106	.0456	.7431	9.8711	0.8378	48° 00′
10	0.7360	.6713	9.8269	.9057	9.9570	1.1041	.0430	.7412	9.8699	0.8348	50
20	0.7389	.6734	9.8283	.9110	9.9595	1.0977	.0405	.7392	9.8688	0.8319	40
30	0.7418	.6756	9.8297	.9163	9.9621	1.0913	.0379	.7373	9.8676	0.8290	30
40	0.7447	.6777	9.8311	.9217	9.9646	1.0850	.0354	.7353	9.8665	0.8261	20
50	0.7476	.6799	9.8324	.9271	9.9671	1.0786	.0329	.7333	9.8653	0.8232	10
43° 00′	0.7505	.6820	9.8338	.9325	9.9697	1.0724	.0303	.7314	9.8641	0.8203	47° 00′
10	0.7534	.6841	9.8351	.9380	9.9722	1.0661	.0278	.7294	9.8629	0.8174	50
20	0.7563	.6862	9.8365	.9435	9.9747	1.0599	.0253	.7274	9.8618	0.8145	40
30	0.7592	.6884	9.8378	.9490	9.9772	1.0538	.0228	.7254	9.8606	0.8116	30
40	0.7621	.6905	9.8391	.9545	9.9798	1.0477	.0202	.7234	9.8594	0.8087	20
50	0.7650	.6926	9.8405	.9601	9.9823	1.0416	.0177	.7214	9.8582	0.8058	10
44° 00′	0.7679	.6947	9.8418	.9657	9.9848	1.0355	.0152	.7193	9.8569	0.8028	46° 00′
10	0.7708	.6967	9.8431	.9713	9.9874	1.0295	.0126	.7173	9.8557	0.7999	50
20	0.7738	.6988	9.8444	.9770	9.9899	1.0235	.0101	.7153	9.8545	0.7970	40
30	0.7767	.7009	9.8457	.8827	9.9924	1.0176	.0076	.7133	9.8532	0.7941	30
40	0.7796	.7030	9.8469	.9884	9.9949	1.0117	.0051	.7112	9.8520	0.7912	20
50	0.7825	.7050	9.8482	.9942	9.9975	1.0058	.0025	.7092	9.8507	0.7883	10
45° 00′	0.7854	.7071	9.8495	1.0000	.0000	1.0000	.0000	.7071	9.8495	0.7854	45° 00′
		Value Cosine	Log	Value Cotangent	Log	Value Tangent	Log	Value Sine	Log	Radian Angle	Degree

TABLE 3
Logarithms

N	0	1	2	3	4	5	6	7	8	9
10	0000	0043	0086	0128	0170	0212	0253	0294	0334	0374
11	0414	0453	0492	0531	0569	0607	0645	0682	0719	0755
12	0792	0828	0864	0899	0934	0969	1004	1038	1072	1106
13	1139	1173	1206	1239	1271	1303	1335	1367	1399	1430
14	1461	1492	1523	1553	1584	1614	1644	1673	1703	1732
15	1761	1790	1818	1847	1875	1903	1931	1959	1987	2014
16	2041	2068	2095	2122	2148	2175	2201	2227	2253	2279
17	2304	2330	2355	2380	2405	2430	2455	2480	2504	2529
18	2553	2577	2601	2625	2648	2672	2695	2718	2742	2765
19	2788	2810	2833	2856	2878	2900	2923	2945	2967	2989
20	3010	3032	3054	3075	3096	3118	3139	3160	3181	3201
21	3222	3243	3263	3284	3304	3324	3345	3365	3385	3404
22	3424	3444	3464	3483	3502	3522	3541	3560	3579	3598
23	3617	3636	3655	3674	3692	3711	3729	3747	3766	3784
24	3802	3820	3838	3856	3874	3892	3909	3927	3945	3962
25	3979	3997	4014	4031	4048	4065	4082	4099	4116	4133
26	4150	4166	4183	4200	4216	4232	4249	4265	4281	4298
27	4314	4330	4346	4362	4378	4393	4409	4425	4440	4456
28	4472	4487	4502	4518	4533	4548	4564	4579	4594	4609
29	4624	4639	4654	4669	4683	4698	4713	4728	4742	4757
30	4771	4786	4800	4814	4829	4843	4857	4871	4886	4900
31	4914	4928	4942	4955	4969	4983	4997	5011	5024	5038
32	5051	5065	5079	5092	5105	5119	5132	5145	5159	5172
33	5185	5198	5211	5224	5237	5250	5263	5276	5289	5302
34	5315	5328	5340	5353	5366	5378	5391	5403	5416	5428
35	5441	5453	5465	5478	5490	5502	5514	5527	5539	5551
36	5563	5575	5587	5599	5611	5623	5635	5647	5658	5670
37	5682	5694	5705	5717	5729	5740	5752	5763	5775	5786
38	5798	5809	5821	5832	5843	5855	5866	5877	5888	5899
39	5911	5922	5933	5944	5955	5966	5977	5988	5999	6010
40	6021	6031	6042	6053	6064	6075	6085	6096	6107	6117
N	0	1	2	3	4	5	6	7	8	9

TABLE 3 (Continued)
Logarithms

N	0	1	2	3	4	5	6	7	8	9
40	6021	6031	6042	6053	6064	6075	6085	6096	6107	6117
41	6128	6138	6149	6160	6170	6180	6191	6201	6212	6222
42	6232	6243	6253	6263	6274	6284	6294	6304	6314	6325
43	6335	6345	6355	6365	6375	6385	6395	6405	6415	6425
44	6435	6444	6454	6464	6474	6484	6493	6503	6513	6522
45	6532	6542	6551	6561	6571	6580	6590	6599	6609	6618
46	6628	6637	6646	6656	6665	6675	6684	6693	6702	6712
47	6721	6730	6739	6749	6758	6767	6776	6785	6794	6803
48	6812	6821	6830	6839	6848	6857	6866	6875	6884	6893
49	6902	6911	6920	6928	6937	6946	6955	6964	6972	6981
50	6990	6998	7007	7016	7024	7033	7042	7050	7059	7067
51	7076	7084	7093	7101	7110	7118	7126	7135	7143	7152
52	7160	7168	7177	7185	7193	7202	7210	7218	7226	7235
53	7243	7251	7259	7267	7275	7284	7292	7300	7308	7316
54	7324	7332	7340	7348	7356	7364	7372	7380	7388	7396
55	7404	7412	7419	7427	7435	7443	7451	7459	7466	7474
56	7482	7490	7497	7505	7513	7520	7528	7536	7543	7551
57	7559	7566	7574	7582	7589	7597	7604	7612	7619	7627
58	7634	7642	7649	7657	7664	7672	7679	7686	7694	7701
59	7709	7716	7723	7731	7738	7745	7752	7760	7767	7774
60	7782	7789	7796	7803	7810	7818	7825	7832	7839	7846
61	7853	7860	7868	7875	7882	7889	7896	7903	7910	7917
62	7924	7931	7938	7945	7952	7959	7966	7973	7980	7987
63	7993	8000	8007	8014	8021	8028	8035	8041	8048	8055
64	8062	8069	8075	8082	8089	8096	8102	8109	8116	8122
65	8129	8136	8142	8149	8156	8162	8169	8176	8182	8189
66	8195	8202	8209	8215	8222	8228	8235	8241	8248	8254
67	8261	8267	8274	8280	8287	8293	8299	8306	8312	8319
68	8325	8331	8338	8344	8351	8357	8363	8370	8376	8382
69	8388	8395	8401	8407	8414	8420	8426	8432	8439	8445
70	8451	8457	8463	8470	8476	8482	8488	8494	8500	8506
N	0	1	2	3	4	5	6	7	8	9

TABLE 3 (Continued)
Logarithms

N	0	1	2	3	4	5	6	7	8	9
70	8451	8457	8463	8470	8476	8482	8488	8494	8500	8506
71	8513	8519	8525	8531	8537	8543	8549	8555	8561	8567
72	8573	8579	8585	8591	8597	8603	8609	8615	8621	8627
73	8633	8639	8645	8651	8657	8663	8669	8675	8681	8686
74	8692	8698	8704	8710	8716	8722	8727	8733	8739	8745
75	8751	8756	8762	8768	8774	8779	8785	8791	8797	8802
76	8808	8814	8820	8825	8831	8837	8842	8848	8854	8859
77	8865	8871	8876	8882	8887	8893	8899	8904	8910	8915
78	8921	8927	8932	8938	8943	8949	8954	8960	8965	8971
79	8976	8982	8987	8993	8998	9004	9009	9015	9020	9025
80	9031	9036	9042	9047	9053	9058	9063	9069	9074	9079
81	9085	9090	9096	9101	9106	9112	9117	9122	9128	9133
82	9138	9143	9149	9154	9159	9165	9170	9175	9180	9186
83	9191	9196	9201	9206	9212	9217	9222	9227	9232	9238
84	9243	9248	9253	9258	9263	9269	9274	9279	9284	9289
85	9294	9299	9304	9309	9315	9320	9325	9330	9335	9340
86	9345	9350	9355	9360	9365	9370	9375	9380	9385	9390
87	9395	9400	9405	9410	9415	9420	9425	9430	9435	9440
88	9445	9450	9455	9460	9465	9469	9474	9479	9484	9489
89	9494	9499	9504	9509	9513	9518	9523	9528	9533	9538
90	9542	9547	9552	9557	9562	9566	9571	9576	9581	9586
91	9590	9595	9600	9605	9609	9614	9619	9624	9628	9633
92	9638	9643	9647	9652	9657	9661	9666	9671	9675	9680
93	9685	9689	9694	9699	9703	9708	9713	9717	9722	9727
94	9731	9736	9741	9745	9750	9754	9759	9763	9768	9773
95	9777	9782	9786	9791	9795	9800	9805	9809	9814	9818
96	9823	9827	9832	9836	9841	9845	9850	9854	9859	9863
97	9868	9872	9877	9881	9886	9890	9894	9899	9903	9908
98	9912	9917	9921	9926	9930	9934	9939	9943	9948	9952
99	9956	9961	9965	9969	9974	9978	9983	9987	9991	9996
N	0	1	2	3	4	5	6	7	8	9

SELECTED ANSWERS

SELECTED ANSWERS

CHAPTER 1

p. 3 (No Answers)

p. 5 **2.** Yes; yes; yes; yes   **4.** No; no; yes; no
6. Yes; yes; yes; yes   **9.** Yes; no; yes; no
11. Yes; yes; yes; yes

pp. 8-9 **1.** Yes   **4.** No   **6.** No   **8.** No

pp. 11-12 **1a.** $3, -\dfrac{1}{3}$ **c.** $-2-\sqrt{3}, 2-\sqrt{3}$ **e.** $-\dfrac{9}{2}, \dfrac{2}{9}$ **2a.** $\triangle$ **c.** Yes
e. $\{\bigcirc\}$ **4.** Yes; yes; no

p. 15 **1.** No   **3.** No   **5.** Yes   **7.** No   **10.** Yes

pp. 18-19 **8a.** $\{4\}$ **b.** $\{3\}$ **c.** $\{6\}$ **d.** $\{-3\}$

pp. 23-24 **1.** Yes; yes   **3.** 0; 1   **7.** Yes; no   **10.** $\{0\}$ **11.** $\{3\}$ **12.** $\{2\}$
14. $\{2\}$ **15.** ϕ

pp. 25-26 **4.** $\{-19\}$ **5.** $\{0\}$ **6.** $\{5\}$ **7.** $\left\{-\dfrac{10}{9}\right\}$ **8.** $\{-22\}$ **9.** $\left\{\dfrac{3}{4}\right\}$

pp. 30-31 **2.** $\left\{x \mid x > \dfrac{1}{2}\right\}$ **4.** $\left\{x \mid x < \dfrac{1}{4}\right\}$ **6.** $\{x \mid x < 10\}$ **8.** $\{x \mid x > -4\}$
10. $\left\{x \mid x > -\dfrac{6}{5}\right\}$ **12.** $\left\{x \mid x > \dfrac{6}{5}\right\}$ **14.** $\{x \mid x < -3\}$
16. $\{x \mid x > -54\}$ **18.** $\{x \mid -\sqrt{3} < x < \sqrt{3}\}$

pp. 32-33 **4.** $5 - 2i$ **6.** $(6\sqrt{2} - 3\sqrt{3}) - (3\sqrt{2} + 6\sqrt{3})i$ **8.** $-\dfrac{29}{10} + \dfrac{17}{10}i$
10. $-9 - 46i$ **12.** $1 + i$ or $-1 - i$

Chapter 1. Review, pp. 33-34

17a. $\{5\}$ **b.** $\{-1, 4\}$ **c.** $\left\{x \mid x < \dfrac{5}{2}\right\}$ **d.** $\{x \mid -2 < x < 2\}$
e. $\left\{x \mid x > \dfrac{1 + \sqrt{13}}{2}\right\}$ **18.** $\dfrac{3 + 2i}{13}$ **19.** $\dfrac{(4\sqrt{2} - \sqrt{6}) + (4\sqrt{3} + 2)i}{18}$
20. $-2 - 2i$

CHAPTER 2

pp. 38-40 **7.** $f(-1) = -4$ **9.** $f(0) = 1$ **11.** $f(0) = 1$ **13.** The set of real
numbers; x **15.** 2   **16a.** 7   **c.** There is none

p. 42 **1.** 3   **3.** 10   **5.** 5   **7.** $2\sqrt{2}$ **9.** 30

pp. 45-46 1. $m = 1$ 3. $m = -\dfrac{5}{4}$ 5. $m = -3$ 8. No slope
9. 2   10. 9 units

p. 47 1. x-intercept $= \dfrac{5}{2}$, no y-intercept, no slope

3. x-intercept $= \dfrac{2}{3}$, y-intercept $= 2$, $m = -3$

5. x-intercept $= -\dfrac{1}{8}$, y-intercept $= \dfrac{1}{2}$, $m = 4$

9. $-\dfrac{4}{3}, \dfrac{4}{3}, \dfrac{4}{9}$ 10. $(8, 5), (-1, 1), (2, -3)$

pp. 51-52 1. $m = \dfrac{3}{2}$, y-intercept $= -\dfrac{7}{2}$ 3. $m = \dfrac{3}{4}$, y-intercept $= 0$

5. $m = 7$, y-intercept $= 0$ 7. $m = \dfrac{7}{2}$ 9. $m = 0$

11. $3x - 5y + 19 = 0$ 13. $4x + y - 7 = 0$ 15. $x + 11y + 18 = 0$
19. (11) $\sqrt{34}$; (13) $\sqrt{17}$; (15) $\sqrt{122}$

p. 53 (No Answers—Graphs)

p. 56 10. Vertices: $(0, 0), (2, 0), (0, 4)$ 11. Vertices: $(1, 0), (3, 0), (3, 5), (0, 5), (0, 1)$
13. Vertices: $(1, -1), \left(\dfrac{8}{3}, \dfrac{2}{3}\right), (1, 4)$

p. 58 1. Minimum: at $(0, 1)$, the value is 9;   Maximum: at $\left(\dfrac{15}{4}, 1\right)$, the value
is 24   2. Maximum: at $(0, 4)$, the value is 9   3. Minimum: at $(0, 3)$, the
value is -1;   Maximum: at $(2, -4)$, the value is 8

pp. 60-61 1. The maximum weight handling purchase is 8 model M hoists and 6
model R hoists. With attachments, the maximum is 4 model M and 10 model R
hoists.   2. Maximum income from 1100 widgets and 1200 gadgets; maximum profit of \$771.00 from 1100 widgets and 1200 gadgets; after increased
costs maximum profit of \$749.00 from 1300 widgets and 1000 gadgets.

Chapter 2. Review, pp. 61-62

1a. $\{6\}$ c. $\{-1, 3\}$ 2a. $f(0) = -5, f(2) = 1, f(-3) = -14$ 4a. $\sqrt{17}$
c. $\sqrt{117}$ 5. $p = 5 + 5\sqrt{5} + \sqrt{74}$ 7a. $m = -4$, y-intercept $= 3$,
x-intercept $= \dfrac{3}{4}$ c. $m = \dfrac{5}{2}$, y-intercept $= \dfrac{7}{2}$, x-intercept $= -\dfrac{7}{5}$
9. $y = 0$ or $y = 6$ 11. $2\sqrt{5}$ units and $2\sqrt{13}$ units   13. $\{x \mid x > 4\}$
15. $\left\{x \mid x < \dfrac{4}{3}\right\}$ 17. $\{x \mid x > 12\}$
24. Maximum: at $(2, 5)$, the value is 50

CHAPTER 3

p. 64 2. -2 4. 0, 1   6. 2, 5   8. $\dfrac{2}{3}, \dfrac{3}{2}$ 9. $\{5\}$ 11. $\{2, 4\}$

p. 66 1. $x + 6$ 3. $x^2 + 2x + 6, R = 15$ 5. $x^3 - 2x^2 - 4x + 8$
8. $x^3 + 3x^2 + 6x + 12, R = 23$

p. 69 1. -1 3. 11   5. 0   7. 12   9. 92
11. 0   13. -4 15. none   17. $-2, 3$ 19. -5

p. 72   **1.** 1   **3.** $-3, -2, -1, 1$ **5.** none   **7.** $-3, \dfrac{1}{2}, 1$ **9.** $\dfrac{3}{4}$

p. 73   **1.** 2   **3.** 1   **5.** 0   **7.** 2   **9.** 1
      11. 1   **13.** 3   **15.** 3   **17.** 1   **19.** 2

p. 77   **1.** Between $x = -3$ and $x = -2$; between $x = -1$ and $x = 0$
      3. Between $x = -1$ and $x = 0$; between $x = 4$ and $x = 5$
      5. Between $x = 1$ and $x = 2$ **7.** The roots are 2 and -1; no other real roots
      9. Least upper limit is 2, greatest lower limit is -5
      11. Least upper limit is 1, greatest lower limit is 0
      13. $x^3 - x^2 - 4x - 4 = 0$
      15. $x^4 - 9x^3 + 30x^2 - 44x + 24 = 0$

pp. 78-79   **3.** $+2i$ **4.** $-\dfrac{1}{2} - \dfrac{1}{2}i$ **6.** $x^3 - 4x^2 + 6x - 4 = 0$ **8.** $x^3 - 1 = 0$
      10. $x^4 - 6x^3 + 13x^2 - 24x + 36 = 0$

p. 82   **1a.** 2   **b.** 0   **3a.** 8   **b.** -4 **5a.** 3   **b.** -1 **7.** -11
      9. $\dfrac{7}{6}$ **10.** $\dfrac{3}{2}$

p. 83   **1.** $4x - y - 4 = 0$ **3.** $7x + y + 2 = 0$ **5.** $4y + 1 = 0$
      7. $12x - y + 17 = 0$

pp. 86-87   **1.** $\left(\dfrac{1}{2}, -\dfrac{25}{4}\right)$ **3.** $(-1, -16)$, minimum   **5.** $y = 3; y = \dfrac{77}{27}$

p. 89   (No Answers—Graphs)

p. 90   **1.** $-1.8, 2.8$ **3.** $-2, -1$ **5.** -2.5 **7.** $-1, 1$

p. 94   **1.** $-2.414, .415$ **3.** 1.86 **5.** $-1.65, 1.65$ **7.** 1.38

p. 96   **2.** $-1, \dfrac{1}{2} + \dfrac{\sqrt{3}}{2}i, \dfrac{1}{2} - \dfrac{\sqrt{3}}{2}i$ **4.** $2, -1 + i\sqrt{3}, -1 - i\sqrt{3}$

Chapter 3. Review, pp. 96-97

      1a. $1, 4$ **c.** $2, -2, 3, -3$ **2a.** $2x^2 + 3x - 4$ **3a.** $-2, -1, 5$
      5a. $D_x y = 3$ **c.** $D_x y = 6x^2 - 1$ **7.** $10x - y - 11 = 0$
      8a. $(4, -12)$, minimum   **9a.** Between -1 and 0, and between 3 and 4; roots are approximately $-.8$ and 3.8 **10a.** 1.4

CHAPTER 4

pp. 102-103   **1.** $\begin{pmatrix} a_{11} & a_{12} & a_{13} & a_{14} & a_{15} \\ a_{21} & a_{22} & a_{23} & a_{24} & a_{25} \\ a_{31} & a_{32} & a_{33} & a_{34} & a_{35} \end{pmatrix}$ **3.** 9   **4.** $(a, b) + (c, d) = (a + c, b + d)$;
      $(a + bi) + (c + di) = [(a + c) + (b + d)i]$ **5.** $x = 7, y = 2$

pp. 104-105   **1.** $\begin{pmatrix} 6 & 3 & -9 \\ -12 & 0 & 21 \end{pmatrix}$ **2.** $\begin{pmatrix} 14 & -29 \\ 3 & 7 \end{pmatrix}$
      4. $a_{11}x + a_{12}y + b_1 = 0, a_{21}x + a_{22}y + b_2 = 0$ **5.** 5×2
      6a. $\begin{pmatrix} 14 & -5 \\ -4 & -6 \end{pmatrix}$ **d.** $\begin{pmatrix} 0 & 3 & 0 \\ -2 & 5 & -2 \\ 1 & 7 & 1 \end{pmatrix}$

pp. 108-109   **4.** $\begin{pmatrix} 0 & 0 \\ 0 & 0 \end{pmatrix}$ **5.** Infinitely many solutions   **6a.** $\begin{pmatrix} -5 & 3 \\ 2 & -1 \end{pmatrix}$
      c. No inverse
      8. $\dfrac{1}{13}\begin{pmatrix} 21 & 13 \\ -10 & -13 \end{pmatrix}$ **9.** $\dfrac{1}{6}\begin{pmatrix} -2 & 7 \\ 16 & -5 \end{pmatrix}$

p. 112   **1.** $\{(-1, 2)\}$ **3.** $\{(-3, 5)\}$ **5.** $\{(-1, 5, -2)\}$

        6. $\left\{\left(\dfrac{62}{35}, \dfrac{113}{70}, -\dfrac{29}{35}, -\dfrac{61}{35}\right)\right\}$

p. 114   **1.** $\sqrt{17}$ **2.** $(6, 3)$ **4.** Yes; yes; yes

pp. 118-119   **1.** $(2, 7)$ **4.** $(1, 1)$ **6.** $(0, 0)$ **7.** $(-3, 2)$ **9.** $(-9, -9)$

        11. $\sqrt{13}$; $5\sqrt{2}$; $9\sqrt{2}$; $\sqrt{2}$ **12a.** 1   **c.** 0   **13.** 2

p. 124   **1.** $\sqrt{14}$ **3.** $\sqrt{2}$ **5.** $\sqrt{13}$ **7.** $\sqrt{17}$ **9.** 9   **11.** 30   **18.** $(4, 12, 16)$

Chapter 4. Review, pp. 124-125

      1. $\begin{pmatrix} 3 & -1 & 1 \\ 1 & -1 & 6 \\ -6 & 2 & 2 \end{pmatrix}$ **2c.** $\begin{pmatrix} 4 & 9 & -15 \\ -4 & 18 & -1 \\ 5 & -5 & -2 \end{pmatrix}$ **3.** $\begin{pmatrix} 6 & 11 \\ 7 & 12 \end{pmatrix}$

      4. $\{(-10, -6, 0)\}$ **5a.** $(7, 0)$ **7a.** $(17, 4)$ **9a.** -16 **10a.** $\sqrt{21}$

      c. $\sqrt{26}$ **d.** $(7, 22, 2)$

CHAPTER 5

pp. 130-131   **2a.** $(-1, 0)$ **c.** $(1, 0)$ **e.** $(-.5, -.9)$ **g.** $(.17, -.99)$

      i. $(.89, .46)$ **4.** $.79, (.7, .7)$; $1.57, (0, 1)$; $2.36, (-.7, .7)$; $3.14, (-1, 0)$;

      $3.93, (-.7, -.7)$; $4.71, (0, -1)$; $5.50, (.7, -.7)$ **6a.** 1.57 **c.** $.25$

      e. 5.18 **7a.** -4.71 **c.** -6.03 **e.** -1.10 **8a.** $7.85 + 2\pi n$, n

      a whole number   **c.** $6.53 + 2\pi n$ **e.** $11.46 + 2\pi n$

pp. 132-133   **2a.** Quadrant I   **c.** Quadrant III   **3.** Least positive value of α:

      2π; fundamental period of each: 2π **4.** Cosine is even, sine is odd; cosine is

      symmetrical about the y-axis; yes

pp. 134-135   **1.** Tangent is odd   **3.** Fundamental period: π

      4. Cotangent is odd, secant is even, cosecant is odd

p. 138   **3a.** $\sin (\pi + s) = -\sin s$ **c.** $\cos (\pi + s) = -\cos s$

      e. $\sin (2\pi + s) = \sin s$ **g.** $\cos (2\pi + s) = \cos s$

      4. $\tan (s_1 + s_2) = \dfrac{\tan s_1 + \tan s_2}{1 - \tan s_1 \tan s_2}$; $\tan (s_1 - s_2) = \dfrac{\tan s_1 - \tan s_2}{1 + \tan s_1 \tan s_2}$

p. 142   **1.** $.17$ **3.** $.48$ **5.** $-.32$ **7.** $.56$ **9.** $-.64$ **11.** Undefined

      13. Quadrant IV   **15.** Quadrant II   **17.** Quadrant III

p. 146   **4a.** 2; $\dfrac{2\pi}{5}$; 0 **c.** Amplitude does not exist; $\dfrac{\pi}{2}$; $\dfrac{\pi}{2}$ **e.** 243; $\dfrac{2\pi}{15}$; $\dfrac{8}{3}$

      g. Amplitude does not exist; $\dfrac{\pi}{3}$; $\dfrac{\pi}{2}$

pp. 147-148   **1.** $\tan 2s = \dfrac{2 \sin s \cos s}{\cos^2 s - \sin^2 s}$; $\tan 2s = \dfrac{2 \tan s}{1 - \tan^2 s}$

      2. $\tan \dfrac{r}{2} = \dfrac{\sin r}{1 + \cos r}$ **3.** $\dfrac{\sqrt{2}}{2}$ **4.** $\dfrac{\sqrt{3}}{2}$ **6.** $.26, .97$

pp. 150-151   **4a.** $\dfrac{7\pi}{6} + 2\pi n$, $\dfrac{11\pi}{6} + 2\pi n$, n an integer

      c. $.61 + 6.28n$, $3.75 + 6.28n$ **5a.** $\dfrac{\pi}{3}$ or 1.047 **c.** $-\dfrac{\pi}{4}$ or $-.785$

      e. $\dfrac{\pi}{3}$ or 1.047 **g.** $\dfrac{\pi}{2}$ or 1.57 **6a.** $.89$ **c.** 1.29 **e.** -1.27

      g. -1.54 **7a.** $\dfrac{1}{2}$ or $.500$ **c.** $\dfrac{\sqrt{2}}{2}$ or $.707$ **e.** $\dfrac{\sqrt{3}}{2}$ or $.866$

Chapter 5. Review, pp. 152-153

      1a. $(0, 1)$ **c.** $\left(\dfrac{\sqrt{3}}{2}, \dfrac{1}{2}\right)$ or $(.866, .5)$ **e.** $\left(\dfrac{\sqrt{3}}{2}, -\dfrac{1}{2}\right)$ or $(.866, -.5)$

g. $(-.70, .72)$　　**i.** $(-.05, .999)$　　**2a.** 1.40　　**c.** $.37$　　**e.** 5.79
g. $.93$　　**i.** 1.63　　**3a.** $.998$　　**c.** $.500$　　**e.** 0　　**6a.** $3; 6\pi; 0$
7a. $\dfrac{\pi}{3}$　　**c.** $\dfrac{\pi}{2}$　　**8a.** $.6$　　**c.** $\dfrac{1}{2}$ or $.5$

CHAPTER 6

p. 157　**1.** $\sin \alpha = \dfrac{3}{5},\quad \cos \alpha = \dfrac{4}{5},\quad \tan \alpha = \dfrac{3}{4},\quad \cot \alpha = \dfrac{4}{3},\quad \sec \alpha = \dfrac{5}{4},\quad \csc \alpha = \dfrac{5}{3}$

4. $\sin \theta = \dfrac{8}{17},\quad \cos \theta = \dfrac{15}{17},\quad \tan \theta = \dfrac{8}{15},\quad \cot \theta = \dfrac{15}{8},\quad \sec \theta = \dfrac{17}{15},\quad \csc \theta = \dfrac{17}{8}$

6. $\sin \alpha = \dfrac{3\sqrt{13}}{13},\quad \cos \alpha = \dfrac{2\sqrt{13}}{13},\quad \tan \alpha = \dfrac{3}{2},\quad \cot \alpha = \dfrac{2}{3},\quad \sec \alpha = \dfrac{\sqrt{13}}{2},$

$\csc \alpha = \dfrac{\sqrt{13}}{3};\quad \sin \beta = \dfrac{2\sqrt{13}}{13},\quad \cos \beta = \dfrac{3\sqrt{13}}{13},\quad \tan \beta = \dfrac{2}{3},\quad \cot \beta = \dfrac{3}{2},$

$\sec \beta = \dfrac{\sqrt{13}}{3},\quad \csc \beta = \dfrac{\sqrt{13}}{2}$

p. 159　**1.** $\dfrac{1+\sqrt{3}}{2}$　　**3.** $\dfrac{\sqrt{2}+1}{2}$　　**5.** $\dfrac{\sqrt{2}-2}{2}$　　**7.** $\sqrt{3}-1$

pp. 160-161　**3.** $32°$ approximately　　**7.** $\tan x = \sqrt{3}$　　**10.** $R = 34°$ approximately

pp. 162-163　**1.** $.4384$　　**3.** $.8098$　　**5.** $.8331$　　**11.** $17°30'$　　**15.** $67°12'$
17. $38°32'$

pp. 163-164　**1.** $\cos B = \dfrac{\sqrt{3}}{3}$　　**3.** $.109$　　**5.** $\cos 45° = \dfrac{\sqrt{2}}{2}$　　**7.** $\sin 79° = .9816$

p. 164　**1.** $\csc A = 2$　　**3.** $\cot C = \dfrac{5\sqrt{2}}{2}$　　**5.** $\cos Y = \dfrac{10}{17}$　　**7.** $\cos A = \dfrac{10}{13}$

p. 167　**1.** $\cos A = \dfrac{3}{5}$　　**3.** $\sec A = \dfrac{\sqrt{53}}{2}$　　**5.** $\csc X = \dfrac{\sqrt{41}}{5}$　　**7.** $\sec N = \dfrac{\sqrt{15}}{2}$

9. $\tan A = \dfrac{\sin A}{\sqrt{1 - \sin^2 A}}$

pp. 170-171　**1.** Yes　　**2.** No　　**21.** $\tan x = 1$　　**22.** $\sin x = 0,\ \sec x = 1$
25. $\tan x = \pm\dfrac{\sqrt{2}}{2}$　　**29.** $\dfrac{1}{9}$

pp. 172-173　**1a.** $\dfrac{\pi}{6}$　　**c.** $\dfrac{3\pi}{2}$　　**e.** $\dfrac{7\pi}{6}$　　**g.** $\dfrac{5\pi}{12}$　　**2a.** $45°$　　**c.** $158°$　　**e.** $108°$
3a. $.42$　　**c.** 5.50　　**e.** $.06$　　**4a.** $28°40'$　　**c.** $35°30'$　　**e.** $573°0'$
5a. $237°18'$　　**6a.** 3π

p. 174　**1a.** $5.2''$　　**c.** $21''$　　**e.** $.87''$　　**3.** $28°40'$　　**4a.** 1 radian or $57°18'$
c. $\dfrac{5}{2}$ radians or $143°20'$　　**e.** $.81$ radian or $46°30'$

p. 178　**1.** $\sin 45°$　　**3.** $-\tan 40°$　　**5.** $-\sin 20°$　　**7.** $\tan 24°$　　**9.** $-\csc 49°$
11. $\cos 9°$　　**13.** $-\tan 40°$　　**15.** $\cot 30°$　　**17.** $-\csc 35°$　　**22.** $-\sin 30°$
23. $-\tan 50°$　　**24.** $\cos 20°$

pp. 179-180　**3.** If k is even, $\tan (k\,90°) = 0$; if k is odd, $\tan (k\,90°)$ is undefined.
5. $\sin (k\,90°) = \csc (k\,90°)$ when k is an odd integer.

p. 181　**1.** $\sin (90° + 10°)$ or $\sin (2 \times 90° - 80°)$; $\cos 10°$ or $\sin 80°$
3. $\tan (2 \times 90° + 60°)$ or $\tan (3 \times 90° - 30°)$; $\tan 60°$ or $\cot 30°$
5. $\sec (2 \times 90° + 15°)$ or $\sec (3 \times 90° - 75°)$; $-\sec 15°$ or $-\csc 75°$
13. $-\cos x$　　**15.** $-\sin x$　　**17.** $\tan x$

pp. 183-184 **1.** $\sin 105° = \dfrac{\sqrt{6} + \sqrt{2}}{4}$, $\cos 105° = \dfrac{\sqrt{2} - \sqrt{6}}{4}$ **2.** $\tan 75° = 2 + \sqrt{3}$

5. $\sin 75° = \dfrac{\sqrt{6} + \sqrt{2}}{4}$, $\cos 75° = \dfrac{\sqrt{6} - \sqrt{2}}{4}$ **7.** $\sin(\alpha + \beta) = 1$

8. $\cos(\alpha - \beta) = \dfrac{63}{65}$; $\tan(\alpha + \beta) = \dfrac{56}{33}$ **11.** $\sin(\alpha + \beta + \gamma) =$

$\sin \alpha \cos \beta \cos \gamma + \sin \beta \cos \alpha \cos \gamma + \sin \gamma \cos \alpha \cos \beta - \sin \gamma \sin \alpha \sin \beta$

p. 186 **1.** $\cos 60° = \dfrac{1}{2}$ **3.** $\sin 45° = \dfrac{\sqrt{2}}{2}$ **5.** $\sin 90° = 1$, $\cos 90° = 0$,

$\tan 90°$ is undefined **7.** $\tan 2y = \dfrac{120}{119}$; $\tan \dfrac{y}{2} = \dfrac{1}{5}$

9. $\sin 7°30' = .13$ approximately **10.** $\sin 3\alpha = 3 \sin \alpha - 4 \sin^3 \alpha$

12. $\tan 3\alpha = \dfrac{3 \tan \alpha - \tan^3 \alpha}{1 - 3 \tan^2 \alpha}$

pp. 187-188 **3.** $.9397$ **5.** $2 \sin A - 4 \sin^3 A$ **7.** $\cos 10° = .9848$

9a. $2 \sin 8° \cos 2°$ **b.** $-2 \sin 8° \sin 2°$ **14.** $\sin 8\alpha + \sin 2\alpha$

p. 189 (No Answers)

Chapter 6. Review, pp. 189-191

4. $\sin x = \sqrt{1 - \cos^2 x}$, $\tan x = \dfrac{\sqrt{1 - \cos^2 x}}{\cos x}$, $\cot x = \dfrac{\cos x \sqrt{1 - \cos^2 x}}{1 - \cos^2 x}$,

$\sec x = \dfrac{1}{\cos x}$, $\csc x = \dfrac{\sqrt{1 - \cos^2 x}}{1 - \cos^2 x}$ **5a.** $-\cos \theta$ **c.** $-\tan \theta$

6. $\cos A = \dfrac{12}{13}$, $\tan A = \dfrac{5}{12}$, $\cot A = \dfrac{12}{5}$, $\sec A = \dfrac{13}{12}$, $\csc A = \dfrac{13}{5}$

7a. $-.9205$ **c.** -1 **e.** $-.7330$ **g.** $-.5972$

9a. $\dfrac{63}{65}$ **c.** $-\dfrac{63}{16}$ **e.** $\dfrac{56}{65}$ **10.** $\dfrac{\sqrt{6} + \sqrt{2}}{4}$

CHAPTER 7

pp. 195-196 (No Answers—Graphs)

p. 198 **3.** $A = 4$; $P = 2\pi$ **5.** A is undefined; $P = \dfrac{\pi}{4}$ **7.** $A = \dfrac{1}{4}$; $P = 4\pi$

9. $A = 2$; $P = 2$

p. 200 (No Answers—Graphs)

p. 203 (No Answers—Graphs)

Chapter 7. Review, p. 203

1. $A = 4$; $P = \pi$ **3.** A is undefined; $P = 2\pi$ **5.** $A = \sqrt{3}$;

$P = 2\pi$

CHAPTER 8

pp. 207-210 **1.** $A = 44°26'$, $B = 45°34'$, $b = 21.4$ cm. **3.** $A = 47°23'$
5. $s = 6.98$ inches, $h = 5.89$ inches **6.** 3.26 in.
7. $s = 10.8$ cm., $r = 9.18$ cm. **9.** $\alpha = 29°13'$ **10.** $d = 3558$ ft.
15. $r = 11$ in. **18.** Area $= 31.7$ sq. in. **21.** 132 ft. **22.** 99.8 ft.

p. 214 **1.** $C = 91°10'$, $a = 76$ cm., $b = 98$ cm. **3.** (The ambiguous case)
$K = 47°33'$ or $132°27'$, $J = 93°45'$ or $8°51'$, $j = 274$ yards or 42.3 yards
7. 28.8 in. or 11.4 in. **8.** 54.9 ft.

p. 217 **1.** $p = 6.4$ cm., $Q = 47°50'$, $R = 80°$ **3.** $a = 459$ ft., $B = 69°20'$, $C = 58°$ **5.** $k = 9.50$ in., $H = 38°21'$, $J = 36°21'$

7. $\cos C = \dfrac{a^2 + b^2 - c^2}{2ab}$ **9.** 101 in., 76.9 in.

p. 218 **1.** 33.2 sq. in. **3.** 13410 sq. in. **5.** 20240 sq. cm. **7.** 173 sq. cm.

pp. 222-223 **1.** 261 mph at $3°31'$ west of north; 266 mph at $3°14'$ west of north **3.** 172 lbs., $28°$ **5.** $68°22'$; 312 g. **6.** $9°$

p. 224 **1.** Sector, 38.1 sq. cm.; segment, 11.7 sq. cm. **3.** 837 sq. cm. **5.** 3.01 sq. in.

pp. 224-226 Miscellaneous Exercises **1.** $b = 10.9$ in., $C = 76°33'$, $c = 15.8$ in. **3.** $c = 8.76$ cm., $B = 8°1'$, $A = 111°17'$ **5.** $a = 24.6$ ft., $B = 88°20'$, $C = 63°51'$ **7.** $A = 43°29'$, $B = 76°15'$, $C = 60°16'$ **9.** 1066 sq. cm. **11.** 2405 sq. cm. or 766 sq. cm. **13.** 1295 ft. **15.** 14370 sq. ft. **16.** 11 sq. in. **17.** 68.2 ft. **23.** 109 mph

Chapter 8. Review, pp. 226-227

1. $B = 48°31'$ **2.** 5.1 cm., 3.5 cm. **3.** Area = 7.69 sq. in. **6.** $h = 106$ ft. **7.** 2190 sq. in. **9.** 357 sq. ft.

CHAPTER 9

pp. 230-231 **1.** $0°, 180°$ **3.** $45°, 225°$ **5.** $63°26', 243°26'$ **7.** $60°, 300°$ **9.** $25°, 205°$ **11.** $\dfrac{1}{2}$ **13.** $\dfrac{1}{2}$ **15.** 2 **17.** $\dfrac{4}{5}$ **19.** 1 **20.** $\dfrac{\sqrt{3}}{3}$

pp. 232-233 **1.** $60°$ **3.** $41°$ **5.** $-45°$ **7.** $36°52'$ **9.** $135°$ **11.** $60° + n360°, 120° + n360°$ **13.** $45° + n360°, 315° + n360°$ **15.** $78°41' + n180°$ **17.** $270° + n360°$ **19.** $26°34' + n180°$

pp. 234-235 **1.** $\{x \mid -1 \leqq x \leqq 1\}$; $\left\{y \mid -\dfrac{\pi}{2} \leqq y \leqq \dfrac{\pi}{2}\right\}$ **2.** $\{x \mid -1 \leqq x \leqq 1\}$; $\{y \mid 0 \leqq y \leqq \pi\}$ **3.** No, x is any real number; $\left\{y \mid -\dfrac{\pi}{2} < y < \dfrac{\pi}{2}\right\}$

p. 236 **1.** $60° + n360°, 300° + n360°; 60°$ **3.** $45° + n360°, 225° + n360°; 45°$ **5.** $30° + n360°, 330° + n360°; 30°$ **7.** $150° + n180°; -30°$ **9.** $20° + n120°, 100° + n120°; 20°$

p. 237 **1.** $-30°, 90°$ **3.** $60°$ **5.** $45°, 135°$ **7.** $90°$ **9.** $30°, 90°$ **11.** $-24°28'$

p. 240 **1.** $0°, 180°$ **2.** $90°, 30°$ **3.** $20°$ **4.** $30°$ **5.** $45°$ **7.** $-45°$ **9.** $45°, -45°$ **11.** $90°, 150°$ **13.** $18°$

Chapter 9. Review, pp. 240-241

1. $30°$ **3.** $71°34'$ **5.** $180°$ **7.** $36°52'$ **9.** $\sqrt{3}$ **11.** 1 **15.** $60°; 60° + n360°, 120° + n360°$ **17.** $30°, 150°; 30° + n180°, 150° + n180°$ **19.** $26°34'; 26°34' + n360°, 206°34' + n360°$

CHAPTER 10

p. 243 **1.** $a = 1; d = 1; 4, 5, 6, 7, 8$ **3.** $a = 17; d = 12; 53, 65, 77, 89, 101$ **5.** $a = 0; d = 7; 21, 28, 35, 42, 49$ **12.** $a = x; d = x; 4x, 5x, 6x, 7x, 8x$ **15.** $a = b; d = -2b; -5b, -7b, -9b, -11b, -13b$

p. 244   **1.** $l = -25$ **2.** $n = 11$ **3.** $a = 15$ **4.** $d = 6$ **7.** $l = 149$
          9. $l = 3 - 4\sqrt{3}$

p. 245   **2.** $\dfrac{33}{2}$ **3.** $-1, 2$ **5.** $\dfrac{10 + 2\sqrt{2}}{3}, \dfrac{20 + \sqrt{2}}{3}$ **7.** $l = 2m - a$

p. 246   (First List)   **1.** 77   **3.** 8   **5.** 13

p. 246   (Second List)   **1.** $-2, -\dfrac{4}{3}, -\dfrac{8}{9}, -\dfrac{16}{27}$ **3.** Yes; $r = \sqrt{2}$ **5.** Yes;
          $3\sqrt[3]{9}, 9, 9\sqrt[3]{3}$

p. 247   **1.** $\dfrac{27}{3^8}$ **2.** $\dfrac{3}{2}$ **3.** 10^{-13}

p. 248   **2.** ± 1 **3.** $3, 9$ **4.** $6, -18$

p. 249   **1.** $\dfrac{127}{128}$ **3.** $\dfrac{147620}{3}$ **5.** $\dfrac{10101 + 6734\sqrt{3}}{1024}$

p. 251   **1.** $\dfrac{4}{3}$ **3.** $\dfrac{3\sqrt{3} + 3}{2}$ **5.** $\dfrac{3}{11}$ **7.** $\dfrac{2203}{999}$

p. 252   **1.** \$1216.65   **3.** \$1426.33

p. 254   **1.** Convergent; $\dfrac{1}{6}$ **3.** Divergent   **5.** Divergent

pp. 257-258   **1.** Divergent   **3.** Divergent   **5.** Convergent   **7.** Divergent

p. 259   **1.** Convergent   **3.** Convergent   **5.** Convergent

p. 261   **1.** $8x^3 - 36x^2y + 54xy^2 - 27y^3$ **5.** $\dfrac{x^5}{y^5} + \dfrac{5x^4v}{y^4} + \dfrac{10x^3v^2}{y^3} + \dfrac{10x^2v^3}{y^2} + \dfrac{5xv^4}{y} + v^5$
          8. $16x^4 + 32\sqrt{3}\, x^3 + 72x^2 + 24\sqrt{3}\, x + 9$

pp. 261-262   **1.** 120   **3.** 362,880   **5.** 2160   **7.** 144   **9.** 120   **11.** 90
          13. 6!   **15.** 8!   **17.** $x(x - 1)$ **19.** $x(x + 1)$ **21.** $x - y$

p. 262   **1.** $35a^4b^3$ **3.** $90x^3y^2$ **5.** $-112\sqrt{2}\, a^5$

p. 266   **6.** 630   **7.** 300   **8.** 330

p. 268   (No Answers—Proofs)

p. 268   (No Answers)

Chapter 10. Review, pp. 268-270

     1. 7.5, 9, 10.5, 12, 13.5   **3.** $-1, 2, 5$ **5.** 109   **7.** 25   **9.** $\dfrac{9}{2}$

     11. Divergent   **13.** Convergent   **16.** 126   **20.** 2.45 approximately

CHAPTER 11

p. 273   **1.** $\sqrt{2}\left(\cos\dfrac{\pi}{4} + i\sin\dfrac{\pi}{4}\right)$ **3.** $3\left(\cos\dfrac{\pi}{2} + i\sin\dfrac{\pi}{2}\right)$

         5. $3\sqrt{2}\left(\cos\dfrac{5\pi}{4} + i\sin\dfrac{5\pi}{4}\right)$ **7.** 2   **9.** -1 **11.** $6 - 6i\sqrt{3}$

         13. $1\left(\cos\dfrac{\pi}{2} + i\sin\dfrac{\pi}{2}\right), 1\left(\cos\dfrac{3\pi}{2} + i\sin\dfrac{3\pi}{2}\right)$

p. 275   **1.** $10\,(\cos\pi + i\sin\pi)$ **3.** $3\left(\cos\dfrac{\pi}{12} + i\sin\dfrac{\pi}{12}\right)$ **5.** $16\,(\cos 0 + i\sin 0)$

         7. $-2i$ **9.** $-2\sqrt{3} + 2i$ **11.** (1) -10 (2) $-\dfrac{21\sqrt{2}}{2} - \dfrac{21\sqrt{2}}{2}\,i$

         (3) $2.90 + .78i$

p. 277 1. $-4 + 4i$ 3. $54 + 54i$ 5. $-527 - 336i$

p. 279 1. $1.08 + .29i$ 3. $.72 + 1.08i$ 5. $.809 + .588i$ 7. $-1, \frac{1}{2} + \frac{\sqrt{3}}{2}i,$
$\frac{1}{2} - \frac{\sqrt{3}}{2}i$ 9. $1, -1, i, -i$

p. 281 2. $\frac{1}{2}$ 3. 2 4. $\frac{1}{2}$

p. 283 (No Answers)

p. 284 1. 2.718 2. 7.389

p. 286 1. $\$271.83$ 3. $\$64.98$

p. 288 2. $\log_e 4 + i\pi$ or $1.386 + 3.142i$ 7. $2e^{i\frac{\pi}{3}}$ 8. $1e^{i\frac{7\pi}{4}}$ 11. $e^{-\frac{\pi}{2}}$

Chapter 11. Review, pp. 288-289

1a. $2\sqrt{2}\left(\cos\frac{\pi}{4} + i\sin\frac{\pi}{4}\right); 2\sqrt{2}e^{i\frac{\pi}{4}}$ 2a. $-2\sqrt{3} + 2i; 4e^{i\frac{5\pi}{6}}$

3a. $-2; 2(\cos\pi + i\sin\pi)$ 5. $2, .618 + 1.902i, .618 - 1.902i,$
$-1.618 + 1.176i, -1.618 - 1.176i$ 7. $.866$ 8. 20.1 9. $\$6,389.10$

CHAPTER 12

pp. 293-294 1. $2x - y = 0$ 3. $4x - 7y - 28 = 0$ 5. $3x - 4y - 12 = 0$
7. $3x - y + 6 = 0$ 11. No 14. $(-1, 4)$ 15. $4\sqrt{2} + \sqrt{61} + \sqrt{85}$
17. $(1, 2 + 3\sqrt{3})$ and $(1, 2 - 3\sqrt{3})$ 19. 22 sq. units; $5\frac{1}{2}$ sq. units

pp. 295-296 (No Answers—Proofs)

pp. 297-298 1. $3x + 2y + 1 = 0$ 3. $2x - 7y - 10 = 0$ 5. -4
7. There are four possible solutions. 9. $x + y - b = 0$

p. 299 1. $-26°34'$ 5. $3x + y - 9 = 0$ and $x - 3y + 7 = 0$ 7. $25°21'$
10. 16 sq. units

p. 301 1. $x + \sqrt{3}y - 6 = 0$ 3. $x + y - \sqrt{6} = 0$ and $x + y + \sqrt{6} = 0$
5. $x\cos\phi + y\sin\phi - 5 = 0$

p. 303 1. $\frac{3}{5}x - \frac{4}{5}y - \frac{3}{2} = 0; \frac{3}{2}$ 3. $\frac{2\sqrt{10}}{10}$ or $\frac{\sqrt{10}}{5}; 18°26'$
5. $4x + 3y - 15 = 0$ and $4x + 3y + 15 = 0$

p. 305 1. $.186$ approx. 3. $.316$ approx. 5. 1.37 approx.
7. 7.78 approx., 5.97 approx., 6.82 approx.

p. 307 1. $(\sqrt{5} + 2\sqrt{2})x + (\sqrt{2} - \sqrt{5})y + 3\sqrt{5} - \sqrt{2} = 0$
2. $(3\sqrt{29} - 2\sqrt{10})x + (\sqrt{29} - 5\sqrt{10})y - 7\sqrt{29} = 0$

p. 309 (No Answers—Graphs)

p. 310 1. $\left(5, \arctan\frac{4}{3}\right)$ or $(5, .93)$ 3. $(\sqrt{2}, \arctan 1)$ or $(1.4, .79)$
5. $(\sqrt{10}, \arctan 3)$ or $(3.16, 4.39)$ 7. $(2, 0)$ 9. $(0, 1.5)$ 11. $(.135, .210)$

p. 313 3. $\frac{\sqrt{13}}{13} = \rho\cos(\theta - 56°19')$ 5. $x + \sqrt{3}y - 8 = 0$ 6. $x = 1$

Chapter 12. Review, pp. 313-314

1. $5x + 2y - 8 = 0$ 3. $3x + 4y - 28 = 0$ 5. $3x + (k + 4)y - 3k = 0$
6. $\frac{\pi}{4}$ 9. $5x + 12y - 13 = 0$ and $5x + 12y + 13 = 0$
11a. $(2\sqrt{5}, 2.68)$ b. $(3\sqrt{2}, 3\sqrt{2})$

CHAPTER 13

pp. 317-318 1. The circle passes through the origin.   3. Center: $(0, .5)$; radius: 1

5. $(x + 2)^2 + (y - 3)^2 = 25$ 7. $(x - 5)^2 + (y - 12)^2 = \dfrac{1}{5}$

p. 320 1. $x^2 + y^2 - 3x - 7y = 0$ 3. $(x + 2)^2 + (y - 4)^2 = 106$ 5. $x^2 + y^2 = 1$ and $(x - \sqrt{2})^2 + y^2 = 1$

p. 321 1. $2x - \sqrt{15}\,y + 19 = 0$ 3. $y = 5$ and $y = -5$

p. 323 1. $\sqrt{58}$ 3. 0; the point is on the circle   5. $\sqrt{33}$ 7. $2\sqrt{6}$

p. 325 1. Family of circles: $x^2 + y^2 - \dfrac{10}{1 + k}\,x + \dfrac{21 - 4k}{1 + k} = 0$;

radical axis: $10x - 25 = 0$ 3. $10x - 16y - 47 = 0$ 4. $5x - 11 = 0$

p. 326 1. $x^2 + y^2 = 25$ 2. $\rho = 7$

Chapter 13. Review, pp. 326-327

1. Center: $(1, -2)$; radius: 4   2. $(x + 3)^2 + (y - 7)^2 = 9$
3. $5x^2 + 5y^2 - 10x - 42y - 3 = 0$ 5. 8

CHAPTER 14

p. 333 1. $F\left(0, \dfrac{11}{4}\right)$; directrix: $4y + 11 = 0$ 3. $V(3, -1)$; $F\left(3, \dfrac{3}{2}\right)$; directrix:

$y = -\dfrac{7}{2}$; axis: $x = 3$; length of latus rectum: 10   5. $y^2 = 8x$

7. $(y - 1)^2 = 4(x + 2)$ 9. $y^2 = -6\left(x - \dfrac{3}{2}\right)$

pp. 335-336 1. Tangent: $4x - y + 1 = 0$; normal: $x + 4y - 4 = 0$ 3. Tangent: $11x - 5y + 13 = 0$; normal: $25x + 55y + 3 = 0$ 5. $m_1 = 1$; $m_2 = -1$; the tangents are perpendicular   7. $(0, -1)$

p. 338 1. $(x')^2 = 4y'$ 2. $(y')^2 = 4p(x' + 3)$

pp. 339-340 1. $\rho = \dfrac{7}{2 \cos \theta - 2}$ 2. $y^2 = 14x$; $(y')^2 = 14x' + 49$

Chapter 14. Review, p. 340

1. $V(7, 3)$; $F(7, 5)$; directrix: $y = 1$ 3. $y = 0$; endpoints: $(-2, 0)$ and $(10, 0)$ 5. Tangent: $6x - 5y + 8 = 0$; normal: $25x + 30y - 109 = 0$
7. $2x + y + 4 = 0$; $8x + 4y - 9 = 0$

CHAPTER 15

pp. 346-347 1. $\dfrac{x^2}{100} + \dfrac{y^2}{75} = 1$ 3. $e = \dfrac{\sqrt{5}}{3}$; $F(\sqrt{5}, 0)$, $F'(-\sqrt{5}, 0)$; $V(3, 0)$, $V'(-3, 0)$;

directrices: $x = \dfrac{9\sqrt{5}}{5}$ and $x = \dfrac{-9\sqrt{5}}{5}$;   length of latus rectum: $\dfrac{8}{3}$

5. $\dfrac{(x - 2)^2}{49} + \dfrac{9(y + 2)^2}{245} = 1$ 7. Major axis: 10; minor axis: 8

9. $x^2 + y^2 = 13$ 10. 2095.2 miles; 424.8 miles

p. 349 1. $\dfrac{x^2}{49} + \dfrac{y^2}{45} = 1$; $e = \dfrac{2}{7}$ 3. $x^2 + y^2 = 4$ and $x^2 + y^2 = 9$ 5. $e = \dfrac{2}{3}$;

length of latus rectum: $\dfrac{20}{3}$

p. 350   **1.** Tangent: $4\sqrt{3}\,x + 7y - 56 = 0$;   normal: $14x - 8\sqrt{3}\,y - 33\sqrt{3} = 0$
3. $x = 3$ and $x = -3$ **5.** The normal is $25x - 20y - 64 = 0$

p. 352   **1.** Center: $(2, -3)$; $F(2, -3 - 2\sqrt{6})$, $F'(2, -3 + 2\sqrt{6})$; $e = \dfrac{2\sqrt{6}}{5}$;

directrices: $y = -3 + \dfrac{25\sqrt{6}}{12}$ and $y = -3 - \dfrac{25\sqrt{6}}{12}$

3. $49x^2 + 9y^2 + 294x - 126y + 441 = 0$
5. Approximate coordinates: $(.94, 3.36)$ and $(.94, -3.36)$

pp. 353-354   **1.** $\rho = \dfrac{9}{4 - \sqrt{7}\,\cos\theta}$ **3.** $\dfrac{x^2}{9} + \dfrac{y^2}{4} = 1$

Chapter 15. Review, p. 354

1. Center: $(4, 6)$; $F(4 + 3\sqrt{3}, 6)$, $F'(4 - 3\sqrt{3}, 6)$; $V(10, 6)$, $V'(-2, 6)$;

endpoints: $\left(4 + 3\sqrt{3}, \dfrac{15}{2}\right)$, $\left(4 + 3\sqrt{3}, \dfrac{9}{2}\right)$, $\left(4 - 3\sqrt{3}, \dfrac{15}{2}\right)$,

$\left(4 - 3\sqrt{3}, \dfrac{9}{2}\right)$ **3.** $3x^2 + 4y^2 = 3$ **5.** $y = 2$ and $y = -4$

CHAPTER 16

pp. 359-360   **1.** $\dfrac{(x - 3)^2}{9} - \dfrac{4(y + 1)^2}{45} = 1$ **3.** $F(0, 10)$, $F'(0, -10)$; $e = \dfrac{5}{4}$

4. $F(3 + 6\sqrt{2}, -5)$, $F'(3 - 6\sqrt{2}, -5)$;   directrices: $x = 3 + 2\sqrt{2}$ and $x = 3 - 2\sqrt{2}$; $e = \sqrt{3}$; transverse axis: $4\sqrt{6}$; conjugate axis: $8\sqrt{3}$

5. $\dfrac{25(y + 2)^2}{576} - \dfrac{625(x + 2)^2}{22464} = 1$ **7.** $\dfrac{y^2}{4} - \dfrac{(x - 1)^2}{1} = 1$

9. $\dfrac{(x - 4)^2}{4} - \dfrac{(y + 2)^2}{5} = 1$

pp. 362-363   **1.** $3x + 2y = 0$ and $3x - 2y = 0$ **2.** $F(\sqrt{41}, 0)$, $F'(-\sqrt{41}, 0)$; $V(5, 0)$,

$V'(-5, 0)$; length of latus rectum: $\dfrac{32}{5}$; asymptotes: $4x + 5y = 0$, $4x - 5y = 0$

3. $\dfrac{x^2}{4} - \dfrac{y^2}{1} = 1$

pp. 363-364   **1.** Tangent: $5x - 6y - 16 = 0$; normal: $12x + 10y - 75 = 0$
3. Tangents: $5x - 3y - 18 = 0$, $5x + 3y - 18 = 0$, $5x - 3y + 18 = 0$,
$5x + 3y + 18 = 0$;   normals: $9x + 15y - 250 = 0$, $9x - 15y - 250 = 0$,
$9x + 15y + 250 = 0$, $9x - 15y + 250 = 0$

p. 365   **1.** Center: $(5, -3)$; transverse axis: 4;   conjugate axis: 6; $e = \dfrac{\sqrt{13}}{2}$

2. Center: $(-3, 4)$; $F(-3 + \sqrt{74}, 4)$, $F'(-3 - \sqrt{74}, 4)$; $V(2, 4)$, $V'(-8, 4)$;
asymptotes: $7x + 5y + 1 = 0$ and $7x - 5y + 41 = 0$

p. 366   **1.** $\rho = \dfrac{9}{4 + 5\cos\theta}$ **2.** $\dfrac{49x^2}{576} - \dfrac{49y^2}{448} = 1$

Chapter 16. Review, pp. 366-367

1. Center: $(4, 5)$; $F(4 + 2\sqrt{10}, 5)$, $F'(4 - 2\sqrt{10}, 5)$; $V(10, 5)$, $V'(-2, 5)$;

ends of latera recta: $\left(4 + 2\sqrt{10}, \dfrac{17}{3}\right)$, $\left(4 + 2\sqrt{10}, \dfrac{13}{3}\right)$, $\left(4 - 2\sqrt{10}, \dfrac{17}{3}\right)$,

$\left(4 - 2\sqrt{10}, \dfrac{13}{3}\right)$ **4.** $x = 1$ **5.** $\dfrac{(y - 1)^2}{9} - \dfrac{4(x + 5)^2}{45} = 1$; asymptotes:

$2x - \sqrt{5}\,y + 10 + \sqrt{5} = 0$ and $2x + \sqrt{5}\,y + 10 - \sqrt{5} = 0$

6. $\dfrac{(x-2)^2}{9k^2} - \dfrac{(y-1)^2}{16k^2} = 1$ and $\dfrac{(y-1)^2}{16k^2} - \dfrac{(x-2)^2}{9k^2} = 1$

9. $3x^2 + 8xy + 3y^2 - 28x - 28y + 49 = 0$

CHAPTER 17

p. 369　　1. 36　　3. 45　　5. 30

pp. 371-372　　1. 24　　　3. 7　　　5. 39,916,800　　7. 840　　9. 60　　11. $\dfrac{24!}{3!}$

17. 1　　19. 151,200

p. 373　　1. 4200　　3. 180　　5. 60

pp. 375-376　　1. 6　　　3. 4　　　5. 35　　7. 792　　9. 10　　11. 756　　16. 646,646

p. 378　　1. $\dfrac{9}{11}; \dfrac{7}{11}$　　3. $\dfrac{1}{16}$　　5. 2,598,960; 1287; $\dfrac{33}{66,640}$

pp. 381-383　　1. $\dfrac{1}{36}$　　3. $\dfrac{1}{36}$　　5. $\dfrac{2}{3}$　　7. $\dfrac{1}{2}; \dfrac{1}{4}; \dfrac{1}{2^{10^{10}}}$; no　　9. .73 approximately

11. .78 approximately

pp. 387-388　　3. .47178; .16308; .03078　　　5. .62305; .04395　　　7. .52822

8. .00001; .32805; .40951　　10. .31250; .536

Chapter 17. Review, pp. 388-389

1. 40　　3. 3360　　5. $-1,025,024x^5$　　7. $\dfrac{13}{20}$　　9. .09　　10. .30 approximately

CHAPTER 18

p. 392　　1. 83.8　　3. $329\frac{3}{7}$

p. 393　　1. $M_d = 67$; range $= 43$　　　3. $\bar{X} = 165\frac{2}{9}$, $M_d = 166$, $\bar{X} - M_d = -\frac{7}{9}$; $\bar{X} = 161.4$, $M_d = 164$, $\bar{X} - M_d = -2.6$　　5. 68; 52

p. 394　　1. 63.5　　2. .408

p. 395　　1. 8.8　　3. 4.21　　5. $\bar{X} = 4.8$; $M_d = 5$; $G = 4.28$; $H = 3.77$; $Q = 5.25$

p. 397　　1. 11.5　　2. 8.6　　3. M.D. $= 5.89$, $Q = 5$, M.D. is greater

p. 398　　1. .29　　3. $\sigma = 10.6$; M.D. $= 8.6$; σ is greater

p. 401　　(No Answers—Tables)

p. 402　　(No Answers—Graphs)

p. 406　　1. $\bar{X} = 104.7$; $M_d = 104.2$; $\sigma = 10.4$

p. 408　　(No Answers—Graphs)

p. 410　　2. A, 2; B, 10; C, 20; D, 20; E, 10; F, 2

pp. 412-413　　1. A, 6.7%; B, 24.15%; C, 38.3%; D, 24.15%; F, 6.7%

3. .1585; .0225

pp. 415-416　　1. $\sigma_{\bar{x}} = .20$ mm.; $16.2 \pm .33$; $16.2 \pm .39$　　2. .955

Chapter 18. Review, pp. 416-418

3. 2.344　　5. .0025　　6. .0031　　7. .904　　8. .0008　　11. 3.31

12. 3.51　　15. 1.82

CHAPTER 19

p. 423 1. 4   3. 2   4. $\dfrac{8}{3}$ 6. 6   8. No limit   10. 3   13. 1   15. 1

pp. 426-427 1. $5 - \dfrac{1}{30} < x < 5 + \dfrac{1}{30}$ or $|x - 5| < \dfrac{1}{30}$

3. $\left\{ x \mid \dfrac{24}{25} < x < \dfrac{26}{25} \right\}$ 5a. $\left\{ x \mid \dfrac{49}{10} < x < \dfrac{51}{10} \right\}$ c. $\left\{ x \mid \dfrac{1499}{1500} < x < \dfrac{1501}{1500} \right\}$

p. 429 4a. $\dfrac{1}{500}$ c. .01   5a. Continuous   c. Continuous

pp. 431-432 2. $-\dfrac{1}{3}$ 3. 12   5. No limit   7. 0   9. 9

Chapter 19. Review, pp. 432-433

1. $\dfrac{1}{3}$ 3. 1.72   4. 9   6. 0   8. 2   10. $\{x \mid 9.9 < x < 10.1\}$ 13a. $\delta \leqq .005$
14. Continuous   17. -28

APPENDIX

p. 440 1. 3   3. 3   5. 5   7. 4   9. 4

p. 441 (First List)   1. .5; .0068   3. .005; .00018   5. 500,000; .0054

p. 441 (Second List)   1. 47.8   3. 12$\underline{0}$00   5. .0232   7. 41400
9. 3.86×10^{-3}

pp. 443-444 1. 55.5   3. 5$\underline{0}$ sq. cm.   5. 180   7. Maximum, 308.0575;
minimum, 303.1875; actual, 305.62; answer, 310, with 2 significant digits

p. 445 1. 2   3. 2   5. 2   7. 2

pp. 451-452 1. 544   3. .0552   5. 524   7. 15.1

pp. 453-454 1a. 2   c. 3   e. 5   2a. 50   c. .0005   e. .5   3. 23   4a. .027
has greater precision, but 3.81 has greater accuracy.   5. 8.58   6a. 41.2
c. 15.77   9. $\dfrac{38}{9}$

INDEX

INDEX